Aircraft Gas Turbine Engine Technology

Aircraft Gas Turbine Engine Technology

IRWIN E. TREAGER
*Associate Professor, Department of
Aviation Technology*
Purdue University

McGRAW-HILL BOOK COMPANY
*New York   St. Louis   San Francisco   London
Sydney   Toronto   Mexico   Panama*

This book was set in Optima by Progressive Typographers,
and printed on permanent paper by Halliday Lithograph
Corporation, and bound by The Book Press, Inc.   The
designer was Edward Zytko; the drawings were done
by J. & R. Technical Services, Inc.   The editors were
Cary F. Baker, Jr. and Albert Shapiro.   William P. Weiss
supervised the production.

Preface

Although the gas turbine, or jet engine, is a relative youngster to aviation, its growth and refinement have not only given new life to this industry, but also have been so rapid that keeping abreast of developments in this area has become very difficult. A great deal has been written about the gas turbine engine from an engineering viewpoint, but there is relatively little consolidated information treating this type of power plant at the technical level. This book is an attempt to correct this deficiency.

Although the text is designed primarily to provide a source of information about the gas turbine engine for aircraft technicians, it may be used by others interested in this type of power plant.

The author has tried to follow a logical presentation and to use the type of approach that does not assume a great deal of technical information on the part of the reader. Beginning with the background and development of the gas turbine engine the book ends with a discussion of several modern engines of this type. The section of the book dealing with the mathematical relationships, which are an integral part of any study dealing with this type of engine, has been simplified without, it is hoped, sacrificing clarity and completeness to any great degree. As the heading for Chapter 3 implies, all who can add and subtract should have little difficulty reading and understanding this part of the book. The part of Chapter 12 dealing with the fuel control is slightly more detailed than other sections because fuel metering is a critical factor in correct engine operation and because the fuel control is probably the most complicated and difficult to understand unit on the entire engine. The appendixes are devoted to a compilation of appropriate mathematical formulas, a glossary of terms related to the gas turbine engine, and several pages of applicable conversion factors and tables.

IRWIN E. TREAGER

Acknowledgments

....

The information contained in this book has been collected from a great number of sources. It represents the work of many people and organizations, without whose contributions this text could not have been completed. I wish to express my gratitude to the following organizations for their efforts in providing technical information, pictures, charts, tables, and other materials.

AiResearch Mfg. Co., Div. of the Garrett Corp., Phoenix, Ariz.

Air Training Command, U.S.A.F., Randolph A.F.B., Tex.

Allison Div., General Motors Corp., Indianapolis, Ind.

American Petroleum Institute, New York, N.Y.

American Society of Mechanical Engineers, New York, N.Y.

American Society of Tool and Manufacturing Engineers, Dearborn, Mich.

Aviation Power Supply Inc., Burbank, Calif.

Aviation Week and Space Technology, New York, N.Y.

Beech Aircraft Corp., Wichita, Kans.

Bell Helicopter Co., Fort Worth, Tex.

Bendix Products Aerospace Div., Bendix Corp., South Bend, Ind.

Boeing Airplane Co., Commercial Airplane Div., Renton, Wash.

Cessna Aircraft Co., Wichita, Kans.

Chandler Evans Corp., West Hartford, Conn.

Continental Aviation and Engineering Corp., Detroit, Mich.

Convair Div., General Dynamics Corp., San Diego, Calif.

Curtiss-Wright Corp., Wood-Ridge, N.J.

Department of the Air Force, Washington, D.C.

Douglas Aircraft Co., Long Beach and Santa Monica, Calif.

Ex-Cell-O Corp., Detroit, Mich.

Extension Course Institute, U.S.A.F., Gunter A.F.B., Ala.

Fairchild Hiller, Republic Aviation Div., Farmingdale, N.Y.

Federal Aviation Agency, Washington, D.C.

Gas Turbine Publications Inc., Stamford, Conn.

General Dynamics Corp., Fort Worth Div., Fort Worth, Tex.

General Electric Co., Cincinnati, Ohio

General Laboratory Associates Inc., Norwich, N.Y.

Grumman Aircraft Engineering Corp., Bethpage, N.Y.

Hamilton Standard Div., United Aircraft Corp., Windsor Locks, Conn.

Holley Carburetor Co., Warren, Mich.

Hughes Tool Co., Aircraft Div., Culver City, Calif.

Industrial Acoustics Co., Inc., New York, N.Y.

International Nickel Co., Inc., New York, N.Y.

Investment Casting Institute, Chicago, Ill.

Israel Aircraft Industries Ltd., Lod Airport, Israel

Kaman Aircraft Corp., Bloomfield, Conn.

Kelsey Hayes Co., Utica, N.Y.

Koopers Co. Inc., Sound Control Dept., Baltimore, Md.

Lear Jet Industries Inc., Wichita, Kans.

Ling-Temco-Vought Inc., Dallas, Tex.

Lockheed California Co., Div. of Lockheed Aircraft Corp., Burbank, Calif.

Lycoming Div., Avco Corp., Stratford, Conn.

Magnaflux Corp., Chicago, Ill.

Materials Systems Div., Union Carbide Corp., Indianapolis, Ind.

McDonnell Douglas Corp., St. Louis, Mo.

Misco Precision Casting Div., Howe Sound Co., Whitehall, Mich.

Mooney Aircraft Inc., Kerrville, Tex.

Naval Air Training Command, Washington, D.C.

North American Aviation Inc., Los Angeles and El Segundo, Calif.

Northrop Corp., Beverly Hills, Calif.

Pan American World Airways, New York, N.Y.

Pesco Products Div., Borg-Warner Corp., Bedford, Ohio

Phillips Petroleum Co., Bartlesville, Okla.

Philosophical Library Inc., New York, N.Y.

Power Equipment Div., Lear Siegler Inc., Cleveland, Ohio

Pratt & Whitney Aircraft Div., United Aircraft Corp., E. Hartford, Conn.

Rolls Royce Ltd., Derby, England

Ryan Aeronautical Co., San Diego, Calif.

Scintilla Div., Bendix Corp., Sidney, N.Y.

Shell Oil Co., New York, N.Y.

Sikorsky Aircraft Div., United Aircraft Corp., Stratford, Conn.

Society of Automotive Engineers, New York, N.Y.

Socony Mobil Oil Co., Inc., New York, N.Y.

Solar Div., International Harvester Co., San Diego, Calif.

Stalker Development Co., Bay City, Mich.

Sundstrand Aviation Div., Sundstrand Corp., Rockford, Ill.

Texaco, Inc., New York, N.Y.

Thermal Dynamics Corp., Lebanon, N.H.
United Aircraft of Canada Ltd., Longueuil, Canada
Utica Div., Bendix Corp., Utica, N.Y.
Vertol Div., Boeing Airplane Co., Morton, Pa.
Welding Journal, American Welding Society, New York, N.Y.
Westinghouse Research Laboratory, Pittsburgh, Pa.

Woodward Governor Co., Rockford, Ill.
Wyman-Gordon Co., Worcester, Mass.

A special note of thanks to my wife for all her help and encouragement.

IRWIN E. TREAGER

Contents

PART **1**

History
and theory

Chapter 1

Background and development

FIG. 1-2 *Hero's aeolipile.*

Long before man appeared on earth, nature had given some creatures of the sea, such as the squid and the cuttlefish, the ability to jet propel themselves through the water (Fig. 1-1).

There have been many examples of the utilization of the reaction principle during the early periods of recorded history, but because a suitable level of technical achievement in the areas of engineering, manufacture, and metallurgy had not been reached, there was a gap of over 2000 years before a practical application of this principle became possible.

THE AEOLIPILE

Hero, an Egyptian scientist who lived in Alexandria around 100 B.C. is generally given credit for conceiving and building the first "jet engine." His device, called an *aeolipile* (Fig. 1-2), consisted of a boiler or bowl

FIG. 1-1 *The squid, a jet-propelled fish.*

which held a supply of water. Two hollow tubes extended up from this boiler and supported a hollow sphere which was free to turn on these supports. Attached to the sphere were two small pipes or jets whose openings were at right angles to the axis of rotation of the sphere. When the water in the bowl was made to boil, the steam shooting from the two small jets caused the sphere to spin, very much like the lawn sprinkler is made to spin from the reaction of the water leaving its nozzles. (This phenomenon will be explained in Chap. 3.) Incidentally, the aeolipile was only one of a number of inventions credited to Hero, which include a water clock, a compressed air catapult, and a hydraulic organ. He also wrote many works on mathematics, physics, and mechanics.

LEONARDO DA VINCI

Around A.D. 1500 Leonardo Da Vinci described the *chimney jack* (Fig. 1-3), a device which was later widely used for turning roasting spits. As the hot air from the fire rose, it was made to pass through a series of fanlike blades which, through a series of gears, turned a roasting spit, thus illustrating another application of the reaction principle.

FIG. 1-3 *Da Vinci's chimney jack.*

ROCKETS AS A FORM OF JET PROPULSION

The invention of gunpowder allowed the continued development of the reaction principle. Rockets, for example, were constructed apparently as early as 1232 by the Mongols for use in war and for fireworks displays. One daring Chinese scholar named Wan Hu intended to use his rockets as a means of propulsion (Fig. 1-4). His plan was simple. A series of rockets were lashed to a chair under which sledlike runners had been placed. Unfortunately, when the rockets were ignited, the blast that followed completely obliterated Wan Hu and the chair, making him the first martyr in man's struggle to achieve flight. In later times rockets were used during several wars, including the Napoleonic Wars. The phrase "the rocket's red glare" in our national anthem

FIG. 1-5 *Branca's jet turbine.*

refers to the use of rockets by the British in besieging Fort McHenry in Baltimore, during the war of 1812. And, of course, the German use of the V-2 rocket during World War II, and the subsequent development of space vehicles is contemporary history.

BRANCA'S STAMPING MILL

A further application of the jet-propulsion principle, utilizing what was probably the first actual impulse turbine, was the invention of a stamping mill built in 1629 by Giovanni Branca, an Italian engineer (Fig. 1-5). The turbine was driven by steam generated in a boiler. The jet of steam from a nozzle in this boiler impinged on the blades of a horizontally mounted turbine wheel which, through an arrangement of gearing, caused the mill to operate.

SIR ISAAC NEWTON

It was at this point in history (1687) that Sir Isaac Newton formulated the laws of motion (discussed in detail in Chap. 3) on which all devices utilizing the jet-propulsion theory are based. The vehicle illustrated in Fig. 1-6, called Newton's wagon, applied the principle of jet propulsion. It is thought that Jacob Gravesand, a Dutchman, actually designed this "horseless carriage," and that Isaac Newton may have only supplied the idea. The wagon consisted essentially of a large boiler

FIG. 1-4 *Chinese rocket sled.*

FIG. 1-6 *Newton's steam wagon.*

FIG. 1-7   *Barber's British patent—1791.*

FIG. 1-8   *Dr. Sanford Moss.*

mounted on four wheels.   Steam generated by a fire built below the boiler was allowed to escape through a nozzle facing rearward.   The speed of the vehicle was controlled by a steam cock located in the nozzle.

THE FIRST GAS TURBINE

In 1791 John Barber, an Englishman, was the first to patent a design utilizing the thermodynamic cycle of the modern gas turbine and suggested its use for jet propulsion (Fig. 1-7).   The turbine was equipped with a chain-driven reciprocating type of compressor, but was otherwise basically the same as the modern gas turbine in that it had a compressor, a combustion chamber, and a turbine.

SIR FRANK WHITTLE

During the period between 1791 and 1930, many men supplied ideas which laid the foundation for the modern gas turbine engine as we know it today.   When in 1930 Frank Whittle submitted his patent application for a jet aircraft engine, he had the contributions of many men to draw from.   For example:

Sir George Caley—Invented the reciprocating hot air engine.   This engine (1807) operated on the same cycle principle as the modern closed cycle gas turbine.

Dr. F. Stoltz—Designed an engine (1872) approaching the concept of the modern gas turbine engine.   The engine never ran under its own power because component efficiencies were too low.

Sir Charles Parsons—Took out many comprehensive gas turbine patents (1884).

Dr. Sanford A. Moss (Fig. 1-8)—Did much work on the gas turbine

engine, but whose chief contribution lies in the development of the turbosupercharger. Credit for the basic idea for the turbosupercharger is given to Rateau of France; it is in reality very similar to a jet engine, lacking only the combustion chamber (Fig. 1-9).

Dr. A. A. Griffith—Member of the British Royal Aircraft establishment who developed a theory of turbine design based on gas flows past airfoils, rather than through passages.

The work of many others, in addition to those mentioned, preceded Whittle's efforts.   In addition, there were several jet-engine developments occurring concurrently in other countries.   These developments are discussed on the following pages.   Whittle is considered by many to be the father of the jet engine, but his contribution lies mainly in the application to aircraft of this type of engine which, as indicated previously, was already somewhat refined.

In 1928, at the time that Dr. Griffith was involved in his work with compressors and other parts of the gas

FIG. 1-9   *A turbosupercharger.*

FIG. 1-10 *Sir Frank Whittle.*

turbine, Whittle (Fig. 1-10), then a young air cadet at the R.A.F. College in Cramwell, England, submitted a thesis in which he proposed the use of the gas turbine engine for jet propulsion. It was not until 18 months later that this idea crystallized, and he began to think seriously about using the gas turbine engine for jet propulsion. By January of 1930, Whittle's thinking on the subject had advanced to the point that he submitted a patent application on the use of the gas turbine for jet propulsion (Fig. 1-11). In this patent was included ideas for the athodyd, or ramjet, but this was removed from the specifications when it was determined that the ramjet idea had already been proposed.

The period between 1930 and 1935 was one of frustration for Whittle and his coworkers. During this time his idea had been turned down by the British Air Ministry, and by several manufacturing concerns be-

FIG. 1-11 *Whittle's patent drawing. (G. G. Smith, "Gas Turbines and Jet Propulsion," Philosophical Library, Inc., New York, 1955.)*

cause the gas turbine was thought to be too impractical for flight. In 1935, while he was at Cambridge studying engineering, he was approached by two former R.A.F. officers, Williams and Tinling, with the suggestion that Whittle should acquire several patents (he had allowed the original patent to lapse), and they would attempt to raise money in order to build an experimental model of Whittle's engine. Eventually, with the help of an investment banking firm, Power Jets Ltd. was formed in March of 1936.

Before the new company was formed, the banking firm had placed an order with the British Thomson-Houston Company at Rugby for the actual construction of the engine, minus the combustion chamber and instrumentation. Originally Whittle had planned to build and test each component of the engine separately, but this proved to be too expensive. As planned, the new engine was to incorporate specifications beyond any existing gas turbine. As Whittle explains in his book, "Jet—The Story of a Pioneer":

> Our compressor was of the single stage centrifugal type generally similar to, but much larger than, an aero-engine supercharger (or fan unit of a vacuum cleaner). The turbine was also a single stage unit. Thus the main moving part of the engine—the rotor—was made up of the compressor impeller, the turbine wheel and the shaft connecting the two. It was designed to rotate at 17,750 revolutions per minute, which meant a top speed of nearly 1500 feet per second for the 19 inch diameter impeller and 1250 feet per second for the 16½ inch diameter turbine. [Author's note: $fps = (\pi D/12)(rpm/60)$.]
>
> Our targets for performance for the compressor, combustion chamber assembly and turbine were very ambitious and far beyond anything previously attained with similar components.
>
> The best that had been achieved with a single stage centrifugal compressor was a pressure ratio of 2.5 with an efficiency of 65 percent (an aero-engine supercharger). Our target was a pressure ratio of 4.0 with an efficiency of 80 percent.
>
> Our designed airflow of 1500 pounds per minute (25 pounds per second) was far greater in proportion to size than anything previously attempted (that was one of the reasons why I expected to get high efficiency). For this pressure ratio and airflow the compressor required over 3000 horsepower to drive it. Power of this order from such a small single stage turbine was well beyond all previous experience. Finally, in the combustion chamber, we aimed to burn nearly 200 gallons of fuel per hour in a space of about six cubic feet. This required a combustion intensity many times greater than a boiler furnace.

The design and manufacture of the combustion chamber, which was let to an oil burner firm, Laidlaw, Drew and Company, proved to be one of the most difficult design problems in the engine. But by April 1937, testing on the first engine began, and although the engine's performance did not come up to specifications and there was much heartbreaking failure, the machine showed enough promise to prompt the official entry of the Air Ministry into the picture (Fig. 1-12). With new funds, the original engine was rebuilt and the combustion chamber design was improved somewhat. Testing was continued at a new site because of the danger involved.

FIG. 1-12 *Whittle's first experimental engine—1937. (G. G. Smith, "Gas Turbines and Jet Propulsion," Philosophical Library, Inc., New York, 1955.)*

FIG. 1-14 *The Gloster E28/39, which flew in 1941.*

The original engine was reconstructed several times (Fig. 1-13). Most of the rebuilding was necessitated by turbine blade failures due to faulty combustion. But enough data had been collected to consider the engine a success, and by the summer of 1939, the Air Ministry awarded to Power Jets Ltd. a contract to design a flight engine. The engine was to be flight tested in an experimental airplane called the Gloster E28. On May 15, 1941, the W1 Whittle engine installed in the Gloster E28 made its first flight, with Flight Lieutenant P. E. G. Sayer as pilot. In subsequent flights during the next few weeks, the airplane achieved a speed of 370 mph in level flight, with 1000 lb of thrust. The Gloster/Whittle E28/39 is shown in Fig. 1-14. Sayer was later killed flying a conventional aircraft.

GERMAN DEVELOPMENT

Work on the gas turbine engine was going on concurrently in Germany with Whittle's work in Britain. Serious efforts toward jet propulsion of aircraft were started in the middle 1930s. Two students at Gottingen, Germany, Hans von Ohain and Max Hahn, apparently unaware of Whittle's work, patented, in 1936, an engine for jet propulsion based on the same principles as the Whittle engine. These ideas were adapted by the Ernst Heinkel Aircraft Company and the second engine of this development made a flight with Erich Wahrsitz as pilot on August 27, 1939, which is now generally considered to be the *earliest date* of modern jet propulsion. The HE178 was equipped with a centrifugal flow jet engine, the Heinkel HeS-3b, which developed 1100 lb of thrust and had a top speed of over 400 mph (Fig. 1-15).

Subsequent German development of turbojet-powered aircraft produced the ME262, a 500-mph fighter, powered by two axial flow engines. (The terms centrifugal flow and axial flow will be examined in Chap. 2.) More than 1600 ME262 fighters were built in the closing stages of World War II, but they reached operational status too late to seriously challenge the overwhelming air superiority gained by the Allies (Fig. 1-16). These engines were far ahead of contemporary British developments and they foreshadowed many of the features of the more modern engine, such as blade cooling, ice prevention, and the variable area exhaust nozzle. An interesting sidelight to the German contribution was

FIG. 1-13 *Early Whittle engine designs.*

FIG. 1-15 *The HE178 was the first true jet-propelled aircraft to fly (1939). (J. V. Casamassa and R. D. Bent, "Jet Aircraft Power Systems," 3d ed., McGraw-Hill Book Company, New York, 1965.)*

FIG. 1-16 *The ME262 German operational jet fighter.*

FIG. 1-18. *The Caproni-Campini CC-2 flew using the engine configuration shown in Fig. 1-17. (G. G. Smith, "Gas Turbines and Jet Propulsion," Philosophical Library, Inc., New York, 1955.)*

that on September 30, 1929, a modified glider using Opel rockets was the world's first airplane to achieve flight using a reaction engine.

ITALIAN CONTRIBUTION

Although strictly speaking not a gas turbine engine in the present sense of the term, an engine designed by Secundo Campini of the Caproni Company in Italy utilized the reaction principle (Fig. 1-17). A successful flight was made in August 1940, and was reported, at the time, as the first successful flight of a jet-propelled aircraft (Fig. 1-18). The power plant of this aircraft was not a "jet" because it relied upon a conventional 900-hp reciprocating engine instead of a turbine to operate the three-stage compressor. Top speed for this aircraft was a disappointing 205 mph, and the project was abandoned in late 1948.

10

DEVELOPMENT IN AMERICA

America was a late-comer to the jet-propulsion field, although it must be said that at the time it was felt that the war would have to be won with airplanes using conventional reciprocating engines.

In September of 1941, under the auspices of the N.A.C.A. (National Advisory Committee for Aeronautics), the W.1X engine, which was the forerunner of the W.1, and a complete set of plans and drawings for the more advanced W.2B gas turbine, were flown to the United States under special arrangements between the British and American governments. A group of Power Jets engineers was also sent. The General Electric Corporation was awarded the contract to build an American version of this engine because of their previous experience with turbosuperchargers and Moss' pioneering work in this area.

11

The first jet airplane flight in this country was made in October 1942, in a Bell XP-59A (Fig. 1-19) with Bell's chief test pilot Robert M. Stanley at the controls. The two General Electric I-A engines (Fig. 1-20) used in this experimental airplane were adaptations of the Whittle design. But while the Whittle engine was rated at 850 lb of thrust, the I-A was rated at about 1300 lb of thrust and with a lower specific fuel consumption. (Specific fuel consumption will be defined later in the book.) To make the story even more dramatic, both engine and airframe were designed and built in one year. A project of similar proportions would take several years at the present time.

General Electric's early entry into the jet-engine field gave the company a lead in the manufacturing of gas turbines, but they were handicapped somewhat by having to work with preconceived ideas, after having seen Whittle's engine and drawings. Now, the N.A.C.A. Jet Propulsion Committee began to look about for a manufacturer to produce an all-American engine. Their choice was the Westinghouse Corporation, because of this company's previous experience with steam

FIG. 1-17 *The CC-1, a proposed Italian design never flown. This illustration shows the compressors being driven by a reciprocating engine.*

FIG. 1-19 *America's first jet airplane, the Bell XP-59A powered by two General Electric I-A engines.*

turbines. The contract was let late in 1941 by the Navy, but it was decided not to inform the Westinghouse people of the existence of the Whittle engine. As it turned out, this decision was a correct one, for the Westinghouse engineers designed an engine with an axial compressor and an annular combustion chamber. Both of these innovations, or variations thereof, have stood the test of time and are being used in contemporary engines.

Shortly thereafter, several other companies began to design and produce gas turbine engines. Notable

FIG. 1-20 *General Electric I-A, the first jet engine built in the U.S.*

among these are Allison, AiResearch, Boeing, Continental, Lycoming, Pratt & Whitney, Solar, and Wright. Of these, Boeing, Westinghouse, and Wright are no longer manufacturing jet engines. The several companies offer a variety of gas turbines to the user, some of which are discussed in Chap. 2, along with the airplanes in which these engines are installed.

REVIEW AND STUDY QUESTIONS

1 How old is the idea of jet propulsion?
2 Describe the first practical device utilizing the reaction principle.
3 What was Leonardo Da Vinci's contribution to the development of a jet engine?
4 Who were the first people to use rockets? Give an example of the use of rockets in war.
5 Between the years 1600 and 1800, who were the contributors to the development of the gas turbine engine? What were those contributions?
6 What was Sir Frank Whittle's chief contribution to the further development of the gas turbine engine?
7 Give a brief outline of the efforts of Whittle and his company to design a jet engine.
8 Describe the German contributions to the jet engine.
9 Which country was the first to fly a jet-powered aircraft? What was the designation of this airplane and with what type of engine was it equipped?
10 When considering who was first with the development of a jet engine, why should the Italian engine be discounted?
11 What American company was chosen to build the first jet engine? Why?
12 Describe the series of events leading up to the first American jet airplane. Who built this plane?
13 List several American companies who manufacture gas turbine engines.

Chapter 2

Types, variations, and applications

THE GAS TURBINE ENGINE

Gas turbine engines can be classified according to the type of compressor used, the path the air takes through the engine, and how the power produced is extracted or used (Fig. 2-1).

Compressor types fall into three categories:

1 Centrifugal flow
2 Axial flow
3 Centrifugal-axial flow

while power usage produces the following divisions:

1 Turbojet engines
2 Turbofan engines
3 Turboprop engines
4 Turboshaft engines

Compression is achieved in a centrifugal-flow engine by accelerating air outward perpendicular to the longitudinal axis of the machine, while in the axial-flow type, air is compressed by a series of rotating and stationary airfoils moving the air parallel to the longitudinal axis. The centrifugal-axial design uses both kinds of compressors to achieve the desired compression.

In relation to power usage, the turbojet engine directly uses the reaction resulting from a stream of high-energy gas emerging from the rear of the engine at a higher velocity than it had at the forward end. The turbofan engine also uses the reaction principle, but the gases exiting from the rear of this engine type, have a lower energy level, since some power has to be extracted to drive the fan. (See pages 59–60 for a more detailed explanation of the operating principles of the fan engine.)

Turboprop and turboshaft engines both convert the majority of the kinetic (energy of motion), static (energy of pressure), and temperature energies of the gas into torque to drive the propeller in one case, and a shaft in the other. Very little thrust from reaction is produced by the exiting gas stream.

From these basic types of gas turbine engines have come the literally dozens of variations that are either in actual service, or are in various stages of development. Many combinations are possible, since the centrifugal- and axial-flow compressor engines can be used for turbojet, turbofan, turboprop, or turboshaft applications. Furthermore, within the major classifications, are a host of variations, some of which are discussed on the following pages.

CENTRIFUGAL COMPRESSOR ENGINES

Variations of this type of compressor include the single-stage, two-stage, and single-stage double-entry compressor (Fig. 2.2). The centrifugal design works well for small engines where a high compression ratio (pressure rise across the compressor) is not too essential, or where other design or operational considerations may take precedence.

The principal advantages of the compressor are:

1 Light weight
2 Ruggedness, and therefore resistance to foreign object damage
3 Simplicity
4 Low cost

Probably the most famous example of this type of power plant is the Allison J33 (Fig. 2-3), used in the first U.S.A.F. jet, the Lockheed P-80. Newer versions are still being used in the T-33 (Fig. 2-4), which is a training version of the P-80. Centrifugal compressors have found wide acceptance on smaller gas turbine engines. An example of this application is the Continental J69 (Fig. 2-5). Models of this engine are being used in the Cessna T-37 (Fig. 2-6), the U.S.A.F.'s primary trainer. Another example of an engine equipped with a form of the centrifugal compressor is the Rolls Royce Dart (Fig. 2-7). This is a highly produced turboprop engine incorporating a two-stage compressor and integral propeller reduction gearbox (see Fig. 2-33 for an example of an engine equipped with a separate propeller reduction gearbox) and is used in the Convair Conversion 600, Grumman Gulfstream, and Fairchild F-27 (Fig. 2-8).

Several illustrations of the centrifugal compressor used in ground power or auxiliary engines are shown in Figs. 2-9, 2-10, and 2-11. An interesting feature to note on some of these engines is the radial inflow gas-producer turbine shown in Fig. 2-11a and b, and the ''free-power'' turbine shown in Figs. 2-10 and 2-11a

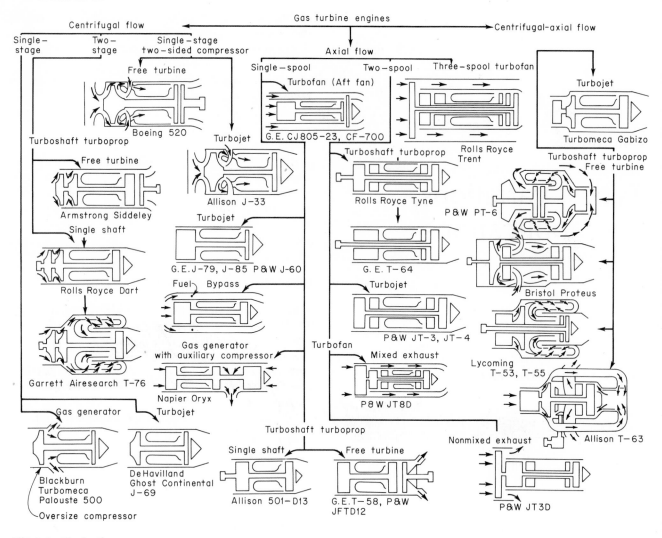

FIG. 2-1 *The family tree.*

FIG. 2-2 *Drawings showing the three basic forms of centrifugal compressors and schematics showing the airflow through each.* (**a**) *and* (**b**) *Single-stage compressor.* (**c**) *Two-stage compressor.* (*Continued on following page.*)

Two — stage compressor
(d)

(e)

Double — entry compressor
(f)

FIG. 2-2 *Drawings showing the three basic forms of centrifugal compressors and schematics showing the airflow through each (continued).* (**d**) *Two-stage compressor airflow.* (**e**) *and* (**f**) *Double-entry compressor.*

(a)

(b)

FIG. 2-3 *Allison J33.* (**a**) *External view.* (**b**) *Cutaway.*

ALLISON J33 *(Fig. 2-3)*

Although this engine is no longer in production, it is included here as an example of a centrifugal-flow turbojet with a double-sided compressor. Since several models were produced, engine operating parameters are given as ranges and/or approximations. The compression ratio is approximately 4.5:1, flows 90 to 110 lb of air per second at 11,800 rpm, and is driven by a single-stage turbine. Fourteen can-type combustion chambers are interconnected by cross ignition tubes. Specific fuel consumption is about 1 lb/(lbt)(hr). The engine weighs approximately 1900 lb and produces thrusts up to 6000 lb.

to *c*. The free-power turbine has no mechanical connection to the primary or gas generator turbine which, in this situation, is used only to turn the compressor in order to supply high-energy gases to drive the free-power turbine. The design lends itself to variable speed operation better than the single shaft, and it produces high torque at low free-power turbine speeds. In addition, this type of power plant has the advantage of requiring no clutch when applying a load or when starting. An example of the single shaft engine is shown in Fig. 2-12.

Some centrifugal and axial engines incorporate a heat exchanger called a regenerator or recuperator. The purpose of the regenerator or recuperator is to return some of the heat energy that would normally be lost with the exhaust to the front of the combustion chamber. By doing this, less fuel needs to be added to reach the turbine limiting temperatures and this will result in high thermal efficiency, low specific fuel consumption, and low exhaust gas temperature. Two basic regenerator

or recuperator types are the rotary drum shown in Fig. 2-10, and the stationary or nonrotating type designed for the Allison T-78 turboprop shown in Fig. 2-34.

AXIAL-FLOW COMPRESSOR ENGINES *(Fig. 2-13)*

Engines using this type of compressor may incorporate one, two, or three spools (a spool is defined as a group of compressor stages rotating at the same speed; see Figs. 2-23, 2-14, and 2-35 for examples of a single-spool, two-spool, and three-spool engine, respectively), forward or rear fans, afterburners, and free-power turbines, and may be used in a variety of applications such as turbojet, turbofan, turboprop, and turboshaft engines.

Practically all of the larger gas turbine engines use this type of compressor because of its ability to handle large volumes of airflow at pressure ratios in excess of 12:1. Unfortunately it is more susceptible to foreign-object damage, it is expensive to manufacture, and it is very heavy in comparison to the centrifugal compressor with the same compression ratio.

Examples of axial-flow machines are even more numerous than those of the centrifugal-flow types and include all of the uses to which gas turbines may be put. Two of the most widely used axial-flow engines are the Pratt & Whitney JT3 (J57) and JT4 (J75) series power plants (Fig. 2-14). These engines were used in early model Boeing 707s, 720s, and Douglas DC-8s, and except for dimensional and thrust values, are essentially the same in construction. Newer designs are installed in several military aircraft. A forward fan version of this engine, the JT3D (Fig. 2-15), is currently powering later versions of the 707, 720, DC-8, and many new military aircraft. Other Pratt & Whitney forward fan engines are the JT9D (Fig. 2-16) used on the Boeing 747, the JT8D (Fig. 2-17) used in the Boeing 727, 737, and Douglas DC-9, and the TF30 (Fig. 2-18)

FIG. 2-4 *Lockheed T-33, training version of the F-80 Shooting Star with one Allison J33 engine.*

CONTINENTAL J69 *(Fig. 2-5)*

The Continental J69 is a centrifugal-flow turbojet engine. The single-stage compressor flows 20 lb of air per second, and has a compression ratio of 3.8:1 at 21,730 rpm. The engine has an annular side-entry combustion chamber, and a single-stage turbine. Specific fuel consumption is 1.11 lb/(lbt)(hr). The engine weighs 364 lb and produces 1025 lb of thrust. Variations include auxiliary power engines with oversized compressors and engines incorporating an axial stage and/or an aft fan. Thrust and/or power ratings for these engines will vary accordingly.

(a)

1. TURBINE SHAFT ASSEMBLY
2. FUEL DISTRIBUTOR
3. FRONT BALL BEARING
4. FUEL SEAL
5. ACCESSORY GEAR TRAIN
6. ACCESSORY CASE
7. STARTER-GENERATOR DRIVE
8. STARTER-GENERATOR REPLACEMENT COVER
9. AIR INLET
10. COMPRESSOR-HOUSING STRUT
11. INDUCER ROTOR
12. COMPRESSOR ROTOR
13. COMPRESSOR COVER
14. RADIAL DIFFUSER
15. COMPRESSOR HOUSING
16. AXIAL DIFFUSER
17. STARTING-FUEL NOZZLE
18. IGNITER PLUG
19. AIR INLET TUBE
20. COMBUSTION CHAMBER
21. TURBINE HOUSING
22. OUTER-COMBUSTOR SHELL
23. INNER-COMBUSTOR SHELL
24. TURBINE INLET NOZZLE
25. TURBINE ROTOR
26. REAR-BEARING HOUSING SUPPORT
27. OIL PASSAGE
28. STREAMLINE STRUT
29. EXHAUST DIFFUSER
30. REAR ROLLER BEARING
31. TUBULAR AIR PASSAGE
A. INLET AIR
B. PRIMARY AIR
C. PRIMARY AIR, COOLING
D. SECONDARY AIR

STARTING FUEL NOZZLES AND IGNITER PLUGS ARE IN LOWER PART OF ACTUAL ENGINE, AND ARE SHOWN ON TOP TO FACILITATE SECTIONING.

(b)

FIG. 2-5 *The Continental J69.* (**a**) *External view.* (**b**) *Sectioned view.*

13

FIG. 2-6 *Cessna T-37B with two Continental J69 engines.*

ROLLS ROYCE DART (*Fig. 2-7*)

The Rolls Royce Dart is another of the most highly produced engines in the world. It has undergone a number of design changes since it was first produced. Basically, the engine is a turboprop with a two-stage centrifugal compressor, two or three turbines and an integral propeller-reduction gearbox. Depending upon the model, the compression ratio is 5.6 to 6.35:1, and mass airflow is from 20 to 27 lb/sec at 15,000 rpm (approximately 1400 propeller rpm). There are seven can-type burners set at an angle to the center line of the engine. Specific fuel consumption is approximately 0.57 lb/(eshp)(hr). The engine weighs 1250 lb and produces about 1800 to 3000 eshp. Some of these engines are equipped with water-alcohol injection.

(a)

(b)

OIL COOLER   2nd-STAGE ROTOR   COMBUSTION CHAMBER

AIR INTAKE   1st-STAGE ROTOR   HIGH-PRESSURE TURBINE   LOW-PRESSURE TURBINE

EXHAUST UNIT

COOLING AIR OUTLET

ROTATING GUIDE VANE   2nd-STAGE DIFFUSER   BURNER   FLAME TUBE

1st-STAGE DIFFUSER   CASCADE VANES   EXPANSION CHAMBER   AIR CASING

FIG. 2-7 *Rolls Royce Dart.* (**a**) *Cutaway view of the Rolls Royce Dart RDa 7 turboprop engine with three turbines.* (**b**) *Airflow through an early Rolls Royce engine.*

(a)

(b)

(c)

FIG. 2-8 (**a**) *Two Rolls Royce Dart MK 529-8X engines are installed in the Grumman Gulfstream.* (**b**) *The Fairchild Hiller F-27 powered by two Rolls Royce Dart engines. The stretched version is called the FH-227.* (**c**) *The Convair Conversion 600 with two Rolls Royce Da 10 engines.*

installed in the General Dynamics/Grumman F-111 and Ling-Temco-Vought Corsair II. Typical of the two-spool design used by the Pratt & Whitney Company is the J52 (Fig. 2-19), a straight turbojet engine used in the Douglas Skyhawk and Grumman Intruder. One of the few supersonic cruise engines, the J-58, is also manufactured by this company (Fig. 2-50).

Pratt & Whitney makes the JT12 (J60), a small axial-flow engine in the 3000-lb thrust class (Fig. 2-20). One of these engines is installed in the North American Buckeye, two JT12's are installed in the North American Sabreliner, while four are used to power the Lockheed Jetstar. Note the placement of the engine(s) on these aircraft. This company also manufactures an axial-flow turboprop, the T34 (Fig. 2-21), which is used in the Douglas C-133, and a free-power turboshaft engine, the JFTD12 (Fig. 2-22), two of which are used in the Sikorsky Skycrane.

Another major manufacturer of both large and small axial-flow gas turbines in this country is the General Electric Company. One of their most highly produced machines is the J79 series (Fig. 2-23) used in many supersonic U.S. Air Force and Navy airplanes. A commercial version of this engine is called the CJ805-3 (Fig. 2-24) and an aft fan counterpart, the CJ805-23 (Fig. 2-25) is used in the Convair 880 and the Convair 990, respectively. Two points worth noting about these engines are the variable angle inlet guide vanes, the variable angle first six stator stages in the compressor, and the location and the method of driving the fan in the CJ805-23 engine. The fan, located in the rear, is "gas coupled" to the primary engine as opposed to the mechanical coupling used in many of the Pratt & Whitney designs and others. Placing the fan in the rear and having it gas coupled is claimed to compromise basic engine performance to a lesser degree. In addition, the engine can be accelerated faster and the aft fan blades are automatically anti-iced by thermal conduction. Forward, mechanically coupled, fan designers claim fewer problems resulting from foreign-object damage, since most of the foreign material will be thrown radially outward and not passed through the rest of the engine, and furthermore, that the forward fan is in the cold section of the engine for highest durability, reliability, and minimum sealing problems.

In addition to their aft fan designs, General Electric also produces a forward fan engine called the TF39 (Fig. 2-26) which powers the Lockheed C5A Galaxy, the largest airplane in the world, and an afterburning commercial pure jet, the GE4 (Fig. 2-27) for use in the Boeing 2707 supersonic transport.

Like Pratt & Whitney, General Electric manufactures a series of smaller gas turbine engines. The CJ610 or J85 (Fig. 2-28) is used in the Lear Jet, Northrop Talon (F-5), and Jet Commander. As might be expected, General Electric has developed an aft fan version of this engine called the CF700 (Fig. 2-29), two of which are installed on the Falcon Fan Jet.

In addition to the jet and fan engines, General Electric manufactures the T58 (Fig. 2-30) and the T64 (Fig. 2-31). Both are free-power turbine engines with a major difference being the location of the power take-off shaft.

CONTROL ISLAND

RADIAL DIFFUSER AXIAL DIFFUSER FUEL DISTRIBUTOR COMPRESSED-AIR DISCHARGE

EXHAUST DIFFUSER

INDUCER
COMPRESSOR
1st-STAGE NOZZLE 1st-STAGE TURBINE

2nd-STAGE TURBINE
2nd-STAGE NOZZLE

(a)

(b)

FIG. 2-9 *Two models of Continental engines showing an oversized compressor and a side-entry combustor.* (a) *This Continental engine is used to provide a high volume of air for starting other gas turbine engines.* (b) *This engine can supply shaft power in addition to air.*

Still other examples of axial-flow machines are the Allison J71 (Fig. 2-32) powering the Douglas B-66, and the Allison 501-D13 or T56 engine (Fig. 2-33) used in the Lockheed Hercules and Electra, Grumman Hawkeye, and the Convair 580 Conversion. Since the 501-D13 is a turboprop, the compressor plus the load of the propeller requires the use of four turbine wheels, as can be seen in Fig. 2-33. Allison has also designed an axial-flow turboprop engine incorporating a regenerator (Fig. 2-34). The advantages of this design are discussed on page 47.

British manufacturers have come up with some interesting variations of the axial-flow engine. For example, the Rolls Royce Trent (Fig. 2-35) is a three-spool turbofan engine for installation in the Fairchild-Hiller F-228. The Rolls Royce Spey (Fig. 2-36), which powers the DeHavilland Trident, B.A.C. One-Eleven, and Grumman Gulfstream II aircraft, is a multispool turbofan engine with a mixed exhaust (see pages 59–60 for a discussion of mixed and nonmixed exhaust systems), and the Rolls Royce Tyne (Fig. 2-37) is a two-spool turboprop engine with an integral gearbox for use in the Canadair 440.

FIG. 2-10 *The Allison GMT-305 regenerative gas turbine. The engine is designed to be used as a prime source of power for land vehicles, but is included here to show the rotating regenerator. The GMT-305 Whirlfire is shown in above cutaway with some of the frame parts omitted for clarity. The arrows show the airflow through the engine. Air enters the inlet (1), is compressed to over 3 atm by a centrifugal compressor (2), and absorbs exhaust heat as it passes through two rotating regenerators (3). The heated compressed air then enters the combustors (4) where the fuel nozzles (5) inject fuel for combustion. The combustion gases pass through the turbine vanes (6) and drive the gasifier turbine (7). The gases then drive the power turbine (8) which is not mechanically connected to the gasifier shaft. Hot exhaust gas is cooled (to 300–500°F) as it passes through the self-cleaning rotating regenerators (9) and is directed out the exhaust ports (10). The power turbine drives the power output shaft (11) through a single-stage helical reduction gear. The gasifier turbine drives the accessory shaft (12) through a set of reduction gears.*

1 COMPRESSOR INLET
2 COMPRESSOR
3 COMPRESSOR COLLECTOR
4 BURNER

5 GAS-PRODUCER TURBINE
6 OUTPUT TURBINE
7 EXHAUST

FIG. 2-11 *The Boeing 520 (T60).* (**a**) *Cutaway view.* (**b**) *The Boeing T60 engine.* (**c**) *The Boeing T50 engine.*

BOEING 520 (T60) *(Fig. 2-11)*

Although this engine is no longer in production, it is included here as an example of an engine equipped with a double-sided centrifugal compressor, a radial-inflow turbine, and an axial-flow power turbine. Since the engine is obsolete, no specifications are included except to note that it was rated at approximately 430 shp. The Boeing T50 shown in Fig. 2-11c is an example of another engine with a centrifugal compressor and a free-power turbine.

The Oryx (Fig. 2-38) manufactured by D. Napier and Son Ltd. is another unusual design of British manufacture. The power produced by the gas generator section of the engine is used to drive another axial-flow compressor. The airflow from both the gas generator and the air pump is mixed together resulting in an extremely high volume airflow. The engine is specifically designed to drive helicopter rotor blades by a jet reaction at the tips.

CENTRIFUGAL-AXIAL-FLOW COMPRESSOR ENGINES

Lycoming Division of the Avco Manufacturing Corporation is, at the time of this writing, one of the largest producers of centrifugal-axial-flow engines in this coun-

AIRESEARCH TPE 331 (T76) *(Fig. 2-12)*

The Garrett AiResearch TPE 331 is a single-shaft turboprop engine. The compressor has two centrifugal stages that are driven by three turbine wheels. Compression ratio is 7.9:1 and mass airflow is 5.8 lb/sec at 41,730 rpm. Propeller rpm is reduced to 2000 by means of a 20.86:1 integral gearbox equipped to sense torque. A reverse-flow combustion chamber is used. Specific fuel consumption is 0.66 lb/(eshp)(hr), and the engine weighs 307 lb. Power is 605 eshp or 575 shp plus 75 lb of thrust.

FIG. 2-12 *(Opposite)* *The AiResearch TPE 331 (T76).* (**a**) *Cutaway view.* (**b**) *Airflow through the engine.*

CARRIER, GEAR PLANET
HOUSING ASSY-DRIVE & ACCESSORY CASE
HOUSING ASSY-INTAKE
TORQUE SENSOR ASSY
COMPENSATOR ASSY
TORQUE SENSOR PRESSURE
REGULATOR UNFEATHERING
VALVE ASSY
GEAR & BEARING
SET ASSY

IMPELLER, 1ST. STAGE COMPRESSOR
DIFFUSER ASSY, 1ST. STAGE
SUPPORT ASSY
CROSS-OVER DUCTS, COMPRESSOR
IMPELLER.
DIFFUSER ASSY, 2ND STAGE
PLENUM ASSY
COMBUSTION CHAMBER ASSY
STATOR ASSY, 1ST STAGE, TURBINE
WHEEL ASSY, 1ST STAGE, TURBINE
STATOR, 2ND STAGE, TURBINE
FUEL NOZZLE JET ASSY
CONE, TAIL PIPE

TAILPIPE SENSOR
PUMP ASSY, OIL SCAVENGE
WHEEL ASSY, 3RD STAGE, TURBINE
STATOR ASSY, 3RD STAGE, TURBINE
WHEEL ASSY, 2ND STAGE, TURBINE
FUEL CONTROL

OIL PUMP ASSY
PUMP ASSY, OIL SCAVENGE
BOOST PUMP, OIL

HOUSING ASSY-FRONT GEAR CASE
GEAR, INTERNAL PLANETARY
PROPELLER ROTOR

(a)

INTEGRAL INLET DUCT
REDUCTION GEARS
PROPELLER SHAFT
FRONT BEARING
ACCESSORIES
TWO STAGE CENTRIFUGAL COMPRESSOR
THREE STAGE AXIAL TURBINE
ANNULAR COMBUSTION
CHAMBER
FUEL NOZZLES
REAR BEARING

REDUCTION-GEAR
SECTION
COMPRESSOR
SECTION
TURBINE SECTION

(b)

19

(c)

(d)

FIG. 2-12 *The AiResearch TPE 331 (T76) (continued).* (**c**) *and* (**d**) *Two models of the 331 engine.* (**c**) *Compressors, turbine, and load on the same shaft (model TSE 331-7).* (**d**) *This version incorporates a free-power turbine (model TSE 331-50).* *(Continued on following page.)*

try. Their T53 and T55 series of engines (Fig. 2-39) in their several versions have been designed for wide application in both conventional and rotary wing aircraft. Both engines utilize the same basic concept and arrangement of parts; the main difference is in the number of compressor and free-power turbine stages. The mechanically independent free-power turbine drives a coaxial through-shaft to provide cold, front-end power extraction. An interesting feature of the engine is the reverse-flow combustion chamber designed to keep the engine as short as possible.

The Canadian Pratt & Whitney PT6A engine (Fig. 2-40) also uses a reverse-flow combustion chamber. On this machine the air enters toward the rear and flows forward, with power takeoff at the front. It is currently in use in several aircraft, including the Beech King Air. The engine has also been used to power the STP Special at the Indianapolis 500 Race.

Allison's bid for the small turbine market, the T63 (Fig. 2-41), has a centrifugal-axial compressor. It incorporates many unusual design features, including disassembly in minutes with ordinary hand tools, a

(e)

(f)

(g)

(h)

FIG. 2-12 *The AiResearch TPE 331 (T76) (continued).* (**e**) *North American's OV-10A Counterinsurgency (COIN) aircraft with two Garrett AiResearch T76 (TPE 331) engines.* (**f**) *The Turbo II Aero Commander with two Garrett AiResearch TPE 331 engines.* (**g**) *Two Garrett AiResearch TPE 331 turbines installed in the Mooney MU-2.* (**h**) *Volpar Super Turbo 18 Conversion using Garrett AiResearch TPE 331 engines.*

single combustion chamber, and an interchangeable gearbox. The axial part of the compressor is only about 4.5 in. in diameter, and the engine weighs about 140 lb, yet produces approximately 317 hp. The turboshaft version of this engine is installed in the Hughes OH-6 Light Observation Helicopter (L.O.H.) and the Bell Jet Ranger helicopter.

Most small gas turbines utilize the free-power turbine method of driving the load and the Boeing engine is no exception. As shown in Fig. 2-42, air is compressed by a single axial stage, followed by a single centrifugal stage. The compressed air is mixed with fuel and ignited in twin reverse-flow combustors. The hot gases pass into an annular chamber and expand through the single-stage gas producer and power turbines. Exhaust is through either a single or double exhaust nozzle.

(*Text continues on page 57.*)

FIG. 2-13 *The axial-flow compressor rotor and stator assembly.*

(a)

(b)

IGNITION — OIL TANK — HIGH-SPEED COMPRESSOR — COMBUSTION-CHAMBER LINER

AIR INLET —

FRONT (LOW-SPEED) COMPRESSOR — ACCESSORIES — FUEL NOZZLES — REAR-COMPRESSOR DRIVE TURBINE — FRONT-COMPRESSOR DRIVE TURBINES

(c)

FIG. 2-14 *The Pratt & Whitney J57.* (**a**) *Cutaway view.* (**b**) *Compressor and turbine arrangement.* (**c**) *Description and cutaway view of the Pratt & Whitney J75.* (*Continued on following page.*)

FIG. 2-14 *The Pratt & Whitney J57 (continued).* **(d)** *McDonnell Douglas RF 101 Voodoo with two Pratt & Whitney J57 engines.* **(e)** *The Ling-Temco-Vought F-8E Crusader equipped with one Pratt & Whitney J57 engine.* **(f)** *Republic Aviation Division, Fairchild Hiller Corporation F-105 Thunderchief with one late-model Pratt & Whitney J57 engine.* **(g)** *The Boeing B-52G with eight Pratt & Whitney J57 engines.* **(h)** *The Pratt & Whitney J57 with afterburner installed in the North American Aviation F-100 Super Sabre.* **(i)** *The Convair F-106 with one Pratt & Whitney J75 engine. This engine is a more powerful version of the J57.*

PRATT & WHITNEY J57 (JT3)

(Fig. 2-14a and b)

The J57 is an axial-flow, two-spool turbojet. It has a nine-stage low-pressure compressor driven by the second- and third-stage turbines, and a seven-stage high-pressure compressor driven by the first-stage turbine. The can-annular combustor has eight burner cans with six fuel nozzles in each can. Mass airflow at 9500 rpm (high-pressure compressor) is 180 lb/sec, with a compression ratio of 13:1 total. Specific fuel consumption is 0.77 lb/(lbt)(hr) without afterburner, and 2.8 lb/(lbt)(hr) with afterburner. Engine weights run from approximately 3800 to 4800 lb. Various engines may be equipped with an afterburner or water injection system. Thrusts range from approximately 11,000 to 18,000 lb, depending upon configuration.

PRATT & WHITNEY J75 (JT4) *(Fig. 2-14c)*

The J75 is similar in construction features to the J57. It is a two-spool axial-flow turbojet engine. The eight-stage low-pressure compressor is driven by the second- and third-stage turbine, and the seven-stage high-pressure compressor is driven by the first-stage turbine. The combustor is of the can-annular design with six fuel nozzles in each can. It may be equipped with an afterburner or a water injection system. Mass airflow at 8650 rpm is 265 lb/sec, and the compression ratio is 12:1. The engine weighs 5000 to 6000 lb, produces 16,000 to 26,000 lb of thrust, and has a specific fuel consumption of 0.79 to 2.2 lb/(lbt)(hr), depending upon configuration.

23

(a)

(b)

(c)

1 COMPRESSOR BLEED CONTROL
2 FRONT ACCESSORY SUPPORT
3 FIRST-STAGE BLADES (FAN)
4 SECOND-STAGE BLADES (FAN)
5 FRONT-COMPRESSOR EXIT VANES
6 FRONT-COMPRESSOR ROTOR
7 COMPRESSOR INTER-MEDIATE INLET VANES
8 REAR-COMPRESSOR ROTOR
9 COMPRESSOR EXIT GUIDE VANES

10 FRONT-COMPRESSOR DRIVE TURBINE ROTOR SHAFT
11 COMBUSTION CHAMBER
12 REAR-COMPRESSOR DRIVE TURBINE ROTOR SHAFT
13 FIRST-STAGE TURBINE VANES
14 SECOND-STAGE TURBINE VANES
15 THIRD-STAGE TURBINE VANES
16 FOURTH-STAGE TURBINE VANES
17 NO. 6 BEARING SUMP AREA
18 TURBINE EXHAUST CASE
19 FOURTH-STAGE TURBINE DISK AND BLADES
20 THIRD-STAGE TURBINE DISK AND BLADES
21 SECOND-STAGE TURBINE DISK AND BLADES
22 FIRST-STAGE TURBINE DISK AND BLADES
23 TURBINE NOZZLE CASE
24 COMBUSTION-CHAMBER REAR OUTER CASE
25 COMBUSTION-CHAMBER FRONT OUTER CASE
26 DIFFUSER CASE
27 ACCESSORY COMPONENTS GEARBOX
28 COMPRESSOR BLEED VALVE
29 COMPRESSOR INTER-MEDIATE CASE
30 FRONT-COMPRESSOR REAR CASE
31 ANTI-ICING AIR VALVE AND ACTUATOR
32 FRONT-COMPRESSOR FRONT CASE
33 COMPRESSOR INLET CASE

FIG. 2-15 *The Pratt & Whitney TF33 (JT3D).* (**a**) *External view.* (**b**) *Sectioned view.* (**c**) *Compressor and turbine arrangement.* (*Continued on following page.*)

(d)

(e)

(f)

(g)

(h)

(i)

FIG. 2-15 *The Pratt & Whitney TF33 (JT3D) (continued).* (**d**) *The Boeing 720 uses four Pratt & Whitney JT3D engines.* (**e**) *The Boeing 707 comes equipped with four Pratt & Whitney JT3D engines.* (**f**) *The McDonnell Douglas DC-8 with four Pratt & Whitney JT3D engines.* (**g**) *General Dynamics' RB-57F powered by two Pratt & Whitney TF33 (JT3D), and two Pratt & Whitney J60 (JT12) engines.* (**h**) *The Lockheed Georgia Division C-141 Starlifter equipped with four Pratt & Whitney TF33 (JT3D) engines.* (**i**) *The Boeing B-52H with eight Pratt & Whitney TF33 (JT3D) engines.*

PRATT & WHITNEY TF33 (JT3D)
(Fig. 2-15)

The TF33 is the fan version of the JT3 series engine. It has a two-spool compressor with the six-stage low-speed spool and two-stage fan being driven by the second-, third-, and fourth-stage turbines, and the seven-stage high-speed spool being driven by the first-stage turbine. The can-annular combustor contains eight burner cans, each with six nozzles. Total compression ratio of the compressors is 13:1 to 16:1, with a mass airflow of 180 to 220 lb/sec at 9800 rpm. Fan compression ratio is 1.66:1 to 2:1, with a mass airflow of 280 lb/sec at 6650 rpm. Specific fuel consumption is 0.53 lb/(lbt)(hr). The engine weighs approximately 4600 lb, and produces 17,000 to 21,000 lb of thrust, depending upon the model.

(a)

(b)

(c)

FIG. 2-16   *The Pratt & Whitney JT9D.* **(a)** *External view.* **(b)** *Internal view.* **(c)** *The Boeing 747 with four Pratt & Whitney JT9D engines.*

PRATT & WHITNEY JT9D   *(Fig. 2-16)*

The Pratt & Whitney JT9D is a two-spool turbofan engine.   The large single front fan has mid-span supports, flows 1210 lb of air per second, and has no inlet guide vanes.   Fan and three-stage low-pressure compressor are driven by a four-stage low-pressure turbine, while the eleven-stage high-pressure compressor is driven by a two-stage turbine.   Mass airflow through the compressor is 240 lb/sec with an overall compression ratio of 24.5:1.   Combustion chamber is of the annular variety.   Turbine inlet temperature is 2100°F as a result of cooled and coated combustors and blades.   Specific fuel consumption is 0.64 lb/(lbt)(hr).   The engine weighs approximately 8400 lb and produces 42,000 lb of thrust.   Growth versions of this engine are intended to produce thrusts of approximately 45,000 lb.

PRATT & WHITNEY JT8D   *(Fig. 2-17)*

Like many of Pratt & Whitney's engines, the JT8D is a two-spool turbofan.   The four-stage low-pressure compressor is connected to the two-stage fan, and is driven by the second-, third-, and fourth-stage turbine wheels.   The seven-stage high-pressure compressor is driven by the first-stage turbine.   A can-annular combustion chamber with nine burner cans is used.   Fan mass airflow is 163 lb/sec, with a compression ratio of 1.9:1.   Compressor mass airflow is 153 lb/sec, with a compression ratio of 16:1 at 11,450 rpm.   The fan air mixes with the primary air at the nozzle.   Specific fuel consumption is 0.6 lb/(lbt)(hr).   The engine weighs 3096 lb, and produces 12,000 to 15,000 lb of thrust in various configurations.

(a)

1	ANTI-ICING AIR DISCHARGE PORTS	**10**	REAR-COMPRESSOR ROTOR REAR HUB
2	FAN INLET CASE	**11**	DIFFUSER CASE AIR MANIFOLD
3	FIRST-STAGE FAN BLADES	**12**	FUEL NOZZLE
4	FRONT COMPRESSOR ROTOR	**13**	NO. 4 BEARING OIL NOZZLE
5	FAN DISCHARGE VANES	**14**	COMBUSTION CHAMBER
6	FAN DISCHARGE INTER-MEDIATE CASE	**15**	COMBUSTION-CHAMBER INNER CASE
7	FAN DISCHARGE INTER-MEDIATE CASE STRUTS	**16**	FIRST-STAGE TURBINE BLADES
8	NO. 2 AND 3 BEARINGS OIL NOZZLE	**17**	SECOND-STAGE TURBINE DISK AND BLADES
9	REAR-COMPRESSOR ROTOR		

18	THIRD-STAGE TURBINE DISK AND BLADES	**23**	THIRD-STAGE TURBINE VANES
19	FOURTH-STAGE TURBINE DISK AND BLADES	**24**	SECOND-STAGE TURBINE VANES
20	EXHAUST STRUT	**25**	FIRST-STAGE TURBINE VANES
21	NO. 6 BEARING HEAT-SHIELD	**26**	IGNITER PLUG
22	FOURTH-STAGE TURBINE VANES	**27**	GEARBOX DRIVE BEVEL GEAR
		28	NO. 1 BEARING TUBE CONNECTOR

PRIMARY AIRSTREAM →
SECONDARY AIRSTREAM ▷

(b)

(c)

(d)

(e)

FIG. 2-17 *The Pratt & Whitney JT8D.* (**a**) *Sectioned view.* (**b**) *Airflow through the engine.* (**c**) *The Boeing 737 with two Pratt & Whitney JT8 engines.* (**d**) *The McDonnell Douglas DC-9 with two Pratt & Whitney JT8D engines.* (**e**) *The Boeing 727 (standard and stretched versions) use three Pratt & Whitney JT8D engines.*

(a)

(b)

(c)

FIG. 2-18 *The Pratt & Whitney TF30.* (**a**) *External view.* (**b**) *Sectioned view.* (**c**) *General Dynamics F-111 with two Pratt & Whitney TF30 engines. In this view the wings are partially swept.* (Continued on following page.)

PRATT & WHITNEY TF30 (*Fig. 2-18*)

The Pratt & Whitney TF30 is a two-spool turbofan engine. The fan has three stages and is connected to the low-pressure compressor which has six stages. Together they rotate at 9300 rpm. The high-pressure compressor has seven stages, and rotates at 14,500 rpm. Mass airflow through the fan is 141 lb/sec with a compression ratio of 2:1. Mass airflow through the compressor is 129 lb/sec, with a compression ratio of 17:1. The engine is equipped with a can-annular combustion chamber having eight flame tubes. The low-pressure compressor and fan are driven by the second-, third-, and fourth-stage turbine wheels, and the high-pressure compressor is driven by the first-stage turbine wheel. Specific fuel consumption is 0.8 to 1.8 lb/(lbt)(hr), depending upon whether the engine is equipped with an afterburner. Weights range from 2500 to 4100 lb and thrust from 11,500 to 21,000 lb, depending upon configuration.

(d)

(e)

FIG. 2-18 *The Pratt & Whitney TF30 (continued).* (**d**) *General Dynamics F-111 with wings extended.* (**e**) *Ling-Temco-Vought A-7A Corsair II powered by one Pratt & Whitney TF30 nonafterburning engine.*

(a)

FIG. 2-19 *The Pratt & Whitney J52 (JT8).* (**a**) *External view.* (*Continued on following page.*)

(b)

(c)

FIG. 2-19 *The Pratt & Whitney J52 (JT8) (continued).* (**b**) *McDonnell Douglas TA-4F Skyhawk with one Pratt & Whitney J52.* (**c**) *Grumman A2F Intruder with two Pratt & Whitney J52 engines.*

PRATT & WHITNEY J52 (JT8) *(Fig. 2-19)*

The J52 is an axial-flow two-spool turbojet engine. It has a five-stage low-pressure compressor and a seven-stage high-pressure compressor with a total compression ratio of 12:1. The combustor is of the can-annular design with nine flame tubes. The two-stage turbine is divided so that the first stage drives the rear, or high-pressure compressor, and the second stage drives the front, or low-pressure compressor. Mass airflow at 11,000 rpm is 120 lb/sec. Specific fuel consumption is 0.79 lb/(lbt)(hr). The engine produces approximately 9300 lb of thrust and weighs 2118 lb.

(a)

FIG. 2-20 *The Pratt & Whitney J60 (JT12).* (**a**) *External view.* *(Continued on following page.)*

PRATT & WHITNEY J60 (JT12) *(Fig. 2-20)*

The Pratt & Whitney J60 is a single-spool single-shaft axial-flow turbojet engine. The compressor has nine stages and is driven by a two-stage turbine. The can-annular combustion chamber has eight flame tubes. Mass airflow at 16,000 rpm is 50 lb/sec with a compression ratio of 6.5:1. Specific fuel consumption is 0.89 lb/(lbt)(hr). The engine weighs 468 lb, and produces approximately 3000 lb of thrust, depending upon the model. An afterburner may be installed.

(b)

(c)

(d)

(e)

FIG. 2-20 *The Pratt & Whitney J60 (JT12) (continued).* (**b**) *Sectioned view.* (**c**) *Lockheed Georgia Division Jet Star (C-140) equipped with four Pratt & Whitney JT12 (J60) engines.* (**d**) *Standard and stretched versions of the North American Sabreliner equipped with two Pratt & Whitney JT12 engines.* (**e**) *North American Aviation T-2B Buckeye with two Pratt & Whitney J60 engines.*

(a)

(b)

FIG. 2-21 *The Pratt & Whitney T34.* (**a**) *External view.* (**b**) *McDonnell Douglas C-133 Cargomaster with four Pratt & Whitney T34 engines.*

PRATT & WHITNEY T34 *(Fig. 2-21)*

The T34 is a turboprop engine equipped with an integral gearbox. The compressor has 13 stages, with a compression ratio of 6.7:1. The combustor is a can-annular type with eight flame tubes. Mass airflow at 11,000 rpm is 65 lb/sec. The propeller and compressor are driven by a three-stage turbine. Specific fuel consumption is 0.70 lb/(shp)(hr), and horsepower equals 6000 to 7000, depending upon the use of water injection and/or configuration. The engine weighs 2870 lb without the propeller.

(a)

(b)

FIG. 2-22 *The Pratt & Whitney JFTD12.* (**a**) *Cutaway view.* (**b**) *Sikorsky S-64 (CH54A) Skycrane equipped with two Pratt & Whitney JFTD12 engines—the free-turbine version of the JT12.*

PRATT & WHITNEY JFTD12 *(Fig. 2-22)*

The Pratt & Whitney JFTD12 engine is a free-power turbine version of the JT12 (J60). It is basically the same as the JT12, except it has a two-stage free-power turbine. Specific fuel consumption is 0.90 lb/(shp)(hr). The engine weighs 870 lb, and produces 4050 shp at 9000 power turbine rpm.

(a)

(b)

(c)

(d)

(e)

(f)

FIG. 2-23 *The General Electric J79.* (**a**) *External view of one model.* (**b**) *Cutaway view of another model.* (**c**) *North American Aviation RA5C Vigilante incorporates two General Electric J79 engines.* (**d**) *Lockheed F-104A Starfighter with one General Electric J79-19 engine.* (**e**) *The B-58 Hustler manufactured by General Dynamics, Fort Worth Division, uses four General Electric J79 engines, and is capable of Mach 2.2 speeds.* (**f**) *McDonnell Douglas F4B Phantom II with two General Electric J79 engines.*

GENERAL ELECTRIC J79 (*Fig. 2-23*)

This is one of the most highly produced engines in the world. The General Electric J79 has a 17-stage axial-flow compressor with variable inlet guide vanes and variable stators on the first six stages. Engine operating parameters are approximate values because of the number of different models produced. Compression ratio is 13:1, mass airflow is 170 lb/sec, and rpm is 7680. The combustion section is of the can-annular design with 10 flame tubes. A three-stage turbine drives the compressor. Specific fuel consumption ranges from 0.84 to 1.96 lb/(lbt)(hr). The engine weighs 3670 lb, and produces from 10,900 to 17,900 lb of thrust, depending upon the model, and whether the afterburner is in operation.

GENERAL ELECTRIC CJ805-3 (*Fig. 2-24*)

The General Electric CJ805-3 engine is the commercial turbojet version of the J79. Specifications for the engine are the same as for the CJ805-23 model, except the engine weighs 2815 lb, produces 11,200 lb of thrust, has a specific fuel consumption of 0.81 lb/(lbt)(hr), and has no aft fan. (See Fig. 2-25 for specifications.)

(a)

(b)

FIG. 2-24 *The General Electric CJ805-3.* (**a**) *Cutaway view.* (**b**) *Convair 880 powered by four General Electric CJ805-3 engines, the commercial version of the J79 engine without the afterburner.*

(a)

1 COMPRESSOR, COM-
  BUSTION, AND TURBINE
  SECTIONS
2 CONICAL COMPRESSOR/
  TURBINE SHAFT
3 THREE MAIN BEARINGS

4 VARIABLE STATORS
5 HYDROMECHANICAL
  CONTROL SYSTEMS
6 TURBOFAN: COMBINATION
  TURBINE BUCKETS AT ROOT
  AND FAN BLADES AT TIP

(b)

FIG. 2-25 *The General Electric CJ805-23.* (**a**) *Cutaway view.*
(**b**) *Convair 990 powered by four General Electric CJ805-23 aft-fan engines.*

GENERAL ELECTRIC CJ805-23 (*Fig. 2-25*)

This General Electric engine is the aft turbofan version of the J79. It has a 17-stage axial-flow compressor, with the inlet guide vanes and the first six stages of stator vanes being variable. The compressor has a compression ratio of 13:1 and a mass airflow of 171 lb/sec at 7310 rpm. The can-annular combustion chamber has 10 flame tubes. A three-stage turbine drives the compressor, and a single-stage turbine blade-fan blade combination (bluckets) is located to the rear. The fan rotates at 5560 rpm, has a pressure ratio of 1.65:1, and flows 251 lb of air per second. Specific fuel consumption is 0.53 lb/(lbt)(hr). The engine weighs 3760 lb, and produces 16,100 lb of thrust.

FAN

COMPRESSOR

VARIABLE
STATOR
SYSTEM

LUBE OIL TANK

COMBUSTOR

HP TURBINE

LP FAN TURBINE

SCAVENGE
PUMP

ACCESSORY GEAR BOX

LUBE PUMP

FUEL PUMP

FUEL CONTROL

AIRFRAME CSD & ALTERNATOR

(a)

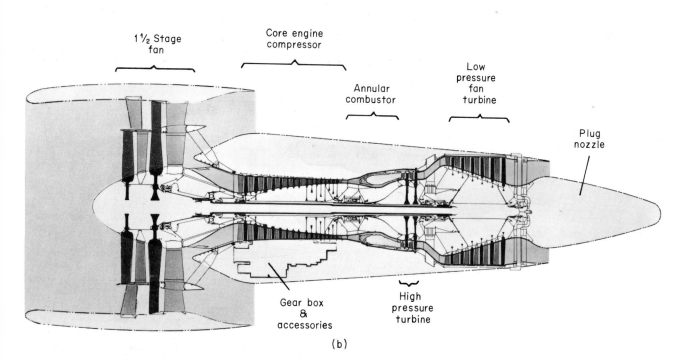

1½ Stage
fan

Core engine
compressor

Annular
combustor

Low
pressure
fan
turbine

Plug
nozzle

Gear box
&
accessories

High
pressure
turbine

(b)

FIG. 2-26 *The General Electric TF39.* (**a**) *External view.* (**b**) *Schematic view.* (*Continued on following page.*)

(c)

FIG. 2-26 *The General Electric TF39 (continued).* **(c)** *Lockheed Georgia C-5A Galaxy with four General Electric TF39 engines.*

GENERAL ELECTRIC TF39 (Fig. 2-26)

The TF39 engine is one of General Electric's latest designs. It is a two-shaft, high-bypass-ratio, front-turbofan engine. The fan has 1½ stages and no inlet guide vanes. It flows 1333 lb of air per second and has a compression ratio of 2:1. The compressor is a 16-stage axial-flow design, with the first seven stages having variable stator vanes. Mass airflow through the compressor is 167 lb/sec, and total compression ratio is 25:1. The engine has an annular combustion chamber. The first two high-pressure turbines drive the compressor, and the last six turbine stages drive the fan. Air-cooled blades permit a turbine inlet temperature of 2300°F as opposed to 1800°F for most engines. Specific fuel consumption is 0.6 lb/(lbt)(hr). The engine weighs 7400 lb and produces 41,000 lb of thrust.

SPECIFICATIONS		
Thrust Class:	**60,000 pounds**	
Length:	**25 feet**	
Diameter:	**6 feet**	
Cruise capability:	**Mach 2.7 (with growth capability to Mach 3)**	

(a)

FIG. 2-27 *The General Electric GE4.* **(a)** *Sectioned view.* **(b)** *Proposed Boeing supersonic transport.*

GENERAL ELECTRIC GE4 (*Fig. 2-27*)

This is the first afterburner equipped commercial turbojet engine.   The nine-stage axial-flow compressor has three rows of variable stator vanes, two rows of fixed stator vanes, and four rows of variable vanes.   Mass airflow is 620 lb/sec.   The engine has an annular combustion chamber.   The compressor is driven by a two-stage turbine with a relatively high inlet temperature of 2200°F.   A thrust reverser and fully modulating afterburner nozzle are part of the engine.   All controls are encapsulated in an insulated steel pod beneath the engine.   Specific fuel consumption is 0.7 to 1.72 lb/(lbt)(hr) with thrust ratings from 43,000 to 63,000 lb, depending upon the use of the afterburner.   The engine weighs 10,500 lb.

GENERAL ELECTRIC J85 (CJ610)
  (*Fig. 2-28*)

The General Electric J85 is a turbojet engine which has an eight-stage axial-flow compressor.   The compressor handles 44 lb of air per second, and has a compression ratio of 6.5:1 to 7:1 at 16,500 rpm.   Variable inlet guide vanes and compressor bleed valves are linked together.   The engine has an annular combustion chamber and a two-stage turbine drives the compressor.   Specific fuel consumption is 0.95 to 2.2 lb/(lbt)(hr) and thrust is 2400 to over 4000 lb, depending upon the model and whether the engine is equipped with an afterburner.   Weights range from 400 to 600 lb.

(a)

1 FORWARD FRAME	**6** TURBINE NOZZLE
2 EIGHT-STAGE AXIAL-FLOW COMPRESSOR	**7** TWO-STAGE AXIAL-FLOW TURBINE
3 COMPRESSOR CASING	**8** TURBINE CASING
4 MAIN FRAME	**9** EXHAUST SECTION AND JET NOZZLE
5 COMBUSTOR	

FIG. 2-28 *The General Electric J85 (CJ610).* (**a**) *Cutaway view.* (*Continued on following page.*)

(b)

(c)

(d)

FIG. 2-28   *The General Electric J85 (CJ610) (continued).* (**b**) *Two General Electric CJ610 engines are installed in the Lear Jet.* (**c**) *Northrop T-38 Talon jet trainer. Training version of the F-5 uses two General Electric J85 (CJ610) engines.* (**d**) *Jet Commander formerly manufactured by the Rockwell Standard Corporation, is now built by Israel Aircraft Industries, Ltd. At the present time it is equipped with two General Electric CJ610 engines.*

GENERAL ELECTRIC CF700 *(Fig. 2-29)*

This engine is General Electric's aft fan version of their CJ610 engine. The eight-stage axial compressor has a compression ratio of 6.8:1, and a mass airflow of 44 lb/sec at 16,500 rpm. The compressor also has variable inlet vanes and bleed valves that operate together. The engine has an annular combustion chamber. Two turbines drive the compressor. The free-power turbine bluckets rotate at the rear at 8160 rpm, have a compression ratio of 1.6:1, and flow 82 lb of air per second. Specific fuel consumption is 0.68 lb/(lbt)(hr). The engine weighs 725 lb and produces 4125 lb of thrust.

(a)

1	FORWARD FRAME
2	EIGHT-STAGE AXIAL-FLOW COMPRESSOR ROTOR
3	COMPRESSOR CASING
4	MAIN FRAME
5	COMBUSTOR
6	TURBINE NOZZLE
7	TWO-STAGE AXIAL-FLOW TURBINE
8	TURBINE CASING
9	FAN FRONT FRAME
10	BUCKETS
11	FAN REAR FRAME

FIG. 2-29   *The General Electric CF700.* (**a**) *Cutaway view. (Continued on following page.)*

(b)

FIG. 2-29 *The General Electric CF700 (continued).* **(b)** *The Fan Jet Falcon built by Dassault of France and marketed by the Business Jets Division of Pan American World Airways, Inc., is powered by two General Electric CF700 turbofan engines.*

(a)

1 TEN-STAGE, AXIAL-FLOW COMPRESSOR WITH ONE-PIECE STEEL CONSTRUCTION FOR LAST EIGHT STAGES OF ROTOR HUB
2 SHORT, SMALL-DIAMETER ANNULAR COMBUSTOR
3 TWO-STAGE, AXIAL-FLOW GAS GENERATOR TURBINE
4 EXHAUST POSITION, ADJUSTABLE 90° LEFT OR

RIGHT [OPTIONAL TORQUE SENSING SPEED DECREASER GEAR (NOT SHOWN) PROVIDES FORE AND AFT POWER TAKEOFF]
5 ANTI-ICED INLET STRUTS AND INLET GUIDE VANES
6 HYDROMECHANICAL CONTROL
7 SINGLE-STAGE, AXIAL-FLOW FREE-POWER TURBINE

FIG. 2-30 *The General Electric T58.* **(a)** *Cutaway view. (Continued on following page.)*

FIG. 2-30 *The General Electric T58 (continued).* (**b**) *Boeing Vertol Division 107-11 Airliner with two General Electric CT58 engines.* (**c**) *Bell model UH-1F with one General Electric T58 engine.* (**d**) *Kaman UH-2 Seasprite with one General Electric T58 engine.* (**e**) *Boeing Vertol Division CH-46 Sea Knight with two General Electric T58 engines.* (**f**) *Sikorsky S-62 with one General Electric CT58 engine.* (**g**) *Sikorsky S-61 (HH-3E) with two General Electric T58 engines.*

GENERAL ELECTRIC T58 *(Fig. 2-30)*

The General Electric T58 is a free-power axial-flow turboshaft engine. The compressor has 10 stages, with variable inlet guide vanes and variable stators on the first three rows. The compressor has a compression ratio of 8.3:1, and flows approximately 13 lb of air per second at 26,300 gas producer rpm. The combustion chamber is of the annular design. Two turbines drive the compressor, and one turbine drives the load through the rear at 19,500 rpm. Specific fuel consumption is 0.64 lb/(shp)(hr). The engine weighs approximately 350 lb, and produces approximately 1300 shp, depending upon the model.

GENERAL ELECTRIC T64 *(Fig. 2-31)*

The General Electric T64 is a turboprop/turboshaft engine incorporating a two-stage gas generator turbine and a two-stage free-power turbine. The compressor has 14 stages with the inlet guide vanes and the first four stages being variable. The combustion chamber is of the annular variety. Mass airflow at 16,900 rpm is 25 lb/sec, and the compression ratio is approximately 13:1, depending upon the model. Specific fuel consumption is approximately 0.5 lb/(eshp)(hr). Weight with propeller reduction gearbox is 1130 lb. The shaft version weighs approximately 700 lb. Equivalent shaft horsepower is 2850 (2770 shp plus 210 lbt) at 15,600 power turbine rpm for the turboprop, to 3435 shp at 13,600 power turbine rpm for the shaft engine. Power takeoff is at the front.

(a)

1 TORQUE SENSOR ON POWER SHAFT (EXCEPT T64-16)
2 HIGH-PRESSURE-RATIO COMPRESSOR
3 BALANCED MOMENT WEIGHT BLADES AND BUCKETS
4 ANTI-ICED FRONT FRAME AND INLET GUIDE VANES
5 FUEL CONTROL, PUMPS, FILTERS, AND ACCESSORY PADS
6 EXTERNAL NOZZLES AND IGNITORS
7 ANNULAR COMBUSTOR
8 TWO-STAGE GAS-GENERATOR TURBINE AND TWO-STAGE FREE-POWER TURBINE

(b)

FIG. 2-31 *The General Electric T64.* **(a)** *Cutaway view.* **(b)** *Sikorsky S-65 (CH53A) with two General Electric T64 engines.* *(Continued on following page.)*

(c)

(d)

FIG. 2-31 *The General Electric T64 (continued).* (**c**) *Late version of the Sikorsky S-65 (HH53B) powered by two General Electric T64 engines.* (**d**) *Ling-Temco-Vought XC-142A triservice VISTOL with four General Electric T64 engines.*

(a)

FIG. 2-32 *The Allison J71.* (**a**) *External view. (Continued on following page.)*

ALLISON J71 *(Fig. 2-32)*

The 16-stage axial-flow compressor of this turbojet engine flows 160 lb/sec at a compression ratio of 8:1 at 6100 rpm. The can-annular combustor has 10 interconnected flame tubes. A three-stage turbine drives the compressor. Specific fuel consumption is 1.8:1 lb/(lbt)(hr) with the afterburner in operation. The engine weighs 4900 lb, and produces 10,000 to 14,000 lb of thrust under normal and reheat (afterburner) operation.

(b)

(c)

FIG. 2-32 *The Allison J71 (continued).* **(b)** *Sectioned view.* **(c)** McDonnell Douglas B-66 with two Allison J71 engines.

ALLISON T56 (501-D13) *(Fig. 2-33)*

This is a single-shaft turboprop engine equipped with a separate propeller reduction gearbox which reduces the propeller rpm to 1020. The 14-stage axial-flow compressor is driven by a 4-stage turbine. Compression ratio is 9.25:1 and airflow is 33 lb/sec at 13,820 rpm. The combustion chamber is the can-annular type with six flame tubes. Specific fuel consumption is 0.53 lb/(eshp)(hr), and the weight of the engine is approximately 1800 lb. The power produced ranges from 3750 eshp (3460 shp plus 726 lb of thrust) to almost 5000 eshp, depending upon the model.

(a)

FIG. 2-33 *The Allison T56 (501-D13).* **(a)** *External view.* *(Continued on following page.)*

(b)

(c)

(d)

(e)

(f)

FIG. 2-33 *The Allison T56 (501-D13) (continued).* (**b**) *Sectioned view.* (**c**) *Grumman E-2A Hawkeye with two Allison T56 engines.* (**d**) *Lockheed Electra with four Allison 501-D13 turboprop engines.* (**e**) *Allison 580 Convair Conversion uses two Allison 501-D13 engines.* (**f**) *Lockheed Georgia HC-130P. The Aerospace Rescue and Recovery version with heli-copter refueling capabilities is equipped with four Allison T56 engines.*

FIG. 2-34 *Allison's T78 regenerator turboprop incorporating a variable stator compressor and a fixed recuperator or regenerator. This engine promises a 36 percent reduction in specific fuel consumption over comparable nonregenerative turboprop engines. The engine has relatively unusual side-entry burners. This engine was never placed in production, but is included here as an example of an engine incorporating a fixed regenerator.*

No variable stators on intermediate- or high-pressure systems

Simple 2-shaft gas producer

Suitable for short, medium, or long cowl

Conservative operating temperatures

Independent single-stage fan without inlet guide vanes

All accessories driven from high-pressure shaft

High bypass ratio

Annular combustion chamber

(a)

(b)

FIG. 2-35 *The Rolls Royce Trent.* (**a**) *Cutaway view.* (**b**) *F-228 short haul aircraft manufactured by Fairchild Hiller is designed to use two Rolls Royce Trent engines.*

ROLLS ROYCE TRENT *(Fig. 2-35)*

The Rolls Royce Trent is an interesting three-spool (shaft) turbofan engine. The fan and low-speed and high-speed compressors are all driven by their own individual turbine wheel. The single-stage fan has no inlet guide vanes, and flows 225 lb of air per second at 8755 rpm. The low-pressure compressor has four stages, and turns at 13,050 rpm, while the high-pressure compressor has five stages and turns at 15,855 rpm. Mass airflow through the compressor is 75 lb/sec, and the total compression ratio is 16:1. An annular combustion chamber is used. Specific fuel consumption is 0.72 lb/(lbt)(hr). The engine's weight is 1750 lb, and it produces 9730 lb of thrust.

ROLLS ROYCE SPEY (ALLISON TF41) *(Fig. 2-36)*

The Spey is a two-shaft turbofan engine having a four- or five-stage front fan driven by the third- and fourth-stage turbine, and a 12-stage high-pressure compressor driven by the first and second turbine stages. The fan compression ratio is approximately 2.7:1 and flows 85 lb of air per second at 8500 rpm. The high-pressure compressor has a compression ratio of 20:1 overall, and the airflow is 123 lb/sec at approximately 12,600 rpm. The can-annular combustion chamber has 10 flame tubes. Specific fuel consumption is 0.6 to 1.95 lb/(lbt)(hr) depending upon whether or not the afterburner is used. The engine weighs 2300 to 3600 lb and produces from 10,000 to 20,000 lb of thrust, depending upon the model. The Allison TF41 is an advanced version of this engine having a 3-stage fan, an 11-stage compressor, and other modifications for installation in the Ling-Temco-Vought A-7D Corsair II. The TF41 was designed and developed jointly by Allison Division of General Motors and Rolls Royce Ltd.

(a)

(b)

(c)

(d)

FIG. 2-36 *The Rolls Royce Spey (Allison TF41).* **(a)** *Cutaway view (four-stage fan).* **(b)** *Schematic.* **(c)** *The Rolls Royce Spey 25 engine (five-stage fan).* **(d)** *Cutaway view of the Allison TF41.* *(Continued on following page.)*

(e)

(f)

FIG. 2-36 *The Rolls Royce Spey (Allison TF41) (continued).* (**e**) *Two Rolls Royce Spey engines drive the Grumman Gulfstream II.* (**f**) *The A-7D Corsair II with one Allison TF41 engine.*

ROLLS ROYCE TYNE (*Fig. 2-37*)

The Tyne is a two-spool axial-flow turboprop engine with an integral propeller reduction gearbox turning the propeller at 975 rpm. The six-stage low-pressure compressor is driven by the second-, third-, and fourth-stage turbines, while the nine-stage high-pressure section is powered by the first-stage turbine. The compression ratio is 13.5:1, and the mass airflow is 46.5 lb/sec at 15,250 rpm. The can-annular combustor has 10 flame tubes. Specific fuel consumption is 0.39 lb/(eshp)(hr) in cruise. Weight of the engine is 2177 lb, and it produces 5500 eshp (5095 shp plus 1065 lb of thrust).

(a)

FIG. 2-37 *The Rolls Royce Tyne 20 turboprop engine.* (**a**) *External view.* (*Continued on following page.*)

HIGH PRESSURE SHAFT

3-STAGE LOW PRESSURE TURBINE

FUEL BURNER

EXHAUST UNIT

SINGLE-STAGE HIGH PRESSURE TURBINE

LOW PRESSURE SHAFT

FLAME TUBE

9-STAGE HIGH PRESSURE COMPRESSOR

6-STAGE LOW PRESSURE COMPRESSOR

REDUCTION GEAR

AIR INTAKE

PROPELLER SHAFT

(b)

FIG. 2-37 *The Rolls Royce Tyne 20 turboprop engine (continued).* (**b**) *Cutaway view.*

(a)

FIG. 2-38 *The Napier Oryx.* (**a**) *External view.* (*Continued on following page.*)

(b)

(c)

FIG. 2-38 *The Napier Oryx (continued).* (**b**) *Schematic showing the airflow.* (A) *Compressor inlets,* (B) *compressor turbine,* (C) *air-pump outlet,* (D) *throttle valve.* (**c**) *Proposed Napier Oryx installation.*

(a)

1	ANNULAR INLET	**7**	COMBUSTION CHAMBER
2	VARIABLE INLET GUIDE VANE	**8**	VAPORIZER TUBES (IN EARLIER VERSIONS) OR ATOMIZERS
3	FIVE-STAGE AXIAL COMPRESSOR	**9**	COMBUSTION TURNING ZONE
4	SINGLE CENTRIFUGAL COMPRESSOR STAGE	**10**	AIR-COOLED FIRST TURBINE NOZZLE
5	RADIAL DIFFUSER	**11-12**	TWO-STAGE COMPRESSOR TURBINE
6	AREA SURROUNDING COMBUSTION CHAMBER		

13	FREE-POWER TURBINE NOZZLE
14-15	TWO-STAGE FREE-POWER TURBINE
16	THROUGH-SHAFT
17	PLANETARY REDUCTION GEAR
18	INLET HOUSING

(b)

1	ANNULAR INLET	**9**	180° TURNING AREA
2	INLET GUIDE VANES	**10**	AIR-COOLED FIRST TURBINE NOZZLE
3	SEVEN AXIAL STAGES	**11**	COMPRESSOR TURBINE ROTOR ASSEMBLY
4	SINGLE-STAGE CENTRIFUGAL COMPRESSOR ASSEMBLY	**12**	FREE-POWER TURBINE NOZZLE
5	RADIAL DIFFUSER	**13**	TWO-STAGE FREE-POWER TURBINE ASSEMBLY
6	AREA SURROUNDING THE COMBUSTION CHAMBER	**14**	STRUT
7	ANNULAR, REVERSE FLOW, COMBUSTION CHAMBER	**15**	CONCENTRIC OUTPUT SHAFT
8	ATOMIZER OR VAPORIZER TUBES		

FIG. 2-39 *The Lycoming T53 (T55).* (**a**) *Cutaway view of the T53-L-13.* (**b**) *Cutaway view of the T55-L-7.* *(Continued on following page.)*

(c)

(d)

(e)

(f)

(g)

FIG. 2-39 *The Lycoming T53 (T55) (continued). (c) Boeing helicopter Vertol Division CH-47 with two Lycoming T55 turboshaft engines. (d) Bell 204B, civil version of the military UH-1 Iroquois helicopter uses a Lycoming T53 engine. (e) Kaman HH43B Huskie powered by one Lycoming T53 engine. (f) Three Bell helicopters using the Lycoming T53 engine (Top to bottom—UH-1D, UH-1B, Huey Cobra). (g) The Lycoming T53 turboprop powers the Grumman OV-1A Mohawk.*

LYCOMING T53 (T55) *(Fig. 2-39)*

This engine incorporates a five-stage axial and single-stage centrifugal compressor. The compression ratio is 6.1:1, and mass airflow is 11.1 lb/sec at 25,200 rpm. Combustion chamber is a reverse-flow annular type. Some models are equipped with a single gas generator turbine and a single free-power turbine, while others have two of each kind. The load (turboprop or turboshaft) is driven at the front of the engine by means of a concentric shaft. Specific fuel consumption, weight, and power ratings all vary with the model engine, but run from approximately 0.6 to 0.7 lb/(shp)(hr), 500 to 600 lb of weight, and 1100 to 1400 shp, respectively. The T55 is a growth version of this engine.

(a)

Power turbine
inlet

Exhaust outlet   Exhaust inlet   Compressor   Burner inlet   Compressor   Engine inlet
                               turbine inlet   inlet

(b)

(c)

(d)

FIG. 2-40 *The United Aircraft of Canada (Pratt & Whitney) PT6A.* (**a**) *Cutaway view.*
(**b**) *Sectioned view.* (**c**) *American Turbine Beech 18 Conversion uses two Canadian Pratt &
Whitney PT6 engines.* (**d**) *The Beechcraft King Air with two Canadian Pratt & Whitney
PT6A engines.*

UNITED AIRCRAFT OF CANADA (PRATT & WHITNEY) PT6A *(Fig. 2-40)*

The Canadian Pratt & Whitney PT6A is a two-shaft turboprop engine. The air enters the three-stage axial compressor from the side of the engine through an inlet screen, and flows forward to a single centrifugal stage. The pressure ratio is 6.3:1 and airflow is 5.5 lb/sec at 37,500 rpm. A reverse-flow combustion chamber surrounds the turbine wheels. One turbine wheel drives the compressor, while the free-power turbine drives the propeller through a 15:1 ratio integral gearbox. Propeller rpm is 2200 maximum. Specific fuel consumption at cruise is 0.65 lb/(eshp)(hr). The engine weighs 275 lb and produces 579 eshp, or 550 shp plus 72 lb of thrust. Several versions of this engine have higher power ratings.

ALLISON T63 *(Fig. 2-41)*

This is a centrifugal-axial-flow, free-power turbine, turboshaft-turboprop engine. The five-stage axial and single-stage centrifugal compressors provide a compression ratio of 6.2:1, and an airflow of 3 lb/sec at 51,600 rpm. There is a single reverse-flow combustor at the rear. The compressor is driven by a two-stage turbine and the load is driven by a two-stage turbine which turns at 35,000 rpm. Specific fuel consumption is 0.7 lb/(shp)(hr). The engine weighs 140 lb, and produces 317 shp. Shaft rpm is 6000, and propeller rpm is 2200.

(a)

FIG. 2-41 *The Allison T63.* **(a)** *Cutaway view.* *(Continued on following page.)*

(b)

(c)

(d)

FIG. 2-41 *The Allison T63 (continued).* (**b**) *Sectioned view.* (1) Compressor: air enters the inlet and is compressed to over 6 atm by the six axial stages and one centrifugal stage of the compressor. (2) Air-transfer tubes: the high-pressure discharge air from the compressor is transferred rearward to the combustion section through the two air-transfer tubes. (3) Combustor: the single combustor regulates and evenly distributes the engine airflow. (4) Fuel nozzle: fuel is injected through a single duplex-type fuel nozzle. (The fuel is ignited by a single ignitor plug adjacent to the fuel nozzle and used only during the starting cycle.) (5) Turbines: the hot combustion gases pass forward through the first two-stage axial turbine which drives the compressor and thence through the second two-stage axial turbine which drives the power output shaft. (6) Exhaust: after passing forward through the turbine section, the gases are exhausted upward through twin exhaust ducts. (7) Power output shaft—6000 rpm: the energy of the turbine section, after passing through appropriate gearing in the accessories gear case, is available from an internally splined shaft at either the front or rear output pad. (**c**) The Allison T63 (Civil model 250-C18) installed in a Bell Jet Ranger 206A helicopter. (**d**) Hughes Tool Company Aircraft Division OH-6A light observation helicopter powered by one Allison T63 engine.

(a)

(b)

(c)

FIG. 2-42 *A Boeing engine incorporating an axial-centrifugal compressor and a free-power turbine.* (**a**) *Boeing T50-BO-10, commercial version model 550.* (**b**) *Airflow schematic of the Boeing engine.* (**c**) *Model 550 rotor system.*

Once again, British designers and manufacturers have produced one of the most unusual centrifugal-axial-flow engines. The Bristol Proteus (Fig. 2-43) incorporates a reverse-flow centrifugal-axial compressor and a two-stage free-power turbine driving the propeller output shaft through a series of reduction gears. The engine is used in the Britannia aircraft.

MIXED-FLOW COMPRESSOR ENGINES

This compressor does not fall into any of the three main categories. The mixed-flow design is similar in appearance to the single-entry centrifugal compressor, but the blade arrangement provides a different type of

BRISTOL PROTEUS *(Fig. 2-43)*

The unusual design and arrangement of the parts in this engine warrant its inclusion in this section. Air enters toward the middle of the engine and flows forward through a 12-stage axial compressor and a single-stage centrifugal compressor. The compressor is driven by a two-stage turbine and has a compression ratio of 7.2:1, a mass airflow of 44 lb/sec, and rotates at 11,755 rpm. Eight can-type combustion chambers are located on the outside of the compressor. A two-stage free-power turbine drives the propeller by means of a concentric shaft through the engine. An integral gearbox reduces the propeller rpm by a ratio of 11.593:1 in relation to the free-power turbine rpm. Specific fuel consumption is 0.48 lb/(eshp)(hr) in cruise. The engine weighs 2900 lb without the propeller and produces 4445 eshp, or 3960 shp plus 1260 lb of thrust. It may be equipped with water injection.

FAIRCHILD J44 *(Fig. 2-44)*

Although this engine is obsolete, it is included here as an example of a mixed-flow compressor. In this type of compressor the air transitions from a centrifugal to axial flow over a single stage. The compression ratio is 2.7:1 and airflow is 25 lb/sec at 15,780 rpm. The engine has an annular combustion chamber and a single-stage turbine. Specific fuel consumption is 1.4 to 1.6. Engine weight is 370 lb and it produces 1000 lb of thrust.

FIG. 2-43   *Sectioned view of the Bristol Proteus.*

(a)

FIG. 2-44   *The Fairchild J44.*   (**a**) *Sectioned view showing airflow.*   (*Continued on following page.*)

FIG. 2-44 *The Fairchild J44 (continued).* (**b**) *The Fairchild J44 mixed-flow compressor.*

airflow. The compressor receives its air axially as do many other types, but it discharges this air at some angle between the straight through flow of the axial compressor and the radial flow of the centrifugal compressor. The Fairchild J44 engine (Fig. 2-44) uses this design.

CHARACTERISTICS AND APPLICATIONS OF THE TURBOJET, TURBOPROP, AND TURBOFAN ENGINES

THE TURBOJET ENGINE

Chapter 3, which deals with engine theory, points out that a turbojet derives its thrust by highly accelerating a small mass of air, all of which goes through the engine. Since a high "jet" velocity is required to obtain an acceptable amount of thrust, the turbine of a turbojet is designed to extract only enough power from the hot gas stream to drive the compressor and accessories. All of the propulsive force produced by a jet engine is derived from the imbalance of forces within the engine itself (Fig. 2-45).

THE TURBOPROP ENGINE

Propulsion in a turboprop engine is accomplished by the conversion of the majority of the gas stream energy into mechanical power to drive the compressor, accessories, and the propeller load. Only a small amount (approximately ten percent) of "jet" thrust is available

in the relatively low-pressure, low-velocity gas stream created by the additional turbine stages needed to drive the extra load of the propeller.

THE TURBOFAN ENGINE

The turbofan engine has a duct enclosed fan mounted at the front or rear of the engine and driven either mechanically at the same speed as the compressor, or by an independent turbine located to the rear of the compressor drive turbine. (Refer to Figs. 2-15, 2-17, 2-25, and 2-29 to see these variations.) Figures 2-15 and 2-17 also illustrate two methods of handling the fan air. Either the fan air can exit separately from the primary engine air, or it can be ducted back to mix with the primary engine's air at the rear. If the fan air is ducted to the rear, the total fan pressure must be higher than the static gas pressure in the primary engine's exhaust, or air will not flow. By the same token, the static fan discharge pressure must be less than the total pressure in the primary engine's exhaust, or the turbine will not be able to extract the energy required to drive

FIG. 2-45 *Energy distribution of the turbojet, turboprop, and turbofan engines.*

the compressor and fan.   By closing down the area of flow of the fan duct, the static pressure can be reduced and the dynamic pressure increased.   (See Chap. 3 for a discussion of static, dynamic, and total pressure.)

The efficiency of the fan engine is increased over that of the pure jet by converting more of the fuel energy into pressure energy rather than the kinetic (dynamic) energy of a high-velocity exhaust gas stream.   As shown in Chap. 3, pressure times the area (*PA*) equals a force.   The fan produces this additional force or thrust without increasing fuel flow.   As in the turboprop, primary engine exhaust gas velocities and pressures are low because of the extra turbine stages needed to drive the fan.   One fundamental difference between the turbofan and turboprop engine is that the airflow through the fan is controlled by design so that the air velocity relative to the fan blades is unaffected by the aircraft's speed.   This eliminates the loss in operational efficiency at high airspeeds which limits the maximum airspeed of the turboprop engine.

The emphasis on the use and development of the turbofan engine in recent years is due largely to the development of the transonic blade.   The large diameter fan would require a much lower rpm to keep the blade tips below the speed of sound (see Chap. 3) and this would not be conducive to good gas turbine design.

Fan engines show a definite superiority over the pure jet engines at speeds below Mach 1 (Fig. 2-46), the speed of present day commercial aircraft.   The increased frontal area of the fan presents a problem for high-speed aircraft which, of course, require small frontal areas.   At high speeds, the increased drag offered by the fan more than offsets the greater net thrust produced.   The disadvantage of the fan for high-speed aircraft can be offset at least partially by burning fuel in the fan discharge air.   This would expand the gas, and in order to keep the fan discharge air at the same pressure, the area of the fan jet nozzle is increased. This action results in an increase in gross thrust due to an increase in pressure times an area (*PA*), and an increase in thrust specific fuel consumption.   (See Chap. 3.)

COMPARISON AND EVALUATION OF TURBOJET, TURBOPROP, AND TURBOFAN ENGINES

By converting the shaft horsepower of the turboprop into pounds of thrust, and the fuel consumption per horsepower into fuel consumption per pound of thrust, a comparison between turbojet, turboprop, and turbofan can be made.   Assuming that the engines are equivalent as to compressor ratio and internal temperatures and that the engines are installed in equal-sized aircraft best suited to the particular type of engine being used, Fig. 2-46 shows how the various engines compare as to thrust and thrust specific fuel consumption versus airspeed.   As the graphs indicate, each engine type has its advantages and limitations.   Summaries of these characteristics and uses follow.

Turbojet characteristics and uses

1   Low thrust at low forward speeds.
2   Relatively high TSFC at low altitudes and airspeeds. This disadvantage decreases as altitude and airspeed increase.
3   Long takeoff roll required.
4   Small frontal area results in reduced ground clearance problems.
5   Lightest specific weight (weight per pound of thrust produced).
6   Ability to take advantage of high ram-pressure ratios.

These characteristics would indicate that the turbojet engine would be best for high speed, high altitude, long distance flights.

Turboprop characteristics and uses

1   High propulsive efficiency at low airspeeds, which falls off rapidly as airspeed increases.   This results in shorter takeoff rolls.   The engine is able to develop very high thrust at low airspeeds because the propeller can accelerate large quantities of air at zero forward velocity of the airplane.   A discussion of propulsive efficiency follows in the next chapter.
2   More complicated and heavier than a turbojet.
3   Lowest TSFC.
4   Large frontal area of propeller and engine combination necessitates longer landing gears for low-wing airplanes, but does not necessarily increase parasitic drag.
5   Efficient reverse thrust possible.

These characteristics show that turboprop engines are superior for lifting heavy loads off short and medium runways.   Turboprops are limited in speeds to approximately 500 mph, since propeller efficiencies fall off rapidly with increasing airspeeds.

Turbofan characteristics and uses

1   Increased thrust at forward speeds similar to a turboprop results in a relatively short takeoff.   But unlike the turboprop, the turbofan thrust is not penalized with increasing airspeed, up to approximately Mach 1 with current fan designs.
2   Weight falls between the turbojet and turboprop.
3   Ground clearances are less than turboprop, but not as good as turbojet.
4   TSFC and specific weight fall between turbojet and turboprop (Figs. 2-47 and 2-48).   This results in increased operating economy and aircraft range over the turbojet.
5   Considerable noise level reduction of 10 to 20 percent over the turbojet reduces acoustic fatigue in surrounding aircraft parts and is less objectionable to people on the ground.   No noise suppressor is needed.   On newer fan engines such as the Pratt & Whitney JT9D and General Electric TF39 shown in Figs. 2-16 and 2-26, the inlet guide vanes have been eliminated in an attempt to reduce the fan noise which is considered to be a large problem for high-bypass-ratio fan engines.   The noise level is reduced by the elimination of the discrete frequencies that are generated by the fan blades cutting through the wakes behind the vanes. Other fan-noise-reducing features are also incorporated.
6   Superior to the turbojet in "hot day" performance (Fig. 2-49).

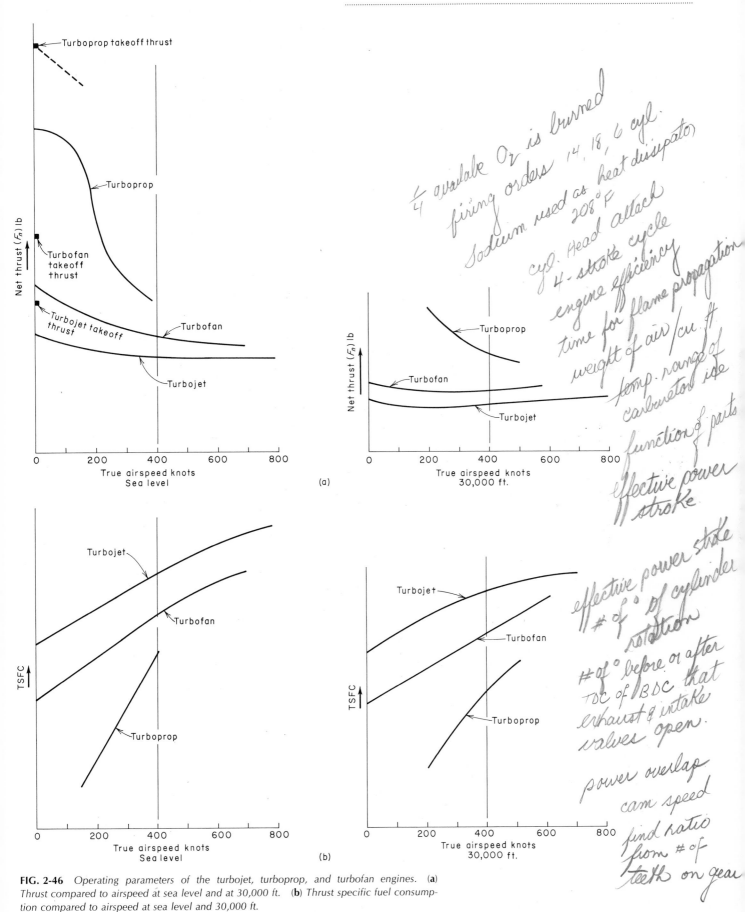

FIG. 2-46 *Operating parameters of the turbojet, turboprop, and turbofan engines.* (**a**) *Thrust compared to airspeed at sea level and at 30,000 ft.* (**b**) *Thrust specific fuel consumption compared to airspeed at sea level and 30,000 ft.*

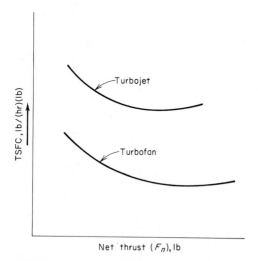

FIG. 2-47 *Comparison of thrust specific fuel consumption to thrust for the turbojet and turbofan engine shows the superiority of the turbofan.*

7   Two thrust reversers are required if the fan air and primary engine air exit through separate nozzles. The advantage of the separate fan nozzle is the short fan duct with corresponding low duct loss.

From the above characteristics it is obvious that the fan engine is suitable for long-range, relatively high speed flight, and has a definite place in the prolific gas turbine family.

REVIEW AND STUDY QUESTIONS

1   What are two methods of classifying gas turbine engines?
2   List some variations of centrifugal-type engines. Name some airplanes in which this type of engine is installed.
3   What are the advantages and disadvantages of the centrifugal compressor?
4   Define "gas generator" and "free-power turbine."
5   What is a regenerator? Of what advantage and disadvantage is this type of device?
6   List some variations of the axial-compressor engine. Name some airplanes in which this type of engine is installed.
7   What are the advantages and disadvantages of the axial compressor?
8   Where is the fan located on the fan-type engine? How is it driven?
9   What are three ways of using a gas turbine engine to power an airplane?
10   What is meant by mixed exhaust and nonmixed exhaust fan engines?
11   Make a table that lists the characteristics and uses of the turbojet, turboprop, and turbofan engines.

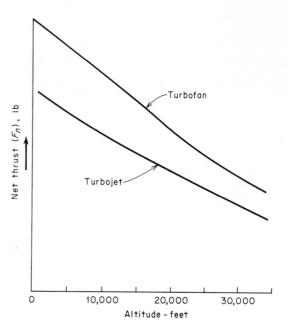

FIG. 2-48 *The turbofan engine maintains its superior thrust rating over the turbojet engine at all altitudes.*

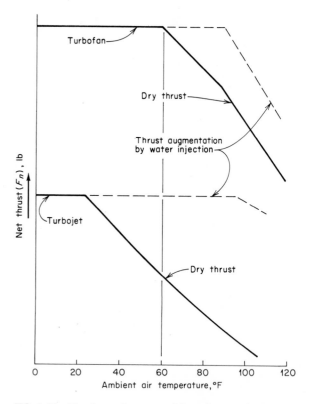

FIG. 2-49 *Hot-day performance of the turbojet and turbofan engines at sea level.*

(a)

(b)

FIG. 2-50 *The Pratt & Whitney J58.* (**a**) *External view.* (**b**) *The Lockheed SR-71 (similar to the F12A) is powered by two Pratt & Whitney J58 engines. Speed is over 2000 mph (Mach 3).*

PRATT & WHITNEY J58 (*Fig. 2-50*)

This engine is a single-shaft, supersonic cruise engine equipped with an afterburner. It has an eight-stage compressor driven by a two-stage turbine. Six large tubes are used to bypass a part of the compressor airflow to the afterburner. The combustion chamber is a can-annular design with eight flame tubes. No rpm, compression ratio, or mass airflow figures are available. Specific fuel consumption is 0.8 to 1.9 lb/(lbt)(hr). The engine weighs 6500 lb and produces up to 34,000 lb of thrust with the afterburner in operation. At the time of this writing the engine is still highly classified.

Chapter 3

Engine theory: two plus two

In order to understand some of the operating fundamentals of the gas turbine engine, it might be well to list the sections of such an engine and then very briefly discuss the series of events that occur.

Basically a gas turbine engine consists of five major sections: an inlet duct, a compressor, a combustion chamber (or chambers), a turbine wheel (or wheels), and an exhaust duct (Fig. 3-1). In addition to the five major sections, each gas turbine is equipped with an accessory section, a fuel system, a starting system, a cooling system, a lubrication system, and an ignition system. Some engines might also incorporate a water injection system, an afterburner system, a variable area exhaust nozzle and system, a variable geometry compressor, a fan, a free-power turbine, a propeller reduction gearbox, and other additional systems and components to improve or change engine operation, performance, and usage.

TYPICAL OPERATION

The front, or inlet, duct is almost entirely open to permit outside air to enter the front of the engine. The compressor works on this incoming air and delivers it to the combustion or burner section with as much as 12 times or more the pressure the air had at the front. In the burner section, fuel, similar to a mixture of gasoline and kerosine, is sprayed and mixed with the compressor air. The air-fuel mixture is then ignited by devices similar to spark plugs. When the mixture is lighted, the ignitor can be turned off, as the burning process will continue without further assistance as long as the engine is supplied with the proper fuel/air ratio. The fuel-air mixture burns at a relatively constant pressure with only about 25 percent of the air taking part in the actual combustion process. The balance of the air is mixed with the products of combustion for cooling before the gases enter the turbine wheel. The turbine extracts a major portion of the energy in the gas stream and uses this energy to turn the compressor and accessories. After leaving the turbine, there is still enough pressure remaining to force the hot gases through the exhaust duct and jet nozzle at the rear of the engine at very high speeds. The engine's thrust comes from taking a large mass of air in at the front end and expelling it from the tailpipe at a much higher speed than it had when it entered the compressor. Thrust, then, is equal to *mass flow rate times change in velocity*. In order to appreciate this statement, a review of some basic physics is necessary.

REVIEW OF PHYSICS CONCEPTS

Force

A *force* is defined as a push or a pull which will produce or prevent motion. Gravity, for example, is a force that attracts bodies toward the earth at a rate that will cause the object to increase its velocity by 32.2 fps for each second the object is falling. That is, at the end of 2 sec, the speed would be 64.4 fps, at the end of 3 sec it would be 128.8 fps, etc. The figure 32.2 feet per second per second (32.2 ft/sec^2) is called the acceleration due to gravity and is represented in formulas by the letter g. This value can also be used to determine the amount of resistance an object of given weight offers to motion. By dividing the weight by the acceleration constant, the quotient is called the mass of the object. (See page 67.)

$$M = \frac{w}{g}$$

Force is also a vector quantity; that is, it has both magnitude and direction. When we speak of 1000 lb of force acting upon an object, we cannot know its effect unless we know the direction of the force. Two or more forces acting on a body will produce a resultant force. Vectors and their resultants will be used in Chaps. 5 and 7 to help explain the operation of compressors and turbines.

Work

Mechanical *work* is done when a force acting on a body causes it to move through any distance (Fig. 3-2).

Work = force × distance
$$W = Fd$$

Atmosphere supplies both mass and oxygen

Energy of fuel

Turbine absorbs energy to drive compressor

Reaction is combustion

Front entry of compressor

Mass to rear entry of compressor passes between cylindrical ducts

Centrifugal flow

Nozzle action

Jet

Energy of fuel

Axial flow

FIG. 3-1 *Airflow through a centrifugal- and axial-flow engine.* (*USAF AFM 52-5*)

It is important to remember that work is accomplished only when an object is moved some distance by an applied force. For example, if an object that is pushed as hard as possible fails to move, then by the textbook definition, no work has been done.

Force is most often expressed in pounds, distance in feet, and work in foot-pounds.

EXAMPLE: A jet engine that is exerting 1000 lb of

55 lb x 10 ft = 550 ft – lb

FIG. 3-2 *Work equals force times distance.* (*U.S.A.F. Extension Course Institute and Air University, Course 4301*)

force moves an airplane 10 ft. How much work is being accomplished?

$$\text{Work} = Fd$$
$$= 1000 \times 10$$
$$W = 10,000 \text{ ft-lb}$$

Power

Nothing in the definition of work states how fast the work is being done. The rate of doing work is known as *power*.

$$\text{Power} = \frac{\text{force} \times \text{distance}}{\text{time}}$$
$$P = \frac{Fd}{t}$$

As will be learned later when developing a formula for converting thrust to power, power may be expressed in any one of several ways, depending upon the units used for the force, the distance, and the time. Power is often expressed in units of horsepower. One *horsepower* is equal to 33,000 foot-pounds per minute or

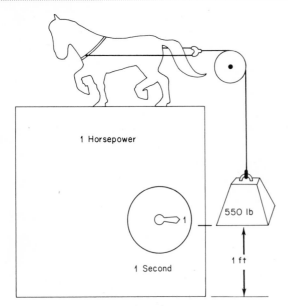

1 Horsepower

1 ⬤ 1

550 lb

1 Second

1 ft

FIG. 3-3   *Most horses are capable of more power than this.*   (U.S.A.F. Extension Course Institute and Air University, Course 4301)

550 foot-pounds per second.   In other words, a 1-hp motor can raise 33,000 lb a distance of 1 ft in 1 min or 550 lb a distance of 1 ft in 1 sec (Fig. 3-3).

$$hp = \frac{power\ (ft\text{-}lb/min)}{33,000}$$
$$= \frac{Fd/t(min)}{33,000}$$

or

$$hp = \frac{power\ (ft\text{-}lb/sec)}{550}$$
$$= \frac{Fd/t(sec)}{550}$$

EXAMPLE: A 5000-lb weight is lifted a distance of 10 ft in 2 min.   How much horsepower is required?

$$P = \frac{Fd}{t}$$
$$= \frac{5000 \times 10}{2}$$
$$= 25,000\ ft\text{-}lb/min$$
$$hp = \frac{P}{33,000}$$
$$= \frac{25,000}{33,000}$$
$$= 0.75 \quad or \quad ¾$$

Energy

Energy is defined as the capacity for doing work.   The energy which bodies possess can be classified into two categories: *potential* and *kinetic*.   Potential energy may be due to position, such as water in an elevated storage

tank, distortion of an elastic body such as a compressed spring, or a chemical action, for example, from coal.

EXAMPLE: A 20,000-lb airplane is held 5 ft off the floor by a jack.   How much potential energy does this system possess?

$$PE = WH$$
$$= 20,000 \times 5$$
$$= 100,000\ ft\text{-}lb$$

where PE = potential energy, ft-lb
       W = weight of object, lb
       H = height of object, ft

   Kinetic energy is energy of motion.   Gases striking the turbine wheel exhibit kinetic energy.   If the mass and speed of a body is known, the kinetic energy can be determined from the formula

$$KE = \frac{WV^2}{2g}$$

where W = weight, lb
       V = velocity, fps
       g = acceleration due to gravity = 32.2 fps²
       KE = kinetic energy, ft-lb

Notice that the kinetic energy is directly proportional to both the weight and the square of the velocity.

EXAMPLE: An airplane weighing 6440 lb has a velocity of 205 mph (300 fps).   Find the kinetic energy.

$$KE = \frac{WV^2}{2g}$$
$$= \frac{6440 \times 300^2}{2 \times 32.2}$$
$$= 9,000,000\ ft\text{-}lb\ of\ energy$$

Speed

   The *speed* of a body in motion is defined as the distance it travels per unit of time.

$$Speed = \frac{distance}{time}$$

Speed units are commonly expressed in miles per hour or feet per second.

Velocity

   Velocity can be defined as speed in a given direction. The symbol *V* is used to represent velocity.

Acceleration

   The *acceleration* of a body in motion is defined as the rate of velocity change.   The definition is not based on the distance traveled, but on the loss (deceleration) or gain (acceleration) of velocity with time.

$$\text{Acceleration} = \frac{\text{change in motion}}{\text{unit of time}}$$
$$= \frac{\text{final velocity minus initial velocity}}{\text{time}}$$
$$= \frac{V_2 - V_1}{t}$$

where V_1 is the original velocity and V_2 is the final velocity.

Mass

The *mass* of an object is the amount of fundamental matter of which it is composed; it is in a sense the measure of a body's inertia. Mass and weight are often confused because the common method of determining a quantity of matter is by weighing. But, weight is only a measure of the pull of gravity on a quantity of matter. An object that weighs 36 lb on earth will weigh 6 lb on the moon. Yet the mass is exactly the same. Mass then, is derived by dividing the weight of the object by the acceleration due to gravity, which, as previously stated is equal to 32.2 ft/sec² on earth.

$$M = \frac{W}{g}$$

Momentum

Mass times velocity or *MV* defines *momentum*. It is the property of a moving body which determines the length of time required to bring it to rest under the action of a constant force. Large objects with a lot of mass but very little velocity can have as much momentum as low-mass objects with very high velocity. A boat must dock very slowly and carefully because if it touches the dock even gently, it may crush it. On the other hand, a bullet weighs very little but its penetrating power is very high because of its velocity.

NEWTON'S LAWS OF MOTION

The fundamental laws of jet propulsion were demonstrated many years ago by recognized scientists and experimenters. These laws, and the equations derived from them, must be discussed in order to understand the operating principle of the gas turbine engine. Foremost among these scientists was Sir Isaac Newton of England, who derived three laws pertaining to bodies at rest and in motion, and the forces acting on these bodies.

Newton's first law states that "A body (mass) in a state of rest tends to remain at rest, and a body in motion tends to continue to move at a constant speed, in a straight line unless acted upon by some external force." The portion of the law which states "a body in a state of rest tends to remain at rest" is acceptable from our own experience. But the second part which states "a

body in motion tends to remain in motion at a constant speed and in a straight line" is more difficult to accept. For example, the less friction that a bearing offers, the longer a wheel will coast. Therefore, according to this law, if all friction were removed, the wheel would coast forever.

The second law of motion says that "An unbalance of force on a body tends to produce an acceleration in the direction of the force, and that the acceleration, if any, is directly proportional to the force and inversely proportional to the mass of the body."

$$a = \frac{F}{M}$$

where a = acceleration
F = force
M = mass

A ball thrown with a force that accelerates it at the rate of 50 ft/sec² will need double this force to accelerate the ball to 100 ft/sec². On the other hand if the mass of the ball is doubled, the rate of acceleration would be halved, or 25 ft/sec². If each side of the equation is multiplied by M, then

$$F = Ma$$

Newton's third law states that "For every acting force there is an equal and opposite reacting force." The term *acting* force means the force exerted by one body on another, while the *reacting* force means the force the second body exerts on the first. These forces always occur in pairs but never cancel each other because, although equal in magnitude, they always act on different objects. Examples of the third law are to be found in everyday life (Fig. 3-4). When a man jumps from a boat, it is pushed backwards with the same force that pushes the man forward. It should be noted that the man gains the same amount of momentum as the boat received, but in the opposite direction.

The equation for momentum equals mass times velocity. Since the momentum of both the man and the boat must be equal, then

$$M_1V_1 = M_2V_2$$

EXAMPLE: A man weighing 150 lb jumps from his boat to shore at a velocity of 2 fps. If the boat weighs 75 lb, what will be its velocity?

$$M_1V_1 = M_2V_2$$
$$\frac{150}{32.2} \times 2 = \frac{75\ V_2}{32.2}$$
$$V_2 = 4 \text{ fps}$$

Everyone knows that when a balloon is blown up and released, it will travel at a fairly high speed for a few seconds. The *gas turbine engine* operates *like a toy*

FIG. 3-4   *Applications of Newton's third law of motion.*   (U.S.A.F. Extension Course Institute and Air University, Course 4301)

balloon, and the operation of both can be explained using Newton's third law of motion.

When the balloon is inflated, the inside air pressure, which is stretching the skin, is greater than the outside pressure, and if the stem is tied closed, the inside air pushes equally in all directions and the balloon will not move (Fig. 3-5). If the balloon is placed in a vacuum and the stem is released, the escaping air obviously has nothing to push against. Yet the balloon will move in a direction away from the stem just as it does in a normal atmosphere, proving that *it is not the escaping air pushing against anything outside that makes the balloon move.*

Releasing the stem removes a section of the skin on that side of the balloon against which the air has been pushing. On the side directly opposite the stem, however, the air continues to push on an equal area of skin, and it is the uncanceled push on this area that causes the balloon to move in the direction away from the stem.

The balloon's flight is short because the pressure within the skin is lost quickly. This handicap could be overcome by pumping air into the balloon with a bicycle pump so the pressure and airflow are maintained.

To transform this apparatus into a self-contained jet engine, the hand pump is replaced with a compressor. And if the compressor is turned at high speed, a large quantity of air is passed through the balloon while holding a high pressure inside. For energy to turn the compressor, a burner is placed in the airstream. Burning the fuel raises the air temperature rapidly, and

the air volume is greatly increased. Since the compressor pressure blocks the forward flow, the air can only move rearward on the less restricted path leading to the exit. By placing a turbine in the path of the heated air, some of this energy is used to spin the turbine, which in turn, spins the compressor by means of a connecting shaft. The remaining energy is expended in expelling the hot gases through the stem of the balloon, which is in effect a jet nozzle. The transformation is now complete and the balloon "jet engine" can operate as long as there is fuel to burn.

The *acting force* that Newton's third law refers to is the acceleration of the escaping air from the rear of the balloon. The reaction to this acceleration is a force in the opposite direction. In addition, the amount of force acting on the balloon is the product of the mass of air being accelerated times the acceleration of that air. Since the forces always occur in pairs, it can be said that if it takes a certain force to accelerate a mass rearward, the reaction to this force is thrust in the opposite direction.

$\overleftarrow{\text{Force}} = \overrightarrow{\text{thrust}}$

Action = reaction

Thrust computation

Using Newton's second law of motion permits the solution of the simple problem that follows.

EXAMPLE: How much force would be necessary to accelerate an object weighing 150 lb at the rate of 10 ft/sec²?

$F = Ma$

where F = force

$M = \dfrac{\text{weight of the object}}{\text{acceleration of gravity}}$

a = change in velocity

$$F = \frac{w}{g} \times a$$
$$= \frac{161}{32.2} \times 10$$
$$= 50 \text{ lb}$$

The same formula applies to the jet engine.

EXAMPLE: A large jet engine handles 100 lb of air per sec. The velocity of this air at the jet nozzle is 659 mph (approximately 966 fps). What is the thrust of the engine?

$$F = Ma$$
$$= \frac{W_a}{g} \times a$$
$$= \frac{100}{32.2} \times 966$$
$$= 3000 \text{ lb} = \text{thrust}$$

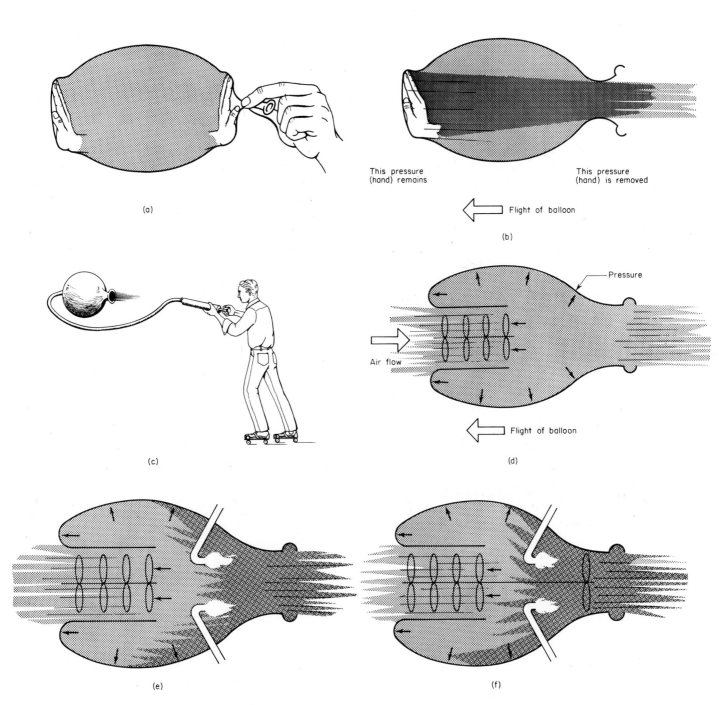

(a)

This pressure
(hand) remains

This pressure
(hand) is removed

Flight of balloon

(b)

(c)

Pressure

Air flow

Flight of balloon

(d)

(e)

(f)

FIG. 3-5 *Balloon analogy of the jet engine (Pratt & Whitney).* (**a**) *Pressures are equal in all directions.* (**b**) *An unbalance of force is created when the stem is opened.* (**c**) *Maintaining pressure in the balloon.* (**d**) *Replacing the hand pump with a compressor.* (**e**) *Raising the air temperature and increasing the volume.* (**f**) *The turbine extracts some of the energy in the air to turn the compressor.*

From the preceding example, if a 3000-lb force or action is required to produce the 966-fps velocity change of 100 lb/sec airflow, then an equal but opposite 3000 lb of reaction or thrust will be felt in the structure of the engine.

Gross and net thrust

When the *gross thrust* is computed, the velocity of the air coming into the engine due to the velocity of the airplane is disregarded and, as shown in the previous problem, the velocity of the gas leaving the engine is used as the acceleration factor. True acceleration of the gas is the *difference* in the velocity between the incoming and outgoing air, and this difference is used in computing *net thrust*. The loss in thrust involved in taking the air in at the front of the engine is known as the *ram drag*. Net thrust is then gross thrust minus ram drag.

$$F_n = F_g - F_r$$

Engine inlet air velocity times the mass of airflow is the *initial momentum*. The faster the airplane goes, the greater the initial momentum and the less the engine can change this momentum.

$MV_2 - MV_1 =$ the acceleration of gases through the engine

where $MV_2 =$ gross thrust or momentum of exhaust gases

$MV_1 =$ ram drag or momentum of incoming air due to airplane speed

EXAMPLE: Using the same engine and values shown in the previous problem, but with the airplane moving at a speed of 220 mph, the net thrust would be

Net thrust $= Ma$

$$= \frac{W_a}{g}(V_2 - V_1)$$

where $V_2 =$ velocity of air at the jet nozzle, fps
$V_1 =$ velocity of the airplane, fps (220 mph = 322 fps = ram drag)

Net thrust $= \dfrac{100}{32.2}(966 - 322)$

$= 2000$ lb

Completing the jet engine equation

Since fuel flow adds some mass to the air flowing through the engine, the same formula must be applied to the weight of the fuel as was applied to the weight of the air, and this must be added to the basic thrust equation

$$F_n = \frac{W_a}{g}(V_2 - V_1) + \frac{W_f}{g}(V_f)$$

where $W_f =$ weight of fuel
$V_f =$ velocity of fuel

Notice that because the fuel is carried along with the engine it will never have any initial velocity relative to the engine. Some formulas do not consider the fuel flow effect when computing thrust because the weight of air leakage through the engine is approximately equivalent to the weight of the fuel added.

This formula was complete until the development of the "choked" nozzle. When a nozzle is choked, the pressure is such that the gases are traveling through it at the speed of sound and cannot be further accelerated. Any increase in internal engine pressure will pass out through the nozzle still in the form of pressure. Even though this pressure energy cannot be turned into velocity energy it is not lost. The pressure inside the nozzle is pushing in all directions, but when the neck is open, the air can no longer push in the direction of the nozzle. The pressure in the other direction continues undiminished, and as a result the pressure of the gases will push the engine forward (Fig. 3-6). Any ambient air (air outside the nozzle) is in the way and will cancel out part of the forward thrust. The completed formula for a turbojet engine with a choked nozzle will be

$$F_n = \frac{W_a}{g}(V_2 - V_1) + \frac{W_f}{g}(V_f) + A_j(P_j - P_{am})$$

where $A_j =$ area of jet nozzle
$P_j =$ static pressure of jet nozzle
$P_{am} =$ ambient static pressure

Thrust distribution   *(Fig. 3-7)*

The net thrust of an engine is a result of pressure and momentum changes within the engine. Some of these changes produce forward forces while others, rearward forces. Whenever there is an increase in total pressure (by compression) or by a change from kinetic energy to pressure energy, as in the diffuser, forward forces are produced. Conversely, rearward forces result when pressure energy decreases or is converted into kinetic energy, as in the nozzle. The rated net thrust of any

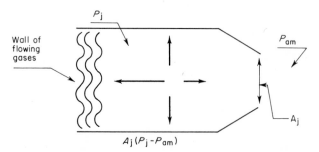

FIG. 3-6   *The choked nozzle.*

FIG. 3-7   *Thrust diagram of an axial-flow jet engine.*

engine is determined by how much the forward thrust forces exceed the rearward thrust forces.

If the areas, pressures acting across these areas, velocities, and mass flows are known at any point in the engine, the forces acting at that point can be calculated. For any point in the engine, the force would be the sum of

$$F_n = \frac{W_a}{g}(V_2 - V_1) \quad \text{or} \quad \text{mass} \times \text{acceleration} = Ma$$

plus

$$F_n = A_j(P_j + P_{am}) \quad \text{or} \quad \text{pressure} \times \text{area} = PA$$

The completed formula would then read

$$F_n = Ma + PA$$

Using the following values for an engine at rest:

Weight of air	= 160 lb/sec
Inlet velocity	= 0 fps
Exhaust gas velocity	= 2000 fps
Area of exhaust nozzle	= 330 sq in.
Pressure at exhaust nozzle	= 6 lb/sq in. gage
Ambient pressure	= 0 lb/sq in. gage
Acceleration due to gravity	= 32 fps²

the thrust of this engine will be, neglecting fuel flows and losses,

$$F_n = \frac{W_a}{g}(V_2 - V_1) + A_j(P_j - P_{am})$$
$$= {}^{160}/_{32}(2000 - 0) + 330(6 - 0)$$
$$= 11,980 \text{ lb}$$

The various forward and rear loads on the engine are determined by using the pressure times the area (*PA*) plus the mass times the acceleration (*Ma*) at given points in the engine.

Compressor outlet

Mass flow	= 160 lb/sec
Velocity	= 400 fps
Pressure	= 95 lb/sq in. gage
Area	= 180 sq in.

NOTE: The pressure and velocity at the face of the compressor is zero. To compute the forces acting on the compressor, it is necessary to consider only outlet conditions.

$$F_{n,comp} = Ma + PA$$
$$= {}^{160}/_{32}(400) + (95 \times 180)$$
$$= 19,100 \text{ lb of forward thrust}$$

Diffuser outlet

Mass flow	= 160 lb/sec
Velocity	= 350 fps
Pressure	= 100 lb/sq in. gage
Area	= 200 sq in.

NOTE: Since the condition at the inlet of the diffuser is the same as that at the outlet of the compressor, that is, 19,100 lb, it is necessary to subtract this from the force value found for the diffuser outlet.

$$F_{n,diff} = Ma + PA - 19,100$$
$$= {}^{160}/_{32}(350) + (100 \times 200) - 19,100$$
$$= 21,750 - 19,100$$
$$= 2650 \text{ lb of forward thrust}$$

Combustion chamber outlet (burner)

Mass flow	= 160 lb/sec (neglecting fuel flow)
Velocity	= 300 fps
Pressure	= 95 lb/sq in. gage
Area	= 550 sq in.

NOTE: The condition at the inlet of the combustion

chamber is the same as that at the outlet of the diffuser, that is, 21,750 lb.

$$F_{n,burner} = Ma + PA - 21,750$$
$$= {}^{160}/_{32}(300) + (95 \times 550) - 21,750$$
$$= 53,750 - 21,750$$
$$= 32,000 \text{ lb of forward thrust}$$

Turbine outlet

Mass flow = 160 lb/sec
Velocity = 900 fps
Pressure = 20 lb/sq in. gage
Area   = 500 sq in.

NOTE: The condition at the inlet of the turbine is the same as that at the outlet of the combustion chamber, that is, 53,750 lb; therefore

$$F_{n,turbine} = Ma + PA - 53,750$$
$$= {}^{160}/_{32}(900) + (20 \times 500) - 53,750$$
$$= 14,500 - 53,750$$
$$= -39,250 \text{ lb of rearward thrust}$$

Exhaust duct outlet

Mass flow = 160 lb/sec
Velocity = 650 fps
Pressure = 25 lb/sq in. gage
Area   = 600 sq in.

NOTE: The condition at the inlet of the exhaust duct is the same as that at the outlet of the turbine, that is, 14,500 lb; therefore

$$F_{n,exh.\ duct} = Ma + PA - 14,500$$
$$= {}^{160}/_{32}(650) + (25 \times 600) - 14,500$$
$$= 18,250 - 14,500$$
$$= 3750 \text{ lb of forward thrust}$$

Exhaust nozzle outlet

Mass flow = 160 lb/sec
Velocity = 2000 fps
Pressure = 6 lb/sq in. gage
Area   = 330 sq in.

NOTE: The condition at the inlet of the exhaust nozzle is the same as that at the outlet of the exhaust duct, that is, 18,250 lb; therefore

$$F_{n,nozzle} = Ma + PA - 18,250$$
$$= {}^{160}/_{32}(2000) + (6 \times 330) - 18,250$$
$$= 11,980 - 18,250$$
$$= -6270 \text{ lb of rearward thrust}$$

The sum of the forward and rearward forces is:

	FORWARD	REARWARD
Compressor	= 19,100	
Diffuser	= 2650	
Combustion chambers	= 32,000	
Turbine	=	−39,250
Exhaust duct	= 3750	
Exhaust nozzle	=	− 6270
	57,500	−45,520
	−45,520	
	11,980	

Thrust computed for the complete engine (from page 71) equals 11,980. Thrust computed for the individual sections of the engine equals 11,980.

Fitting the engine with an afterburner will have two large effects on engine operating conditions.

Mass flow = 160 lb/sec (neglecting fuel flow)
Velocity = 2500 fps
Pressure = 6 lb/sq in. gage
Area   = 450 sq in.

$$F_{n,nozzle} = Ma + PA - 18,250$$
$$= {}^{160}/_{32}(2500) + (6 \times 450) - 18,250$$
$$= 15,200 - 18,250$$
$$= -3050 \text{ lb of rearward thrust}$$

The amount of rearward thrust for the nonafterburning engine is −6270 lb, and for the afterburning engine it is −3050 lb, a difference of 3220 lb. If 3220 lb is added to the thrust of the nonafterburning engine, the total thrust will be

$$11,980 + 3220 = 15,200 \text{ lb}$$

The thrust for the entire engine under afterburning conditions is

$$F_n = \frac{W_a}{g}(V_2 - V_1) + A_j(P_j - P_{am})$$
$$= {}^{160}/_{32}(2500 - 0) + 450(6 - 0)$$
$$= 15,200 \text{ lb}$$

Thrust compared to horsepower

Thrust and horsepower cannot be directly compared because, by definition, power is a force applied through a distance in a given period of time. All of the power produced by a jet engine is consumed internally to turn the compressor and drive the various engine accessories. Therefore, the jet engine does not develop any horsepower in the normally accepted sense, but supplies only one of the terms in the horsepower formula. The other term is actually provided by the vehicle in which the engine is installed. To determine the horsepower of the jet engine, the following formula is used:

thp =

$$\frac{(W_a/g)\,(V_2 - V_1) + A_j\,(P_j - P_{am}) \times \text{velocity of plane (fps)}}{550}$$

This can be simplified to

$$thp = \frac{\text{net thrust} \times \text{velocity of plane (fps)}}{550}$$

or

$$thp = \frac{F_n V}{550}$$

Since airplane speeds are often given in miles per hour, it may be desirable to compute the thrust using mile-pounds per hour. If such is the case

$$thp = \frac{\text{net thrust} \times \text{velocity of plane (mph)}}{375}$$

The denominator in these formulas is arrived at in the following manner.

1 hp	= 550 (ft) (lb)/sec
550 (ft) (lb)/sec × 60	= 33,000 (ft) (lb)/min
33,000 (ft) (lb)/min × 60	= 1,980,000 (ft) (lb)/hr
$\frac{1,980,000 \text{ (ft) (lb)/hr}}{5280}$	= 375 (mi) (lb)/hr
375 (mi) (lb)/hr	= 1 hp

If an airplane is flying at a velocity of 375 mph and developing 4000 lb of thrust, the thrust horsepower will be:

$$thp = \frac{F_n V_p}{375}$$

where F_n = net thrust, lb
V_p = airplane velocity, mph

$$thp = \frac{4000 \times 375}{375}$$
$$= 4000$$

From this it can be seen that at 375 mph each pound of thrust will be converted to one horsepower, and that for each speed of the airplane there will be a different thp. At 750 mph this 4000-lb-thrust jet engine will produce 8000 thp.

Factors affecting thrust

The jet engine is much more sensitive to operating variables than is the reciprocating engine. Such variables can be divided into two groups: those that change because of design or operating characteristics of the engine, and those that change because of the medium in which the engine must operate.

In the first category are such factors as:

1 Engine rpm
2 Size of nozzle area
3 Weight of fuel flow

4 Amount of air bled from the compressor
5 Turbine inlet temperature
6 Use of water injection

Nondesign factors include:

7 Speed of the aircraft (ram pressure rise)
8 Temperature of the air ⎫
9 Pressure of the air   ⎬ density effect
10 Amount of humidity   ⎭

For the present, only factors 1, 7, 8, 9, and 10 are discussed. The effect of the other variables on engine operation are covered elsewhere in the book in the appropriate sections.

RPM EFFECT (*Fig. 3-8*) Engine speed in revolutions per minute has a very great effect on the thrust developed by a jet engine. Figure 3-8 shows that very little thrust is developed at low rpm as compared to the thrust developed at high engine rpm, and that a given rpm change has more effect on thrust at higher engine speeds than at lower engine speeds. The weight of air pumped by a compressor is a function of its rpm. Recalling the formula

$$F_n = \frac{W_a}{g}\,(V_2 - V_1)$$

it is evident that increasing the weight of air being pumped will result in an increase in F_n or thrust. As we shall see when we get to the section on compressors, engine speed may not be indiscriminately varied, but must be controlled within very close limits. (See Chap. 5.)

SPEED EFFECT The formula

$$F_n = \frac{W_a}{g}\,(V_2 - V_1)$$

shows that any increase in the forward velocity of the airplane will result in a decrease in thrust. The faster

Engine speed, % rpm
Effect of rpm on net thrust

FIG. 3-8 *A nonlinear relationship exists between engine rpm and thrust.*

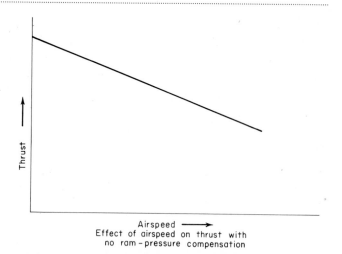

FIG. 3-9 *Thrust loss is due to $V_2 - V_1$ difference becoming smaller.*

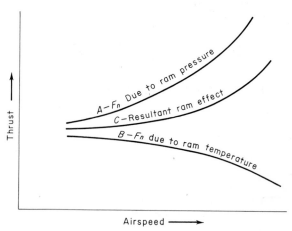

FIG. 3-11 *The ram effect result comes from two factors.*

the airplane goes, the greater will be the initial momentum of the air in relation to the engine (V_1 increasing). But the jet nozzle velocity is generally fixed by the speed of sound. Obviously, the $V_2 - V_1$ difference or momentum change will become smaller as airplane speed increases (Fig. 3-9). This loss of thrust will be partially offset by the increase in the W_a due to ram (Fig. 3-10). Not as much thrust is recovered due to the ram pressure rise as would seem to be indicated on first examination. At high airplane speeds there is a considerable temperature rise in addition to the rise in pressure (Fig. 3-11). The actual weight of airflow increase into the engine will be directly proportional to the rise in pressure and inversely proportional to the square root of the rise in temperature. (See Chap. 5.)

$$W_a \frac{\delta_t}{\sqrt{\theta_t}}$$

where δ_t = total pressure
θ_t = total temperature

Losses may also occur in the duct during high speeds as a result of air friction and shock-wave formation. (See Chap. 4.)

TEMPERATURE EFFECT The gas turbine engine is very sensitive to variations in the temperature of the air (Fig. 3-12). All engines are rated with the air at a standard temperature of 59°F. If the engine operates in air temperatures hotter than standard, there will be less thrust produced. Conversely, engine operation in air temperatures colder than standard day conditions will produce a greater than rated thrust.

A rise in temperature will cause the speed of the molecules to increase so that they run into each other harder and move further apart. When they are further apart, a given number of molecules will occupy more space. And when a given number of molecules occupy more space, fewer can get into the engine inlet area. This results in a decrease in W_a into the engine with a corresponding decrease in thrust.

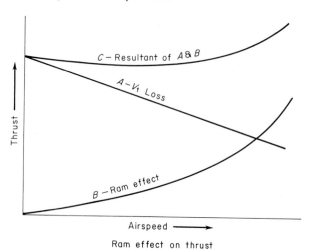

Ram effect on thrust

FIG. 3-10 *Combining thrust loss due to $V_2 - V_1$ difference decrease with thrust gain due to ram-pressure rise.*

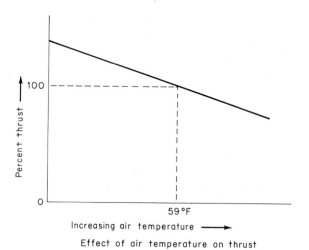

Effect of air temperature on thrust

FIG. 3-12 *Thrust may vary as much as 20 percent from the specified rating on cold or hot days.*

Effect of air pressure on thrust

FIG. 3-13 *Air pressure drops as altitude is gained.*

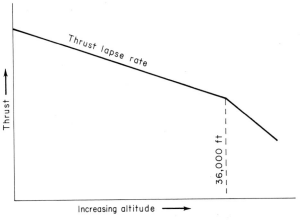

Effect of altitude on thrust

FIG. 3-14 *Combining thrust loss due to pressure decrease with altitude and thrust gain due to temperature decrease with altitude.*

PRESSURE EFFECTS An increase in pressure results when there are more molecules per cubic foot. When this situation occurs, there are more molecules available to enter the engine inlet area and as a result, an increase in W_a occurs through the engine (Fig. 3-13). How pressure changes effect thrust will become clearer when we examine the gas turbine cycle later in this chapter.

DENSITY EFFECT Density is defined as the number of molecules per cubic foot, and is affected by both pressure and temperature. When the pressure goes up, the density goes up, and when the temperature goes up, the density goes down. This may be expressed mathematically as

Density ratio $= K \dfrac{P}{T}$

where $K =$ a constant
$P =$ pressure, in. Hg
$T =$ temperature, °R

or density is directly proportional to pressure and inversely proportional to temperature times a constant. A constant of 17.32 is necessary in order to make the density ratio equal 1 under standard conditions of temperature (518.7°R) and pressure (29.92 in. Hg).

$$\begin{aligned} \text{Density ratio} &= K \frac{P}{T} \\ &= 17.32\,\frac{29.92}{518.69} \\ &= 1 \end{aligned}$$

Density changes are most noticeable, of course, with changes in altitude. The effect of altitude change on thrust is really a function of density. Figure 3-14 shows the result of combining Figs. 3-12 and 3-13. The higher the altitude the less air pressure there is. This should result in a decrease in thrust as shown in Fig. 3-13. But

the higher the altitude, the colder it gets, and this should result in an increase in thrust as shown in Fig. 3-12. However, the pressure drops off faster than the temperature, so that there is actually a drop in thrust with increased altitude.

At about 36,000 ft, essentially the beginning of the tropopause, the temperature stops falling and remains

Altitude, thousands of ft
pressure – temperature – density variation with altitude increase

FIG. 3-15 *At 36,000 ft, temperature stops falling.*

FIG. 3-16 *The effects of engine rpm, airspeed, altitude (at a constant temperature), ram efficiency, and air temperature on fuel flow, specific fuel consumption, airflow, and thrust for a General Electric J79 engine. (Continued on following page.)*

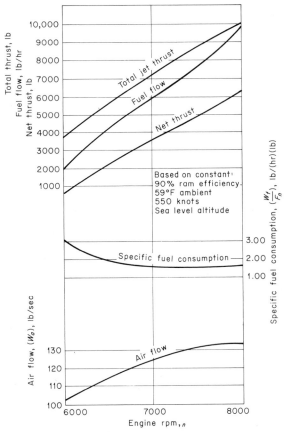

FIG. 3-16 *(continued)*.

constant while the pressure continues to fall (Fig. 3-15). As a result, the thrust will drop off more rapidly above 36,000 ft because the thrust loss due to the air pressure drop will no longer be partially offset by the thrust gain due to temperature drop. This makes 36,000 ft the optimum altitude for long-range cruising, because at this altitude, even though the engine's thrust is reduced, the relationship between the thrust produced and the diminished drag on the airplane is most favorable.

HUMIDITY EFFECT While humidity has a fairly large effect on the reciprocating engine, its effect on the gas turbine engine is negligible. Since water vapor weighs only five-eighths as much as dry air, increasing humidity will decrease the weight per unit volume. Since a carburetor is essentially a volume-measuring device, it will not sense this decrease in the *weight* of the air and, as a result, will continue to supply the same amount of fuel to the engine, causing the fuel-air mixture ratio to become too rich and the engine to lose power.

On the other hand, a jet engine operates with an excess of air needed for combustion. (Refer to Chap. 6.) Any air needed for the combustion process will come from the cooling air supply. In addition, the fuel control does not measure the volume of air directly, but rather meters fuel flow as a function of pressures, temperatures, and rpm (Fig. 3-16). (Refer to Chap. 12.)

Pressure, temperature, and velocity changes

At the beginning of this chapter, a general description of the series of events that take place in a typical gas turbine was briefly given. A somewhat more specific examination of airflow changes will help to better understand the thrust phenomenon. Refer to Fig. 3-17a and b, both of which illustrate pressure, temperature, and velocity changes through typical gas turbine engines.

PRESSURE CHANGES Air usually enters the front of the compressor at a pressure that is less than ambient, indicating that there is considerable suction at the inlet to the engine. This somewhat negative pressure at the engine inlet may be partly or completely overcome by ram pressure as the airplane speed increases. From this point on, there is a considerable pressure rise through the successive compression stages, with the rate of rise increasing in the later stages of compression. The exit area of the exhaust nozzle, the exit area of the turbine nozzle, and rate of fuel flow all can determine the compression ratio of the compressor. (Refer to Chap. 5.) A final pressure rise is accomplished in the divergent section of the diffuser. From the diffuser, the air passes through the combustion section where a slight pressure loss is experienced. The combustion-chamber pressure must be lower than the compressor discharge pressure during all phases of engine operation in order to establish a direction of airflow toward the rear of the engine and allow the gases to expand as combustion occurs. A sharp drop in pressure occurs as the air is accelerated between the converging passages of the turbine nozzle. The pressure continues to drop across the turbine wheel as some of the pressure energy in the hot gas is converted to a rotational force by the wheel. If the engine is equipped with more than one turbine stage, a pressure reduction occurs across each turbine wheel. Pressure changes after the turbine depend upon the type of exhaust nozzle used, and whether the nozzle is operating in a choked (gas velocity at the speed of sound) or nonchoked condition. When the gases leave the exhaust nozzle, the pressure continues to drop to ambient.

TEMPERATURE CHANGES Air entering the compressor at sea level on a standard day is at a temperature of 59°F. Due to compression, the temperature through the compressor gradually climbs to a point that is determined by the number of compressor stages and its aerodynamic efficiency. (Refer to Chap. 5.) On some large commercial engines, the temperature at the front of the combustion section is approximately 600°F. As the air enters the combustion chambers, fuel is added and the temperature is raised to about 3500°F in the hottest part of the flame. Since this temperature is above the melting point of most metals, the combustion chamber and surrounding parts of the engine are protected by a cooling film of air which is established through proper design of the combustion chamber.

(a)

(b)

FIG. 3-17 (**a**) *Temperature, pressure, and velocity diagram for a typical turbojet engine with and without afterburner operation.* (*Wright Corporation*) (**b**) *Temperature, pressure, and velocity diagram for a typical turboprop engine.* (*Allison Division of General Motors*)

(Refer to Chap. 6.) Because of this cooling film, the air entering the turbine section is considerably cooler. The acceleration of air through the turbine section further reduces the temperature. If the engine is operating without the use of an afterburner, there is a slight temperature drop through the exhaust pipe. If the engine is operating with the use of the afterburner, there will be a sharp temperature rise in the exhaust pipe.

VELOCITY CHANGES Since a jet engine derives its thrust mainly from the reaction to the action on a stream of air as it flows through the jet engine, the pressure and temperature changes just discussed are important only because they must be present to accomplish the action part of the action-reaction process. What is really desired is a jet of air flowing out of the engine at a speed faster than the speed with which it entered.

The velocity of the air at the front of the compressor must be less than sonic for most present-day compressors. In order to achieve this goal, the design of the inlet duct of the airplane is of paramount importance. (Refer to Chap. 4.) If the ambient air velocity is zero, the air velocity increases as it is drawn into the compressor. On the other hand, if the airplane speed is supersonic, the air's velocity is slowed in the duct. Airflow velocity through the majority of compressors is essentially constant, and in some compressors may decrease slightly. A fairly large drop in airspeed occurs in the enlarging diffuser passage. The turning point where flow velocity starts to increase is in the combustion chamber as the air is forced around the forward end of the combustion chamber inner liner and through the holes along the sides. A further increase occurs at the rear of the combustion chamber as the hot gases expand and are forced through the slightly smaller area of the transition liner. An extremely sharp rise in velocity, with a corresponding loss of pressure, occurs as the air passes through the converging partitions of the turbine nozzle. This exchange of pressure for velocity is very desirable, since the turbine is designed to operate largely on a velocity drop. As previously explained, the velocity increase is accompanied by a temperature and pressure drop. A large portion of the velocity increase through the nozzle is absorbed by the turbine wheel and applied to drive the compressor and engine accessories. Velocity changes from this point on depend upon the design of the engine. As shown in Fig. 3-17a, if the engine is not using the afterburner, the velocity is reduced as the air enters the afterburner section because it is a diverging area. As the air is discharged through the orifice formed by the exhaust nozzle, the velocity increases sharply. If the engine is running with the afterburner in operation, the rise in temperature caused by the burning of the afterburner fuel will cause a tremendous velocity increase. In most cases, use of the afterburner produces an increase in exhaust veloc-

ity which is approximately equal to the reduction in velocity through the turbine wheel. Notice that the only changes which occur with the use of the afterburner are those of the temperature and velocity in the exhaust pipe. Pressure, temperature, and velocity changes in the basic engine remain the same because the variable-area exhaust nozzle used with afterburner equipped engines is designed to open to a new position that will maintain the same turbine discharge temperature and pressure that existed when operating at full power without the afterburner. Figure 3-17b shows that there is little velocity change after the turbine section of a turboprop. In both engines there is always energy in the form of temperature, pressure, and velocity remaining in the exhaust gases after they leave the turbine, but this energy level is much lower in the turboprop because the turbine extracts more from the gases in order to drive the propeller (Fig. 3-18a and b). This

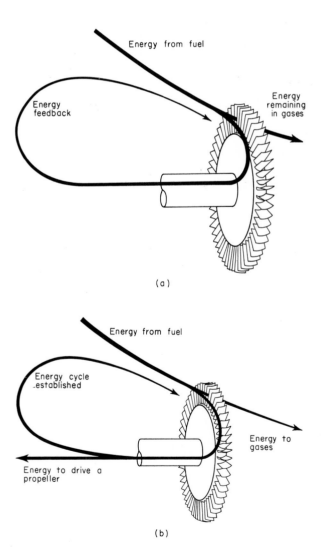

(a)

(b)

FIG. 3-18 *More energy is extracted by the turboprop turbine section than in a turbojet. (U.S.A.F. Extension Course Institute and Air University, Course 4301)* (**a**) *Turbojet turbine.* (**b**) *Turboprop turbine.*

is also true for fan-equipped engines. Of course the jet effect is reduced a proportionate amount. In addition, part of the energy is lost because the exhaust gases have not cooled to the same temperature as the air which entered the engine. This problem will be examined in the discussion on engine cycles that follows.

The gas turbine cycle *(Fig. 3-19)*

A cycle is a process that begins with certain conditions and ends with those same conditions. Both reciprocating and jet engines operate on cycles which can be illustrated graphically. As shown in Fig. 3-19, reciprocating and jet engines are similar in many respects.

Both types of power plants are called air-breathing engines. Both work by providing rearward acceleration to a mass of air. In the case of the reciprocating engine, the propeller imparts a relatively small acceleration to a large mass of air, while the gas turbine imparts a relatively large acceleration to a small mass of air (Fig. 3-20). Although both convert the energy in expanding gas into thrust, the reciprocating engine does this by changing the energy of combustion into mechanical energy which is used to turn a propeller, while the gas turbine engine produces and uses the propulsive force directly. The same series of events, i.e., intake, compression, power, and exhaust, occur in both, the

Piston descends, inlet valve open. Air drawn in at constant pressure (line 1-2).

Piston ascends, both valves closed. Pressure increases and volume decreases to point 3. Combustion at constant volume results in sharp pressure rise to point 4.

Increased pressure at constant volume forces piston down, resulting in increase in volume and drop in pressure (line 4-5).

Exhaust valve opens, releasing combustion charge with rapid drop in pressure at constant volume (line 5-2). Piston rises and forces remaining gases out exhaust at constant pressure (line 2-1). Cycle begins again at point 1.

The Otto Cycle

Air enters at atmospheric pressure and constant volume at point 1.

Air enters compressor and pressure increases as volume decreases to point 2 above. Combustion at point 2 at constant pressure results in sharp volume rise to point 3.

Gas at increased volume and constant pressure enters turbine and expands through it, resulting in further increase in volume and sharp drop in pressure (line 3-4).

Combustion charge released through jet with rapid drop in volume at constant pressure (line 4-1). Cycle is continuous, starting at point 1.

The Brayton Cycle

FIG. 3-19 *Pressure-volume changes in the reciprocating and gas turbine engines.*

The propeller gives a SMALL acceleration to a LARGE weight of air

The turbojet engine gives a LARGE acceleration to a SMALL weight of air

FIG. 3-20 *Propulsive efficiency is high for a propeller and low for a jet.*

difference being that in the jet engine all of these events are happening simultaneously, whereas in the reciprocating engine, each event must follow the preceding one. It should also be noted that in the turbine engine each operation in the cycle is not only performed continuously, but also is performed by a separate component designed for its particular function, whereas in the reciprocating engine, all the functions are performed in one section of the engine.

The Otto cycle (the constant-volume engine)
(Fig. 3-21)

The reciprocating engine operates on what is commonly termed a closed cycle. In the series of events shown in Fig. 3-21, air is drawn in on the intake stroke at point 1, where compression by the piston raises the temperature and decreases the volume of the gases. Near the end of the compression stroke, point 2, ignition occurs, which greatly increases the temperature of the mixture. The term "constant volume" is derived from the fact that from point 2 to 3 there is no appreciable change of volume while the mixture is burning. Point 3 to 4 represents the expansion stroke with a loss of temperature and pressure, and a corresponding increase in volume. It might be noted that this is the only stroke of the four from which power may be extracted. When the exhaust valve opens near the end of the power stroke (point 4 to 1), the gases lose their remaining pressure and temperature and the closed cycle starts all over again.

The Brayton cycle (the constant-pressure engine)

Since all of the events are going on continuously, it can be said that the gas turbine engine works on what is commonly called an open cycle. As in the reciprocating engine, air is drawn in and compressed (point 1 to 2) with a corresponding rise in pressure and temperature, and a decrease in volume. Point 2 to 3 represents the change caused by the fuel mixture burning in the combustion chamber at an essentially constant pressure, but with a very large increase in volume. This increase in volume shows up as an increase in velocity because the engine area does not change much in this section. From the burner, the gases expand through the turbine wheel causing an increase in volume and a decrease in temperature and pressure (point 3 to 4). This process continues from point 4 to 5 through the exhaust nozzle.

In comparing the two engines, it is interesting to note that the reciprocating engine obtains its work output by employing very high pressures (as much as 1000 lb/sq in.) in the cylinder during combustion. With these high pressures, a larger amount of work can be obtained from a given quantity of fuel, thus raising the *thermal efficiency* (the relationship between the potential heat energy in the fuel and the actual energy output of the engine) of this type of engine. On the other hand, a jet engine's thermal efficiency is limited by the ability of the compressor to build up high pressures without an excessive temperature rise. The shaded area shown in Fig. 3-21 is called the area of useful work, and any increase in this area indicates more energy available for useful output, thus thrust. But increasing the compression ratio would also increase the compressed air temperature. Since most gas turbine engines are already operating at close to maximum temperature limits, this would result in a mandatory decrease in fuel flow (Fig. 3-22), thus making it extremely difficult to increase compression ratios without designing more efficient compressors, i.e., compressors able to pump air with

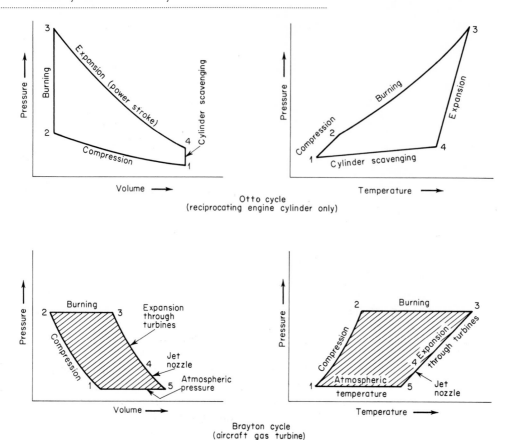

FIG. 3-21   *Comparing the Otto and Brayton cycle.*   (Pratt & Whitney)

FIG. 3-22   *Effect of increasing compressor pressure; pressure-temperature engine cycle diagram.*   (Pratt & Whitney)

a minimum temperature rise. Ideally, we would like to be able to burn as much fuel as possible in the jet engine in order to raise the gas temperature and increase the area of useful output.

One last illustration will help to understand how the gas turbine works. Note that Fig. 3-23 is similar to the pressure-temperature graph for the gas turbine engine shown in Fig. 3-21.

During steady-state operation, the work done by the turbine must be almost exactly the same as the work needed by the compressor. Although the temperature drop available to obtain work from the very hot gases passing through the turbines is very much greater than the actual temperature rise through the compressor, the mass (or weight) flow available to the turbine is exactly the same as the mass or weight handled by the compressor. (This assumes that air bleed loss is equal in weight to the fuel added. Refer to page 70.) Therefore, a temperature drop takes place through the turbine that is approximately equivalent to the temperature rise which occurred in the compressor. However, Fig. 3-23 shows that although the compressor temperature rise x equals the turbine temperature drop y, the pressure change needed is much less at the higher temperature.

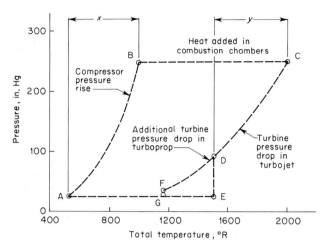

FIG. 3-23 *Compression and expansion curves (Pratt & Whitney).*

This difference (point D to E) is why pressure is left to produce thrust in the turbojet. In the turboprop, more energy is taken out by the turbines to drive the propeller, with a correspondingly small amount of pressure left over to induce a jet thrust (point F to G). The energy added in the form of fuel has been *more than enough* to drive the compressor. The energy remaining produces the thrust or power for useful work.

Efficiencies

Engine thermal efficiency is defined as the engine's energy output divided by the fuel's energy input. One of the principal measures of jet engine efficiency is called *specific fuel consumption* SFC, or *thrust specific fuel consumption* TSFC. Specific fuel consumption is the ratio between the fuel flow (in pounds per hour) and the thrust of the engine (in pounds).

$$SFC = \frac{W_f}{F_n}$$

EXAMPLE: A 9100-lb-thrust engine consumes 700 gal of fuel per hour. What is the SFC? (One gallon of fuel equals 6.5 lb.)

$$SFC = \frac{W_f}{F_n}$$
$$= \frac{4550}{9100}$$
$$= 0.5 \text{ lb of fuel per hour per pound of thrust}$$

Obviously the more thrust we can obtain per pound of fuel, the more efficient the engine is. Specific fuel consumption enables valid comparisons to be made between engines because the fuel consumption is reduced to a common denominator. For example: If one engine produces 5000 lb of thrust and consumes 2500 lb of fuel per hour, while another engine produces 10,000 lb of thrust and burns 4000 lb of fuel per hour, which engine is the most efficient?

$$SFC = \frac{W_f}{F_n}$$
$$= \frac{2500}{5000}$$
$$= 0.5 \text{ lb of fuel per hour per pound of thrust}$$

$$SFC = \frac{W_f}{F_n}$$
$$= \frac{4000}{10,000}$$
$$= 0.4 \text{ lb of fuel per hour per pound of thrust}$$

The 10,000-lb-thrust engine produces twice as much thrust as the 5000-lb-thrust engine, but does not consume twice the fuel.

The term *equivalent specific fuel consumption* ESFC is used to compare fuel consumption between turboprop engines.

$$ESFC = \frac{W_f}{eshp}$$

The eshp, or *equivalent shaft horsepower,* is found by the following formula when the aircraft is not moving:

$$eshp = shp + \frac{F_n}{2.6} \quad \text{approximately}$$

NOTE: Under static conditions one shaft horsepower equals approximately 2.6 pounds of thrust.

If the airplane is moving, the equivalent shaft horsepower can be found as follows:

$$eshp = shp + \frac{F_n V}{550}$$

where F_n is in pounds and V is in feet per second.

There are many factors that affect the overall efficiency of an engine. Some of these factors are:

1 Component efficiency—Since none of the engine components are perfect, there will always be a certain amount of inefficiency present. For instance, if the compressor is 85 percent efficient, the combustion chamber 95 percent, and the turbine 90 percent, the engine will have an overall efficiency of 72.7 percent (85 percent × 95 percent × 90 percent).

2 Type of fuel used—Some fuels have a higher potential heat value than others.

3 Engine operating factors—Already mentioned are rpm, use of water injection or afterburning, density of the air, flight speed, and fuel flow.

While the conversion of fuel energy into kinetic energy determines the thermal or internal efficiency, the efficient conversion of the kinetic energy to propulsive work determines the propulsive or external efficiency. This depends on the amount of kinetic energy wasted by the propelling mechanism which in turn depends on the mass airflow multiplied by the square of its velocity. From this we can see that the high-velocity, relatively-low-weight jet exhaust wastes considerably more energy than the propeller with its low-velocity, high-weight airflow (Fig. 3-24). This condition changes however as the aircraft speed increases, because although the jet stream continues to flow at high

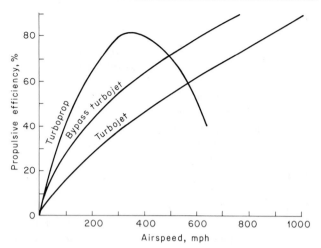

FIG. 3-24 *Comparison of propulsive efficiency of the turbojet, turbofan (bypass), and turboprop with changing airspeed.*

velocity from the engine, its velocity relative to the surrounding atmosphere is lessened by the forward speed of the aircraft. Thus the energy wasted is reduced. One hundred percent propulsive efficiency would occur if the airplane speed equalled the exhaust velocity.

On some fan engines the fan air is mixed with the exhaust gases, thereby reducing the exit velocity and consequently increasing the propulsive efficiency of the system. This in turn is reflected in lower SFC.

Air behavior at low and high velocities

The very nature of the jet engine with its high-speed flight characteristics requires a discussion of the behavior of moving air. Even though a great deal can be written on this subject, coverage here must necessarily be brief.

At low airflows, air is normally treated as an incompressible fluid similar to water because, at these low airspeeds, the air can undergo change in pressure with relatively little change in density. Since this condition

of low-speed airflow is analogous to the flow of water or any other incompressible fluid, Bernoulli's theorem and other relationships developed for an incompressible fluid may be used.

BERNOULLI'S THEOREM Most simply stated, Bernoulli's theorem says that when a gas or fluid is flowing through a restricted area, as in a nozzle or venturi, its speed will increase and its temperature and pressure will decrease. If the area is increased as in a diffuser, the reverse is true. The total energy in a flowing gas is made up of static and dynamic temperatures, and static and dynamic pressures. A nozzle or a diffuser does not change the total energy level, but rather changes one form of energy to another (Fig. 3-25). For example, a nozzle will increase the flow, or dynamic pressure, at the expense of the static pressure. If the gas is moving through the pipe at so many pounds per second, the air must continue to flow at the same rate through the nozzle. The only way it can do this is to speed up. A diffuser will do the opposite. Thus by varying the area of the pipe, velocity can be changed into pressure, and pressure into velocity. The jet engine is just such a pipe, with changing areas where the air pressure and velocity are constantly being changed to achieve desired results.

MACH NUMBER At high speeds the pressure changes that take place are very large, resulting in significant changes in air density. The air no longer acts as an incompressible fluid. *Compressibility effects* due to high-speed airflow, are of great importance in the design of both the airplane and the engine. The compressibility phenomenon and the speed of sound are closely related to each other. The speed of sound is the rate at which small pressure disturbances will be propagated through the air. This propagation speed is solely a function of temperature. (See the Appendix for variation of the speed of sound with temperature.)

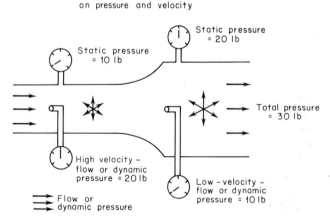

FIG. 3-25 *Pressure and velocity changes at subsonic flow.*

Flow direction changes ahead of
leading edge

(a)

No change of flow direction apparent
ahead of leading edge

(b)

FIG. 3-26 *Airflow behavior over an airfoil at subsonic and supersonic speeds.* (**a**) *Typical subsonic flow pattern.* (**b**) *Typical supersonic flow pattern.*

As an object moves through the air, velocity and pressure changes occur which create pressure disturbances in the airflow surrounding the object. Since these pressure disturbances are propagated through the air at the local speed of sound, if the object is traveling below the speed of sound, these pressure disturbances are propagated ahead of the object (as well as in all other directions) and influence the air immediately in

front of the object (Fig. 3-26). On the other hand, if the object is traveling at some speed above the speed of sound, the airflow ahead of the object will not be influenced, since the pressure disturbances cannot be propagated ahead of the object. In other words the object is outspeeding its own pressure waves. Thus, as the speed of the object nears the speed of sound, a compression wave will form and changes in velocity, pressure, and temperature will take place quite sharply and suddenly. The compression or shock wave results from the "piling up" of air molecules as they try to move forward, away from the pressure disturbance as fast as the object is moving forward through the air. The shock waves are very narrow areas of discontinuity where the air velocity slows from supersonic to subsonic.

It becomes apparent that all compressibility effects depend upon the relationship of the object's speed to the local speed of sound. The term used to describe this relationship is the Mach number, so named for the Austrian physicist Ernst Mach. Mach number then is the ratio of the speed of an object to the local speed of sound.

$$M = \frac{V}{c_s}$$

where V = velocity of object
c_s = speed of sound

Since the speed of sound varies with temperature, the M number is a very convenient measure of high-speed

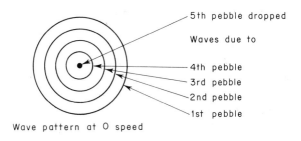

5th pebble dropped

Waves due to

4th pebble
3rd pebble
2nd pebble
1st pebble

Wave pattern at 0 speed

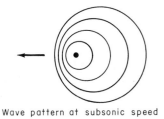

Wave pattern at subsonic speed

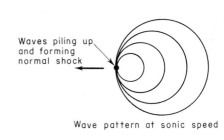

Waves piling up
and forming
normal shock

Wave pattern at sonic speed

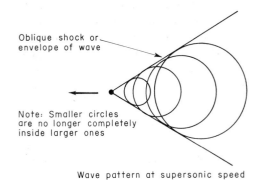

Oblique shock or
envelope of wave

Note: Smaller circles
are no longer completely
inside larger ones

Wave pattern at supersonic speed

FIG. 3-27 *Water wave analogy of shock formation; disturbance caused by pebbles dropped into water at equal time intervals.*

flow. For example, at sea level, the speed of sound equals 1116 fps. If an airplane's speed is also 1116 fps, we would say that the airplane was traveling at Mach 1.0. At 36,000 ft, where the speed of sound is only 968 fps, M = 1.15.

PROBLEM: An airplane is traveling at M 2.0 at 30,000 ft. What is the plane's airspeed? (Speed of sound at 30,000 ft = 995 fps or 680 mph.) How fast is the airplane moving?

$$V = Mc_s \qquad\qquad V = Mc_s$$
$$= 2 \times 995 \quad\text{or}\quad = 2 \times 680$$
$$= 1990 \text{ fps} \qquad = 1360 \text{ mph}$$

Reference was made on page 70 of this section to a choked nozzle, and it was stated that when a nozzle is choked, the gases are traveling through it at the speed of sound and cannot be further accelerated. It can now be seen that the velocity of these exhaust gases are much higher than 763 mph (the speed of sound at the standard temperature of 59°F). In fact, if the exhaust gas temperature is 1040°F, the exhaust velocity may reach 1896 fps or 1293 mph before the speed of sound is reached.

In review, a sonic shock wave is the accumulation of sound-wave energy (pressure) developed when a sound moving away from a disturbance (object) is held in a stationary position by the flow of air in the opposite direction. The velocity of airflow across a shock wave will decrease because the air molecules are moving with the sound wave against the air velocity. This decrease in air velocity is accompanied by a pressure rise, because the sound-wave motion, in slowing the air velocity, will convert most of the kinetic energy of velocity into a pressure rise.

There are two types of shock waves, oblique and normal (Fig. 3-27). The oblique shock wave stands off of the moving object at an oblique angle; it occurs at high supersonic velocities, and the velocity drop across this shock is to a *lower supersonic* velocity. The normal shock wave stands perpendicular to the airstream; it occurs at low supersonic speed and its velocity drop is from *supersonic* to *subsonic* behind the normal shock front. In both types, a pressure rise occurs. If the velocity and pressure changes are small, it is called a weak shock; if the velocity drop and pressure rise are high, it is called a strong or forced shock. Keep in mind that across all shock waves there is a temperature increase. (See Chap. 4.)

REVIEW AND STUDY QUESTIONS

1 Name the five basic sections of the gas turbine engine. What additional sections and/or components may also be present?

2 Briefly describe the series of events that take place in the gas turbine engine.

3 Define the following terms: force, work, power, energy, kinetic energy, speed, velocity, vector, acceleration, mass, and momentum.

4 What is one horsepower equal to in terms of foot-pounds per minute?

5 State Newton's three laws of motion.

6 Using the balloon analogy, explain the reaction principle.

7 What is the relationship between thrust and force?

8 What is the difference between gross thrust and net thrust? How does ram drag enter into this difference?

9 Write the *complete* formula for determining the thrust of a jet engine.

10 What do the words "choked nozzle" mean? How does this effect enter into the determination of thrust?

11 Give the formula for determining the thrust at any given point in the engine.

12 At what major points in the engine is forward thrust being applied? Rearward thrust?

13 State the relationship between thrust and horsepower. At what point are they equal?

14 Make a table to show the effects of increasing and decreasing rpm, airplane speed, temperature, pressure, density, and humidity.

15 How do pressure, temperature, and velocity change through an operating engine? How does the use of the afterburner affect these parameters?

16 Why is the Otto cycle engine called a constant-volume engine? Why is the Brayton cycle engine called a constant-pressure engine?

17 Compare the Otto cycle and Brayton cycle as to differences and similarities.

18 Compare pressure and temperature increases and decreases through the compressor and turbine.

19 Define "specific fuel consumption." Why is this a good way to compare engine efficiencies?

20 List the factors which affect the overall efficiency of the gas turbine engine.

21 Define thermal and propulsive efficiency.

22 What is the relationship between pressure and velocity when a fluid passes through a restriction (venturi) at subsonic velocity? Through a diffuser?

23 What do the terms compressible and incompressible fluid mean? Using these terms, how does air act at subsonic speeds? At supersonic speeds?

24 What influences the speed of sound? Define Mach number.

25 Explain how a shock wave forms.

26 What is the difference between a normal and oblique shock wave?

PART 2

Construction
and design

Chapter 4

Inlet ducts

Although the inlet duct is made by the aircraft manufacturer, during flight operation, as shown in Chap. 3, it becomes very important to the overall jet engine performance and will greatly influence jet engine thrust output. The faster the airplane goes, the more critical the duct design becomes. Engine thrust can be high only if the inlet duct supplies the engine with the required airflow at the highest possible pressure.

The inlet duct must operate from static ground run up to high aircraft Mach numbers with a high duct efficiency at all altitudes, attitudes, and flight speeds (Fig. 4-1). To compound the problem, the amount of air required by a turbojet engine is approximately ten times or more than that of a piston engine of comparable size.

Inlet ducts should be as straight and smooth as possible, and should be designed in such a way that the boundary layer air (a layer of still, dead air lying next to the surface) be held to a minimum. The length, shape, and placement of the duct is determined to a great extent by the location of the engine in the aircraft.

Not only must the duct be large enough to supply the proper airflow, but it must be shaped correctly to deliver the air to the front of the compressor with an even pressure distribution. Poor air pressure and velocity distribution at the front of the compressor may result in compressor stall. (See Chap. 5.)

Another primary task a duct must do during flight operation is to convert the kinetic energy of the rapidly moving inlet airstream into a ram pressure rise inside the duct. To do this it must be shaped so that the ram velocity is slowly and smoothly decreasing, while the ram pressure is slowly and smoothly rising.

Inlet ducts are rated in two ways: the duct pressure efficiency ratio and the ram recovery point. The duct pressure efficiency ratio is the ratio of the compressor inlet total pressure to the ram pressure. It will have a high value of 98 percent if the friction loss is low and if the ram pressure rise is accomplished with small losses. The ram recovery point is that aircraft speed at which the ram pressure rise is equal to the friction pressure losses, or that airspeed at which the compressor inlet total pressure is equal to the outside ambient air pressure. A good subsonic duct will have a low ram recovery point (about 160 mph).

Inlet ducts may be divided into two broad categories.

1 Single entrance ducts
2 Divided entrance ducts

Figure 4-2 illustrates the variety of possible inlet duct designs falling within these categories. It is interesting to note that the engine manufacturers rate their engines using a bellmouth inlet (Fig. 4-3). This type of inlet is essentially a bell-shaped funnel having carefully rounded shoulders, which offer practically no air resistance. The duct loss is so small that it is considered zero, and all engine performance data can be gathered without any correction for inlet duct loss being necessary. (See Chap. 18.) Normal duct inefficiencies may cause thrust losses of 5 percent or more because a decrease in duct efficiency of 1 percent will decrease airflow 1 percent, decrease jet velocity ½ percent, and result in 1½ percent thrust loss. The decrease in jet velocity occurs because it is necessary to increase the area of the jet nozzle in order to keep the turbine temperature within limits when duct losses occur.

SUPERSONIC DUCTS

The supersonic inlet duct must operate in three speed zones (Fig. 4-4).

1 Subsonic
2 Transonic
3 Supersonic

Although each of these speed zones needs a slightly different inlet duct design, good overall performance can be achieved by designing to the supersonic shape with some modifications.

The supersonic duct problems start when the aircraft begins to fly at or near the speed of sound. As illustrated in the preceding chapter, at these speeds sonic shock waves are developed which, if not controlled, will give high duct loss in pressure and airflow, and will set up vibrating conditions in the inlet duct called inlet buzz. Buzz is an airflow instability caused by the shock wave rapidly being alternately swallowed and expelled at the inlet of the duct.

Air which enters the compressor section of the engine must usually be slowed to subsonic velocity, and this process should be accomplished with the least possible

Air velocity decreasing
and pressure increasing

(a)

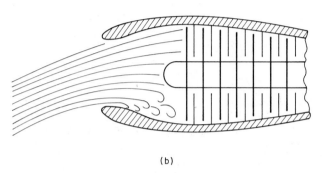

(b)

FIG. 4-1 (**a**) *Normal and* (**b**) *distorted flow through an inlet duct. Distorted flow is the result of unusual flight attitudes or ice buildup; the problem is especially critical with short ducts.*

waste of energy. At supersonic speeds the inlet duct does the job by slowing the air with the weakest possible series or combination of shocks to minimize energy loss and temperature rise.

At transonic speeds (near Mach 1), the inlet duct is usually designed to keep the shock waves out of the duct. This is done by locating the inlet duct behind a spike or probe (Fig. 4-4*b*) so that at airspeeds slightly above Mach 1.0 the spike will establish a normal shock (bow wave) in front of the inlet duct. This normal shock wave will produce a pressure rise and a velocity decrease to subsonic velocities before the air strikes the actual inlet duct. The inlet will then be a subsonic design behind a normal shock front. At low supersonic Mach numbers, the strength of the normal shock wave is not too great, and this type of inlet is quite practical. But at higher Mach numbers, the single normal shock wave is very strong and causes a great reduction in the total pressure recovered by the duct and an excessive air temperature rise inside the duct.

At slightly higher airspeeds the normal bow wave will change into an oblique shock (Fig. 4-4*c* and *d*). Since the air velocity behind an oblique shock is still supersonic, to keep the supersonic velocities out of the inlet duct, the duct will need to set up a normal shock wave at the duct inlet. The airflow is controlled so that

the air velocity at the duct inlet is exactly equal to the speed of sound. At this time the duct pressure rise will be due to

1 An oblique shock pressure rise
2 A normal shock pressure rise
3 A subsonic diverging section pressure rise

As the airspeed is increased, the angle of the oblique shock will be forced back by the higher air velocity until the oblique shock contacts the outer lip of the duct. When this occurs there will be a slight increase in thrust due to an increase in engine inlet pressure and airflow, because the energy contained in the shock front is now enclosed within the duct and delivered to it with less pressure loss. This point is called the *duct recovery point* (Fig. 4-4*e*).

At higher Mach numbers (about 1.4 and above) the inlet duct must set up one or more oblique shocks and a normal shock (Fig. 4-4*f*). The oblique shocks will slow the supersonic velocities, the normal shock will drop the velocity to subsonic, then the subsonic section will further decrease the velocity before the air enters the compressor. Each decrease in velocity will produce a pressure rise.

VARIABLE GEOMETRY DUCT

A complication of the supersonic inlet is that the optimum shape is variable with the inlet flow direction and the Mach number. In the higher Mach aircraft the inlet duct geometry is made variable by either

1 Moving the inlet spike in and out so as to maintain the oblique shock on the edge of the outer lip of the duct (axisymmetric duct)
2 Moving the side wall or ramp to a higher angle so as to force a stronger oblique shock front (two-dimensional duct)
3 Varying the normal shock throat area so as to force a stronger normal shock (expanding center-body)
4 Varying the inlet lip area so as to vary the intake area

All of these methods have advantages and disadvantages insofar as cost, ease and speed of control, good efficiencies at all flight speeds, and integration into the aircraft aerodynamic and structural design are concerned.

In summation, the supersonic inlet duct must:

1 Have a high duct efficiency and deliver the highest possible ram pressure
2 Deliver the airflow required, although at low supersonic speed it must dump an excess airflow
3 Set up and maintain sonic shock waves and keep these shock waves and supersonic velocities out of the engine
4 Produce the least ram temperature rise, which temperature rise the engine design must take into account. (On some supersonic airplane-engine combinations, compressor inlet temperatures may reach 250°F or more from ram air effects)
5 Deliver ram pressure and airflow that will produce an increase in the net thrust output

Nose Inlet Variations

F8U-1, F-84

FJ4, F-86

F-100

Annular Inlet

Navy Demon

Pod Inlet

B-47, B-52, 707, DC-8

Flush-Scoop Inlet

F-80

Wing Inlet Variations

F-101, F9F-8, T-37

F-105, F4D-1

Avro Vulcan

Scoop Inlet Variations
F-104, F-102, F-106, T-33,
F-94, F-89, A4D-1, P6M-1,
F11F-1

FIG. 4-2 *Inlet duct variations.*

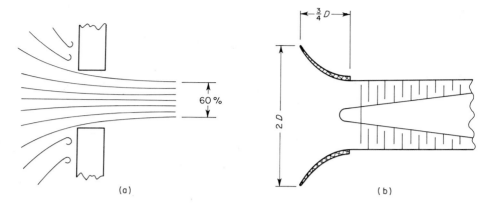

FIG. 4-3 *Purpose of the bellmouth inlet.* (**a**) *Low-velocity approach showing vena contracta effect (necking down).* (**b**) *Bellmouth inlet eliminates contraction and allows engine all the air it can handle.*

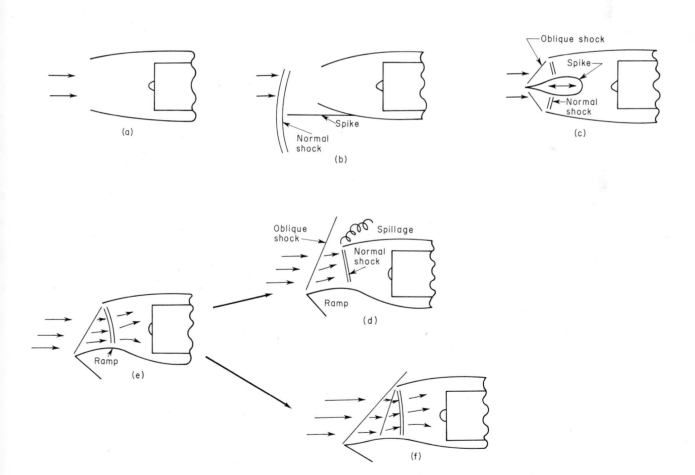

FIG. 4-4 *Types of inlet ducts.* (**a**) *Subsonic duct.* (**b**) *Transonic duct.* (**c**) *Supersonic duct with variable geometry operating at design speed.* (**d**) *Ramp- or wedge-type duct below design speed.* (**e**) *Ramp- or wedge-type duct at design speed.* (**f**) *Ramp- or wedge-type duct establishing multiple oblique shocks.*

REVIEW AND STUDY QUESTIONS

1 What is the function of the inlet duct? Why is its correct design so important?

2 Define duct pressure efficiency and ram recovery point. What is the importance of these terms in the design of a good inlet duct?

3 What is a bellmouth inlet? When is it used?

4 Into what two broad categories do inlet ducts fall?

5 What are the three speed zones in which the supersonic inlet duct must operate? Give a brief description of the inlet duct airflow under these three conditions.

6 What is the action of inlet duct airflow across a normal shock? Across an oblique shock?

7 Why is it desirable for a high-speed supersonic inlet duct to produce a series of weak oblique shocks?

8 Why must supersonic aircraft be equipped with variable geometry inlet ducts?

9 List some methods of constructing the variable geometry ducts.

Chapter 5

Compressors

The role of the compressor in a gas turbine engine is to provide a maximum of high-pressure air which can be heated in the limited volume of the combustion chamber and then expanded through the turbine. The energy that can be released in the combustion chamber is proportional to the mass of air consumed; therefore the compressor is one of the most important components of the gas turbine engine since its efficient operation (maximum compression with minimum temperature rise) is the key to high overall engine performance. The compressor efficiency will determine the power necessary to create the pressure rise of a given airflow and will affect the temperature change which can take place in the combustion chamber. (See Chap. 3.) Present-day compressors have compression ratios approaching 15:1, efficiencies near 90 percent, and airflows up to approximately 350 lb/sec. With the addition of a fan, total pressure ratios of 25:1 and mass airflows of over 1000 lb/sec have been achieved.

TYPES OF COMPRESSORS

All gas turbine engines use one of the following forms of compressor:

1 Centrifugal flow
2 Axial flow

The centrifugal-axial-flow compressor is a combination of the two, with operating characteristics of both.

It will be the purpose of this chapter to examine, in some detail, the construction and operation of each of these compressors.

The centrifugal-flow compressor

The centrifugal compressor consists basically of an impeller and a diffuser manifold (Fig. 5-1). Other com-

ponents such as a compressor manifold may be added to direct the compressed air into the combustion chamber. As the impeller revolves at high speed, air is drawn in at the eye. Centrifugal force provides high acceleration to this air and causes it to move outward from the axis of rotation toward the rim of the rotor where it is ejected at high velocity and high kinetic energy. The pressure rise is produced in part by expansion of the air in the diffuser manifold by conversion of the kinetic energy of motion into static pressure energy (Fig. 5-2).

In Chap. 2 we saw that centrifugal compressors could be manufactured in a variety of designs including single-stage, multiple-stage, and double-sided types. The centrifugal compressor has a number of features to recommend its use in certain types of gas turbine engines. Chief among its attributes are its simplicity, ruggedness, and low cost. Because of its massive construction, it is much less susceptible to damage from the ingestion of foreign objects. The centrifugal compressor is capable of a relatively high compressor ratio per stage. About 80 percent efficiency may be reached with a compression ratio of 4 or 5 to 1. Above this ratio, efficiency drops off at a rapid rate because of excessively high impeller tip speeds and attending shock-wave formation. This rules out this type of compressor for use in larger engines since high compression ratios are necessary for low fuel consumption (Fig. 5-3). Some centrifugal-flow engines obtain somewhat higher ratios through the use of multistage compressors as shown in Chap. 2, Figs. 2-2, 2-7, and 2-12. Although the tip speed problem is reduced, efficiency is again lost because of the difficulty in turning the air as it passes from one stage to another. Double-entry compressors also help to solve the high tip speed problem, but this advantage is partially offset by the complications in engine design necessary to get air to the rear impeller, and by the requirement of a large plenum or

IMPELLER   DIFFUSER   COMPRESSOR MANIFOLD

FIG. 5-1 *Typical single-stage centrifugal compressor.*

FIG. 5-2 *Centrifugal-compressor flow, pressure, and velocity changes.* (**a**) *Airflow through a typical centrifugal compressor.* (**b**) *Pressure and velocity changes through a centrifugal compressor.*

air chamber, where the air from the inlet duct is brought to a slower speed for efficient direction change and higher pressures. The plenum chamber acts as a diffuser by which means the rear impeller can receive its air. Examples of airplanes incorporating a plenum chamber are the Air Force T-33 (Fig. 2-3c), and the Navy F9F. Both of these airplanes use the Allison J-33 engine (Fig. 2-3).

Because of the problems inherent in this type of design, the centrifugal compressor finds its greatest application on the smaller engines where simplicity, flexibility of operation, and ruggedness are the principal requirements rather than small frontal area, and ability to handle high airflows and pressures with low loss of efficiency.

The axial-flow compressor

The axial-flow compressor is made up of a series of rotating airfoils called rotor blades, and a stationary set of airfoils called stator vanes. As its name implies, the air is being compressed in a direction parallel to the axis of the engine (Fig. 5-4). A row of rotating and stationary blades is called a stage. The entire compressor is made up of a series of alternating rotor and stator vane stages. Some axial-flow designs have two or more compressors or spools which are driven by separate turbines and are therefore free to rotate at different speeds.

Axial compressors have the advantage of being capable of very high compression ratios with relatively high efficiencies (Fig. 5-5). In addition, the small frontal area created by this type of compressor lends itself to installation in high-speed aircraft. Unfortunately, the delicate blading, especially toward the rear, makes this type of air pump especially susceptible to foreign-object damage. Furthermore, the number of compressor blades and stator vanes (which can exceed 1000 in a large jet engine), the close fits required for efficient air pumping, and the much narrower range of possible operating conditions, makes this type of compressor very complex and very expensive to manufacture. Modern manufacturing techniques are bringing down the cost for small axial-flow compressors. For these reasons the axial-flow design finds its greatest application where the demands of efficiency and output predominate considerations of cost, simplicity, flexibility of operation, etc. As we shall see later, most manufacturers utilize several dodges to increase flexibility and to improve the operating characteristics of the axial-flow compressor.

COMPRESSOR THEORY

Any discussion of the operation of the compressor must take into account both aerodynamic and thermodynamic considerations since it is impossible to compress air without incurring a temperature rise.

FIG. 5-3 *Specific fuel consumption decreases with increasing pressure ratio.*

FIG. 5-4 *A modern high-performance compressor assembly.* (*General Electric*)

The temperature rise is a result of the work being done by the rotor blades. In 1843, James Joule demonstrated that the temperature rise in a substance (in this case, air) was always proportional to the energy or work expended. This proposition will be examined in more detail in the section called Compressor Thermodynamics.

Compressor aerodynamics

A vector analysis will help to show airflow, pressure, and velocity changes through a typical axial-flow compressor. Starting with inlet air (Fig. 5-6), notice that the length of arrows (vectors) *A* and *B* are the same. This indicates that no change in velocity occurred at this point. The inlet guide vanes only deflect the air to a predetermined angle toward the direction of rotation of the rotor. At points *C* and *D* the vectors are of different lengths showing that work is being done upon the air in the form of a velocity loss and a pressure gain. The stator entrance (vector *E*) and the stator discharge (vector *F*) show another velocity loss and pressure gain exactly like that occurring through the rotor. The discharge air (*D*) seems to be at an incorrect angle to

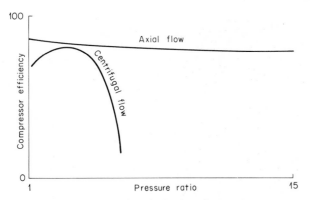

FIG. 5-5 *Comparison of centrifugal- and axial-flow compressor efficiencies with increasing pressure ratios.*

FIG. 5-6 *Airflow through an axial-flow compressor. (Pratt & Whitney)*

enter the first-stage stator, but due to the presence of rotary air motion caused by the turning compressor, the resultants (*E*) and (*G*) are produced which shows the true airflow through the compressor. Notice that these vectors are exactly in line for entrance into the next stage of the compressor. One final aerodynamic point to note is the stator entrance (vector *E*) is longer than the stator discharge (vector *F*) because of the addition of energy to the air by the rotor rotation *X*. Thus, as each set of blades, rotors, and stators, cause a pressure rise to occur at the expense of their discharge velocity, the air's rotary motion restores the velocity energy at each blade's entrance for it in turn to convert to pressure energy.

You will notice that both the rotor blades and the stator blades are diffusing the airflow. It is much more difficult to obtain an efficient deceleration (diffusion or pressure increase) of airflow than it is to get efficient acceleration, because there is a natural tendency in a diffusing process for the air to break away from the walls of the diverging passage, reverse its direction, and flow back in the direction of the pressure gradient or lower pressure (Fig. 5-7). It has been determined that a pressure rise of approximately 1.2 is all that can be handled by a single compressor stage since higher rates of diffusion and excessive turning angles on the blades result in excessive air instability, hence low efficiency. A desired compression ratio is achieved by simply adding more stages onto the compressor. The amount of pressure rise or compression ratio depends on the mass of air discharged by the compressor, the restrictions to flow imposed by the parts of the engine through which the air must pass, and the operating conditions (pressures) inside the engine compared to the ambient air pressure at the compressor intake. The final pressure is the result of multiplying the pressure rise in each stage.

EXAMPLE: A 13-stage compressor has a pressure ratio across each stage of 1.2 and an ambient inlet pressure of 14.7. What is the final pressure? What is the pressure ratio?

stage 1	stage 2	stage 3
$14.7 \times 1.2 = 17.64$	$\times 1.2 = 21.12$	$\times 1.2 =$

stage 4	stage 5	stage 6
$25.34 \times 1.2 = 30.41$	$\times 1.2 = 36.49$	$\times 1.2 =$

stage 7	stage 8	stage 9
$43.79 \times 1.2 = 52.55$	$\times 1.2 = 63.06$	$\times 1.2 =$

stage 10	stage 11	stage 12
$75.67 \times 1.2 = 90.80$	$\times 1.2 = 108.96$	$\times 1.2 =$

stage 13
$130.75 \times 1.2 = 156.90$

Final pressure = 156.9 psi
Initial pressure = 14.7 psi

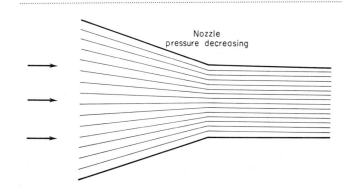

FIG. 5-7 *Diffusing air is unstable.*

or

$$C.R. = \frac{156.9}{14.7}$$
$$= 10.6 : 1$$

Notice that the pressure rise across the first stage is

17.6 psi	pressure at back of 1st stage
−14.7 psi	pressure at front of 1st stage
2.9 psi	pressure rise across 1st stage

and the pressure rise across the last stage is

156.90 psi	pressure at back of 13th stage
−130.75 psi	pressure at front of 13th stage
26.15 psi	pressure rise across 13th stage

The pressure ratio is the same in both cases but the actual increase in pressure is much greater toward the rear of the compressor (Fig. 5-8) than the front. The compression ratio will increase and decrease with engine speed. It will also be affected by compressor inlet temperature. As the inlet temperature (due to ram) increases, the compression ratio will tend to decrease due to the combined effects of air density decrease and the temperature effects on the angle of attack.

The ideal compression ratio is that which will produce the maximum pressure in the tailpipe. Normally, the higher the compression ratio the higher the tailpipe pressure. However, at high compression ratios and high compressor inlet temperatures, and with turbine inlet temperature limited to a specific value, the com-

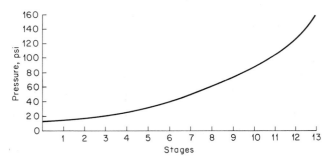

FIG. 5-8 *The result of compressor pressure multiplication.*

pressor discharge temperature would be so high that main fuel flow would have to be limited, and the turbine rotor would have to use more pressure energy in place of combustion energy to drive the compressor. This, then would result in increased turbine pressure loss in comparison to the compressor pressure increase. (See Chap. 7.)

High-speed flight also has a profound effect on compressor discharge pressure and temperature. High aircraft speeds will cause a ram pressure and ram temperature rise of considerable proportions to exist at the front of the compressor. These high ram pressure ratios and high ram temperature ratios when multiplied by the pressure and temperature rise across the compressor will produce pressures and temperatures in the engine which will be in excess of design limitations. For example, at Mach 3 the pressure ratio due to ram alone will be approximately 30:1. When this is multiplied by a compressor ratio of only 10:1 it will give a total pressure ratio of 300:1. This is far beyond what the combustion chamber can stand. Furthermore, at this high speed, the ram temperature ratio when multiplied by the compressor temperature ratio will give very high temperatures at the compressor discharge, and this in turn will limit the amount of fuel that can be added to obtain a useful temperature rise.

By bypassing some of the excess compressor discharge air around the combustion chambers and turbine, and discharging it into the primary airstream at the jet nozzle, and/or by reducing the number of compressor stages, these high compressor discharge pressures may be used to advantage. A system of "blow-in" doors will be necessary to ensure the proper pressure relationship between the bypassed air and primary air.

A cross-sectional view of the engine (Fig. 5-9) shows that the space formed by the compressor disk rim and the stator casing gradually reduces in area. Figure 3-17 in Chap. 3 shows that the airflow velocity is relatively constant through the compressor. If air is compressed and the volume is not decreased, its velocity will decrease toward the rear stages and the stall area (discussed on pages 99–101), will be approached. Two methods of reducing the volume toward the rear stage

FIG. 5-9   *Sectioned view showing a typical compressor taper, and constant-diameter case.*

are to use a compressor whose case has a constant diameter and whose compressor rotor tapers, or, to use a compressor with a tapering case and a constant diameter rotor.   Figure 2-15 shows both types used on one engine.   Since rpm and airflow are related, the compressor should be turned as fast as possible.   Keeping in mind that the blade tips must not exceed the speed of sound in order to avoid shock-wave formation that would destroy pumping efficiency, the tip speed is kept to approximately Mach 0.85.

By using the formula

$$V_{\text{fpm}} = \pi D \times \text{rpm}$$

or

$$V_{\text{fps}} = \frac{\pi D}{12} \times \frac{\text{rpm}}{60}$$

where V_{fpm} = velocity, ft/min
V_{fps} = velocity, fps
D = diameter, ft
$\dfrac{D}{12}$ = diameter, in.
$\dfrac{\text{rpm}}{60}$ = revolutions per second

the tip speed of any rotating wheel, i.e., the compressor or turbine, may be found.   For example, if the diameter of a particular compressor is 18 in. from tip to tip, the compressor rpm is 20,000, and the temperature at this point in the compressor is standard, the tip speed of the blades would be:

$$\begin{aligned}
V_{\text{fps}} &= \frac{\pi D}{12} \times \frac{\text{rpm}}{60} \\
&= \frac{3.14 \times 18}{12} \times \frac{20,000}{60} \\
&= 1570
\end{aligned}$$

Always keeping in mind that the speed of sound is a function of temperature, and that under standard day temperatures the speed of sound is equal to 1117 fps, we can see that the rpm of this compressor would be much too high, being limited to 1117 × 0.85, or 950 fps.   But as already indicated, there is a considerable temperature rise at the rear stages of the compressor.   This will permit a higher tip speed at the rear stages without exceeding the speed of sound.   The Pratt & Whitney two-spool compressor design (Fig. 2-15) takes advantage of this fact.   Figure 5-10 shows the advantage of the constant outside case diameter.

Other forms of the same formula will allow us to find the maximum rpm or the maximum diameter of a given compressor or turbine.

EXAMPLE: What is the maximum rpm of a compressor whose diameter equals 18 in. and whose blade-tip speed is limited to Mach 0.8?   Note: The speed of sound

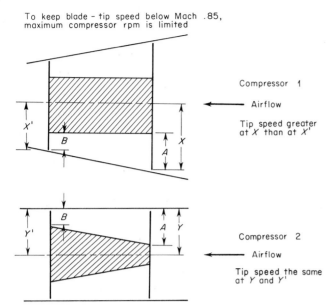

To keep blade – tip speed below Mach .85, maximum compressor rpm is limited

Compressor 1

Airflow

Tip speed greater at *X* than at *X'*

Compressor 2

Airflow

Tip speed the same at *Y* and *Y'*

FIG. 5-10 *Comparison of airflow through a constant-outside-diameter and constant-inside-diameter compressor. Conditions: (1) Outlet air temperature for compressors 1 and 2 = 500°F. (2) A = A and B = B. Critical dimensions for both compressors are the same. Conclusion: A temperature of 500°F would permit a speed of 15,000 rpm, but the speed of compressor 1 is limited by tip speed at X. It is potentially capable of pumping more air.*

equals 1100 fps under existing conditions, therefore the tip speed is limited to 1100 × 0.8, or 880 fps.

$$\text{rpm} = \frac{12 \times 60 \times V_{\text{fps}}}{\pi D}$$
$$= \frac{12 \times 60 \times 880}{3.14 \times 18}$$
$$= 11,210$$

EXAMPLE: What is the maximum diameter of a compressor whose rpm equals 10,000 and whose blade-tip speed is limited to Mach 0.7? Note: Again the local speed of sound equals 1100 fps.

$$D = \frac{V_{\text{fps}} \times 12 \times 60}{\pi \times \text{rpm}}$$
$$= \frac{770 \times 12 \times 60}{3.14 \times 10,000}$$
$$= 17.65 \text{ in.}$$

As was mentioned previously, the air velocity is fairly constant throughout the compressor and a given air molecule will not wander much more than 180° around the compressor, for although the rotors impart a rotational component to the air, the stators take this rotational component and turn the velocity into pressure.

Compressor stall

Since an axial-flow compressor consists of a series of alternately rotating and stationary airfoils or wings, the same rules and limitations which apply to an airfoil or

wing will apply to the entire compressor. The picture is somewhat more complicated than is the case for a single airfoil, because the blades are close together, and each blade is affected at the leading edge by the passage through the air of the preceding blade. This "cascade" effect can be more readily understood if the airflow through the compressor is viewed as flow through a series of ducts formed by the individual blades, rather than flow over an airfoil that is generating lift. The cascade effect is of prime importance in determining blade design and placement (Fig. 5-11).

The axial compressor is not without its difficulties, and the most vital of these is the stall problem. If for some reason the angle of attack, i.e., the angle at which the airflow strikes the rotor blades, becomes too low, the pressure zones shown in Fig. 5-11 will be of low value and the airflow and compression will be low. (The angle of attack should not be confused with the angle of incidence, which is a fixed angle determined by the manufacturer when he constructs the compressor.) If the angle of attack is high, the pressure zones will be high and airflow and compression ratio will be high. If it is too high the compressor will stall. That is, the airflow over the upper foil surface will become turbulent and destroy the pressure zones. This will, of course, decrease the compression and airflow. The angle of attack will vary with engine rpm, compressor inlet temperature, and compressor discharge or burner pressure. From Fig. 5-12 it can be seen that decreasing the velocity of airflow or increasing engine rotor speed will tend to increase the angle of attack. In general, any action that decreases airflow *relative* to engine speed will increase the angle of attack and increase the tendency to stall. The decrease in airflow may result from the compressor discharge pressure becoming too high, for example from excessive fuel-flow schedule during acceleration. Or compressor inlet pressure may become too low in respect to the compressor discharge

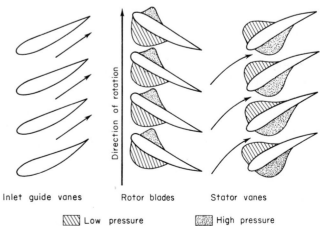

Inlet guide vanes   Rotor blades   Stator vanes

▨ Low pressure   ▨ High pressure

FIG. 5-11 *The cascade effect.*

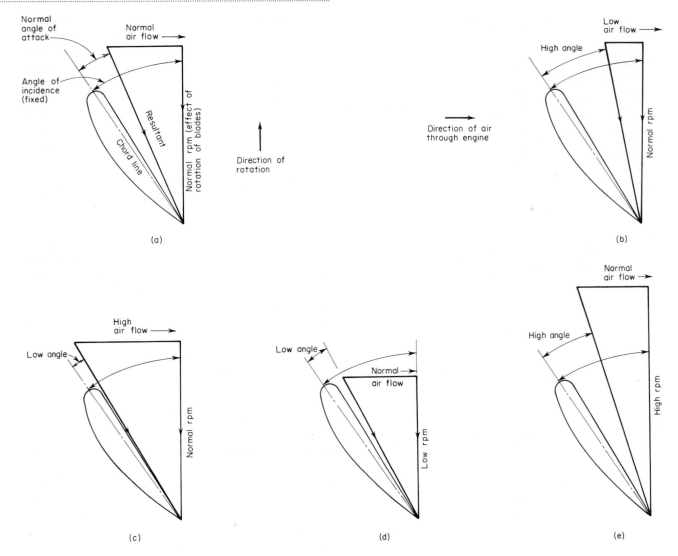

FIG. 5-12 *The result of changing airflow velocity and rpm on the angle of attack.* (**a**) *Normal air velocity, rpm, and angle of attack.* (**b**) *Low air velocity, normal rpm, high angle of attack (stall).* (**c**) *High air velocity, normal rpm, low angle of attack (choke).* (**d**) *Normal air velocity, low rpm, low angle of attack (choke).* (**e**) *Normal air velocity, high rpm, high angle of attack (stall).*

pressure because of high inlet temperatures or distortion of inlet air. Several other causes are possible (Fig. 5-12).

During ground operation of the engine, the prime action that tends to cause a stall is choking. If the engine speed is decreased from the design speed, the compression ratio will decrease with the lower rotor velocities as shown in Fig. 5-12d. With a decrease in compression, the volume of air in the rear of the compressor will be greater. This excess volume of air causes a choking action in the rear of the compressor with a decrease in airflow, which in turn decreases the air velocity in the front of the compressor and increases the tendency to stall illustrated in Fig. 5-12b. If no corrective design action is taken, the front of the compressor will stall at low engine speeds.

Another important cause of stall is high compressor inlet air temperatures. High-speed aircraft may experience an inlet air temperature of 250°F or higher because of the ram effect. These high temperatures cause low compression ratios (due to density changes) and will also cause choking in the rear of the compressor. This choking-stall condition is the same as that caused by low compression ratios due to low engine speeds. High compressor inlet temperatures will cause the length of the airflow vector to become longer since the air velocity is directly affected by the square root of any temperature change.

Each stage of a compressor should develop the same pressure ratio as all other stages. But as stated in the two preceding paragraphs, when the engine is slowed

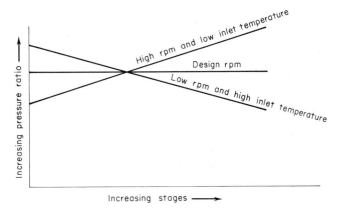

FIG. 5-13 *The effect of rpm and temperature on the angle of attack and the pressure ratio per stage.*

down or the compressor inlet temperature climbs, the front stages supply too much air for the rear stages to handle and the rear stages will choke (Fig. 5-13).

There are five basic solutions which can be utilized to correct this front-end, low-speed, high-temperature stall condition.

1   Derate or lower the angles of attack on the front stages so that the high angles at low engine speed are not stall angles.

2   Introduce a bleed valve into the middle or rear of the compressor and use it to bleed air and increase airflow in the front of the compressor at lower engine speeds.

3   Divide the compressor into two sections or rotors (the two-spool rotor) and design the front rotor speed to fall off more than the rear rotor at low speeds so that the low front rotor speed will equal the low choked airflow.

4   Place variable guide vanes at the front of the compressor and variable stator vanes in the front of the first several compressor stages so that the angles of attack can be reset to low angles by moving the variable vanes at low engine speeds.   Some advanced engine designs also utilize the variable stator concept on the last several compressor stages.

5   Use a variable-area exhaust nozzle to unload the compressor during acceleration.

NOTE: A combination of these methods may be used.

One last point on compressor aerodynamics needs discussion. Every compressor has a certain ability to maintain a compression ratio for a given mass airflow. Figure 5-14 shows a typical compressor's ability to maintain a compression ratio as mass flow varies.   Any point located above the compressor's stall curve represents a compression ratio too high for the existing mass airflow.   The normal operating line shows the actual pressure ratio the compressor would be subject to with variations in mass airflow.   Any point on this line represents the compression ratio that will exist in a given engine with a specific mass flow.   The normal operating line can be raised or lowered by changing the downstream restrictions.   Any time the normal operating line crosses the compressor stall curve, the compressor will be subject to compression ratios it

cannot maintain.   Stall will result.   Figure 5-14 illustrates that, while this engine will run unstalled at a compression ratio of 9:1 with a mass airflow of 100 lb/sec, it cannot get to this point without encountering the stall zone.   All of the listed methods in the preceding paragraph for correcting stall either change the shape of the normal operating line so that it will conform more closely with the compressor stall line or move the compressor stall line to a higher point.

Compressor thermodynamics

Thermodynamically, the compressor follows natural gas laws which state that a pressure rise is normally accompanied by a temperature rise.   In addition, any aerodynamic inefficiencies cause an additional temperature rise and correspondingly less pressure output than the ideal compressor.   Since this is not a text on thermodynamics, this phenomena will be investigated only rather briefly.

THE BEHAVIOR OF AIR

Air is a mixture of gases, principally oxygen and nitrogen with some water vapor always present.   The gases are made up of molecules which are very widely separated in relation to their size.   These molecules travel at very high average velocity and cause pressure by hitting the sides of any container.

The force with which any molecule will strike the walls of a container is equal to the mass of the molecule times twice its speed.   Two times the speed is used because when a mass has its direction changed, a force results which is equal to the mass times the amount of change, and when a given molecule strikes the wall of the container at a given speed it will rebound with the same speed.

Force = $2mc$

where m = mass of molecule
c = speed of molecule

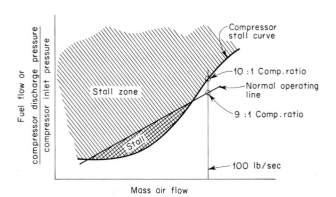

FIG. 5-14 *Typical compressor operating curve.*

In addition, the total number of molecules in the container must be considered. Although not all of the molecules strike the container walls, those in the middle form the boundary for the molecules that are hitting the walls, so all of the molecules contribute to the pressure or force in the container.

Force = 2mc × number of molecules

Further, each molecule in a container will eventually strike all sides of that container. If a force in one direction is of interest, i.e., pressure on a specific area, the total force must be divided by 3.

$$\text{Force} = \frac{2mc \times \text{number of molecules}}{3}$$

One other factor needs to be considered, and that is the number of times each molecule will hit the wall. This is equal to the molecule's speed in feet per second divided by two times the distance the molecule has had to travel to strike the wall. Two times the distance is used because the molecule must travel back to its original point before it can start again.

$$\text{Force} = \frac{2mc \times \text{number of molecules}}{3} \times \frac{c}{2d}$$

where c = speed of molecule, fps
   d = molecule distance to wall

Since the mass of the molecule times the number of molecules equals the mass of the whole body, then

$$F = \frac{Mc^2}{3d}$$

where M = mass of entire body.
   Pressure times an area equals a force, so

$$PA = \frac{Mc^2}{3d}$$

where P = pressure, lb/sq ft
   A = area, sq ft
By rearranging the formula,

$$P = \frac{Mc^2}{3dA}$$

It is also known that an area times a distance equals a volume.

$$P = \frac{Mc^2}{3V}$$

Mass is equal to w/g and the formula then becomes:

$$P = \frac{wc^2}{3gV}$$

From this formula it can be seen that the internal energy or static pressure will increase as the square of the molecular speed (a function of temperature) and directly in relation to the density. Rearranging the formula again and solving for c^2,

$$c^2 = \frac{3gPV}{w}$$

Pressure × volume = WRT

where W = weight of air
   R = gas constant for air (see page 104)
   T = absolute temperature, °R
Rearranging this formula gives

$$\frac{PV}{w} = RT$$

Now if

$$c^2 = \frac{3gPV}{w}$$

then

$$c^2 = 3gRT$$

In this formula the 3, g, and R are all constants, and it can be seen that the temperature varies as the square of the molecular speed. The letter K is often used for the combined constant for the 3, g, and R, and this results in the formula:

$$c^2 = KT \qquad \text{or} \qquad c = \sqrt{KT}$$

which states that the molecular speed is directly related to the square root of the temperature of the gas.

High temperature = high molecular speed
Low temperature = low molecular speed

At absolute zero (−460°F) the velocity of the gas molecule would theoretically equal zero and the pressure would be zero. On a standard day, and at sea level, the average molecular speed would be 1116 fps or 761 mph (speed of sound) with the pressure equal to 14.7 lb/in.². (See Appendix.)

Air is capable of expanding and contracting, and of absorbing and giving up heat. These effects are interrelated and closely follow known gas laws. For example, adding heat to a fixed volume of air raises its temperature, causes the molecules to move faster and the pressure to increase. Compressing the air delivers energy to the molecules, resulting in higher molecular speed and thus higher temperatures. When the same number of molecules occupies less space, they hit the side of the enclosure with greater frequency, which results in higher pressure. The principal point to remember is that whenever work is done on a gas the gas gets hotter in *proportion* to the amount of work being done on the gas.

BOYLE'S LAW

The three possible properties of air are volume, temperature, and pressure. Since the gas turbine engine is continuously changing these variables, an understanding of the relationship between volume, temperature, and pressure is important. If any two values are known, the third can be determined, assuming that the weight or mass of air has not changed. Boyle's law states that: If the *temperature of a given quantity of gas is kept constant*, absolute pressure is inversely proportional to volume.

$$\frac{P_1}{P_2} = \frac{V_2}{V_1} \qquad \text{or} \qquad P_1 V_1 = P_2 V_2$$

where P_1 = initial absolute pressure
P_2 = final absolute pressure
V_1 = initial volume, cu ft
V_2 = final volume, cu ft
Transposing will give us

$$P_2 = \frac{P_1 V_1}{V_2} \qquad \text{or} \qquad V_2 = \frac{P_1 V_1}{P_2}$$

CHARLES' LAW (Fig. 5-15)

Charles' law states that: If the *pressure on a given quantity of gas is held constant*, the volume is directly proportional to the absolute temperature.

$$\frac{V_1}{V_2} = \frac{T_1}{T_2} \qquad \text{or} \qquad \frac{T_1}{V_1} = \frac{T_2}{V_2}$$

where V_1 = initial volume, cu ft
V_2 = final volume, cu ft
T_1 = initial absolute temperature
T_2 = final absolute temperature
Transposing will give us

$$V_2 = \frac{V_1 T_2}{T_1} \qquad \text{or} \qquad T_2 = \frac{T_1 V_2}{V_1}$$

This law may also be written: If the *volume of a given quantity of gas is held constant*, the pressure is directly proportional to the absolute temperature.

$$\frac{P_1}{P_2} = \frac{T_1}{T_2} \qquad \text{or} \qquad \frac{T_1}{P_1} = \frac{T_2}{P_2}$$

Transposing will give us

$$P_2 = \frac{P_1 T_2}{T_1} \qquad \text{or} \qquad T_2 = \frac{T_1 P_2}{P_1}$$

By combining Boyle's and Charles' laws we get the *general gas law* which can be used to find the pressure, volume, or temperature of a gas when any of the other conditions change.

$$\frac{P_1 V_1}{T_1} = \frac{P_2 V_2}{T_2}$$

Transposing will give

$$P_2 = \frac{P_1 V_1 T_2}{V_2 T_1}$$

or

$$V_2 = \frac{P_1 V_1 T_2}{P_2 T_1}$$

or

$$T_2 = \frac{P_2 V_2 T_1}{P_1 V_1}$$

SPECIFIC HEAT

The *British thermal unit* is a standard measure of energy and is defined as the amount of energy required to raise the temperature of one pound of water one degree Fahrenheit at a constant volume. If the temperature of 1 lb of air is raised the same amount only 0.1715 Btu is required to do the job. The numerical comparison of Btu's between water and air is called the

10 psig (24.7 psia)   19 psig (33.7 psia)
32 °F (492 °R)   212 °F (672 °R)

At a constant volume, pressure and temperature vary directly

FIG. 5-15 *Diagram illustrating Charles' law.*

V = 10 cu ft   V = 13.6 cu ft
32 °F (492 °R)   212 °F (672 °F)

At a constant pressure, volume and temperature vary directly *specific heat* at a constant volume (c_v). According to Charles' law, the pressure of a given weight of gas, when heated at a constant volume, varies directly as the absolute temperature. When a gas does not expand, its volume remains the same and no external work is done. All of the heat added to a gas at a constant volume is effective only in raising its temperature. But a gas will require *more than* 0.1715 Btu to raise its temperature 1°F at a constant pressure than at a constant volume, because at a constant pressure the gas can expand and do useful work. In other words, the heat added must be sufficient to raise the gas temperature 1°F as well as to supply energy equal to the external work done. The specific heat of air at a constant pressure (c_p) is 0.24 Btu. Now if it takes 0.1715 Btu to raise the gas temperature 1°F at a constant volume, and 0.24 Btu to raise the gas temperature and furnish expansion energy for useful work at a constant pressure, then

$$
\begin{array}{rl}
0.2400 & c_p \\
-0.1715 & c_v \\
\hline
0.0685 & = \text{amount of Btu that went into the} \\
& \quad \text{expansion of 1 lb of air when the} \\
& \quad \text{temperature was raised 1°F}
\end{array}
$$

It has been determined, through experimentation, that 1 Btu = 778 ft-lb. Multiplying the energy (Btu's) that goes into the expansion of 1 lb of air by 778 will give the work in foot-pounds that the air is capable of doing for each degree of temperature rise per pound of air. This is the mechanical equivalent of heat.

$$
\begin{aligned}
1 \text{ Btu} &= 778 \, (c_p - c_v) \\
&= 778 \, (0.24 - 0.1715) \\
&= 53.3 \text{ ft-lb of mechanical work done by the} \\
& \quad \text{expansion of 1 lb of air at a constant} \\
& \quad \text{pressure when its temperature is raised} \\
& \quad \text{1°F}
\end{aligned}
$$

The number 53.3 is practically constant for all temperatures and pressures of air and is designated by the letter R. Other gases will have other gas constants.

PERFECT-GAS EQUATION

According to Boyle's law, the product of the pressure times the volume of one pound of air at a given temperature equals a constant.

$PV = \text{constant}$

According to Charles' law the volume varies as the temperature varies. In addition it is known that the pressure will vary as the temperature. Combining these statements will give:

$$\frac{PV}{T} = \text{const} \quad \text{or} \quad R$$

By transposing,

$PV = RT$

If the value for R (53.3 for air as found above) and any two of the quantities P, V, or T is known, the third can be found by using one of the following equations.

$$P = \frac{RT}{V} \qquad V = \frac{RT}{P} \qquad T = \frac{PV}{R}$$

HORSEPOWER REQUIRED TO DRIVE THE COMPRESSOR

The compressor requires a considerable amount of shaft horsepower to pump air and to give this air a pressure and temperature rise. The horsepower requirements can be determined by finding out how much energy has been put into the air by the compressor. Multiplying the specific heat of air at a constant pressure by the temperature rise across the compressor will give the energy put into each pound of air during the pressurizing process. If this result is then multiplied by the total weight of airflow through the compressor, the total energy put into the air by the compressor can be obtained:

$c_p T W_a = \text{Btu/sec being put into the air, or total}$
$\qquad\qquad \text{energy of air}$

Since 1 Btu = 778 ft-lb, and 1 hp equals 550 ft-lb/sec, the horsepower requirements for the compressor are

$$\frac{c_p T W_a \times 778}{550}$$

NOTE: The specific heat of air at a constant pressure is used any time the volume of a gas is increasing or decreasing because while the c_v and c_p both take into account the energy required to increase molecular speed, only the c_p takes into consideration the change in volume or change in distance the molecules travel.

PROBLEM: An axial-flow engine is running at 100 percent rpm under standard day conditions. The compressor is pumping 200 lb of air per second, and the temperature rise across the compressor is 600°F. How much power is needed by this compressor? Disregard any losses and assume 100 percent efficiency.

$$
\begin{aligned}
\text{Compressor horsepower} \atop \text{requirements} \;
&= \frac{c_p T W_a 778}{550} \\
&= \frac{0.24 \times 600 \times 200 \times 778}{550} \\
&= 40{,}703 \quad \text{at 100 percent}
\end{aligned}
$$

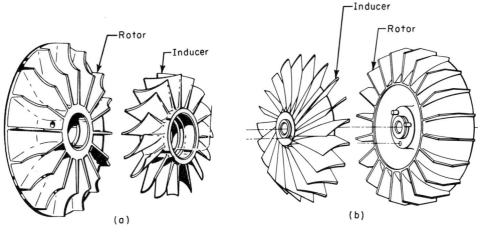

FIG. 5-16 *Typical single-stage centrifugal compressors.* (**a**) *Continental J69.* (**b**) *Fairchild J44.*

Construction features

Centrifugal-flow jet engines usually use heat-treated forged aluminum compressors, although cast compressors are being used on small engines of this type. The aluminum or magnesium diffuser is also generally manufactured by casting. In many cases the inducer or guide vanes, which smooth and direct the airflow into the engine and thus minimize the shock in the impeller, is manufactured separately from the impeller or rotor. Rotor vanes may either be all full length as in Fig. 5-16, or some may be half length as shown in Fig. 5-17. A close fit is important between the compressor and its case in order to obtain maximum compressor efficiency. The clearance is usually checked with a feeler gage or with a special fixture. Balancing of the rotor may be accomplished by removing material from specified areas of the compressor or by using balancing weights installed in holes in the hub of the compressor. On some engines in which the compressor and turbine wheel are balanced as a unit, special bolts or nuts having slight variations in weight are used. Compressor support bearings may be either ball or roller, although most manufacturers use at least one ball bearing on the compressor to support both axial and radial loads.

Axial-flow engines have compressors that are constructed of several different materials depending upon the load and temperature under which the unit must operate. The rotor assembly illustrated in Fig. 5-18

1	IMPELLER FRONT SHAFT	5	REAR ROTATING GUIDE VANE
2	OIL PLUG	6	IMPELLER REAR SHAFT
3	FRONT ROTATING GUIDE VANE	7	OIL PLUG
4	IMPELLER	8	IMPELLER BOLT

FIG. 5-17 *Double-sided centrifugal compressor with half-vanes (Allison J33).*

FIG. 5-18 *Compressor construction features of the General Electric CJ805-23 engine.*

FIG. 5-19 *The Allison 501-D13 compressor is held together with a tie bolt. Notice the dovetail blade base, balancing weight, and lock pin.*

consists of stub shafts, disks, blades, ducts, spacers, and torque cones. The rotor blades are generally machined from stainless-steel forgings, although some blades may be of titanium in the forward or colder part of the compressor; the remainder of the components are machined, low-alloy steel forgings. The clearance between the rotating blades and the outer case is most important with many manufacturers depending upon a "wear fit" between the blade and the compressor case. Many companies design their blades with knife-edge tips so that the blades will wear away and form their own clearance as they expand from the heat generated from compression of the air. Other companies coat the inner surface of the compressor case with a soft material which can be worn away without damage to the blade. The several stages of the compressor are composed of disks which can be joined together by means of a tie bolt as shown in Fig. 5-19. Serrations or splines prevent the disks from turning in relation to each other. Other manufacturers eliminate the tie bolt and join the stages together at the disk rim (Figs. 5-18 and 5-20). Methods of attaching the blade to the disk also vary between manufacturers, with the majority using some variation of the dovetail to hold the rotor blade in the disk. Various locking methods are used to anchor the blades in place. The blades do not have a tight fit in the disk, but rather are seated by centrifugal force during engine operation. By allowing the blades some movement, vibrational stresses, produced by the high-velocity airstreams from between the blades, are reduced.

Stator cases also show great variability in design and construction features. Figure 5-21 shows most of the features to be found in a typical compressor case, with an additional feature being the variable stator vanes. The stator vanes may be either of solid or hollow construction and may or may not be connected together at their tips by a shroud. The shrouding serves two purposes. First, it provides support for the longer stator vanes located in the forward stages of the compressor, and second, it provides the absolutely necessary air seal between rotating and stationary parts. Allison, General Electric, Lycoming, and others use split compressor cases (Figs. 5-22 and 5-23), while Pratt & Whitney favors a weldment, forming a continuous case. The advantage to the split case lies in the fact that the com-

FIG. 5-20 *Low-speed (N1) compressor construction for the Pratt & Whitney JT3C. Notice the dovetail blade attachment. (1) Front hub, (2) spacer assembly, (3) rear hub.*

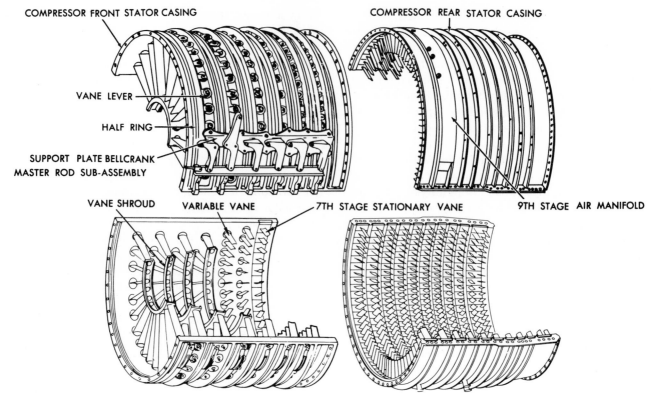

FIG. 5-21 *Stator case for the General Electric CJ805-23 engine.*

FIG. 5-22 *Rotor and stator assembly for the General Electric CJ610 (J85). Note the first-stage blade attachment.*

FIG. 5-23 *The Lycoming T53 has a split compressor case.*

pressor and stator blades are readily available to inspection. On the other hand, the continuous case offers simplicity and strength, since it requires no horizontal parting surface (Fig. 5-24).

Both the case and the rotor are very highly stressed parts. Since the compressor turns at very high speeds, the disks must be able to withstand very high centrifugal force, and, in addition, the blades must resist bending loads and high temperatures. When the compressor is constructed, each stage is balanced separately and after assembly, the compressor is balanced as a unit. Figure 5-19 shows the balance method used by Allison on their 501-D13 engine. The compressor case in most instances is one of the principal structural, load-bearing members of the engine, and may be constructed of aluminum as shown in Fig. 5-25 or steel as shown in Figs. 5-21, 5-22, and 5-24.

FIG. 5-24 *Disassembly of a Pratt & Whitney N1 compressor having a continuous, one-piece case.*

FIG. 5-25 *Sectioned Rolls Royce Dart showing aluminum compressor housing and diffuser construction.*

REVIEW AND STUDY QUESTIONS

1   How would you define an efficient compressor?

2   List some typical operating specifications in terms of compression ratios, airflows, and efficiencies for a large axial-flow compressor.

3   Name the two basic types of gas turbine compressors. Describe the operating principles of each.

4   Using vectors, show the pressure and velocity changes through an axial compressor.

5   What is the practical maximum pressure rise per stage for an axial-flow compressor? For a centrifugal-flow compressor? Why?

6   What is the purpose of the curved section at the front of the centrifugal-flow compressor?

7   Compare the pressure increase per stage at the front and rear of the axial-flow compressor.

8   Determine the compression ratio for a 10-stage axial-flow compressor (1.2 C.R. and 14.7 psi ambient pressure).

9   What are two methods of reducing the flow area toward the rear of the compressor? Why is it necessary to do this?

10   What formula is used to determine the tip speed of the compressor?

11   Explain the phenomenon of compressor stall. What conditions bring a compressor closer to stall? How may the stall problem be reduced?

12   What is the relationship between temperature and the speed of sound? Between temperature and work done on a gas?

13   State Boyle's law and Charles' law.

14   What is meant by specific heat?

15   Give the formula for determining the power required by the compressor.

16   Describe the construction features and materials of the axial and centrifugal compressors.

Chapter 6

Combustion chambers

The development of burner systems for aircraft gas turbine engines presents a number of challenging problems. These problems involve thermodynamics, fluid mechanics, heat transfer, chemistry, metallurgy, and many other phases of development.

There are three basic types of burner systems in use today. They are the can type (Fig. 6-1), the annular type (Fig. 6-2), and the combination of the two called the can-annular or cannular type (Fig. 6-3). Variations of these basic designs are used in a number of engines, examples of which can be seen in Figs. 2-3, 2-7, and 2-43 for the can type and its variations; in Figs. 2-5, 2-12, 2-26 to 2-31, 2-35, 2-39, and 2-40 for the annular type and its variations; and in Figs. 2-14, 2-15, 2-18 to 2-25, 2-32, 2-33, 2-36, 2-37, and 2-50 for the can-annular type and its variations.

TYPES OF BURNERS

In the can type, individual burners, or cans, are mounted in a circle around the engine axis, with each one receiving air through its own cylindrical shroud. One of the main disadvantages of can-type burners is that they do not make the best use of available space in the engine. On the other hand, the burners are individually removable for inspection. The annular burner is essentially a single chamber made up of concentric cylinders mounted coaxially about the engine axis. This arrangement makes more complete use of available space and fits well with the axial compressor and turbine, but has a disadvantage in that structural problems may arise due to the large-diameter, thin-wall cylinder required with this type of chamber. The prob-

lem is more severe for larger engines. There is also some disadvantage in that the entire combustor must be removed from the engine for inspection and repairs. The can-annular design also makes good use of available space, but employs a number of individual cylindrical liners that receive air through a common annular housing. The can-annular arrangement has the added advantage of greater structural stability and lower pressure loss than that of the can type (Fig. 6-4).

OPERATION OF THE COMBUSTION CHAMBER

Fuel is introduced at the front end of the burner in either a highly atomized spray from specially designed nozzles (see Chap. 12), or in a prevaporized form from devices called vaporizing tubes. Air flows in around the fuel nozzle and through the first row of combustion air holes in the liner. The burner geometry is such that the air near the nozzle stays close to the front wall of the liner for cooling and cleaning purposes, while the air entering through opposing liner holes mixes rapidly with the fuel to form a combustible mixture. Additional air is introduced (Fig. 6-5) through the remaining air holes in the liner. The air entering the forward section of the liner tends to recirculate and move upstream against the fuel spray. During combustion this action permits rapid mixing and prevents flame blowout by forming a low-velocity stabilization zone which acts as a continuous pilot for the rest of the burner. The air entering the downstream part of the liner provides the correct mixture for combustion, and it creates the intense turbulence that is necessary for mixing the fuel and air and for transferring energy from the burned to the unburned gases.

Since there are usually only two ignitor plugs in an engine, cross ignition tubes are necessary in the can and can-annular types of burners in order that burning may be initiated in the other cans or inner liners. The ignitor plug is usually located in the upstream reverse-flow region of the burner. After ignition, the flame quickly spreads to the primary or combustion zone where there is approximately the correct proportion of air to completely burn the fuel. If all the air flowing through the engine were mixed with the fuel at this point, the mixture would be outside the combustible limits for the fuels normally used. Therefore only about one-third to one-half is allowed to enter the combustion zone of the burner. About 25 percent of the air actually takes part in the combustion process. The gases that result from combustion have temperatures of 3500°F. Before entering the turbine the gases must be cooled to approximately half this value, which is determined by the design of the turbine and the materials involved. Cooling is done by diluting the hot gases with secondary air that enters through a set of

(a)

(b)

FIG. 6-1 (a) *The can-type burner.* (b) *Sectioned view of a typical can-type burner.*

relatively large holes located toward the rear of the liner. The liner walls must also be protected from the high temperatures of combustion. This is usually accomplished by introducing cooling air at several stations along the liner, thereby forming an insulating blanket between the hot gases and the metal walls (Fig. 6-6).

PERFORMANCE REQUIREMENTS

1 *High combustion efficiency*—This is necessary for long range.
2 *Stable operation*—Free from blowout at airflows ranging from idle to maximum power and at pressures representing the aircraft's entire altitude range is essential.
3 *Low-pressure loss*—It is desirable to have as much pressure as pos-

sible available in the exhaust nozzle to accelerate the gases rearward. High-pressure losses will reduce thrust and increase specific fuel consumption.

4 *Uniform temperature distribution*—The average temperature of the gases entering the turbine should be as close to the temperature limit of the burner material as possible to obtain maximum engine performance. High local temperatures or hot spots in the gas stream will reduce the allowable average turbine inlet temperature in order to protect the turbine. This will result in a decrease in total gas energy and a corresponding decrease in engine performance (Fig. 6-7).

5 *Easy starting*—Low pressures and high velocities in the burner make starting difficult; therefore, a poorly designed burner will start within only a small range of flight speeds and altitudes, whereas a well designed burner will permit easier air restarts.

6 *Small size*—A large burner requires a large engine housing with a corresponding increase in the airplane's frontal area and an

(a)

secondary air
distribution cup

burner primary
air and fuel tube

(c)

1   OUTER COMBUSTION
    CASING
2   INNER COMBUSTION
    CASING
3   COMBUSTION LINER
4   SHAFT SHIELD
5   NO. 3 (REAR) BEARING
6   NO. 3 (REAR) CARBON
    SEAL
7   NO. 3 (REAR) SEAL
    SUPPORT
8   NO. 3 (REAR) BEARING
    SUPPORT
9   TURBINE STATIONARY SEAL
10 FIRST-STAGE TURBINE
    NOZZLE

(b)

FIG. 6-2   (**a**) *The annular-type burner.*   (**b**) *Sectioned view of the annular combustion chamber used on the General Electric CJ610 engine.*   (**c**) *An annular combustion chamber using vaporizing tubes instead of injection nozzles.*

FIG. 6-3 (**a**) *The can-annular-type burner.* (**b**) *Sectioned view of the can-annular burner used on the Allison 501-D13 engine. Note how the transition section changes the circular cross section of the liner to an annular shape so that the gases will impinge on the entire nozzle face.*

increase in aerodynamic drag. This will result in a decrease in maximum flight speed. Excessive burner size also results in high engine weight, and for a given aircraft means a lower fuel capacity and payload and shorter range. Modern burners release 500 to 1000 times the heat that a domestic oil burner or heavy industrial furnace of equal unit volume. Without their high heat release the aircraft gas turbine could not have been made practical.

7 *Low smokey burner*—Smoke is not only annoying on the ground, but may also allow easy tracking of high flying military aircraft.

8 *Low carbon formation*—Carbon deposits can block critical air passages and disrupt airflow along the liner walls causing high metal temperatures and low burner life.

All of the burner requirements must be satisfied over a wide range of operating conditions. For example, airflows may vary as much as 50:1, fuel flows as much as 30:1, and fuel/air ratios as much as 5:1. Burner pressures may cover a ratio of 100:1, while burner inlet temperatures may vary by more than 700°F.

EFFECT OF OPERATING VARIABLES ON BURNER PERFORMANCE

The operating variables are:

1 Pressure
2 Inlet air temperature
3 Fuel/air ratio
4 Flow velocity

Combustion efficiency

As the pressure of the air entering the burner increases, the combustion efficiency rises and levels off to a relatively constant value. The pressure at which this leveling off occurs is usually about 1 atm, but this may vary somewhat with different burner configurations. As the inlet air temperature is increased, combustion efficiency rises until it reaches a value of substantially 100 percent. If the fuel/air ratio is increased, combustion efficiency first rises, then levels off when the mixture in the combustion zone is close to the ideal value, and then decreases as the fuel-air mixture becomes too rich. An increase in fuel/air ratio will result in increased pressure loss because increasing fuel/air ratios cause higher temperatures with a corresponding decrease in gas density. In order to maintain continuous flow, these gases must travel at higher velocities and the energy needed to create these higher velocities must come from an increase in pressure loss. Increasing the flow velocity beyond a certain point reduces combustion efficiency, probably because it reduces the time available for mixing and burning.

NO. I REAR INNER LINER
FLAME TUBE
INTER. INNER LINER
COVER SPACER
FUEL NOZZLE SWIRL CUP
FUEL NOZZLE AIR SWIRL GUIDE
INNER LINER SPACER

NO. I OUTER LINER
NO. 2 REAR INNER LINER
NO. 3 REAR INNER LINER
NO. 4 REAR INNER LINER
NO. 5 REAR INNER LINER
NO. 6 REAR INNER LINER

FRONT INNER LINER
LINER COVER
SPARKIGNITER SLEEVE
SPARKIGNITER GUIDE
COMBUSTION CHAMBER AIR PRESSURE TRANSFER TUBE
LOCATING FLANGE

NO. 12 OUTER LINER
NO. II OUTER LINER
NO. 10 OUTER LINER
NO. 9 OUTER LINER
NO. 8 OUTER LINER
NO. 7 OUTER LINER
NO. 6 OUTER LINER
NO. 5 OUTER LINER
NO. 4 OUTER LINER
NO. 3 OUTER LINER
NO. 2 OUTER LINER

FIG. 6-4 *A variation of the can-annular combustion chamber as used on the Pratt & Whitney JT3 series engines.*

Fuel nozzle
Seal
Outer casing
Igniter plug
Flame tube

FIG. 6-5 *Typical airflow through a burner.*

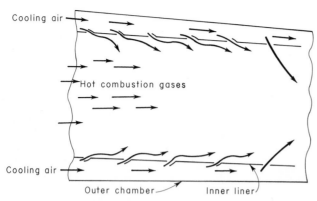

FIG. 6-6 *Cooling the burner walls. Large arrows to the rear represent dilution airflow.*

Stable operating range

The stable operating range of a burner also changes with variations in pressure and flow velocity. As the pressure decreases the stable operating range becomes narrower until a point is reached below which burning will not take place. As the flow velocity increases the stable operating range again becomes narrower until a critical velocity is reached above which combustion will not take place. Increasing the temperature of the incoming charge usually increases the fuel/air ratio range for stable operation. In addition, as the flow velocity is increased, the burner pressure loss will rise. This is mainly due to higher expansion losses as the air flows through the restricting or metering holes in the liner.

Temperature distribution

The temperature distribution of the burner exit is also affected by changes in the operating variables. Reducing the pressure below about 1 atm tends to upset temperature uniformity. On the other hand, for a given size burner, more uniform temperatures may be obtained by creating better mixing of the hot and cold gases at the expense of an increase in pressure loss. If the fuel/air ratio and flow velocity are increased, the exit

FIG. 6-7 *Temperature distribution.*

temperatures tend to become less uniform because more heat is released and there is less time for mixing.

Starting

Starting is usually easier with high temperature, high pressure, and low velocity. In addition there is an optimum fuel/air ratio for starting, above or below which ignition of the fuel-air mixture becomes increasingly difficult.

Carbon deposits

The operating variables have some effect upon the accumulation of carbon deposits in the burner, but their effects may vary with different burner types and configurations. Generally, deposits get worse with increasing temperatures and pressures until a point is reached where they begin to burn off. Increasing the fuel/air ratio has a tendency to increase deposits, probably because the proportion of oxygen in the combustion zone becomes too low to burn the fuel completely. In addition, changes in fuel/air ratios may change the location of carbon deposits within the burner. It should also be noted that the properties of the fuel have a significant effect on carbon accumulation and burner performance, and must be considered in the design of the burner.

Temperature and cooling requirements

Changes in the operating variables have a direct bearing on the temperature and cooling requirements of the liner. If the pressure and temperature of the incoming charge are increased, more heat is transferred from the burning gases to the liner, partly by radiation through the insulating blanket of cool air and partly by forced convection, and the lining temperature goes up. If the fuel/air ratio is increased, combustion temperatures become higher, and again the liner temperature goes up, mainly due to increased radiation. On the other hand, an increase in flow velocity outside the liner tends to increase external convection, thereby reducing the temperature of the liner.

INFLUENCE OF DESIGN FACTORS ON BURNER PERFORMANCE

The design factors include:

1 Methods of air distribution
2 Physical dimension of burner
3 Fuel-air operating range
4 Fuel nozzle design

Methods of air distribution

Since the quantity of air required for efficient combustion is much less than the total amount pumped through the engine, an important factor in burner design is the correct distribution of air between the combustion zone and the dilution zone. As more of the total airflow is used for combustion, a higher overall fuel/air ratio is needed to maintain maximum efficiency. The manner in which air is introduced into the burner also has a substantial effect on combustion efficiency, therefore the size, number, shape, and location of the air inlet holes has a marked influence on the burner performance.

Physical dimensions

One method of reducing pressure loss is to increase the diameter or length of the burner. The increase allows more time for the mixing of the hot and cold gases; hence the amount of energy required for mixing which must be supplied by a loss in pressure does not have to be as great. If the burner diameter is made too large, the pressure loss may have to be increased in order to produce adequate mixing and provide sufficient cooling for the added liner surface area. If a greater proportion of air is used to cool the liner, an increase in pressure loss is required since the cooling air filtered in along the liner walls must eventually be mixed with the central high-temperature stream in order to maintain uniform discharge temperatures.

Fuel-air operating range

There are several ways in which the fuel/air ratio operating range or blowout limit of the burner can be increased. One is to cut down the flow velocity through the burner by increasing the diameter. Another is to improve fuel atomization and distribution by increasing the pressure drop across the fuel nozzle, or by improving the design of the nozzle-metering elements. Once proper atomization has been established, an increase in pressure drop or further changes in the metering elements will have no appreciable effect. The fuel-air operating range of a burner can also be increased by improving the manner in which combustion air is introduced and distributed. The starting ability of a burner is closely related to its blowout limits, therefore starting can also be improved by increasing the burner diameter, by improving the distribution of combustion air, or by improving the fuel spray pattern, either through a change in fuel nozzle design or an increase in pressure drop across the nozzle. The life of the burner liner depends, to a large extent, upon its operating temperature. This temperature can be lowered by using a larger portion of the total airflow as a convective cooling film and insulating blanket along the liner wall. However, since an increase in liner cooling requires an increase in pressure loss, the quantity of air used for this purpose should be the least amount needed to maintain safe operating temperatures.

Fuel nozzle design

Fuel nozzle design plays a major part in burner performance. Not only must the nozzle atomize and distribute the fuel, but it must also be able to handle a wide range of fuel flows. For a given fuel system there is a small pressure drop across the nozzle that must be maintained for good atomization, and there is a maximum pressure that a practical fuel pump is able to produce. With a simple swirl-type nozzle like those used in many domestic burners, the range of fuel flows that can be handled within these pressure limitations is usually far short of the engine's requirements. One way of meeting the engine's fuel requirements while still maintaining good atomization is to use a two-stage fuel system. The primary stage functions alone at low fuel flows until the maximum available pressure is reached; then a pressure-sensitive valve is opened and fuel begins to spray through the secondary passages. The total flow in the primary and secondary stages fulfills the engine's fuel requirements without the use of excessive pressures and without a sacrifice in atomization qualities and spray pattern at low fuel flows. (See Chap. 12 on fuel nozzles.)

All of the operating and design variables must be taken into account when the burner is designed and manufactured. The final configuration is, at best, a compromise to achieve the desired operating characteristics, because it is impossible to design and construct a given burner that will have 100 percent combustion efficiency, zero pressure loss, maximum life, minimum weight, and minimum frontal area, all at the same time.

REVIEW AND STUDY QUESTIONS

1 List the three basic types of combustion chambers. Give the advantages and disadvantages of each type.

2 Describe the gas flow through a typical combustion chamber.

3 How many ignitors are generally used in the combustion section? How is the flame front propagated into the rest of the section?

4 List the requirements for a good combustion chamber.

5 Discuss the effects of the operating variables such as pressure, inlet air temperature, fuel/air ratio, and flow velocity on burner performance.

6 What is the relationship between fuel nozzle design and burner performance?

Chapter 7

Turbines

The function of the turbine is to drive the compressor and accessories, and, in the case of the turboprop, the propeller, by extracting a portion of the pressure and kinetic energy from the high-temperature combustion gases. In order to furnish the drive power to compress the air, the turbine must develop as much as 40,000 to 50,000 hp or more for the larger jet engines. One blade or bucket of a turbine can extract about 250 hp from the moving gas stream. This is equivalent to the power produced by a typical eight-cylinder automobile engine. It does all of this in a space smaller than the average automobile engine, and with a considerable advantage in weight. See Chaps. 3 and 5 for a detailed discussion of turbine power output. (Although Chap. 5 deals with the power required to drive the compressor, this power is supplied by the turbine. Therefore the same formula which is used to compute compressor power requirements can also be used to determine turbine power output.)

TYPES OF TURBINES

With a few exceptions, gas turbine manufacturers have concentrated on the axial-flow turbine (Fig. 7-1), although some manufacturers, notably Garrett AiResearch Corporation and Solar Corporation are building engines with a radial inflow turbine (Fig. 7-2). The radial inflow turbine has the advantage of ruggedness and simplicity, and is relatively inexpensive and easy to manufacture when compared to the axial-flow type. On this type of turbine, inlet gas flows through peripheral nozzles to enter the wheel passages in an inward radial direction. The speeding gas exerts a force on the wheel blades and then exhausts the air in an axial direc-

tion to the atmosphere. These turbine wheels used for small engines are well suited for a lower range of specific speeds and work at relatively high efficiency.

The axial-flow turbine is comprised of two main elements consisting of a set of stationary vanes and one or more turbine rotors. The turbine blades themselves are of two basic types, the impulse and the reaction. The modern aircraft gas turbine engine utilizes blades which have both impulse and reaction sections (Fig. 7-3).

The stationary part of the turbine assembly consists of a row of contoured vanes set at an angle to form a series of small nozzles which discharge gases onto the blade of the turbine wheel. For this reason, the stationary vane assembly is usually referred to as the turbine nozzle, and the vanes themselves are called nozzle guide vanes.

FUNCTION OF THE NOZZLE GUIDE VANES
(Fig. 7-4)

The nozzle guide vanes (diaphragm) have two principal functions. First, they must convert part of the gas heat and pressure energy into dynamic or kinetic energy, so that the gas will strike the turbine blades with some degree of force. Second, the nozzle vanes must turn this gas flow so that it will impinge upon the turbine buckets in the proper direction; that is, the gases must impact on the turbine blade in a direction that will have a large component force in the plane of the rotor. The nozzle does its first job by utilizing the Bernoulli theorem. As through any nozzle, when the flow area is restricted, the gas will accelerate and a large portion of the static pressure in the gas is turned into dynamic pressure. The degree to which this effect will occur depends upon the relationship between the nozzle guide vane inlet and exit areas, which, in turn is closely related to the type of turbine blade used.

The turbine nozzle area is a critical part of engine design. Making the nozzle area too small will restrict the airflow through the engine, raise compressor discharge pressure, and bring the compressor closer to stall. This is especially critical during acceleration when the nozzle will have a tendency to choke (gas flowing at the speed of sound). Many engines are designed to have the nozzle operate in this choked condition. Small exit areas also cause slower accelerations because the compressor will have to work against an increased back pressure. Increasing the nozzle diaphragm area will result in faster engine acceleration, less tendency to stall, but higher specific fuel consumption. The area of the nozzle is adjusted at the factory or during overhaul so that the gas velocity at this point will be at or near the speed of sound. (See Chap. 19, Maintenance and Overhaul Procedures.)

The second function, that of turning the gases so that

TURBINE STATOR & CASING

TURBINE ROTOR

TURBINE ROTOR

(a)

TURBINE STATOR & CASING

(b)

FIG. 7-1 (**a**) *A single-stage axial-flow turbine wheel.* (**b**) *A multi-stage axial-flow turbine with turbine stators (nozzles). First-stage nozzle is not shown.*

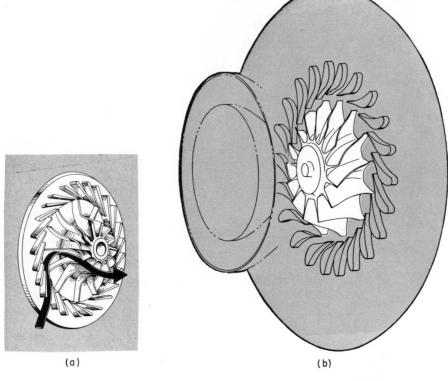

FIG. 7-2 (a) *Airflow through a radial inflow turbine.* (b) *Radial inflow turbines look like centrifugal compressors.*

they strike the turbine blades at the correct angle is accomplished by setting the blades at a specific angle to the axis of the engine.   Ideally, this angle should be variable as a function of engine rpm and gas flow velocity, but in practice, the vanes are fixed in one position.

CONSTRUCTION OF THE NOZZLE

Nozzle vanes may be either cast or forged. Some vanes are made hollow (Fig. 7-5) to allow a degree of cooling using compressor bleed air. In all cases the nozzle assembly is made of very high temperature, high-strength steel to withstand the direct impact of the hot, high-pressure, high-velocity gas flowing from the combustion chamber.

The Curtiss-Wright Corporation and others are ex-

perimenting with transpiration cooled nozzle and turbine blading in which the air flows through thousands of small holes in a porous airfoil made from a sintered wire mesh material. (Refer to Fig. 10-5.) Since the performance of the gas turbine engine is to a large measure dependent upon the temperature at the inlet of the turbine, increasing the turbine inlet temperature from the present limit of about 1750°F to the 2500°F

NOZZLE DIAPHRAGM

FIG. 7-4 *A typical nozzle diaphragm.*

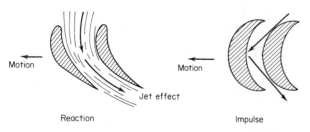

FIG. 7-3 *Reaction and impulse turbine blading (tangential velocity vectors omitted).*

FIG. 7-5 *Typical hollow nozzle vanes.*

possible with transpiration cooled blades will result in about a 100 percent increase in specific horsepower. Transpiration cooling may be a promising development in gas turbine design (Fig. 7-6).

THE IMPULSE TURBINE *(Fig. 7-7)*

A characteristic of an impulse turbine and the nozzle used with it is that gases entering the nozzle diaphragm are expanded to atmospheric pressure. In the ideal impulse turbine all pressure energy of the gas has been converted into kinetic energy; hence, no further pressure drop can occur across the blades.

Gases enter the nozzle diaphragm in the direction A and leave at a specific velocity indicated by vector V_1

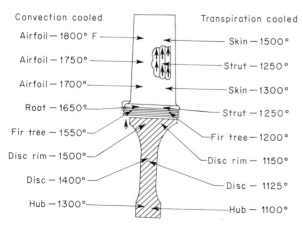

FIG. 7-6 *Typical turbine metal temperatures (°F).*

in the turbine gas flow diagram (Fig. 7-7). The speed of rotation of the turbine wheel is represented by the length of vector U.

In order to determine the speed and angle that the entering gases make with the turbine blades, the *relative* velocity must be found. To find the relative velocity it is necessary to subtract one vector from another ($V_1 - U$). Note: This process is just the opposite of a vector addition in which a resultant is found. From the inlet velocity diagram, the relative velocity is found to be V_R. V_R represents the speed and angle of the entering gases as seen by the rotating turbine blades.

Another characteristic of an impulse turbine is that the area of the inlet and exit between the blades is equal. If the area is equal, then the relative velocity V_R at the exit will be equal to the relative velocity V_R at the inlet, minus friction losses which we will not consider. The descending curve of velocity on the graph is due to the change in direction of V_R as it flows across the blade. A change in velocity may occur in direction and/or magnitude. If the turbine is fixed and unable to rotate, there would be no loss of velocity across the turbine blades. Maximum force would be applied to the blades at this time, but no work will be done because the turbine is not moving.

The speed and direction of the gases at the outlet of the turbine may be determined by a vector addition to find the resultant of V_{R_1} and U. From the gas flow diagram the resultant is found to be V_2. V_2 is less than V_1 due to the rotation of the turbine. The gas gives up some of its kinetic energy to do work on the buckets; that is, the change in momentum of the jet develops

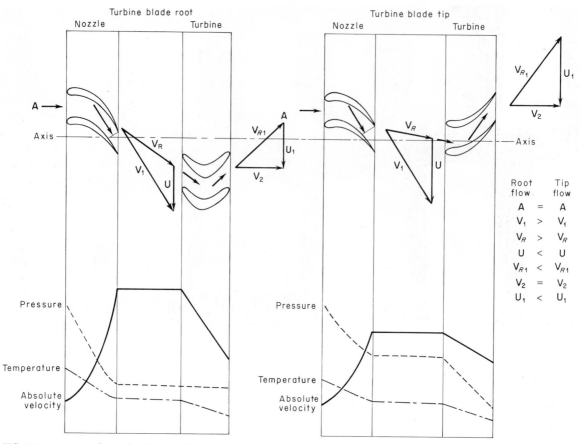

FIG. 7-7 *Vector analysis of turbine gas flow.*

a force on the buckets between which the jet passes. The presence of the turbine blade in the path of the gases results in an impulse force being exerted on the gases, which changes the direction of the V_R across the blade. The greater the mass of gas, the faster the gases strike the blades, and the more they are turned, the greater will be their impulse force. Expressed mathematically:

$$\text{Momentum change} = \frac{2WV_\Delta}{g}$$

where $\dfrac{W}{g}$ = mass gas flow, lb/sec

V_Δ = velocity change, fps

Since the force imparted to the blades is proportional to the momentum change, then

$$\text{Force} = \frac{2WV_\Delta}{g}$$

The impulse force acting on the blade is represented by a vector in Fig. 7-8. From this figure it can be seen that the impulse force does not act directly in the plane of rotation of the turbine wheel, but is resolved into two components. The parallel component acts in the plane of rotation and causes the turbine wheel to rotate. The axial component acts as a thrust along the center line of the shaft and has to be taken up by a thrust bearing.

THE REACTION TURBINE

Again referring to Fig. 7-7, as the gases from the combustion chamber enter the first row of stator blades,

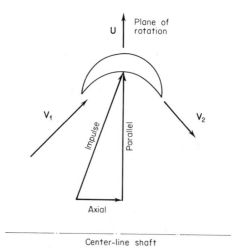

FIG. 7-8 *Forces exerted on an impulse blade.*

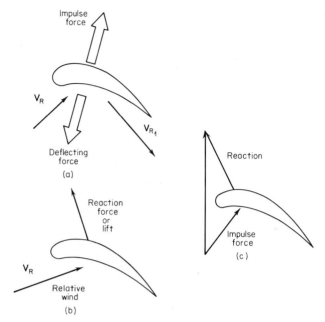

FIG. 7-9 *Forces exerted on a reaction blade.*

they experience a drop in pressure and an increase in velocity through the nozzle, but to a lesser degree than through the nozzle used with the impulse turbine. The gases leave the nozzle at a specific velocity indicated by the vector V_1. The speed of rotation of the turbine wheel is represented by the length of the vector U. From the inlet velocity diagram, the relative velocity is found to be V_R, which is the vector difference of V_1 and U.

On entering the first rotor stage, the gases see the rotor as a convergent passage (outlet area less than inlet area). The change in area produces an increase in the *relative* velocity with an accompanying pressure drop across the blades. The acceleration of the gases generates a reaction force like that produced on a wing. It is from this feature of the reaction turbine that its name is derived. The relative velocity increase is represented by the length of the vector V_{R_1}.

The velocity of the gases at the outlet of the turbine may be determined by the vector addition of the relative velocity of V_{R_1} and the rotational speed U_1 of the turbine wheel. From the outlet velocity diagram, the resultant is found to be V_2. Note: V_2 is less than V_1 which indicates a loss in *absolute* velocity across the blade, but as stated in the preceding paragraph, an increase in *relative* velocity. (The definition of absolute and relative velocity may be viewed as follows: Relative velocity changes assume that the turbine is not turning, whereas absolute velocity changes take into account the rotation of the turbine.)

The presence of the turbine blade in the path of the gases causes a force to be exerted on the gases. The force acting on the gases is represented by the deflecting

force vector in Fig. 7-9a. The deflecting force acts on the gases to change the direction of the relative velocity from V_R to V_{R_1} across the blade. A change in the momentum of the gas flow caused by its change in direction through the rotor blading results in an impulse force also shown in Fig. 7-9a. Note that a certain amount of impulse force is always present in a reaction-type turbine, but reaction force is not present in an impulse turbine.

The reaction force results from the acceleration of the gases across the blade. The direction in which the reaction force acts may be determined by considering the blade as an airfoil. The reaction force, like lift, may be drawn perpendicular to the relative wind which is represented by V_R in Fig. 7-9b.

From Fig. 7-9a and b it can be seen that both impulse and reaction forces are acting on the blade of a reaction turbine. This is why the impulse turbine requires high-velocity gas in order to obtain the maximum rate of momentum change, while the reaction turbine causes its rate of momentum change by the nozzling action of the rotor blading, and therefore does not require excessively high nozzle diaphragm exit velocities. The presence of an impulse and reaction force may then be represented by vectors as shown in Fig. 7-9c. It can be seen that the two forces combine vectorially into a resultant which acts in the plane of rotation to drive the turbine.

REACTION-IMPULSE TURBINE *(Fig. 7-10)*

It is important to distribute the power load evenly from the base to the tip of the blade. An uneven distribution of the work load will cause the gases to exit from the blade at different velocities and pressures. Obviously, the blade tips will be traveling faster than the blade roots (as can be seen by the length of the vector U in Fig. 7-7), because they have a greater dis-

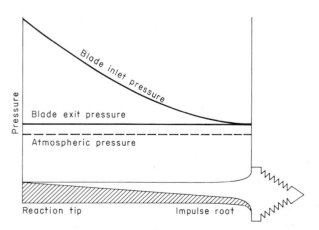

FIG. 7-10 *Pressure changes across the impulse and reaction sections of a turbine blade.*

FIG. 7-11 *An impulse-reaction blade.*

tance to travel in their larger circumference. If all the gas velocity possible is made to impinge upon the blade roots, the difference in wheel speed at the roots and the tips will make the relative speed of the gases less at the tips, causing less power to be developed at the tips than at the roots.

To cope with this problem, in actual practice, the turbine blading is a blending of the impulse type at the roots and the reaction type at the tips (Fig. 7-11). Figure 7-10 shows that by making the blade "impulse" at the root, and "reaction" at the tip, the blade exit pressure can be held relatively constant. The changing height between the two pressure lines indicates the pressure differential across the blade. From previous discussion it can be seen that the required pressure drop for "reaction" is present at the tip, and gradually changes to the "no pressure loss" condition required for "impulse" at the root. In addition, the higher pressures at the tip will tend to make the gases flow toward the base of the blade which counteracts the centrifugal forces trying to throw the air toward the tip.

Of course, with every change in engine speed and gas-flow velocity, the vector triangle will be shaped considerably differently. The angle of the nozzle and the turbine blades are such that optimum performance is achieved only during a small range of engine rpm.

One can see that if the length of the vector U in Fig. 7-7 is changed (rpm varied), the gases will not enter the turbine in the correct direction and loss of efficiency will occur. In addition, it is desirable to have the gases exit from the turbine with as much of an axial-flow component as possible. Changing rpm will cause V_2 to be angled off the axis and the result will be a swirling

motion to the gas with a consequent loss of energy. To counteract the swirling of the gases, straightening vanes are located immediately downstream of the turbine. These vanes also serve the function in many engines of providing one of the main structural components and additionally act as a passageway for oil, air, and other lines (Fig. 7-12).

TURBINE CONSTRUCTION

The turbine wheel is one of the most highly stressed parts in the engine. Not only must it operate at temperatures up to approximately 1700°F, but it must do so under severe centrifugal loads imposed by high rotational speeds of over 40,000 rpm for small engines to 8000 rpm for the larger ones. Consequently, the engine speed and turbine inlet temperature must be accurately controlled to keep the turbine within safe operating limits.

The turbine assembly is made of two main parts, the disk and blades. The disk or wheel is a statically and dynamically balanced unit of specially alloyed steel usually containing large percentages of chromium, nickel, and cobalt. After forging, the disk is machined all over and carefully inspected using x-rays, magnetism, and other inspection methods to assure structural integrity. The blades or buckets are attached to the disk by means of a "fir tree" design (Fig. 7-13) to allow for different rates of expansion between the disk and the blade while still holding the blade firmly against centrifugal loads. The blade is kept from moving axially either by rivets, special locking tabs or devices, or another turbine stage.

Some turbine blades are open at the outer perimeter, as shown in Fig. 7-1, whereas in others a shroud is used, as in Fig. 7-13. The shroud acts to prevent blade-tip losses and excessive vibration. Resistance to distortion under high loads, which tend to twist the blade toward low pitch, is also reduced. The shrouded blade has an aerodynamic advantage in that thinner blade sections can be used and tip losses can be reduced by using a knife edge or labyrinth seal at this point. Shrouding, however, requires that the turbine run cooler or at a reduced rpm because of the extra mass at the tip. On

Straightening vanes

EXHAUST CONE

FIG. 7-12 *Vanes are used for straightening gas flow and for structural support.*

(a)   (b)

FIG. 7-13 (a) *The shroud is formed by the tips of the blades touching each other.* (b) *Notice the "fir tree" attachment.*

blades that are not shrouded, the tips are cut or recessed to a knife edge to permit a rapid "wearing-in" of the blade tip to the turbine casing with a corresponding increase in turbine efficiency.

Blades are forged from highly alloyed steel and are passed through a carefully controlled series of machining and inspection operations before being certified for use. Many engine manufacturers will stamp a "moment weight" number on the blade to retain rotor balance when replacement is necessary.

The temperature of the blade is usually kept within limits by passing relatively cool air bled from the compressor over the face of the turbine, thus cooling the disk and blade by the process of convection. This method of cooling may become more difficult, as high Mach number flights develop high compressor inlet and outlet temperatures.

As shown in Fig. 7-1, some gas turbine engines use a single-stage turbine, whereas others employ more than one turbine wheel. Multistage turbines are used where the power required to drive the compressor would necessitate a very large turbine wheel. Multistage wheels are also used for turboprops where the turbine has to extract enough power to drive both the compressor and the propeller. When two or more turbine wheels are used, a nozzle diaphragm is positioned directly in front of each turbine wheel. The operation of the multiple-stage turbine is similar to that of the single stage, except that the succeeding stages operate at lower gas velocities, pressures, and temperatures. Since each turbine stage receives the air at a lower pressure than the preceding stage, more blade area is needed in the rear stages to assure an equitable load

distribution between stages. The amount of energy removed from each stage is proportional to the amount of work done by each stage.

Most multistage turbines are attached to a common shaft. However, some multistage turbine engines have more than one compressor. In this case, some turbine wheels drive one compressor and the remaining turbines drive the other. (See Fig. 2-15.)

As stated at the beginning of this section, the turbine wheel is subjected to both high speed and high temperature. Because of these extreme conditions, blades can easily deform by growing in length (a condition known as "creep") and by twisting and changing pitch. Since these distortions are accelerated by exceeding engine operating limits, it is important to operate within the temperature and rpm points set by the manufacturer.

REVIEW AND STUDY QUESTIONS

1 What is the function of the turbine?
2 Name two types of turbines. Describe the gas flow in each.
3 What is the function of the nozzle guide vanes? How does the nozzle area influence engine performance?
4 What is meant by impulse and reaction blading? With the use of vectors, show the gas flow through both types of blades.
5 Make a table showing relative and absolute velocity gas-flow changes across an impulse and a reaction blade.
6 Describe the physical construction of the axial-flow turbine wheel.
7 What dictates the number of turbine wheels employed in the gas turbine?

Chapter **8**

....

Exhaust systems

EXHAUST DUCTS

The exhaust duct takes the relatively high-pressure (relative to the exhaust nozzle), low-velocity gas leaving the turbine wheel and accelerates this gas flow to sonic or supersonic speeds. It is desirable in a pure jet engine to convert as much of the pressure energy in the gas into kinetic energy in order to increase the gas momentum and therefore the thrust produced. If a majority of the gas expansion occurs through the turbine section, as for example in a turboprop, the duct does little more than conduct the exhaust stream rearward with a minimum energy loss. However, if the turbine operates against a noticeable back pressure, the nozzle must convert the remaining pressure energy into a high-velocity exhaust. As stated previously, the duct also serves to reduce any swirl in the gas as it leaves the turbine, thereby creating as much of an axial-flow component as possible (Fig. 8-1).

CONSTRUCTION

Basically, the exhaust duct is constructed of two stainless steel cones. The outer cone is usually bolted to the turbine casing with the inner cone supported from the outer cone. The vanes used to support the inner cone straighten the swirling gas flow. Many engines are instrumented at the duct immediately to the rear of the turbine for turbine temperature and for turbine discharge pressure (Fig. 8-2). Although it would be more desirable to measure turbine inlet temperature, most manufacturers prefer to locate the thermocouples at the rear of the turbine since there is no chance of turbine damage in the event of mechanical failure of

the thermocouple. The exhaust gas temperature is an indication of the turbine inlet temperature because the temperature drop across the turbine is calculated when the turbine is designed and the inlet temperature is then indirectly sensed or controlled through the turbine discharge temperature.

The jet nozzle, which on most engines is formed by the converging section or taper at the rear of the outer cone, may be located at the aft end of a tailpipe if the engine is buried in the airplane (Fig. 8-3). The tailpipe will connect the outer cone of the exhaust duct with the nozzle at the rear of the airplane. In order to keep the velocity of the gases low and reduce skin friction losses, tailpipes are made with as large a diameter as possible. The tailpipe is also kept short and constructed with few or no bends in order to reduce pressure-loss effects. If the engine is buried, any bends necessary to duct air in or out of the power plant are made in the inlet duct, since pressure losses are less damaging there than in the exhaust duct.

EXHAUST NOZZLES

Two types of nozzles in use today are the convergent type and the convergent-divergent type. Generally the convergent nozzle will have a fixed area, while the convergent-divergent nozzle area will be variable.

The area of the jet nozzle is critical, since it affects the back pressure on the turbine and hence the rpm, thrust, and exhaust gas temperature. On some engines this area is adjustable, as shown in Fig. 8-3, by the insertion of small metal tabs called *mice*. By use of these tabs, the engine can be trimmed to the correct rpm, temperature, and thrust settings.

FIG. 8-1 *A typical exhaust duct with straightening vanes.*

A – = Alumel lead wire
B + = Chromel lead wire

FIG. 8-2 *Thermocouples, located in the exhaust duct, are all hooked in parallel so that several may fail without losing the temperature indication. Many thermocouples are used to obtain an average reading.*

The convergent nozzle

The typical convergent nozzle is designed to maintain a constant internal pressure and still produce sonic velocities at the nozzle exit. In this type of nozzle the gas flow is subsonic as it leaves the turbine. Each individual gas molecule is, in effect, being squeezed by the converging shape and pushed from behind. This three-dimensional squirting action causes the velocity to increase. Since this velocity increase is faster than the volume expansion, a converging area is necessary to maintain the pressure or squirting action. In the convergent nozzle, the gas velocity cannot exceed the speed of sound because, as the gas velocity increases, the ability of the gas pressure to move the molecules from behind becomes less. In fact, the pushing action will drop to zero when the gas moves at the speed of sound. The speed of sound is the speed of a natural pressure wave movement. It is dependent upon the natural internal molecular velocity which is limited by the amount of internal temperature energy of these gas molecules. In other words, the speed of sound, although a pressure wave, is limited by the molecular velocity (or sound-temperature energy).

The convergent-divergent nozzle

If the pressure at the entrance to a convergent duct becomes approximately twice that at the exhaust nozzle, the change in velocity through the duct will be enough to cause sonic velocity at the nozzle. At high Mach numbers the pressure ratio across the duct will become greater than 2.0, and unless this pressure can be turned into velocity before the gases exit from the nozzle, a loss of efficiency will occur. Since the maximum velocity that a gas can attain in a convergent nozzle is the speed of sound, a convergent-divergent nozzle must be used. In the diverging section, the gas velocities can be increased above the speed of sound. Since the individual gas molecules cannot be pushed by the pressure or molecules behind them, the gas molecules can be accelerated only by increasing the gas volume outward and rearward. The diverging section of the convergent-divergent nozzle allows expansion outward, but also holds in the expansion so that most of the expansion is directed rearward off the side wall of the diverging section. In other words, the diverging action accelerates the airflow to supersonic velocities by controlling the expansion of the gas so that the expansion (which is only partially completed in the converging section) will be rearward and not outward to the side and wasted.

An example of the action that produces an increase in thrust through a diverging nozzle can be shown with the following experiment. If a greased rubber ball is pushed down into a funnel and then released, the ball would shoot out of the funnel (Fig. 8-4). If only the funnel were released, it would move away from the

RESTRICTOR SEGMENTS

FIG. 8-3 *A buried engine requires a tailpipe.   Nozzle adjustment is made by using restrictor segments called mice.*

FIG. 8-4 *The ball analogy showing thrust increase by means of a diverging nozzle.*

ball. What is happening is that the ball is partially compressed when it is pushed down into the funnel, increasing the pressure of the air inside the ball. When the funnel is released, the air in the ball expands, returning the ball to its normal size and pushing the funnel away. This same type of action occurs in the diverging section of a converging-diverging nozzle. As the gases expand against the side of the duct, they produce a pushing effect even though they are decreasing in pressure.

To sum up then, supersonic, or compressible flow through a diverging duct will result in increasing velocity above the speed of sound, decreasing pressure, and decreasing density (increasing volume).

Unfortunately the rate of change in the divergent duct may be too large or small for a given engine operating condition to allow a smooth supersonic flow. That is, the rate of increase in area of the duct is not correct for the increase in the rate of change in volume of the gases. If the rate of increase is too small, maximum gas velocities will not be reached. If the rate of increase is too great, turbulent flow along the nozzle wall will occur. To correct this problem, and for use with an afterburner, all engines capable of supersonic flight incorporate a variable-area exhaust nozzle (Fig. 8-5). Older engines utilized a two-position eyelid, or "clamshell" type of variable-area orifice, but modern jet nozzles are infinitely variable aerodynamic converging-diverging ejector types utilizing primary and secondary nozzle flaps to control the main and secondary airflows. As shown in Fig. 8-5a, the converging section is formed by a series of overlapping primary flaps through which the air is accelerated to sonic velocity. The diverging section is formed by a secondary

airflow instead of a metal wall. The ejector action produced by the main airflow shooting out of the primary nozzle or nozzle flap draws the secondary flow into the outer shroud and ejects it out the rear end. The ejected secondary air which comes from the outside of the engine, will be accelerated to a higher velocity and will therefore contribute to jet thrust. The nozzle and shroud flap segments are linked to open and close together.

In addition to forming an aerodynamically correct shape for supersonic flow, modern variable-area exhaust nozzles can be used to advantage to improve engine performance in other ways. For example, by keeping the nozzle wide open, the engine idle speed can be held high with a minimum of thrust produced (Fig. 8-6).

1 OUTER SHROUD	4 NOZZLE-FLAP SEAL
2 SUPPORT RING	5 SHROUD FLAP
3 NOZZLE FLAP	6 SHROUD-FLAP SEAL

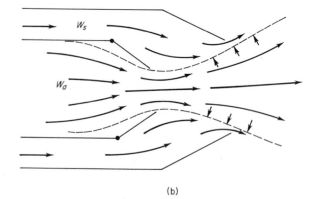

(b)

FIG. 8-5 *(a) The variable-area exhaust nozzle used on the General Electric J79 engine. (b) A convergent-divergent nozzle airflow schematic.*

FIG. 8-6 *The nozzle schedule can be designed so that the nozzle is open in both idle and afterburner regimes.*

This is beneficial since maximum available thrust can then be made available quickly by merely closing the nozzle, thereby eliminating the necessity of having to accelerate the engine all the way up from a low-idle rpm. High-idle rpm will also provide a higher quantity of bleed air for operation of accessories, and in addition,

make "go-arounds" safer. Of course, variable-area nozzles incur a penalty in the form of additional weight and complexity, as indicated in Fig. 8-7, and at the present time are being used only on aircraft operating at sufficiently high Mach numbers to make their use worthwhile.

SOUND SUPPRESSION

THE NOISE PROBLEM

The noise problem created by commercial and military jet takeoffs, landings, and ground operations at airports near residential areas has become a very serious problem within the last several years. Figure 8-8 illustrates the several levels of sound, in decibels, from various sources. The *decibel* (db) is defined as being approximately the smallest degree of difference of loudness ordinarily detectable by the human ear, the range of which includes about 130 db.

The pattern of sound from a jet engine makes the

1	ACTUATOR RING
2	LINK
3	HOUSING
4	INNER LEAF
5	ROLLER
6	HOUSING EXTENSION
7	OUTER LEAF

FIG. 8-7 *The variable-area exhaust nozzle for the General Electric J85.*

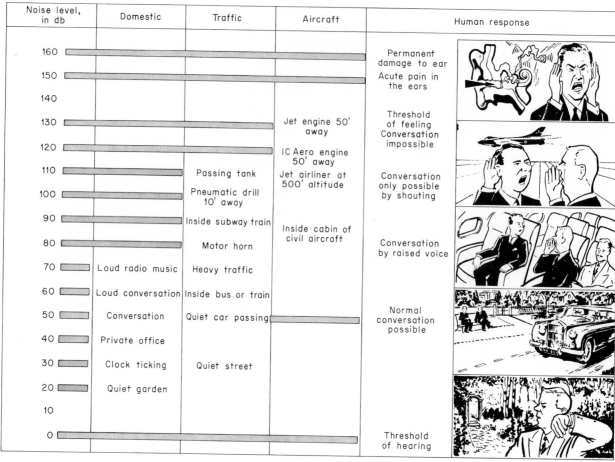

Noise level, in db	Domestic	Traffic	Aircraft	Human response
160				Permanent damage to ear
150				Acute pain in the ears
140				
130			Jet engine 50' away	Threshold of feeling
120			IC Aero engine 50' away	Conversation impossible
110		Passing tank	Jet airliner at 500' altitude	Conversation only possible by shouting
100		Pneumatic drill 10' away		
90		Inside subway train		
80		Motor horn	Inside cabin of civil aircraft	Conversation by raised voice
70	Loud radio music	Heavy traffic		
60	Loud conversation	Inside bus or train		
50	Conversation	Quiet car passing		Normal conversation possible
40	Private office			
30	Clock ticking	Quiet street		
20	Quiet garden			
10				
0				Threshold of hearing

FIG. 8-8 *Comparing the level of sound from various sources.*

noise problem even more bothersome than that coming from other types of engines. For example, the noise from a reciprocating engine rises sharply as the airplane propeller passes an observer on the ground, and then drops off almost as quickly. But as shown in Fig. 8-9 a jet reaches a peak after the aircraft passes, and is at an angle of approximately 45° to him. This noise then stays at a relatively high level for a considerable length of time. The noise from a turbojet is also more annoying because it overlaps the ordinary speech frequencies more than the noise from a reciprocating engine and propeller combination (Fig. 8-10).

Since the noise is produced by the high-velocity exhaust gas shearing through the still air (see pages 130–134), it follows that if the exhaust velocity is slower and the mixing area wider, the exhaust noise levels can be brought down to the point where a sound suppressor is not necessary. The exhaust-gas velocity of a turbofan is slower than a turbojet of comparable size because more energy must be removed by the turbine to drive the fan. The fan exhaust velocity is relatively low and creates less of a noise problem; therefore fan-type engines in general do not need sound suppressors. The

function of the noise suppressor is to lower the level of the sound, about 25 to 30 db, as well as to change its frequency (Fig. 8-11), and to do this with a minimum sacrifice in engine thrust or additional weight.

The two facets of the noise problem, ground operation and airborne operation, lend themselves to two solutions. Noise suppressors can be portable devices for use on the ground by maintenance personnel, or they can be an integral part of the aircraft engine installation. Examples of various types of ground and airborne suppressors can be seen in Figs. 8-12 and 8-13. Of the two, airborne suppressors are more difficult to design because of the weight limitations and the necessity of having the air exit in an axial direction to the engine.

THE SOURCE OF SOUND

Jet engine noise is mainly the result of the turbulence produced when the hot, high-velocity exhaust jet mixes with the cold, low-velocity or static ambient atmosphere around the exhaust. The turbulence increases in

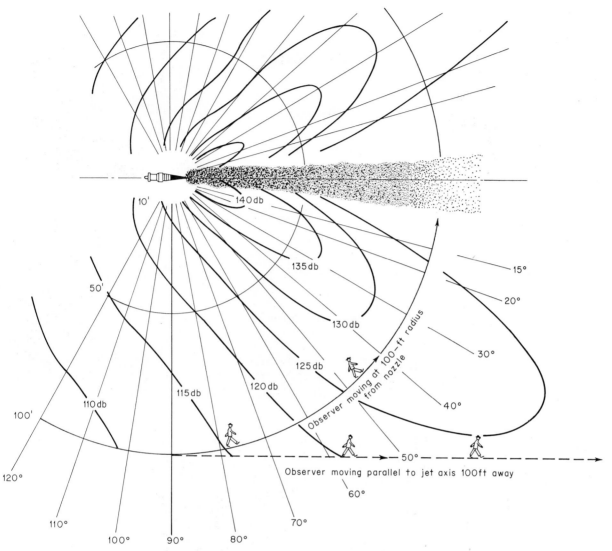

FIG. 8-9 *Typical noise field from jet spreading in still air. The curved lines represent equal sound levels.*

FIG. 8-10 *The jet engine produces its maximum noise in the speech frequency.*

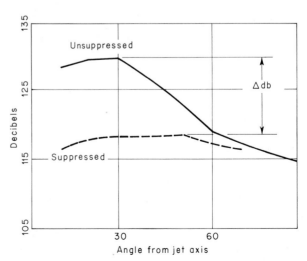

FIG. 8-11 *Sound level intensities are reduced by means of a noise suppressor.*

(a)

(b)

(c)

(d)

(e)

(f)

(g)

(h)

FIG. 8-12 *Typical airborne noise suppressors.*

proportion to the speed of the exhaust stream and produces noise of varying intensity and frequency until mixing is completed (Fig. 8-14). Since there is little mixing close to the nozzle, the fine grain turbulence produces a relatively high frequency sound in this area. But as the jet stream slows down, more mixing takes place, resulting in a coarser turbulence and correspondingly lower frequency. Therefore the noise produced from a jet engine exhaust is a "white" noise (an analogy to white light) consisting of a mixture of all frequencies with intensity peaks at certain frequencies due to the

characteristic note of the turbine wheel which makes an excellent siren (Fig. 8-15). At low power settings, for example during landing, noise generated from the compressor blades may become predominant. The noise emanating from the compressor consists of more discrete higher frequencies. High-frequency sounds are attenuated (weakened) more rapidly by obstructions and distance, and are more directional in nature, whereas low-frequency sounds will travel much further. Therefore compressor noise is less of a problem than noise from the jet exhaust stream.

FIG. 8-13 *Various types of ground noise suppressors.* **(a)** *A ground noise suppressor with water ring for cooling.* *(Air Logistics Corporation)* **(b)**, **(c)**, *and* **(d)** *(Industrial Acoustics Company, Incorporated)* **(e)** *(Emhart Manufacturing Company)*

FIG. 8-14   *The shear layer noise source.*

THEORY OF OPERATION

The high-intensity sound generated by the shearing action of the "solid" jet exhaust in the relatively still air can be reduced and modified by breaking up this "solid" air mass by mechanical means and thus make the mixing process more gentle. Most airborne noise suppressors are of the "corrugated perimeter" design. This type of silencer alters the shape of the exhaust stream as it leaves the engine and permits air to be entrained with the gases which, in turn, encourages more rapid mixing. Examples of the corrugated perimeter can be seen in Fig. 8-12*b*, *f*, and *g*. The *multitube suppressor* (Fig. 8-12*a* and *h*) breaks the primary exhaust stream up into a number of smaller jets, each with its own discharge nozzle which is surrounded by ambient air.

Some suppressor designs (Fig. 8-12*c*, *d*, and *e*) admit a secondary flow of air into the exhaust through the corrugations. In this manner the mixing process is promoted even more quickly.

Deep corrugations give greater noise reduction. But if the corrugations are too deep, excessive drag will

FIG. 8-15   *Typical sound spectrum showing a high noise level over a wide frequency range. The two peaks are fundamental notes of the turbine wheel acting as a siren.*

result because the overall diameter may have to be increased in order to maintain the required nozzle area. Also, a nozzle designed to give a large reduction in noise may involve a considerable weight penalty because of the additional strengthening required.

CONSTRUCTION

Noise suppressors are generally built of welded stainless steel sheet stock and are of relatively simple construction. Overhaul life should be about the same as the engine's, but since the suppressor is exposed to the high-temperature gas flow, periodic inspection must be made for cracks and other signs of impending failure.

PROTECTION AGAINST SOUND

Although the airborne sound suppressor is installed principally for the comfort of those people living in residential areas surrounding the municipal airport, mechanics and others required to work within several hundred feet of operating engines must have some form of ear protection. Not only can noise permanently damage hearing, but at the same time can reduce a person's efficiency by causing fatigue. It also affects both his physical and psychological well being and may result in increasing job errors. Susceptibility to temporary or permanent hearing loss varies with the individual and the quality of the noise. Such factors as frequency, intensity, and the time of exposure to the noise all point up the need for protection. For these reasons, earplugs (Fig. 8-16) and/or ear protectors (Fig. 8-17) are required pieces of equipment for all personnel who must be in the proximity of running jet engines (Fig. 8-18).

A general rule of thumb to follow for determining noise levels with the distance from the source is that as distance is doubled, the noise level decreases 6 db, and conversely, as distance is halved, the noise level increases 6 db. Noise levels of 140 db are not uncommon close to a running engine. Protection is required from approximately 100 db on up, but is difficult to declare a fixed safe distance from an operating engine, since the sound levels vary depending upon the angle of the observer in relation to the engine. Refer to Fig. 8-9.

THRUST REVERSERS

A jet powered aircraft, during its landing run, lacks the braking action afforded by slow turning propellers, which on larger aircraft are capable of going into reverse pitch, thus giving reverse thrust. The problem is further compounded by the higher landing speeds due to the highly streamlined, low-drag fuselage and the

(a)

(b)

FIG. 8-16 (**a**) *Ear insert.* (*1*) *Conforms to the shape of the ear canal.* (*2*) *Diaphragm permits wearer to hear normal conversation.* (*3*) *Prevents plug from being inserted too far into ear.* (*4*) *Tab for removal and insertion.* (**b**) *Placement of ear inserts.* (*American Optical Company*)

heavier gross weights common to modern jet airplanes. Standard wheel brakes are no longer adequate under these adverse conditions, and larger brakes would incur a severe weight and space penalty and decrease the useful load of the aircraft. In addition, brakes can be very ineffective on wet or icy runways.

Many solutions to this problem have been advanced. One method, used extensively by the Air Force, is a

FIG. 8-17 *Ear protectors with fluid-filled ear cushions.* (*Wilson Products*)

"drag chute," or "para-brake" (Fig. 8-19). The para-chute stowed at the rear of the fuselage is deployed upon landing, or in some cases, while the airplane is still airborne to hasten emergency descents. The para-brake does not lend itself to commercial operation, since the chute is easily damaged, must be repacked after each use, and is not absolutely dependable. In addition, once deployed, the pilot has no control over the drag on the aircraft except to release the chute.

Experiments in the use of large nets for stopping air-craft and in the use of arresting gear similar to that used in the Navy for carrier landings, are being performed at some airports. These methods cause fast deceleration which could result in excessive stresses being applied to the airframe and in discomfort to the passengers, and are therefore not suitable for commercial operations at busy airports except for use as an emergency over-run barrier. A simple but effective method of slowing aircraft quickly after landing is to reverse the direction of engine thrust by reversing the exhaust gas stream. Devices in use today allow the pilot to control the degree of reverse thrust. In addition, the modern thrust reverser can be used to slow the aircraft and vary the rate of sink during approaches while still keeping rpm high to minimize the time needed to accelerate the engine in the event of a "go-around." High-idle rpm will also provide sufficient compressor bleed air for the proper performance of air driven accessories.

FIG. 8-18 *Muff-type ear protectors attenuation characteristics.*

TYPES OF THRUST REVERSERS

The two basic types of thrust reversers are the:

1 Mechanical blockage or target type (post-exit)
2 Aerodynamic blockage type (pre-exit)

Mechanical blockage is accomplished simply by placing an obstruction in the jet exhaust stream about one nozzle diameter to the rear of the engine (Fig. 8-20). The gas stream may be deflected in either a horizontal or vertical direction, depending upon the engine's placement on the airframe.

In the aerodynamic blockage type shown in Figs. 8-21 and 8-22 the gases are turned forward by means of airfoils which are normally blocked during forward thrust operation (Figs. 8-21 and 8-22). During reverse thrust, the doors which were covering these airfoils are moved so that they now block the exhaust gas stream. The gas must now exit through the vanes and are deflected in a forward direction. Figure 8-23 shows that on some aircraft the aerodynamic blockage thrust reverser and the noise suppressor are combined into one integrated unit.

FIG. 8-19 *Drag parachute deployed to shorten the landing roll of a McDonnell Douglas F4H.*

(a)

(b)

(c)

FIG. 8-20 *Photographs and drawing of the target or mechanical blockage type of thrust reverser used to reverse both primary and fan streams on the General Electric CJ805-23 aft fan engine.*

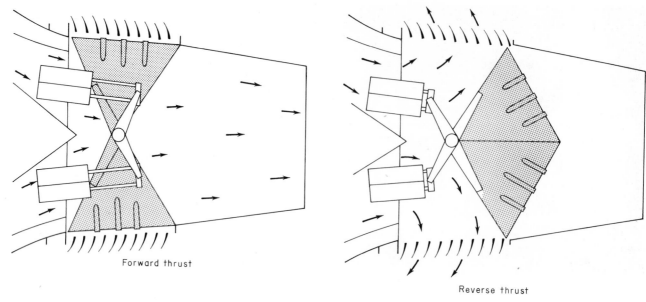

Forward thrust

Reverse thrust

FIG. 8-21 *Schematic of the aerodynamic blockage type of thrust reverser.*

(a)

(b)

(c)

FIG. 8-22 *Typical aerodynamic reversers.*

FIG. 8-23 *Combination suppressor and reverser installed on the General Electric CJ805-3 engine, installed in the Convair 880.*

THRUST REVERSER DESIGNS AND SYSTEMS

A good thrust reverser should:

1 Be mechanically strong and constructed of high-temperature metals to take the full force of the high-velocity jet, and at the same time turn this jet stream through a large angle.

2 Not affect the basic operation of the engine, whether the reverser is in operation or not.

3 Provide approximately 50 percent of the full forward thrust.

4 Operate with a high standard of fail-safe characteristics.

5 Not increase drag by increasing engine and nacelle frontal area.

6 Cause little increased maintenance problems.

7 Not add an excessive weight penalty.

8 Not cause the reingestion of the gas stream into the compressor nor cause the gas stream to impinge upon the airframe. That is, the discharge pattern must be correctly established by the placement and shape of the target or vane cascade.

9 Allow the pilot complete control of the amount of reverse thrust.

10 Not affect the aerodynamic characteristics of the airplane adversely.

Naturally the designer cannot incorporate all of these requirements to the fullest extent. In order to incorporate some of the features listed above, thrust reverser systems can become somewhat complicated. Typical of the systems in use today are the ones used on the Pratt & Whitney JT3D engine and the General Electric CJ805-23 engine, shown in Figs. 8-24 and 8-25, respectively.

Of the two, the Pratt & Whitney system is the more complicated in that there are actually three separate reversers (Fig. 8-26). There is a system for the primary stream and one for each of the bifurcated fan ducts. Actuation of this reverser system is by means of com-

FIG. 8-24 *Pratt & Whitney JT3D thrust reverser control schematic.*

FIG. 8-25 *General Electric CJ805-23 thrust reverser control schematic.*

Reverse thrust

Forward thrust

FIG. 8-26 *The Pratt & Whitney JT3D fan engine requires a separate reverser for primary and secondary airflows.*

pressor bleed air, while actuation of the General Electric system is by means of oil pressure. In both cases, when the pilot moves the power lever past the idle detent, the reverser system operates. The amount of forward or reverse thrust desired may then be controlled by the position of the power lever. It should be noted that forward fan engines designed with mixed-flow exhaust systems (see Chap. 2) require only one reverser.

REVIEW AND STUDY QUESTIONS

1 What is the function of the exhaust duct? How does the type of engine influence duct design?

2 Discuss the physical construction of the exhaust duct.

3 Where are the thermocouples located? Why?

4 Describe the operating principles of the convergent and convergent-divergent exhaust nozzles.

5 Why is it best to incorporate a variable geometry exhaust nozzle on an engine equipped with an afterburner?

6 Describe the sound pattern produced by a jet engine. By a reciprocating engine.

7 Where is sound generated? How does the sound suppressor reduce the sound problem?

8 Why are many modern jet engines not equipped with sound suppressors?

9 Describe the protective devices necessary when standing near a running gas turbine engine.

10 List some methods of stopping high-speed, heavy aircraft. Why were thrust reversers chosen?

11 Name two types of thrust reversers. Describe how each type operates.

12 List the operating features of a good thrust reverser.

Chapter 9

Methods of thrust augmentation

WATER INJECTION

In Chap. 3 we learned that one of the more important determiners of the power output of any gas turbine is the weight of airflow passing through the engine. A reduction in atmospheric pressure due to increasing altitude or temperature will therefore cause a reduction in thrust or shaft horsepower.

Power under these circumstances can be restored or even boosted as much as 10 to 30 percent for takeoff by the use of water or water-alcohol injection (Fig. 9-1). Engine power ratings during the period water injection is used are called "wet thrust" ratings as opposed to "dry thrust" ratings when water injection is off.

The alcohol adds to the power by providing an additional source of fuel, but because the alcohol has a low combustion efficiency, being only about half that of gas turbine fuel, and because the alcohol does not pass through the central part of the combustion chamber where temperatures are high enough to efficiently burn the weak alcohol-air mixture, the power added is small. The addition of alcohol has two other effects. If water only is injected, it would reduce the turbine inlet temperature, but with the addition of alcohol, the turbine temperature is restored. Thus the power is restored without having to adjust the fuel flow. The alcohol also serves to lower the freezing point of the water.

The water provides additional thrust in one of two ways, depending upon where the water is added. Some engines have the coolant sprayed directly into the compressor inlet, whereas others have fluid added at the diffuser. The system described at the end of this section, injects water at both points. (See Fig. 13-2.)

When water is added at the front of the compressor, power augmentation is obtained principally by the vaporizing liquid cooling the air. This increases the density and mass airflow. Furthermore, if water only is used, the cooler, increased airflow to the combustion chamber permits more fuel to be burned before the turbine temperature limits are reached. As shown in Chap. 3, higher turbine temperatures will result in increased thrust.

Water added to the diffuser increases the mass flow through the turbine relative to that through the compressor. This results in a decreased temperature and pressure drop across the turbine which leads to an increased pressure at the exhaust nozzle. Again, the reduction in turbine temperature when water alone is used allows the fuel system to schedule an increased fuel flow, providing additional thrust.

In both cases water is the fluid used because its high heat of vaporization results in a fairly large amount of cooling for a given weight of water flow. Demineralized water is generally used to prevent deposit buildup on compressor blades which will lead to deterioration of thrust requiring more frequent "field cleaning" of the compressor and engine trimming. (See Chap. 18.)

Generally water/air ratios are in the order of 1 to 5 lb of water to 100 lb of air. For example, Fig. 9-2 shows a schematic of the water injection system used on the B-52G and earlier models. Later models of this airplane use the fan engine and there is no provision for water injection. The water tank holds approximately 1200 gal, which is usually exhausted during takeoff. About 110 sec are required to consume all of the liquid. Any water not used during takeoff is drained overboard.

OPERATION (Fig. 9-2)

The first step in the operating procedure is to place the system control switch in the ON position. This supplies electrical power to energize the tank-mounted water-injection boost pumps and to light up the low-pressure warning lights on the control panel to indicate that the engines are *not* receiving water. As the tank boost pumps deliver water to the system, the tank boost pump indicators on the control panel move from the OFF to the ON position.

When the throttle is advanced to approximately 86 percent rpm (this percentage of rpm varies on different engines), a microswitch in the fuel control unit (Fig. 9-2) is actuated. This supplies power to open the motor-operated shutoff valve, thus permitting water to reach the engine-driven water pump. The water pump boosts the water pressure to 385 to 440 psi, with a rated flow of 160 gal/min. At the water-pressure regulators, the water pump output is divided and sent

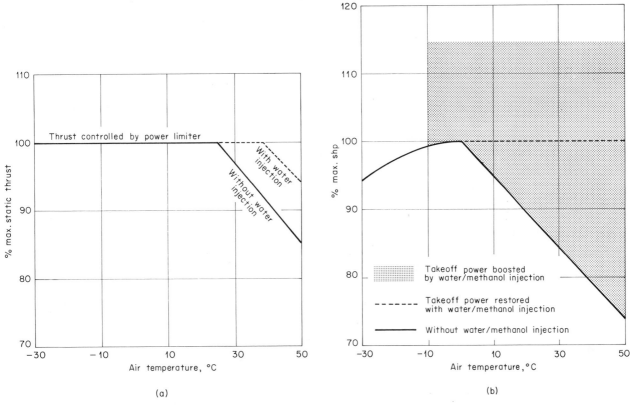

(a)

(b)

FIG. 9-1 *The effect of water injection on a turbojet and turboprop engine.* (**a**) *Turbojet thrust increase with water injection.* (**b**) *Turboprop power with and without water injection.*

SUPPLY
LOW PRESSURE
HIGH PRESSURE
MECHANICAL ACTUATION
ELECTRICAL CIRCUIT

a WATER-INJECTION TANK
b TANK BOOST PUMPS
c BOOST PUMP PRESSURE-INDICATING SWITCHES
d BOOST PUMP OUTLET CHECK VALVES
e TANK DRAIN VALVE
f SURGE CHAMBER
g DRAIN VALVE
h MOTOR-OPERATED WATER SHUTOFF VALVE
i DIFFUSER CASE NOZZLE RINGS
j SIPHON-BREAK VALVE
k LOW-PRESSURE WARNING LIGHTS
l CHECK VALVES
m HIGH-PRESSURE WATER REGULATOR
n PRESSURE SWITCHES
o WATER STRAINERS
p LOW-PRESSURE WATER REGULATORS
q MICROSWITCH ON FUEL CONTROL UNIT
r ENGINE-DRIVEN WATER PUMP
s MANUALLY OPERATED WATER SHUTOFF VALVE
t ENGINE INLET SPRAY RINGS
u THROTTLE LEVERS
v DRAIN SWITCH
w TANK BOOST PUMP PRESSURE INDICATOR
x SYSTEM CONTROL SWITCH

FIG. 9-2 *Water injection system for the B-52G and earlier models.*

to the inlet spray ring and to the diffuser case nozzle ring.

Approximately one-third of the water passes through the low-pressure regulator into the inlet spray ring, and two-thirds of the water passes through the high-pressure regulator into the diffuser case nozzle rings. When the water-pressure regulators receive water from the water pump, the low-pressure warning lights go out, indicating that the engines are receiving water. The water pressure is also directed from the water-pressure regulator to the fuel control unit to reposition the control unit maximum speed limit. This will permit an increased fuel flow during the period of water injection.

As stated previously, the water supply is sufficient to allow 110 sec of continuous maximum takeoff rated (wet) thrust. When the water pressure is lowered by depletion or by placing the system control switch in the OFF position, the water drain valves open automatically and permit the water *remaining in the system* to drain overboard. The drain switch on the water-injection control panel is placed in the OPEN position, and this permits draining of the *water tank*. To ensure proper drainage of the water tank, the eight amber low-pressure warning lights will remain illuminated until the drain switch is moved to the OPEN position, even though the system control switch is off and the system is depleted.

AFTERBURNING

Afterburning or reheating is one method of periodically augmenting the basic thrust of the turbojet, and more recently, the turbofan engine, without having to use a larger engine with its concurrent penalties of increased frontal area, weight, and fuel consumption. The afterburner, whose operation is much like a ramjet, increases thrust by adding fuel to the exhaust gases after they have passed through the turbine section. At this point there is still much uncombined oxygen in the exhaust. (See Chap. 6.) The resultant increase in the temperature raises the velocity of the exiting gases and therefore boosts engine thrust. Most afterburners will produce an approximate 50 percent thrust increase, but with a corresponding 150 percent increase in fuel flow. Since the specific and actual fuel consumption is considerably higher during the time the engine is in afterburning or "hot" operation, as compared to the nonafterburning or "cold" mode of operation, reheating is used only for the time-limited operation of takeoff, climb, and maximum bursts of speed. Afterburning rather than water injection as a method of gaining additional thrust is used extensively in, but not limited to, fighter aircraft because of the higher thrust augmentation ratios possible.

Two late-model engines utilizing an afterburner are the Pratt & Whitney TF30 augmented turbofan engine that is being used in the General Dynamics Corporation "swing wing" F111, and the General Electric GE4, an engine in the 50,000-lb thrust class, for use in the Boeing 2707 supersonic transport. (See Fig. 2-27.) Investigations have indicated the desirability of using this reheating method in combination with the turbofan engine by heating the duct or fan air to high temperatures.

All engines which incorporate an afterburner must, of necessity, also be equipped with a variable-area exhaust nozzle in order to provide for proper operation under afterburning and nonafterburning conditions. The nozzle is closed during nonafterburning operation, but when afterburning is selected, the nozzle is automatically opened to provide an exit area suitable for the increased volume of the gas stream. This prevents any increase in back pressure from occurring which would slow the airflow through the engine and affect the compressor's stall characteristics. A well-designed afterburner and variable-area exhaust nozzle will not influence the operation of the basic turbojet engine.

Specific requirements for a reheat augmentation device are:

1 *Large temperature rise*—The afterburner does not have the physical and temperature limits of the turbine. The temperature rise is limited mainly by the amount of air that is available.

2 *Low dry loss*—The engine does suffer a very slight penalty in thrust during "cold" operation due principally to the restriction caused by the flame holders and fuel spray bars.

3 *Wide temperature modulation*—This is necessary to obtain "degrees" of afterburning for better control of thrust.

CONSTRUCTION

The typical afterburner consists of the following components (Fig. 9-3):

1 Engine or turbine driven afterburner fuel pump
2 Afterburner fuel control
3 Pressurizing valve—if multistage operation is possible
4 Spray nozzles or spraybars
5 Torch ignitor and/or ignition system
6 Flame holders
7 Variable-area exhaust nozzle
8 Connections (mechanical and pressure) from main fuel control, throttle, and engine
9 Screech liner

A detailed examination of an actual afterburner system is made at the end of this chapter, and in Chap. 21.

OPERATION

The gases enter the afterburner at the approximate temperature, pressure, and velocity of 550°C, 40 lb/sq

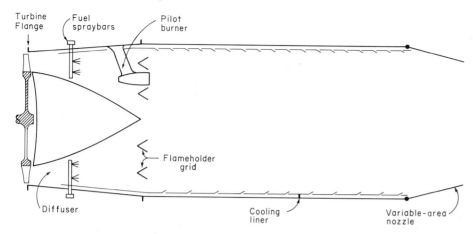

FIG. 9-3 *Simple afterburner schematic.*

in., and 2000 fps, respectively, and leave at about 1600°C, 40 lb/sq in., and 3000 fps, respectively. These values can vary widely with different engines, nozzle configurations, and operating conditions. The duct area to the rear of the turbine is larger than a normal exhaust duct would be in order to obtain a reduced velocity gas stream, and thus reduce gas friction losses. This reduced velocity is still too high for stable combustion to take place, since the flame propagation rate of kerosine is only a few feet per second. It becomes necessary to use a form of flame stabilizer or holder located downstream of the fuel spraybars to provide a region in which turbulent eddies are formed, and where the local gas velocity is further reduced. Fuel is fed into the afterburner through a series of nozzles or spraybars. In some engines the afterburner is either on or off, while in others, degrees of afterburning are available. Ignition occurs in one of several ways.

1 *Hot streak ignition*—In this system an extra quantity of fuel is injected into one of the combustion chambers. The resulting streak of hot gases ignites the afterburner fuel.

2 *Torch ignition*—A "pilot light" located in the area of the spraybars is fed fuel and ignited with its own ignition system. The system works continuously during afterburner operation.

These systems are utilized, since spontaneous ignition of the afterburner fuel cannot be depended upon, especially at high altitudes where the atmospheric pressure is low.

A screech or antihowl liner fits into the inner wall of the duct. The liner is generally corrugated and perforated with thousands of small holes. The liner prevents extreme high frequency and amplitude pressure fluctuations resulting from combustion instability or the unsteady release of heat energy. Screech results in excessive noise, vibration, heat transfer rates, and temperatures which will cause rapid physical destruction of the afterburner components. The screech liner tends to absorb and dampen these pressure fluctuations.

The flame holder mentioned above usually takes the form of several concentric rings with a V cross-sectional shape.

THRUST INCREASE *(Fig. 9-4)*

For a constant pressure ratio, the amount of thrust increase, in terms of percent, due to afterburning, is directly related to the ratio of the exhaust gas temperature before and after the afterburner. For example, if the gas temperature before and after the afterburner is 615°C (1600°R) and 1670°C (3500°R), respectively,

$$\text{Temperature ratio} = \frac{3500}{1600} = 2.19$$

But since the velocity of the jet stream increases as the square root of the temperature, then

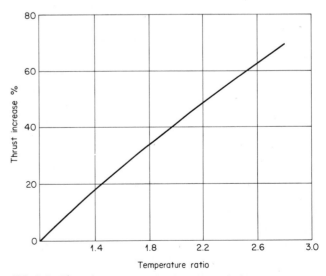

FIG. 9-4 *Thrust increase versus temperature ratio increase.*

$\sqrt{2.19} = 1.48$

or a jet-stream velocity and thrust increase of 48 percent at sea level static conditions. On a "net thrust" basis the advantage increases directly with increases in airplane speed. For example, this same engine-airplane combination with the same cycle temperature would realize a net percentage augmentation of 85 percent at Mach 1, and 130 percent at Mach 2.

There are also small effects on "wet" thrust due to changes in total F/F weight across the nozzle, in total pressure, and in the specific heat of air as the temperature increases.

J57 AFTERBURNER SYSTEM (Fig. 9-5)

This afterburner is composed of the afterburner diffuser and the afterburner duct and exhaust nozzle assembly. The exhaust nozzle assembly is variable and is operated by pneumatic actuating cylinders moved by compressor bleed air, which is metered by the exhaust nozzle control valve. During normal engine operation, the cylinders hold the nozzle iris or flaps in the CLOSED position. When afterburning occurs, the cylinders open the nozzle to permit the less restricted passage of exhaust gases.

Afterburning operation is normally controlled by a switch installed in the throttle quadrant. This switch is actuated when the throttle lever is moved outboard while the engine is operating above the 80 percent range. The switch connects an electrical circuit to a 28-volt dc afterburner actuator motor shown in Fig. 9-5, mounted on the fuel transfer valve body (l). This causes the fuel shuttle valve (m) to open the fuel ports, first in the afterburner exhaust nozzle actuator control, and then in the afterburner ignition fuel valve.

The fuel shuttle valve (m) directs fuel from the afterburner stage of the fuel pump (r) into the afterburner fuel control. Metered fuel from the afterburner fuel control enters the manifold (b) and is atomized for burning by the spray nozzles mounted in the afterburner diffuser. A mechanical afterburner fuel shutoff valve (j) is installed on the engine, in conjunction with the throttle linkage, to prevent fuel flow from going to the afterburner until approximately 80 percent of engine power has been reached. Field adjustment of any of the afterburner fuel regulation and control components should not be attempted. The units must be set with the use of proper flow bench facilities.

The order of the fuel flow through the units of the system is as follows:

The engine and afterburner fuel pump assembly consists of two gear-type pumps and one impeller mounted on the same gear shaft. Fuel routed to the fuel pump inlet (p) enters the throat of the impeller, which discharges fuel under boosted pressure through the pump inlet screen (s). The filtered fuel (t) then passes through the inlet side of the afterburner and engine stages of the pump assembly. Relief valves (u) located in the discharge side of the gear pumps relieve excess fuel pressure back to the inlet side of the fuel pumps. A connecting point is provided on the outlet side of the engine fuel pump for connecting the low-fuel-pressure warning system (o). The afterburner fuel pump (r) is a part of the engine-driven fuel pump assembly, which has a gear stage for each system. The inlet of both stages is fed by a common centrifugal boost pump (q). An automatic emergency transfer valve is incorporated in the pump housing for the purpose of diverting fuel flow from the afterburner stage of the pump to the main fuel system if the main fuel pump fails.

The afterburner fuel shuttle valve and actuator unit (m) is incorporated as a part of the fuel-pump transfer valve assembly to control the flow of fuel to the afterburner fuel system. The actuator, a 28-volt dc motor that opens and closes the valve, is controlled by the afterburner switch located in the cockpit throttle quadrant.

The afterburner fuel control is installed on the right-hand side of the engine at the engine wasp-waist section. The control is provided to meter fuel for use during afterburner operation. Fuel metering is accomplished by an internal mechanical linkage that adjusts the metering valve opening. The internal mechanical linkage is actuated by a static air bellows (h) which extends and retracts with variations of N_2 compressor discharge pressure.

Fuel metering is also affected by spring-loaded fuel pressure valves within the control. Control inlet fuel is routed to the antispring side of the fuel control bypass valve (i). This valve maintains a constant-pressure head across the metering valve. Most of the fuel is then routed through the control filter (g), but some passes through a damping restriction to the spring side of the valve. This permits the spring load on the valve to determine the pressure differential between metered and unmetered fuel.

Ignition for the afterburning system is provided by a "hot streak" type of system. The igniter assembly contains a cylinder and piston (f), which discharges a quantity of fuel through the igniter injection nozzle into the number 3 burner can (combustion chamber, c). The fuel ignites in the burner and travels aft to ignite fuel being supplied by the afterburner discharge manifold (b). The igniter control operates on a combination of fuel pressure, spring tension, and N_2 compressor discharge pressure. At the time of afterburner actuation, the fuel piston (f) is actuated and injects fuel into the burner. The piston then remains in the actuated position until afterburning is terminated and then returns to its preoperational position.

Some of the J-57 engine afterburning systems are

CGQ 1927

a FLAPS ACTUATING
   CYLINDER
b FUEL MANIFOLD
c "HOT STREAK" IGNITER
   (NUMBER 3 COMBUSTION
   CHAMBER)
d FUEL PUMP OUTLET
   PRESSURE
e METERED FUEL PRESSURE

f IGNITER ASSEMBLY PISTON
g FUEL CONTROL FILTER
h STATIC AIR BELLOWS
i FUEL CONTROL BYPASS
   VALVE
j MECHANICAL AFTERBURNER
   FUEL SHUTOFF VALVE
k AFTERBURNER FUEL DRAIN
   VALVE

l FUEL TRANSFER VALVE
   BODY
m FUEL SHUTTLE VALVE
n 28-VOLT DC AFTERBURNER
   MOTOR ACTUATOR
o LOW-FUEL-PRESSURE
   WARNING CONNECTION
p FUEL INLET TO BOOST
   PUMP

q CENTRIFUGAL BOOST PUMP
r AFTERBURNER STAGE OF
   THE FUEL PUMP
s FUEL PUMP FILTER SCREEN
t FILTERED FUEL TO PUMPS
u FUEL PUMP RELIEF VALVES

FIG. 9-5 *Pratt & Whitney J57 afterburner system schematic.*

147

equipped with an afterburner recirculating igniter control, a modification of the "hot streak" afterburner igniter system.   The modification results in continuous fuel circulation through the igniter fuel chamber, thereby reducing igniter coking.   Because the fuel chamber is full at all times, a continuous leakage of fuel will occur from the chamber rather than only during afterburning as on the earlier configuration of the igniter. A check valve is installed in the exhaust nozzle actuator control to the recirculating igniter tube assembly, and another check valve is installed in the diffuser case to the recirculating igniter tube assembly.   The two valves prevent static fuel from leaking to the bottom of the diffuser case and the exhaust nozzle actuator control assembly.

The afterburner exhaust nozzle actuator control is a spring and fuel pressure-actuated component that directs air pressure to the actuating cylinder to open or close the afterburner exhaust nozzle.   Metered fuel pressure (e) and fuel pump outlet pressure (d) are the two pressures used to actuate this component.   The control assembly is equipped with a relay valve, which is spring-loaded to the exhaust nozzle CLOSED position.   At the time of afterburner actuation, afterburner fuel pressure is directed to the exhaust nozzle open end of the relay valve.   This repositions the valve and routes air pressure to open the exhaust nozzle.   The control assembly is equipped with two flapper valves which vent exhaust air from the nozzle actuator pneumatic system.

Multiple exhaust nozzle actuating cylinders (a) are installed around the engine tailpipe to actuate the iris-type or flap-type exhaust nozzle shutters.   The shutters (or flaps) are installed on the aft end of the afterburner to increase or decrease the exhaust nozzle opening. The nozzle must be closed when the afterburner is not in operation to prevent excessive loss of engine thrust. The nozzle must be open during afterburner operation to prevent excessive engine pressures and temperatures.

The actuating cylinders are operated by 16th-stage air pressure from the engine and are directed by the exhaust nozzle actuator control.   Operation of the actuator is begun when the pilot moves his throttle into afterburner range, completing the electrical control circuit to the afterburner fuel shutoff valve.   The afterburner fuel control governs fuel pressure and then actuates the nozzle actuator control valve, which in turn directs air pressure to the nozzle actuators.   The nozzle actuators are protected from excessive heat radiation by a metal insulating blanket installed between the actuators and the afterburner duct.

An afterburner drain valve (k) is installed in the line between the afterburner regulator and the fuel-injection manifold.   This valve is closed by fuel pressure during afterburner operation and is opened by spring pressure to drain the manifold when the afterburner is not in use.

THE GENERAL ELECTRIC J85 AFTERBURNER SYSTEM *(Fig. 9-6)*

In this particular system, the afterburner fuel and nozzle control is designed to maintain the proper fuel

FIG. 9-6   *General Electric J85 afterburner.*

PILOT BURNER
SPRAYBAR

MAIN
SPRAYBAR

MAIN FUEL
CONTROL

MAIN FUEL
CONTROL
PUMP

FUEL IN

AFTERBURNER
PUMP

AFTERBURNER
CONTROL

| HIGH PRESS. | MAIN BURNER | PILOT BURNER | ACCELERATION VALVE LINE |

(a)

Pilot burner
spraybar

Main burner
spraybar

Engine
driven

Afterburner
fuel pump

Afterburner and
nozzle control

Shutoff valve

Filter

From main
fuel control

Drain

Pressure line

To overspeed
governor

Fuel in

To acceleration valve
in main fuel control

| Low pressure | Pump disch pressure | Pilot burner pressure | Main burner pressure | Servo pressure |

(b)

FIG. 9-7 *General Electric J85 afterburner and nozzle system.* (**a**) *Afterburner and fuel system components.* (**b**) *Afterburner fuel system.* (*Continued on following page.*)

FIG. 9-7 General Electric J85 afterburner and nozzle systems (continued). (c) Afterburner and nozzle control.

flow to the engine's afterburner section as a function of power lever angle and compressor discharge pressure; and the proper exhaust nozzle opening as a function of power lever angle, compressor inlet temperature, and turbine discharge temperature. The system consists of the afterburner fuel pump and shutoff valve, the afterburner fuel and nozzle control, the fuel manifold drain valve, the main and pilot burner spraybars, and the turbine discharge temperature sensing system.

Operation (Fig. 9-7)

Fuel enters the afterburner pump through the pump shutoff valve. The valve opens when the power lever is placed in the afterburner ON position, the engine speed is 100 percent and the main fuel acceleration valve is closed. The pump is an engine-driven centrifugal type, and can handle fuel flows in excess of 10,000 lb/hr.

From the pump, the fuel flows to the afterburner fuel

and nozzle control, which is mounted directly on the pump. It is a hydromechanical device consisting of three main parts; the fuel-metering section, the computer section, and the afterburner nozzle control section.

The fuel-metering section meters the fuel flow required during afterburner operation to the pilot burner and main spraybars as determined from information received from the computing section.

The computer section positions the main and pilot burner valves of the fuel-metering section as a function of compressor discharge pressure and power lever angle. The power lever angle input is in turn limited by signals from the nozzle and the turbine discharge temperature system.

The afterburner nozzle control section schedules the afterburner nozzle area, as directed by the power lever, and the turbine discharge temperature. The leaves of the variable-area exhaust nozzle are positioned by three mechanical screwjack actuators powered by the nozzle actuator control via flexible drive cables.

REVIEW AND STUDY QUESTIONS

1 Name two methods of thrust augmentation.

2 Why is alcohol added to water in water injection systems? What effect does the alcohol have on the operation of the engine?

3 Tell how water injection increases thrust. Afterburning.

4 Where can water be injected?

5 How much thrust increase does water injection give; afterburning? Why?

6 Describe a typical water injection system.

7 Discuss the principle behind the afterburner.

8 Why are afterburners used mainly for military aircraft as a method of boosting thrust?

9 Why is it necessary to have a variable-area geometry exhaust on an afterburner equipped engine?

10 What are the requirements of a good afterburner?

11 Describe a typical afterburner system. What type of ignition systems are used?

Chapter 10

Materials and methods of construction

GAS TURBINE MATERIALS

High-temperature, high-strength materials and unique methods of manufacture have made the gas turbine engine a practical reality in a few decades. To a large measure, the performance of turbojet and turboprop engines is dependent upon the temperature at the inlet to the turbine. It can be shown that increasing the turbine inlet temperature from the present limit (for most engines in high production) of approximately 1700 to 2500°F will result in a specific thrust increase of approximately 130 percent along with a corresponding decrease in specific fuel consumption. For this reason, obviously, high cycle temperatures are desirable. Just as obvious is the fact that not all materials can withstand the hostile operating conditions found in parts of the gas turbine engine.

Commonly used terms

Some of the more commonly used terms in the field of metallurgy and metalworking are listed below.

1   *Strength*

   (a) *Creep strength*—Defined as the ability of a metal to resist slow deformation due to stress, but less than the stress level needed to reach the yield point. Creep strength is usually stated in terms of time, temperature, and load.

   (b) *Yield strength*—This point is reached when the metal exhibits a permanent set under load.

   (c) *Rupture strength*—That point where the metal will break

under a continual load applied for periods of 100 and 1000 hr. Metals are usually tested at several temperatures.

   (d) *Ultimate tensile strength*—The load under which the metal will break in a short time.

2   *Ductility*—The ability of a metal to deform without breaking.

3   *Coefficient of expansion*—A measure of how much a metal will expand or grow with the application of heat.

4   *Thermal conductivity*—The measure of the ability of a metal to transmit heat.

5   *Corrosion and oxidation resistance*—An important factor which indicates how well a metal can resist the corrosive effects of the hot exhaust stream.

6   *Melting point*—The temperature at which the metal becomes a liquid.

7   *Critical temperature*—As a metal is cooled, it passes through distinct temperature points where its internal structure and physical properties are altered. The rate of cooling will greatly influence the ultimate properties of the metal.

8   *Heat treatability*—This is a measure of how the metal's basic structure will vary under an operation, or series of operations, involving heating and cooling of the metal while it is in a solid state. Ferritic, austenitic, and martensitic steels all vary as to their heat treatability. (All of these terms have to do with the physical and chemical properties of metal.)

9   *Thermal shock resistance*—The ability of a metal to withstand extreme changes in temperature in short periods of time.

10 *Hardness*—An important characteristic in that it influences ease of manufacture and therefore cost.

Metal working terms include:

1   *Casting*—A process whereby metal, in a molten state, solidifies in a mold.

2   *Forging*—This is a process of plastic deformation under a pressure that may be slowly or quickly applied.

3   *Electrochemical machining (ECM)*—ECM is accomplished by controlled high-speed deplating using a shaped tool (cathode), an electricity conducting solution, and the workpiece (anode).

4   *Machining*—Any process whereby metal is formed by cutting, hot or cold rolling, pinching, punching, grinding, or by means of laser beams.

5   *Extrusion*—Metal is pushed through a die to form various cross-sectional shapes.

6   *Welding*—A process of fusing two pieces of metal together by locally melting part of the material through the use of arc welders, plasmas, lasers, or electron beams.

7   *Pressing*—Metals are blended, pressed, sintered (a process of fusing the powder particles together through heat), and coined out of pre-alloyed powders.

8   *Protective finishes and surface treatments*—This includes plating by means of electrical and chemical processes, by use of ceramic coatings, or painting. Surface treatments for increased wear may take the form of nitriding, cyaniding, carburizing, diffusion coating, and flame plating.

9   *Shot peening*—A plastic flow or stretching of a metal's surface by a rain of round metallic shot thrown at high velocity.

10 *Heat treatment*—A process to impart specific physical properties to a metal alloy. It includes normalizing, annealing, stress relieving, tempering, and hardening.

11 *Inspection*—Strictly speaking, not a part of the metal working

process, inspection is nevertheless integrally associated with it. Inspection methods include magnetic particle and dye penetrant inspection, x-ray inspection, dimensional and visual inspection, and inspection by devices utilizing sound, light, and air. Some of these inspection procedures will be discussed in Chap. 19.

Heat ranges of metals *(Fig. 10-1)*

The operating conditions within a gas turbine engine vary considerably, and metals differ in their ability to satisfactorily meet these conditions.

ALUMINUM ALLOYS Aluminum and its alloys are used in temperature ranges up to 500°F. With low density and good strength to weight ratios, aluminum forgings and castings are used extensively for centrifugal compressor wheels and housings, air inlet sections, accessory sections, and for the accessories themselves.

TITANIUM ALLOYS Titanium and its alloys are used for axial-flow compressor wheels, blades, and other forged components in many large, high-performance engines. Titanium combines high strength with low density and is suitable for applications up to 1000°F.

STEEL ALLOYS This group includes high-chromium and high-nickel iron-base alloys in addition to low-alloy steels. Because of the relatively low material cost, ease of fabrication, and good mechanical properties, the low-alloy steels are commonly used for both rotating and static engine components such as compressor rotor blades, wheels, spacers, stator vanes, and structural members. Low-alloy steels can be heat treated and can be used in temperatures up to 1000°F. High nickel-chromium-iron base alloys can be used up to 1250°F.

NICKEL-BASE ALLOYS The nickel-base alloys constitute some of the best metals for use between 1200°F and 1800°F. Most contain little or no iron. They develop their high-temperature strength by age hardening and are characterized by long-time creep-rupture strength, and high ultimate and yield strength combined with good ductility. Many of these materials, originally developed for turbine bucket applications, are also being used in turbine wheels, shafts, spacers, and other parts. Their use is somewhat restricted because of their cost and because of their requirement for critical materials.

COBALT-BASE ALLOYS Cobalt-base alloys form another important group of high-temperature, high-strength, and high-corrosion-resistant metals. Again, as a group, they contain little or no iron. These alloys are used in afterburners and other parts of the engine subjected to very high temperatures.

Chemical elements used in alloys

The number of alloying materials is large. Several of the most commonly used elements are listed below.

TABLE 10-1

ELEMENT	CHEMICAL SYMBOL	ELEMENT	CHEMICAL SYMBOL
Aluminum	Al	Manganese	Mn
Boron	B	Molybdenum	Mo
Carbon	C	Nitrogen	N
Chromium	Cr	Nickel	Ni
Cobalt	Co	Silicon	Si
Columbium	Cb	Tantalum	Ta
Copper	Cu	Titanium	Ti
Iron	Fe	Vanadium	V
		Zirconium	Zr

The percentages of the various elements used, partially determines the physical and chemical characteristics of the alloy and its suitability to a particular application (Fig. 10-2). Tempering and other processes determine the rest. Three characteristics that must be considered are:

1 High-temperature strength
2 Resistance to oxidation and corrosion
3 Resistance to thermal shock

High-temperature strength *(Fig. 10-3)*

The most highly stressed parts of the gas turbine engine are the turbine blades and disks. Centrifugal forces tending to break the disk vary as the square of the speed. For example, the centrifugal force on a disk rotating at 20,000 rpm will be four times that at 10,000 rpm. Blades weighing only 2 oz may exert loads of over 4000 lb at maximum rpm. The blades must also resist the high bending loads applied by the moving gas stream to produce the thousands of horsepower needed to drive the compressor. There is also a severe temperature gradient (difference) between the central portion of the disk and its periphery of several hundred degrees centigrade. Many metals which would be quite satisfactory at room temperatures will lose much of their strength at the elevated temperatures encountered in the engine's hot section. The ultimate tensile strength of a metal at one temperature is not necessarily indicative of its ultimate tensile strength at a higher temperature. For example, at 1000°F Inconel X has an ultimate tensile strength of 160,000 psi at room temperature, and S 816 at the same temperature has an ultimate tensile strength of 135,000 psi. At 1500°F their positions are reversed. Inconel X has an ultimate tensile strength of 55,000 psi, while S 816 has

Fe BASE ALLOYS	C	Cr	Ni	Co	Mo	Ti	Cb	OTHER
Chromoloy	0.20	1	—	—	1	—	—	0.1 V
Lapelloy	0.30	12	—	—	3	—	—	0.3 V
17-7PH	0.07	17	7	—	—	—	—	1 Al
321 SS	0.05	18	10	—	—	0.4	—	—
A286	0.05	15	26	—	1	2	—	0.2 Al
Incoloy T	0.08	20	32	—	—	1	—	—
Timken 16-25-6	0.10	16	25	—	6	—	—	0.15 N
N-155	0.30	20	20	20	3	—	1	2 W
15-7Mo	0.09	15	7	—	2.5	—	—	1.0 Al
19-9DL	0.32	18.5	9	—	1.4	0.25	—	1.35 W
B5 F5	0.45	.95	—	—	0.55	—	—	0.30 V
M308	0.08	13.75	32.5	—	4.1	2.0	—	6.5 W
V57	0.06	15	25.5	—	1.25	3.0	—	0.25 Al

Ni BASE ALLOYS	C	Cr	Fe	Co	Mo	Ti	Al	OTHER
Inconel	0.05	14	7	—	—	—	—	—
Inconel W	0.05	14	7	—	—	2.5	0.6	—
Inconel X	0.05	15	7	—	—	2.5	0.7	1 Cb
Inco 702	0.02	16	—	—	—	0.5	3.7	—
Inco (Cast)	0.2	12	5	—	4.5	0.75	6.0	2 Si + Mn 2 Cb + Ta
Hastelloy B	0.10	1	5	—	28	—	—	—
Hastelloy X	0.15	22	23	—	9	—	—	—
M-252	0.10	19	2	10	10	2.5	0.8	—
Hastelloy R-235	0.15	16	10	—	6	3	2	—
Udimet 500	0.15	17.5	4 max	16	4	3	3	1.5 Si + Mn
Astroloy	0.055	15.0	0.20	15.0	5.0	3.5	4.4	—
Cosmoloy F	0.04	15.0	0.20	—	3.75	3.45	4.75	2.25 W
Hastelloy C	0.08	15.5	5.5	2.5	16.0	—	—	3.75 W
Rene' 41	0.12	19.0	5.0	11.0	9.75	3.15	1.5	—
U 700	0.10	15.0	4.0	18.5	5.0	3.25	4.25	—
Waspalloy	0.10	19.5	2.00	13.5	4.25	3.0	1.25	—

Co BASE ALLOYS	C	Cr	Ni	Fe	Mo	W	Cb	OTHER
HS 21	0.25	27	3	1	5	—	—	—
HS 25 (L-605)	0.12	20	10	1	—	15	—	—
HS 31 (X-40)	0.40	25	10	1	—	8	—	—
HE1049	0.40	26	10	2	—	15	—	0.4 B
S-816	0.40	20	20	3	4	4	4	—
V-36	0.30	25	20	3	4	3	2	—

Al BASE ALLOYS	Cu	Si	Mg	Mn
355	1.5	5	0.5	—
14 S	4.5	1	1	1

Mg BASE ALLOYS	Al	Zr	Zn	Th
Dow C	9	—	2	—
HK 31	—	—	0.7	3
HZ 32	—	0.75	2.1	3.25

Ti BASE ALLOYS	Al	Mn	Fe	Cr	Mo	V	OTHER
C 130 AM	4	4	—	—	—	—	*
Ti 140A	—	—	2	2	2	—	*
C 110 M	—	8	—	—	—	—	*
6 Al-4 V	6	—	—	—	—	4	*
7Al-4 Mo-Ti	7	—	—	—	4	—	*
A 110 AT	4.0–6.0						2.0–4.5 Sn *

* For all alloys C = 0.2 max; O_2 = 0.25 max; N = 0.1 max; H_2 = 0.015 max.

FIG. 10-1 *Compositions of some jet-engine alloys.*

an ultimate tensile strength of 75,000 psi. The creep strength, which is closely associated with ultimate tensile strength, is probably one of the most important considerations in the selection of a suitable metal for turbine blades (Fig. 10-4). Engine vibration and fatigue resistance will also have some influence on the selection and useful life of both disks and blades.

Although there are many materials which will withstand the high temperatures encountered in the modern gas turbine engine (for example, carbon, columbium, molybdenum, rhenium, tantalum, and tungsten, all have melting points above 4000°F), the ability to withstand high temperatures while maintaining a reasonable tensile strength is not the only consideration. Such factors as critical temperature, rupture strength, thermal conductivity, coefficient of expansion, yield strength, ultimate tensile strength, corrosion resistance, workability, and cost must all be taken into account when selecting any particular metal.

Resistance to oxidation and corrosion

Corrosion and oxidation are results of electrical and chemical reactions with other materials. The hot exhaust gas stream encountered in the engine speeds up this reaction. While all metals will corrode or oxidize, the degree of oxidation is determined by the base alloy and the properties of the oxide coating formed. If the oxide coating is porous, or has a coefficient of expansion different from that of the base metal, the base metal will be continually exposed to the oxidizing atmosphere. One solution to the problem of oxidation at elevated temperatures has been the development and use of ceramic coatings. Ceramic-coated afterburner liners and combustion chambers are in use today. The ceramic coating has two basic functions:

1 Sealing the base metal surface against corrosion
2 Insulating the base metal against high temperatures

These coatings are not without disadvantages, in that they are more susceptible to thermal shock, they must have the same coefficient of expansion as the base metal, they are brittle, and they have low tensile strength which, of course, restricts their use in the engine. Some work which shows promise is being done with various metal-ceramic combinations called *Cermets* or *Ceramels*. Ceramic materials being used include aluminum, beryllium, thorium, and zirconium oxides to name a few.

Thermal shock resistance

Many materials which would otherwise be quite suitable must be rejected because of their poor thermal shock characteristics. Several engine failures have been attributed to thermal shock on the turbine disk. Ceramic coatings in particular are vulnerable to this form of stress. Improved fuel controls, starting techniques, and engine design have lessened this problem.

Transpiration cooling

The effort to achieve higher turbine inlet temperatures, and therefore higher thermal efficiencies, has been approached from two directions. The first has been the development and use of high-temperature materials. The second avenue of approach has been to cool the highly stressed turbine components. A common method of cooling the nozzle guide vanes on gas turbine engines is to pass compressor bleed air through the hollow blades to cool them by convective heat transfer. Some engines also use the air bled from the compressor to cool the front and rear face of the turbine disks and the hollow turbine blades.

Transpiration cooling is a novel and efficient method of allowing the turbine blades and other parts within the hot section to operate at much higher turbine inlet temperatures. The Wright Corporation has constructed and run turbine blades at an inlet temperature of 2500°F (Fig. 10-5).

In this type of cooled blade the air passes through thousands of holes in a porous airfoil made from a sintered wire mesh material. Since the sintered wire mesh is not strong enough by itself, an internal strut is provided as the main structural support carrying all airfoil and centrifugal loads. Fabrication techniques involve rolling layers of woven wire mesh and then sintering these layers to form a porous metal sheet, which is then rolled into an airfoil shape.

Porous materials have been tested for use in combustion chambers and for afterburner liners. A similar material called Rigimesh has also been used in rocket engines to help keep the fuel nozzles cool. Many manufacturers are experimenting with other types of porous materials for use in blades in an attempt to obtain higher turbine inlet temperatures.

Other materials

Relatively new types of materials called composites are coming to the foreground for use in both airframes and engines. In these products, graphite, glass, or boron filaments are embedded in an epoxy-resin matrix or base substance. Other types of filaments and matrices are being tried to meet the demands of higher temperature and/or stress. The chief advantage of the composite material is its very favorable strength to weight ratio, which can lead to the lightening of many structural parts. For example, a lighter fan blade will allow a lighter fan disk, which will in turn permit a lightening of other parts all the way down the line. Composite materials may be used in conjunction with other load-bearing materials to provide a support function. Typical of this type of structure are fan blades made with a steel spar and base and with an airfoil composite shell. Closely associated with the future use of composite materials is the development of new manufacturing techniques to produce these materials.

CHEMICAL COMPOSITION

	DESIGNATION	C	Mn	Si	Cr	Ni	Co	Fe	Mo	W	Others	GENERAL USE
HIGH STRENGTH HIGH TEMPERATURE ALLOYS	21 Alloy (AMS 5385B)	.20 .30	1.0 Max.	1.0 Max.	25.0 29.0	1.75 3.75	Bal.	3.0 Max.	5.0 6.0		B—.007 Max.	Good high tempera strength and shock re ance. Oxidation resist to 2100°F
	X-40 31 Alloy (AMS 5382B)	.45 .55	1.0 Max.	1.0 Max.	24.5 26.5	9.5 11.5	Bal.	2.0 Max.		7.0 8.0	P—.04 Max. S—.04 Max.	Maximum high temp ture strength. Oxida resistance to 2100°F
	Hastelloy "C" (AMS 5388)	.15 Max.	1.0 Max.	1.0 Max.	15.5 17.5	Bal.	2.5 Max.	4.5 7.0	16.0 18.0	3.75 5.25	V—.2—.6	Intermediate high te strength. Oxidation re ance to 2100°F. Re ance to thermal shock
	N-155 (AMS 5376B)	.20 Max.	1.0 2.0	1.0 Max.	20.0 22.0	19.0 21.0	18.5 21.0	Bal.	2.5 3.5	2.0 3.0	Cb +Ta—.75 —1.25 N—.1—.2 P—.04 Max. S—.03 Max.	Good strength at inter diate temperature. Ox tion resistance to 200
	309 Mod. H.R. Crown Max.	.15 .30	1.0 Max.	.75 2.00	22.0 25.0	11.0 14.0		Bal.		2.5 3.5	P—.04 Max. S—.04 Max.	Good strength at inter diate temp. with low loy content
	Inconel X	.08 Max.	.3 1.0	.50 Max.	14.0 16.0	70.0 Min.		5.0 9.0			Cb—.7—1.0 Ti—2.25—2.75 Al—.4—1.0 S—.01 Max.	Maximum elevated te strength properties in heat treated conditic
AUSTENITIC STAINLESS STEELS	Type 302 (AMS 5358)	.25 Max.	2.0 Max.	1.0 Max.	17.0 19.0	8.0 10.0		Bal.	.50 Max.		P—.C4 Max. S—.03 Max. Cu—.5 Max.	Good corrosion resista Oxidation resistance 1600°F
	Type 310 (AMS 5366A)	.18 Max.	2.0 Max.	.50 1.50	23.0 26.0	19.0 22.0		Bal.	.50 Max.		P—.04 Max. S—.03 Max. Cu—.5 Max.	Excellent oxidation re ance to 2000°F. Mod ate high temp. strengt
	Type 316 (AMS 5360)	.15 Max.	2.0 .Max.	.75 Max.	16.0 18.0	12.0 14.0		Bal.	1.50 2.25		P—.04 Max. S—.03 Max. Cu.—.5 Max.	Maximum corrosion re ance and moderate h temperature strength 1600°F
	Type 303	.20 Max.	1.5 Max.	2.0 Max.	18.0 21.0	9.0 12.0		Bal.	.40 .80		P—.05 Max. S—.2—.4	Free machining grade corrosion service
MARTENITIC STAINLESS STEELS	Type 410 (AMS 5350C)	.05 .15	1.0 Max.	1.0 Max.	11.5 13.5	.5 Max.		Bal.	.50 Max.		P—.04 Max. S—.03 Max. Cu—.5 Max.	Moderate corrosion c heat resistance, service 1200°F. Maximum dar ing capacity
	Type 431	.12 .20	1.0 Max.	1.0 Max.	15.0 17.0	1.5 3.0		Bal.	.50 Max.		P—.04 Max. S—.04 Max. Cu—.5 Max.	Moderate corrosion c heat resistance, service 1500°F. Maximum tens strength
CARBON AND LOW ALLOY STEELS	1020	.18 .23	.30 .60	.75 Max.				Bal.			S—.05 Max. P—.04 Max.	Carburized parts or str tural shapes requiri good ductility
	1035	.32 .38	.60 .90	.75 Max.				Bal.			S—.05 Max. P—.04 Max.	Stressed structural sha
	1095	.90 1.05	.30 .50	.75 Max.				Bal.			S—.05 Max. P—.04 Max.	Tools and wear resist parts
	4140	.38 .43	.75 1.00	.75 Max.	.80 1.10			Bal.	.15 .25		S—.04 Max. P—.04 Max.	Highly stressed parts c service to 900°F
	4340	.38 .43	.60 .80	.75 Max.	.70 .90	1.65 2.00		Bal.	.20 .30		S—.04 Max. P—.04 Max.	Highly stressed pa Good impact resista with high strength. Se ice to 1000°F
	8620	.18 .23	.70 .90	.75 Max.	.40 .60	.40 .70		Bal.	.15 .25		S—.04 Max. P—.04 Max.	Highly stressed carb rized parts

FIG. 10-2 *Several representative alloys and their properties.*

CAST-ABILITY	CONDITION	TEST TEMP. °F	Y.S. 2% OFFSET psi	T.S. psi	ELONG. %	R.A. %	HARD-NESS	STRESS RUPTURE DATA 100 HR. LIFE STRESS psi	1000 HR. LIFE STRESS psi	CREEP DATA 1% 10,000 HR. STRESS psi	FATIGUE STRESS 10^8 CY. STRESS psi
Excellent	As Cast	70	80,000	100,000	8	10	$28R_c$				35,000
	As Cast	1200	35,000	70,000	15	40		50,000	45,000		44,000
	As Cast	1500	20,000	65,000	15	30		21,000	15,000	7,000	33,000
	As Cast	1800		33,000	35	50		9,000	6,000		
	Aged (1)	70	100,000	120,000	2	3					
	Aged (1)	1200	70,000	90,000	2	5					
Excellent	As Cast	70	80,000	110,000	8	10	$30R_c$				56,000
	As Cast	1200	40,000	75,000	15	25		55,000	46,000		46,000
	As Cast	1500	25,000	60,000	15	20		28,000	22,000	12,000	
	As Cast	1800		30,000	30	40		10,000	8,000		
	Aged (1)	70	110,000	125,000	2	3					
	Aged (1)	1200	60,000	80,000	5	6					
Good	As Cast	70	50,000	80,000	5	5	$20R_c$				
	As Cast	1200		60,000	15	15		45,000	30,000		
	As Cast	1500		50,000	18	15		18,000	14,000		
	As Cast	1800		20,000	20	50		5,000	2,000		
Excellent	As Cast	70	55,000	95,000	25	15	$85R_b$				
	As Cast	1200	32,000	60,000	25	25		45,000	35,000		
	As Cast	1500	20,000	50,000	15	20		18,000	14,000	7,000	
	As Cast	1800		20,000	25	50		5,000	2,000		
Excellent	As Cast	70	40,000	80,000	15	25	$80R_b$				
	As Cast	1200	25,000	50,000	10	10		25,000	15,000		
	As Cast	1500	20,000	30,000	25	30		12,000	5,000		
Poor	Ht. Tr. (2)	70	85,000	105,000	4	6	$29R_c$				
	Ht. Tr. (2)	1200	70,000	100,000	8	10		75,000	60,000		
	Ht. Tr. (2)	1500	50,000	55,000	20	30		28,000	18,000		
Good	As Cast	70	30,000	80,000	40	50	$80R_b$				
	Ann'ld.(2)	70	25,000	70,000	50	70	$76R_b$				
	As Cast	1200	12,000	40,000	30	40		18,000	13,000		
	As Cast	1500	10,000	20,000	30	40					
Excellent	As Cast	70	25,000	60,000	40	60	$70R_b$				
	Ann'ld. (3)	70	25,000	60,000	50	60					
	As Cast	1200	20,000	50,000	20	25		24,000	18,000		
	As Cast	1500	15,000	25,000	10	15					
Good	As Cast	70	30,000	75,000	40	50	$77R_b$				
	Ann'ld. (3)	70	30,000	70,000	50	60	$75R_b$				
	As Cast	1200	20,000	55,000	30	50		26,000	20,000		
	As Cast	1500	12,000	25,000	20	40					
Good	As Cast	70	30,000	75,000	35	35	$80R_b$				
	Ann'ld. (3)	70	35,000	80,000	40	40	$81R_b$				
Fair	Pro. Ann. (4)	70	90,000	120,000	10	20	$25R_c$				
	H.T. (4&5)	70	110,000	140,000	10	30	$30R_c$				
	H.T. (4&5)	70	85,000	110,000	20	50	$24R_c$				
Fair	Pro. Ann. (4)	70	90,000	120,000	15	20	$26R_c$				
	H.T. (4&6)	70	130,000	180,000	10	15	$42R_c$				
	H.T. (4&5)	70	100,000	140,000	15	30	$30R_c$				
Good	Ann'ld. (7)	70	35,000	70,000	25	40	$77R_b$				
	H.T. (8)	70	100,000	125,000	15	40	$30R_c$				
	H.T. (8)	70	80,000	95,000	20	50	$95R_b$				
Excellent	Ann. (7)	70	45,000	85,000	20	35	$84R_b$				
	H.T. (8)	70	130,000	150,000	5	15	$38R_c$				
	H.T. (8)	70	95,000	110,000	10	30	$28R_c$				
Excellent	Ann. (7)	70	65,000	125,000	5	5	$25R_c$				
	H.T. (8)	70									
Excellent	Ann. (7)	70	50,000	100,000	10	20	$92R_b$				
	H.T. (8)	70	160,000	180,000	5	10	$40R_c$				
	H.T. (8)	70	110,000	140,000	10	20	$33R_c$				
Excellent	Ann. (7)	70	60,000	100,000	20	45	$93R_b$				
	H.T. (8)	70	170,000	200,000	5	20	$43R_c$				
	H.T. (8)	70	130,000	150,000	15	30	$35R_c$				
Good	Ann. (7)	70	40,000	85,000	20	40	$85R_b$				
	H.T. (8)	70	120,000	150,000	10	30	$33R_c$				
	H.T. (8)	70	90,000	110,000	20	50	$22R_c$				

(1) 50 hr. 1350°F

(2) 3 hr. 2100°F, air cooled, 24 hr. 1550°F plus 20 hr. 1300°F

(3) Oil or water quench from 1900 to 2100°F

(4) 4 hr. 1200°F to 1400°F, air cool

(5) 1 hr. 1800°F, oil quench, draw 1 hr. 1100 to 1300°F

(6) 1 hr. 1875°F, oil quench, draw 3 hrs. 675°F or 2 hrs. 1100°F

(7) 2 hr. 1600 to 1650°F, furnace cool

(8) Water or oil quenched from 1600 to 1650°F and drawn to hardness indicated

FIG. 10-2 *Several representative alloys and their properties (continued).*

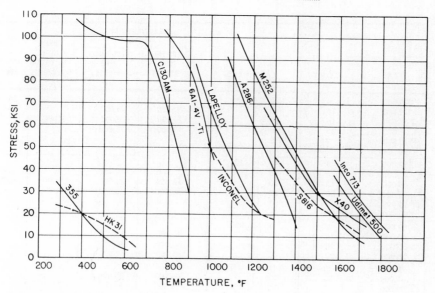

FIG. 10-3   *100-hr stress-rupture strengths of some turbine engine alloys.*

MANUFACTURING TECHNIQUES

The variety of manufacturing techniques is large, and is dependent upon a number of factors such as the material from which the part is made, the duties the part must perform, and the cost of the process. As a result, basic parts of the engine are produced by several casting and forging processes, literally dozens of machine operations, and fabrication procedures using a variety of metal-joining methods.

Casting

Several engine parts are cast in aluminum, magnesium, or steel alloys. These parts include intake and compressor housings, accessory cases, and blading to name a few. Casting methods differ. They include:

1   Sand casting
2   Spin casting
3   Lost-wax or investment casting
4   Resin-shell mold casting
5   Slip casting
6   Mercasting

Sand casting (Fig. 10-6) uses a wood or metal pattern around which a clay-free sand has been packed to form the mold. The mold is then split, the pattern removed, the mold reassembled, and any cores that are necessary added. Molten metal at a precise temperature is poured into the mold and allowed to cool. The mold is removed and various heat treatments may be performed to obtain the desired physical characteristics. The casting may be spun while being poured. Spin casting results in a denser, more sound casting. Spinning is normally performed on small ring sections. Cooling of the metal radially inward results in fewer stresses.

Basically the investment casting process (Fig. 10-7) involves the use of heat-disposable wax or plastic patterns which are surrounded with a refractory material to form a monolithic mold. Patterns are removed from the mold in ovens, and molten metal is poured into the hot mold. Sometimes this pouring is done in a vacuum furnace. After cooling, the mold material is quite fragile and is easily removed from the castings. Because the finished product duplicates the pattern exactly, the production of patterns is a critical factor. They are made by injecting molten wax or plastic into metal dies. The finished castings have an exceptionally smooth surface finish and require very little further machining. Incidentally, this process is not new. It was used by

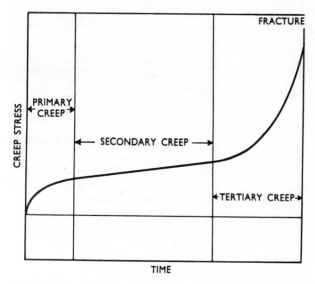

FIG. 10-4   *Typical creep characteristics of turbine blades.*

POROUS TUBE   POROUS AIRFOIL SKIN   STRUT   COMPLETED BLADE

FIG. 10-5 *Steps in the manufacture of a transpiration cooled blade.*

the ancient Greeks and Egyptians to cast light-weight statues, intricate bowls, and pitchers.

Resin-shell mold casting (Fig. 10-8) is a high production method similar to investment casting except that the tolerances are not held as closely. In many ways it rivals sand casting in economy.

Slip casting (Fig. 10-9), borrowed from the ceramics industry, is used to form super-heat-resistant materials. Often it is the only way certain materials can be shaped. Metal ceramics, silicon nitride, and refractory metals cast this way can be used in temperatures over 2200°F.

The Mercast process is a precision-casting technique. It is essentially the same kind of method as the lost-wax precision-investment process, except that frozen mercury is used as a pattern instead of wax. Liquid mercury is poured into a master mold, where it is frozen at temperatures below −40°F. Then it is removed and coated with a cold refractory slurry to a thickness of ⅛ in. or more. The refractory shell is dried at low temperature; then the shell and mercury are brought to room temperature, and the mercury is melted out. The refractory shell is fired to give it strength and then is used as the mold for a usual casting process. Complicated parts can be made by use of the Mercast process, and very close tolerances and excellent surface finish can be obtained. The cost however, is higher than that of some other methods.

Forging *(Fig. 10-10)*

Disks, drive shafts, rings, gears, vanes, blades, and numerous other parts of the gas turbine engine are manufactured by forging. This process allows the development of a grain structure and results in a fine grain, more ductile, strong, dense product (Fig. 10-11). Forging can be accomplished by rapid hammering or slow pressing. The choice of technique depends mainly upon the resistance of metal to rapid deformation. The workpiece is generally heated to improve plasticity and reduce forging forces and will often pass through several different dies before the final shape is obtained (Fig. 10-12). All ductile materials can be forged, but their forgeability varies considerably. At the forging temperature, forgeability generally depends upon the melting point, ductility, yield strength, crystallographic structure, recovery from forging stresses, surface reactivity, die friction, and cost.

Some parts are rolled or swaged, which essentially simulates the forging process. By using this method, a well defined grain structure is established, which increases tensile strength considerably (Fig. 10-13).

Prior to forging some turbine blades, the end of the forging blank (usually a rod) is upset by heating, or the shank is swaged to develop natural "flow lines" in the root and shank section of the blade.

Machining *(Figs. 10-14 and 10-15)*

In addition to the hammers, presses, and other tools mentioned above, the inventory of machinery for manufacturing gas turbine parts includes all of the common varieties such as lathes, mills, broaches, grinders, shapers and planers, polishers and buffers, drills, saws, shears, filers, threaders, contour machines of all kinds, and a host of other devices to cut and form metal. Many of these devices utilize a numerical tape control or other automatic control devices to reduce human error and produce a more uniform, less expensive product.

Some nontraditional machining techniques for removing metal from superhard and supertough alloys, and from other materials whose complex shapes preclude machining with conventional metal cutting tools include chemical milling, electrochemical machining (ECM), electric discharge machining (EDM), electron-beam machining, and laser-beam machining. Other nonconventional machining includes everything from abrasive jet cutting to ultrasonic machining.

Chemical milling involves the removal of metal by dissolving it in a suitable chemical. Those areas that

FIG. 10-6 Typical sand casting procedures. (*Union Carbide Corporation*)

The die is designed.... Skilled designers working from customers' blue-prints plan and detail the die construction.

Then produced.... Master craftsmen construct the die. The accuracy of the desired part depends upon these two steps.

A pattern is formed.... Wax or plastic is injected into the die to make a pattern in the shape of the desired part.

And checked.... To be sure that the tooling is right, a dimensional check is made on the first patterns.

Then assembled into clusters.... As many patterns as is practical are assembled into clusters to facilitate mass-production.

And coated with silica.... A fine silica coating on the pattern gives the cast part a smooth surface. From here, molds can be made in two ways.

Ceramic Shell Method

The pattern is coated with a ceramic shell.... By continual immersion, a thick coating of ceramic mold material is built up around the cluster.

Finally the thick shell is built.... After the ceramic coating has built up to sufficient thickness it is ready for use as a mold.

Mold Flask Method

Or sealed in a container.... The coated clusters are mounted on a square steel base and enclosed in a metal flask.

And investment material added.... The metal flask is filled with an investment material which "sets up" tightly around the patterns.

And inspected.... Every casting is inspected visually and dimensionally. Where specified, a final check on quality can be made with X-Ray, "Zyglo", "Magnaglo" and Gamma-Ray.

Ground and finished.... A rough grinding operation removes the last traces of the gates.

The castings are cut off.... Gates and risers are removed with an abrasive wheel. Then the castings are cleaned.

The shell is removed.... Once the casting is solid, the ceramic shell is blasted away.

Poured into shell.... Molten metal is poured into the inverted shell in a manner similar to that shown below.

Burned out of shell.... The shell is passed through a burnout furnace to remove the patterns.

Burned out of flask.... The flasks are carried through a furnace where the pattern material is burned out.

Poured into flask mold.... Molten alloy is forced under pressure into the cavities of the hot mold.

The mold is broken away.... After the mold cools, the castings are separated from the investment material by hydro-blasting.

FIG. 10-7 *Two methods of investment casting.* (*Union Carbide Corporation*)

Resin-sand is applied to matchplate ...
When the resin-sand mix is applied to the hot matchplate, the mold is formed.

Molds are stripped ...
Heat causes the resin-sand mixture to set. The shell is then removed from the matchplate.

A matchplate is made ...
This is machined to close tolerances since it will be used to make all the molds.

And coated ...
A release agent is sprayed so that later the shells can be stripped off.

Mold halves are joined and poured ...
The two halves are joined to form a complete mold which is then filled with molten metal.

Some types are stacked and poured ...
Shell molds, produced by a special process, facilitate stack molding. This method yields a larger number of castings per pour.

Castings are shaken out ...
Mold material is either removed manually or by shaking on a screen.

Castings are gated and rough ground ...
Very often castings are ready for use after gating and rough grinding only.

Finish inspected and shipped ...
Final inspection makes sure finishing operations were exact.

Machined or ground to final specifications ...
If necessary, finishing can be done to any dimensions.

Inspected for soundness ...
Visual, dimensional, and radiographic inspection methods insure quality.

Then heat-treated ...
Heat-treatment gives optimum properties to the casting.

FIG. 10-8 *Resin-shell mold casting procedure.* (*Union Carbide Corporation*)

Half pattern is mounted... Plaster will be poured over half pattern mounted on board.

Slip is prepared... Metal and ceramic or metal powder are mixed with liquids.

Air is removed from the liquid slip to produce sound, dense castings.

Casting is poured.... Slip is poured into the dried plaster mold. It hardens as moisture is absorbed by the mold wall.

Slip is drained... When sufficient wall thickness is built up, excess slip is drained off.

Casting is removed... Cores and molds are removed from the slip casting.

The casting is dried...

Then sintered...

And then finish machined, if necessary...

FIG. 10-9 Slip casting procedure. (Union Carbide Corporation)

163

FIG. 10-10 *35,000-lb drop hammer forge.*

FIG. 10-11 *Grain flow is developed through forging.*

FIG. 10-12 *Typical forging steps.*

FIG. 10-13 *Forming small compressor blades. Upper drawings show how blade is first squeezed by the press action, then rolled to form the foil section. The bottom drawing points up the problem of controlled forming at the foil root with conventional rolling techniques.*

are not to be dissolved away are masked with nonreactive materials. The process can be used on most metals, including aluminum, magnesium, titanium, steels, and superalloys for surface sculpturing. Both sides of the workpiece can be chemically milled simultaneously. In addition, the process can be used to machine very thin sheets.

FIG. 10-14 *Broaching a fir-tree root on a turbine blade.*

FIG. 10-15 *Milling compressor blades.*

Electrochemical machining is basically a chemical deplating process in which metal, removed from a positively charged workpiece using high-amperage–low-voltage dc, is flushed away by a highly pressurized electrolyte before it can plate out on the cathode tool. The cathode tool is made to produce the desired shape in the workpiece, and both must be electrically conductive. The work proceeds while the cathode and workpiece are both submerged in an electrolyte such as sodium chloride. A variation and extension of electrochemical machining is electro-stream drilling. In this process a negatively charged electrolyte, usually an acid, drills holes in a workpiece that has been positively charged. Holes as small as 0.005 in. in diameter and 0.5 in. deep in superalloys can be drilled in this manner.

In electric discharge machining, high voltages are used to produce a high electrical potential between two conductive surfaces, the workpiece and electrode tool, both of which are immersed in a dielectric fluid. Material is removed from both the electrode and the workpiece by a series of very short electric discharges or sparks between the two, and is swept away by the dielectric fluid. More material is removed from the workpiece than from the tool by proper selection of the two materials. This process can be used to shape complex parts to very close tolerances from refractory metals and alloys that were formerly impossible to machine. The use of electric discharge machining is limited in that it is slower than electrochemical machining, tool replacement can become expensive, and the surface of the workpiece is damaged as a result of the sparks. On the other hand, the EDM process is less expensive than the ECM process.

Electron-beam machining and laser-beam machining are being used experimentally, and may find future use in the production of gas turbines and other aerospace components.

Fabrication

Welding is used extensively to fabricate and repair many engine parts. Fabricated sheet steel is used for combustion chambers, exhaust ducts, compressor casings, thrust reversers, silencers, etc. Common methods include resistance and inert-gas (usually argon) welding. Uncommon methods utilize plasmas (see page 167) and lasers (*Light Amplification by Stimulated Emission of Radiation*). Electric resistance welding is used to make spot, stitch (overlapping spots), and continuous seam welds (Fig. 10-16). Inert-gas welding employs a nonconsumable electrode (tungsten-thorium alloy) surrounded by some inert gas such as argon or helium (Fig. 10-17). The gas prevents an adverse reaction with the oxygen present in the normal atmosphere. The inert gas can be applied in the immediate area of the arc, or in the case of production runs, the workpiece and/or the entire welding machine can be enclosed in a thin plastic balloon, sometimes as large as a room. The entire plastic bubble is filled with and supported by the inert gas. The operator stands on the outside and works through specially designed armholes. After welding, many parts must be stress-relieved. Where temperature or working loads are not large, brazing or silver soldering may be used to join such parts as fittings and tube assemblies.

Electron-beam welding (Fig. 10-18) is showing great promise as a method of fabricating parts from heretofore difficult to weld or unweldable materials. Elec-

(a)

(b)

FIG. 10-16 (**a**) *Spot and* (**b**) *continuous seam welding machines.*

tron-beam welding uses a stream of focused electrons traveling at speeds approaching 60 percent the speed of light. Even though the mass of electrons which form the beam is small, they are traveling at such speeds that they contain a great amount of kinetic energy. When the beam strikes the workpiece, the kinetic energy is transformed into heat energy. The welding usually takes place in a vacuum, although nonvacuum techniques can be used. Deep, narrow welds with a very narrow heat-affected zone in the base metal, the ability to weld materials as thin as 0.00025 in. and as thick as 4 in. of stainless steel, and the ability to weld many

FIG. 10-17 *Heliarc welding.*

FIG. 10-18 *Hamilton Standard electron beam welder.*

different types of materials, make this welding process a valuable one in the gas turbine manufacturing area.

Finishing

The basic material, the properties desired in the finished product, and the kind of protection desired will determine the type of surface and internal treatment received. The variety is considerable and includes the following.

CHEMICAL TREATMENT Chrome pickling is the most commonly used of all chemical treatments of magnesium. The part is dipped in a solution of sodium dichromate, nitric acid, and water.

ELECTROCHEMICAL TREATMENT Anodizing is a common surface treatment for aluminum alloys whereby the surface aluminum is oxidized to an adherent film of aluminum oxide.

PAINTING A thin preservative resin varnish coating is used to protect internal steel, aluminum, and magnesium parts. The characteristic color of this shiny, transparent coating is usually green or blue-green. A graphite powder may be mixed with the varnish to act as an antigallant. Grey, black, or aluminum enamel or epoxy paint is also used extensively as a protective finish.

SHOT PEENING This procedure can increase the life of a part many times. It is essentially a plastic flow or stretching of a metal's surface by a rain of round metallic shot thrown at high velocity by either mechanical or pneumatic means. The 0.005- to 0.035-in. stretched layer is placed in a state of compression with the stress concentration uniformly distributed over the entire surface. Glass beads are sometimes used as the shot for cleaning purposes.

PLATING A great number of plating materials and procedures are used. Plating materials involving the use of chemical or electrochemical solutions include cadmium, chromium, silver, nickel, tin, and others.

FIG. 10-20 *Union Carbide detonation gun.*

The exact procedure is determined by the plating and base metal.

Aluminizing is another plating method whereby pure molten aluminum is sprayed onto the aluminum alloy base material to form a protective coating against oxidation and corrosion.

The Coating Service of Union Carbide Corporation has developed and is producing machines for applying extremely wear-resistant and other specialized coatings to gas turbine parts (Fig. 10-19), tools, and other machines. The different coatings are applied by either of two methods—the *detonation gun* or the *plasma gun*. In the detonation gun (Fig. 10-20), measured quantities of oxygen, acetylene, and suspended particles of the coating material are fed into the chamber of the gun. Four times a second, a spark ignites the mixture and creates a detonation which hurls the coating particles, heated to a plastic state by the 6000°F temperature in the gun, out of the barrel at a speed of 2500 fps. The part to be plated is kept below 300°F by auxiliary cooling streams. The high-level sound of 150 db necessitates housing the gun in a double-walled sound-insulated construction. Operation is controlled from outside of this enclosure.

The plasma gun or *torch* (Fig. 10-21) produces and controls a high-velocity inert-gas stream that can be maintained at temperatures above 20,000°F. Unlike the D-gun process, no combustion takes place. The high-temperature plasma is formed by ionizing argon

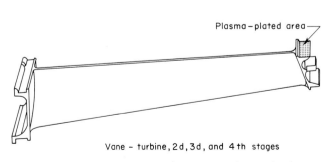

FIG. 10-19 *One of many gas turbine engine plasma-plated parts. This part is plated with chrome carbide.*

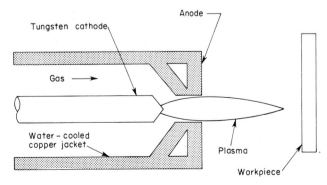

FIG. 10-21 *Plasma torch.*

gas in the extreme heat of an electric arc. Gas mole-cules absorb heat energy from the arc, split into atoms, and then further decompose into electrically charged particles called ions. The hot gas stream can melt, without decomposition, any known material. When the molten particles strike the part being coated, a permanent, welded bond is formed. While the D-gun is a patented Union Carbide machine, other manu-facturers make and distribute a variety of plasma plating and cutting devices.

HEAT TREATMENTS All the following procedures alter the mechanical properties of steel to suit the end use. They include:

1 *Normalizing*—The steel is heated to a temperature above the critical range and allowed to cool slowly. Normalizing promotes uniformity of structure and alters mechanical properties.

2 *Annealing*—Consists of heating to a point at or near the critical range, then cooling at a predetermined rate. It is used to develop softness, improve machineability, reduce stress, improve or restore ductility, and modify other properties.

3 *Stress relieving*—The metal is heated throughout to a point below the critical range and slowly cooled. The object of this treatment is to restore elastic properties or reduce stresses that may have been induced by machining, cold working, or welding.

4 *Hardening*—Involves heating the metal to a temperature above the critical range and then quenching. The cooling rate will determine hardness.

5 *Tempering*—The steel is usually too brittle for use after quenching. Tempering restores some of the ductility and toughness of steel at the sacrifice of hardness or strength. The process is accomplished by heating the hardened steel to a specific point below the critical temperature.

Nonmetallic materials

Teflon, nylon, carbon, rubber, Bakelite, and a host of plastic materials are used in the gas turbine engine mainly as sealing and insulation materials. For example, nylon and Teflon are used to insulate and protect the shielded electrical wiring located on the outside of the engine. Teflon is also used on the J-79 for the seal on the variable-stator-vane actuators. Car-bon is used largely inside the engine in the form of carbon rubbing oil seals. Some of these "face" carbon rubbing seals must be flat to within two helium light bands, or approximately 23 millionths of an inch. Rubber and rubberized fabric materials make up the sealing edge of the fire seal which divides the hot and cold sections of the engine when mounted in the nacelle. Synthetic rubber is used extensively through-out the engine in the form of O-ring or other-shaped seals.

CONCLUSION

Materials and methods of construction for the gas turbine engine are many, and are rapidly changing. This chapter has dealt with some of the more commonly used substances employed in the manufacture of this type of engine. Advances in design, chemistry, and metallurgy are sure to bring some changes in this area.

REVIEW AND STUDY QUESTIONS

1 What is the relationship between the science of metal-lurgy and the gas turbine engine?

2 What is the present turbine inlet temperature limit?

3 Define the following terms: strength, ductility, thermal conductivity, corrosion, critical temperature, heat treat-ability, thermal shock resistance, and hardness.

4 List the methods of working and forming metal.

5 How may the surface or internal properties of a metal be altered?

6 Name some inspection methods.

7 List five alloys that are used in the construction of the gas turbine engine. Describe the properties of each that make it desirable for use in specific locations in the engine.

8 List some of the major metallic elements that are used in gas turbine alloys.

9 What are three characteristics that must be considered in the selection of any metal for use in the gas turbine engine? Discuss these characteristics.

10 What is meant by the term transpiration cooling?

11 List six methods of casting. Give a short description of each method and its advantages and disadvantages.

12 What are the advantages of forging? Give some varia-tions of the forging process.

13 Name as many of the machines as you can that are used in the manufacturing of parts for the gas turbine engine.

14 Discuss the welding processes used in the fabrication of the gas turbine engine.

15 What are some factors which will determine the finishing processes used on a gas turbine part?

16 List the finishing processes and briefly discuss each.

PART 3

Systems and accessories

Chapter 11

Fuels

During the early years of gas turbine development it was popularly believed that this type of engine could use almost any material that would burn—and in theory this is true. Of course we now know that, practically speaking, this is not correct. As a matter of fact, because of the high rate (Table 11-1) of consumption, the effect of any impurities in the fuel will be greatly magnified. This, coupled with wide temperature and pressure variations, results in the modern gas turbine engine having a fussy appetite that calls for fuels with carefully controlled characteristics if the engine is to function efficiently and with a reasonable service life under all operating conditions.

TABLE 11-1
Rate of fuel consumption for some piston and turbine engines

ENGINE MODEL	U.S. GAL/HR OF OPERATION
Piston:	
Pratt & Whitney R-1830	45
Pratt & Whitney R-2800	100
Wright R-3350 Turbo Compound	125
Turbine:	
Rolls-Royce Dart	100
Allison 501	175
Rolls-Royce Avon	400
Rolls-Royce Conway	550
Pratt & Whitney JT-3	450
Pratt & Whitney JT-4	550

FUEL SOURCES

Jet fuel is manufactured or refined from crude oil petroleum, which consists of a great number of hydrocarbons or compounds of the elements hydrogen and carbon. There are literally thousands of combinations that these carbon and hydrogen atoms may form. General families include the paraffins, naphthenes, olefins, and aromatics. Other components in the crude include asphalts, resins, organic acid material, and sulfur compounds. Crude oil from the eastern sections of the country has a relatively large amount of paraffinic hydrocarbons, while crudes taken from the west and gulf coasts contain larger proportions of naphthenic and aromatic hydrocarbons. Crude oil may vary greatly in color, appearance, and in physical characteristics.

JET FUEL FROM CRUDE OIL

The physical process

The first step in the process of turning crude oil into gas turbine fuel is to allow the physical impurities such as mud, water, and salts to settle out. Next, the crude must be separated into its various fractions. This process uses heat and is called *fractional distillation*. Each of the various fractions or families of hydrocarbons is of a different size and has a different boiling temperature. The lighter fractions boil at lower temperatures, and as the molecule size increases, the boiling point becomes higher. The asphalts and resins are very large in size and do not boil at all at the temperatures used in the distillation process.

Distillation takes place in a "bubble tower" (Fig. 11-1). The crude oil is first pumped through a furnace in a rapid continuous flow, where it is heated quickly to a relatively high temperature. Almost all of the crude oil is vaporized simultaneously. The vapors from the furnace are then piped to tall condensers which are the fractionating or bubble towers previously mentioned. As the vapors rise in the towers, the highest boiling point material becomes liquid first, intermediate boiling point materials liquefy next, and lowest boiling point material last. The towers are equipped with a number of trays placed at different levels to catch the liquid that condenses as the vapors are rising. The condensed liquid from each tray is drawn off, separating the crude into as many portions as there are trays. In general practice there are only about seven trays for drawing off distilled fractions of the crude. Each of the fractions will have a range of boiling points, with the fractions and their ranges dependent upon the crude and the number of trays in the fractionating column.

FIG. 11-1 *The bubble tower is widely used for fractional distillation.*

A typical midcontinent crude might yield the following approximate percentages of the various fractions.

Gas	= 3 percent
Gasoline and naphtha	= 18 percent
Kerosine	= 15 percent
Gas-oil	= 39 percent
Lube oil	= 7 percent
Residual material	= 18 percent

The percentages will vary depending upon the source and type of the crude.

The chemical process

From the purely physical processes of separation, the products of distillation are further refined to:

1 Remove undesirable components such as sulfur and gums and resins by means of sulfuric acid and other chemicals, or by a selective solvent extraction process.

2 Split heavy molecules or combine lighter ones to obtain more of a particular fraction of the crude. Thermal and catalytic cracking are two methods of splitting large molecules into smaller ones. While in the process of polymerization, two lighter molecules are combined into one large molecule.

3 Impart to a fraction certain desirable properties with the inclusion of "additives." Such additives might include chemical compounds for inhibiting microbial growths. Other additives reduce the tendency for the ever present water in fuel to form ice crystals at the low temperatures encountered at high altitudes. Lubricating oils also contain many additives.

Step two represents processes performed mainly to develop more gasoline from a barrel of crude.

DEVELOPMENT OF JET FUELS (Table 11-2)

Various grades of jet fuel have evolved during the development of jet engines in an effort to ensure both satisfactory performance and adequate supply. The JP series have been used by the military and its behavior is outlined in Specification Mil-J-5624. For commercial use the American Society for Testing Materials (ASTM) has specification D-1655, which covers Jet A, A-1, and B fuels.

JP-1 fuel

Grade JP-1 fuel was the original low-freezing-point kerosine-type fuel. In the United States, kerosine is required to have a minimum flash point of 120°F and to have an endpoint in the ASTM distillation test of not more than 572°F. (See the following section on fuel tests for a definition of terms used in this section.) Its characteristics were low vapor pressure, good lubricating qualities, and high energy content per unit volume. It was thought to be a safer fuel than gasoline

TABLE 11-2
Comparison of the JP series fuels

	SPECIFICATION MIL-F-	5616	—	5624A	5624A
	NOMINAL GRADE	JP-1	JP-2	JP-3	JP-4
Flash point, min °F		110.0	—	—	—
Reid vapor press., psi min		—	—	5.0	2.0
Reid vapor press., psi max		—	2.0	7.0	3.0
Initial boiling point, min °F		—	150.0	—	—
10% evaporated point, max °F		410.0	—	—	250.0
90% evaporated point, max °F		490.0	—	400.0	—
Endpoint, max °F		572.0	500.0	600.0	550.0
Color		White	White	White	—
Saybolt color, max		+12.0	+12.0	—	—
Freezing point, max °F		−76.0	−76.0	−76.0	−76.0
Sulfur, % by wt max		0.20	0.20	0.40	0.40
Mercaptans, % by wt max		—	—	0.005	0.005
Inhibitors permitted*		No	No	Yes	Yes
Existent gum, mg/100 ml max		5.0	5.0	10.0	10.0
Accelerated gum (7.0 hr), mg/100 ml max		—	8.0	—	—
Accelerated gum (16.0 hr), mg/100 ml max		8.0	—	20.0	20.0
Corrosion, copper strip		None	None	None	None
Water tolerance permitted		None	None	None	None
Specific gravity (60/60) max†		0.850	0.850	0.802	0.825
Specific gravity (60/60) min†		—	—	0.728	0.747
Viscosity at −40°F, centistokes max		10.0	10.0	—	—
Viscosity at 100°F, centistokes min		—	0.95	—	—
Aromatics, % by vol max		20.0	20.0	25.0	25.0
Bromine no. max		3.0	3.0	30.0	30.0
Heating value (lower or net), Btu/lb min		—	—	18,400	18,400

* Inhibitors may be added to the extent required (max 1.0 lb approved inhibitor for each 5000 U.S. gal of finished fuel) to prevent formation of excessive gum during the oxygen bomb test. Several inhibitors are approved for use.

† $\dfrac{\text{Density of fuel at 60°F}}{\text{Density of water at 60°F}}$

because of its higher flash point. Kerosine-type fuels like JP-1 proved to have many disadvantages. Cold-weather starts were quite difficult, and at high altitudes, kerosine was prone to cause engine flameouts, and air starts were nearly impossible. Kerosine has a tendency to hold both water and solids in suspension, making filtration and ice formation a problem. In addition, the potential supply of kerosine is more limited than gasoline since more gasoline can be produced from a barrel of crude than kerosine.

JP-2 fuel

This fuel was an experimental blend of gasoline and kerosine. A large percentage of the blend was kerosine, and therefore did not appreciably save enough crude oil to warrant its widespread adoption.

JP-3 fuel

Grade JP-3 fuel with a Reid vapor pressure of 5 to 7 psi, a flash point of about −40°F, and an endpoint of 550°F, superseded Grade JP-1. The fuel was a blend of 65 to 70 percent gasoline, 30 to 35 percent kerosine,

and had handling characteristics very similar to gasoline. Cold-weather starting was improved, as was the chance of an air restart at high altitude. Its chief disadvantages were high vapor locking tendencies and high fuel losses through the aircraft's fuel tank vents during high rates of climb because of both evaporation of the lighter fractions and entrainment of the liquid fuel with the escaping vapor. JP-3 also had poor lubricating characteristics because of the high gasoline content.

JP-4 fuel

One of the most commonly used fuels for both civil and military jet engines is JP-4. It is a wide-cut blend of kerosine with some naphtha fractions, and gasoline, but has a much lower Reid vapor pressure of 2 to 3 psi and a flash point of about −35°F. Its distillation range is 200 to 550°F, and its freezing point is −76°F. The lower vapor pressure reduces fuel tank losses and vapor lock tendencies. The absence of the lighter ends or fractions not only reduces vapor pressure, but reduces the combustion performance during cold weather and high altitude starting.

TABLE 11-3
Aircraft turbine fuel specifications

TEST	KEROSINE TYPE FUELS			JP-4 TYPE FUELS	
	ASTM D-1655 Jet A	D.Eng.R.D. 2482	MIL-J-5624E JP-5	ASTM D-1655 Jet B	MIL-J-5624F JP-4
Gravity, °API	39–51	40–51	36–48	45–57	45–57
Specific gravity	0.8299–0.7753	0.8251–0.7753	0.8448–0.7883	0.8017–0.7507	0.8017–0.7507
Viscosity, centistokes					
0°F	—	6 max	—	—	—
−30°F	15 max	—	16.5 max	—	—
Flash point, °F	110–150	100 min	140 min	—	—
Freezing point, °F	−40 max	−40 max	−55 max	−60 max	−76 max
Pour point, °F	−40 max	—	—	—	—
Color, 18 in. Lovibond	—	4 max	—	—	—
Distillation, °F					
10% Evap.	400 max	—	400 max	—	—
20%	—	392 (rec.) max	—	290 max	290 max
50%	450 max	—	—	370 max	370 max
90%	—	—	—	470 max	470 max
Endpoint	550 max	572 max	550 max	—	—
Reid vapor pressure, lb	—	—	—	3 max	2–3
Total sulfur, %	0.3 max	0.2 max	0.4 max	0.3 max	0.4 max
Mercaptan sulfur, %	0.003 max	0.005 max	0.001 max	0.003 max	0.001 max
Aromatics, % vol	20 max	20 max	25 max	20 max	25 max
Olefins, %	—	5 max	5 max	5 max	5 max
Net heating value, Btu/lb	18,400 min	18,300 min	18,300 min	18,400 min	18,400 min
Aniline-gravity constant	—	4500 min	4500 min	5250 min	5250 min
Combustion properties					
(1) Luminometer no. min	45	—	—	50	—
or					
(2) Smoke point, min	25	—	19	—	—
or					
(3) Smoke point, min	20	—	—	—	—
Burning test, 16 hr	Pass	—	—	—	—
or					
(4) Smoke point, min	20	—	—	—	—
Naphthalenes, max %	3	—	—	—	—
or					
(5) Smoke volatility index, min	—	—	—	54	52
Burning test, 16 hr	Pass	—	—	—	—
Copper-strip corrosion					
3 hr at 122°F	1 max	—	1 max	—	—
2 hr at 212°F	—	1 max	—	1 max	1 max
Water reaction, ml	2 max	1 max	1 max	1 max	1 max
Separometer	—	—	85	—	95
Existent gum, mg/100 ml	7 max	3 max	7 max	7 max	7 max
Accelerated gum, mg/100 ml	14 max	6 max	14 max	14 max	14 max
Total acidity	—	Nil max	—	—	—
Thermal stability					
Preheater tube deposits, 300°F	Less than code 3	—	Less than code 3	Less than code 3	Less than code 3
Filter pressure drop, 400°F, max	12	—	13	12	13
Additives	See note 3	—			

NOTES

1 The above specifications are considered only a summary. In case of question the detailed specification must be consulted.

2 ASTM Jet A-1 is identical to Jet A except that the freezing point is −58°F max and the pour point is eliminated.

3 In general ASTM specifications permit approved oxidation and corrosion inhibitors and metal deactivators. However, the quantities and types must be declared and agreed to by the consumer. Military specifications permit the inclusion of oxidation inhibitors. MIL-J-5624E, Grade JP-4, requires the addition of anti-icing additive and corrosion inhibitor.

JP-5 fuel

JP-5 fuel was developed as a heavy kerosine to be blended with gasoline to produce a fuel similar to JP-4 for use on aircraft carriers. The gasoline is carried on board the ship for use in reciprocating engine aircraft. JP-5 has a high flash point of 140°F, a very low volatility, a distillation range of 350 to 550°F, and a freezing point of −55°F maximum. Because of this low volatility, it can be stored safely in the skin tanks of the ship rather than in the high-priority, protected space in the center of the ship that is required by Av-Gas. The mixed fuel requires only one protected service tank. Several engines are now designed to use straight JP-5. Although cold-weather starts are marginal, the altitude restarting problem appears to have greatly diminished because of the development of high-energy ignition systems.

JP-6 fuel

This fuel specification was developed by the Air Force for use in supersonic aircraft. Its low freezing point of −65°F makes it suitable for use in cold climates and high altitudes. JP-6 is designated as a wide cut kerosine, with a distillation range of 250 to 550°F.

Jet A and A-1 fuel (Table 11-3)

Both are kerosine-type fuels, and both are alike except that Jet A has a freezing point below −40°F, and Jet A-1 has a freezing point below −58°F. Another kerosine specification used by British manufacturers is D. Eng. R-D-2482.

Jet B fuel

Jet B fuel and JP-4 are basically alike. They are wide boiling range fuels covering the heavy gasoline-kerosine range and are sometimes called gasoline-type fuels. They have an initial boiling point considerably below that of kerosine. They also have a lower specific gravity. Specifications for current fuels are listed in Table 11-3.

FUEL TESTS

In order to determine the physical and chemical characteristics of a fuel, a number of tests are performed. Most of these tests have been devised by the American Society for Testing Materials (ASTM), composed of a group of men representing the oil companies, airline operators, and engine manufacturers. The ASTM has also published several fuel specifications defining properties of fuels suitable for commercial gas turbine use. Among these are the *Specification A*, describing a kerosine-type fuel similar to JP-5, and *Specification B*, describing a gasoline-type fuel like JP-4 (both are listed in the preceding section). The Allison Division of General Motors, and the Pratt & Whitney Division of United Aircraft Corporation both have written their own fuel specifications as a guide for airplane operators to follow when purchasing gas turbine fuel. These specifications will produce a fuel similar in volatility characteristics to both JP-4 and JP-5.

Description of fuel tests (Fig. 11-2)

SPECIFIC GRAVITY This is the ratio of the weight of a substance (fuel in this case) to an equal volume of water at 60°F. Most often the specific gravity is given in terms of degrees A.P.I. This is a scale arbitrarily chosen by the American Petroleum Institute in which the specific gravity of pure water is taken as 10. Liquids lighter than water have values greater than 10, and those liquids heavier than water have a value smaller than 10.

$$\text{Degrees A.P.I.} = \frac{141.5}{\text{sp. gr. at } 60°F} - 131.5$$

For example: JP-4 has a minimum specific gravity in degrees A.P.I. of 40.

$$40 = \frac{141.5}{x} - 131.5$$

$$x = 0.825 \text{ sp. gr.}$$

Specific gravity is an important factor since fuel is metered and sold by volume. To arrive at the correct volume, gravity must be known. Notice that the formula indicates that the specific gravity is affected by temperature (Fig. 11-3).

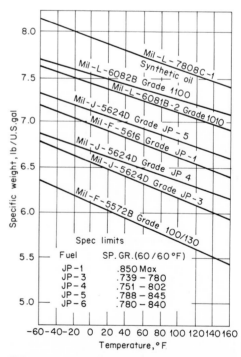

FIG. 11-2 *Temperature effects on density of aviation fuels and oils.*

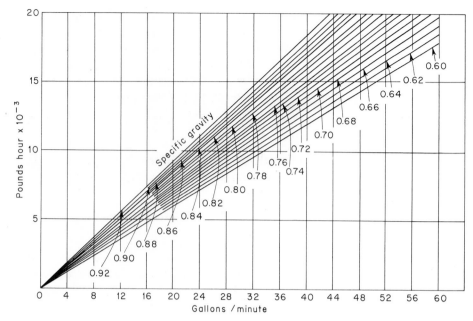

FIG. 11-3 *Fuel conversion chart: gallons per minute to pounds per hour.*

ANILINE-GRAVITY CONSTANT This is the product of two fuel properties which has been related to the net heating value. By measuring fuel aniline point and gravity and using standard conversion tables, it is unnecessary to burn a fuel sample to obtain the heating value.

SMOKE POINT This is the height of a flame in millimeters when the fuel is burned in a special lamp. This height is measured when the flame just starts to smoke.

LUMINOMETER This is a test in which the radiation from a special lamp is measured by a photocell and is compared to the radiation from reference fuels. Increasing luminometer numbers indicate decreasing radiation and therefore better combustion characteristics.

SMOKE VOLATILITY INDEX This is a mathematical combination of smoke point and fuel distillation.

COPPER STRIP CORROSION This is a test to measure the corrosivity of fuel toward copper. Copper appearance is rated numerically with increasing numbers indicating increasing corrosion.

WATER REACTION This is a test to check the separation characteristics of fuel and water. To be accurate it must be conducted under strictest laboratory conditions.

SEPAROMETER This is a test in which a fuel-water emulsion is pumped through a miniature filter separator. Water removal is rated by measuring the haziness of the filtered fuel with a photocell.

EXISTENT GUM This is the amount of nonvolatile material present in fuel. Such material is usually formed by the interaction of fuel and air.

ACCELERATED GUM This is the amount of nonvolatile material formed when a fuel is put into contact with pure oxygen at high pressure and elevated temperature.

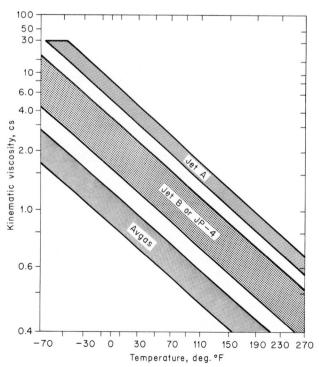

FIG. 11-4 *Viscosity range of aviation fuels. The viscosity change influences the rate of flow through a given size filter.*

BURNING TEST, 16 HR Kerosine is burned in a standard lamp for 16 hr. Changes in flame shape, density, and color of deposit as well as wick condition are reported.

TOTAL ACIDITY This is the acidity of fuel.

VISCOSITY This is measured in centistokes, and gives an indication of the fuel's ability to flow at different temperatures (Fig. 11-4).

REID VAPOR PRESSURE This is the approximate vapor pressure exerted by a fuel when heated to 100°F. This value is important in that it indicates the tendency of fuel to "vapor lock."

A.P.I. GRAVITY This is an indication of liquid density as measured by the buoyancy of special hydrometers. Increasing A.P.I. numbers indicate decreasing liquid density. Water has an A.P.I. gravity of 10/0 at 60°F.

FLASH POINT This is the liquid temperature at which vapors from the heated liquid can first be ignited by a flame under closely controlled conditions.

FREEZING POINT This is the temperature at which solids such as wax crystals separate from a fuel upon cooling.

POUR POINT This is the lowest temperature at which a fuel or oil will pour from a special test tube, cooled at a specified rate. Pour point is measured at 5°F intervals.

COLOR This is the color of a fuel compared to a numbered standard color. Jet fuel grades vary from water white to light yellow.

DISTILLATION These are the temperatures at which various portions of fuel boils under closely controlled conditions. Since any turbine fuel is a mixture of many hydrocarbons which all have differing boiling points, a turbine fuel does not have a single boiling point, but boils over a range of temperatures. The distillation range is an approximation of a fuel's boiling range.

NET HEATING VALUE This is the amount of heat liberated when a pound or gallon of fuel is burned completely. A correction is included for the heat removed to condense the water formed in this burning. This value, which is usually expressed in Btu, influences the range of a particular aircraft, for where the limiting factor is the capacity of the aircraft tanks, the calorific value per unit volume should be as high as possible, thus enabling more energy, and hence more aircraft range, to be obtained from a given volume of fuel. When the useful payload is the limiting factor, the calorific value per unit of weight should be as high as possible, because more energy can then be obtained from a minimum weight of fuel. Other factors, which effect the choice of heat per unit of volume or weight, such as the type of aircraft, the duration of flight, and the required balance between fuel weight and payload must also be taken into consideration (Table 11-4).

TOTAL SULFUR This is the total amount of sulfur in a fuel.

MERCAPTAN SULFUR These are special sulfur compounds which smell unpleasantly and are corrosive to certain materials.

AROMATICS These are certain unsaturated hydrocarbon compounds. These have a higher ratio of carbon to hydrogen than other hydrocarbons.

OLEFINS These are unsaturated hydrocarbons formed by cracking processes. Such compounds are not normally found in crude oils.

NAPHTHALENES These are certain highly unsaturated hydrocarbon compounds felt to have poor combustion characteristics.

THERMAL STABILITY This is the tendency of a fuel at high temperatures to form deposits on a heater tube and to form material which will plug a fuel line filter. Both properties are measured in apparatus which holds the heater tube and the filter at high temperatures.

FUEL HANDLING AND STORAGE

The amount of fuel consumed by many gas turbine engines makes the delivery of clean, dry fuel essential to proper engine performance. This makes handling and storage of the fuel of prime importance to the operator of gas turbine engines. Elaborate methods of filtration for the removal of solids, which may take the form of rust, scale, sand, or dust, pump wear, rubber or elastomers, and lint or other fibrous materials are employed.

Water, in gas turbine fuels, is a particularly troublesome problem in both aircraft and fuel storage tanks because of the fuel's affinity to water. This has led to malfunctioning of fuel controls, ice plugging of fuel filters, and freezing of fuel boost and transfer pumps. In addition, certain microbial and fungal growths thrive on the interface provided by the water environment and the hydrocarbon food supply necessary for their existence. The growth of the "bug" population results in a buildup of bacterial slime which can clog small metering orifices and penetrate the coatings and sealants used in fuel tanks, and thus expose the aluminum surfaces to corrosion.

The Phillips Petroleum Company has developed a

TABLE 11-4
Comparison of net heating values by unit weight and unit volume*

GRAVITY		DENSITY	NET HEAT OF COMBUSTION AT CONSTANT PRESSURE, Q_p		
DEGREES A.P.I. AT 60°F	SPECIFIC AT 60°/60°F	lb/gal	cal/g	Btu/lb	Btu/gal
40	0.8251	6.879	10,280	18,510	127,300
41	0.8203	6.839	10,300	18,530	126,700
42	0.8155	6.799	10,310	18,560	126,200
43	0.8109	6.760	10,320	18,580	125,600
44	0.8063	6.722	10,330	18,600	125,000
45	0.8017	6.684	10,340	18,620	124,400
46	0.7972	6.646	10,360	18,640	123,900
47	0.7927	6.609	10,370	18,660	123,300
48	0.7883	6.572	10,380	18,680	122,800
49	0.7839	6.536	10,390	18,700	122,200
50	0.7796	6.500	10,400	18,720	121,700
51	0.7753	6.464	10,410	18,740	121,100
52	0.7711	6.429	10,420	18,760	120,600
53	0.7669	6.394	10,430	18,780	120,100
54	0.7628	6.360	10,440	18,800	119,500
55	0.7587	6.326	10,450	18,810	119,000
56	0.7547	6.292	10,460	18,830	118,500
57	0.7507	6.258	10,470	18,850	118,000
58	0.7467	6.225	10,480	18,870	117,500
59	0.7428	6.193	10,490	18,880	116,900
60	0.7389	6.160	10,500	18,900	116,400

* Heat energy per pound of fuel decreases with increasing molecular weight or specific gravity but heat energy per gallon of fuel increases under the same conditions.

fuel additive PFA 55MB which is now being added to all JP-4 turbine fuels.   Many commercial fuel suppliers are also using this additive.   This substance provides excellent biocidal and anti-icing protection.   Dispensers are available for adding PFA 55MB at those airports that do not sell treated fuel.

Water in fuel takes two forms.

1   *Dissolved water*—Dissolved water is similar to humidity in the atmosphere, and is a function of the temperature and the type of fuel (Fig. 11-5).   The dissolved water content may be as much as one pint per 1000 gal of fuel.

2   *Free water*—Free water may take two forms,
  (a)   *Entrained water*—when the water in a fuel is suspended in minute globules.   The water may not be perceptible to the naked eye, but it may cause the fuel to take on a hazy appearance.
  (b)   *Water slugs*—visible droplets or pools of water.

The amount of free water is usually checked with litmus paper, with water detecting paste, or by drawing off a small amount of fuel and observing its clarity.

Water problems are solved in a number of ways.

1   *Settling*—Most entrained water will eventually settle out of the fuel, but it takes a much longer time (approximately four times as long) for the water to settle out of turbine fuel than out of Av-Gas

due to its more viscous nature and higher specific gravity (Fig. 11-6).

2   *Coalescing tanks*—These are packed with Fiberglas or other cellulose material which causes the finely divided water particles to join together, creating large globules which then settle to a sump where they can be drained off (Fig. 11-7).

In addition to its slow settling time, and its affinity to water, the fuel vapor-air mixture above the surface of JP-4 and Jet B fuel in a storage tank or fuel cell is nearly always in the explosive range through the wide temperature extremes of 80 to −10°F, whereas Av-Gas in storage forms a mixture that is too rich to burn, and kerosine forms a mixture that is too lean to burn.

Precautions while handling jet fuels

Because of the reasons indicated above, special precautions must be taken when handling or storing jet fuels.

1   Static electrical charges accumulate very rapidly with high fuel flow rates, high gravity fuels, and wider boiling range fuels.   Flow rates must be restricted to a specific maximum, depending upon the hose diameter.   Grounding or bonding is an absolute essential.

2   Observe all "No Smoking" requirements.

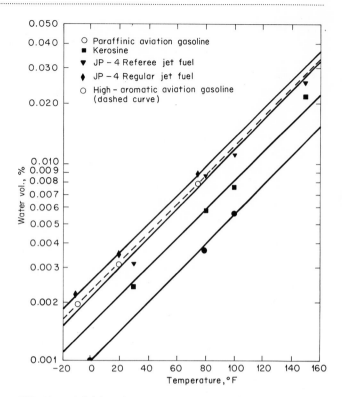

FIG. 11-5 *Solubility of water in aviation fuels.*

FIG. 11-7 *Cutaway view of a typical filter-separator.*

3 Since jet fuels tend to soften asphalt and do not evaporate readily, spillage should be avoided. Remove small amounts of jet fuel with a commercial absorbing agent. Wash large spills with copious amounts of water. Caution should be observed to see that the fuel is not washed into a sanitary or storm sewer system.

4 Approved fire extinguishing equipment should be readily available.

5 Jet fuels should not be used for cleaning purposes. Excessive inhalation and skin contact should be avoided. The skin should be washed thoroughly with soap and water, and clothing should be removed and laundered as soon as possible after contact. Because jet fuels are less volatile than gasoline, they do not evaporate as readily and therefore are more difficult to remove from clothing.

Future developments *(Fig. 11-8)*

In recent years there have been large scale efforts by the government and industry to develop more powerful and more suitable fuels for supersonic and hypersonic aircraft. Trends in this direction include research into the following areas (Fig. 11-9):

1 Jet fuels with a thermal stability up to 700°F and a heat of combustion of 18,400 Btu/lb. Thermal stability is important because at Mach 2, skin temperatures reach 90°C, and at Mach 3, 250°C. Under these conditions, trace components in a fuel concentrate into deposits which plate out on critical surfaces and block fine orifices in the fuel system.

2 Jet fuels that are capable of absorbing the aerodynamic heat generated by aircraft operating in the Mach 3 to Mach 6 range. An interesting development in this area is the endothermic fuel. Basically, the idea is to use a chemical that decomposes into a good fuel mixture as a result of a heat-absorbing (endothermic) reaction. This reaction not only boosts the heat-sink capacity, but also increases the amount of energy that can be extracted from any given fuel. *Reason:* The heat taken up during the reaction has to be released when the fuel is burned. Thus the fuel, which initially enters the system as a liquid, constantly soaks up heat as it cools the engine walls and changes from the liquid to the vapor phase. It continues to absorb heat and then undergoes the endothermic reaction that decomposes the chemical or alters its structure.

3 High-density jet fuels that have a high-energy content per unit

FIG. 11-6 *Settling time of water.*

FIG. 11-8 *U.S.A. aviation fuel requirements. (Military fuel demands are uncertain.)*

volume for use on volume-limited aircraft such as fighter airplanes and missiles.

4 Low volatility fuels because of high engine temperatures and high altitudes.

5 Jet fuels with adequate low-temperature characteristics (viscosity and freezing point) for cold weather starting and subsonic operation.

6 Jet fuels with low water content to prevent the formation of ice resulting from the low temperatures encountered at high altitudes.

7 Gelled fuels to reduce the danger of fire in the event of an abnormal landing.

A radically different approach to the problem of

FIG. 11-9 *Engine operating conditions compared to the fuel properties which affect those conditions. Fuel properties: (1) viscosity, surface tension; (2) volatility, vapor pressure; (3) kinetics; (4) specific heat; (5) thermal stability; (6) heavy aromatics; (7) luminosity; (8) sulfur metals; (9) thermal cracking.*

finding suitable fuels for supersonic engines would involve the use of Liquefied Natural Gas (LNG). The advantage claimed for such a product is greater thermal stability, allowing cleaner burning at Mach 3 temperatures without forming varnishes and other deposits that could foul injectors. In addition, LNG would burn with a lower radiant heat output, resulting in lower metal temperature of the combustion chamber component. Another advantage claimed for this fuel is its high hydrogen/carbon ratio and therefore higher heat content per unit weight.

Because it is a cryogenic fluid with a boiling point of −260°F, LNG offers substantially more heat-sink capacity than present fuels. This greater cooling capacity could be used to cool the turbine cooling air and thus raise cycle efficiency or increase engine life.

Liquefied natural gas also has some drawbacks. Its extremely low temperature and volatility could cause handling and storage problems. The low density of LNG—roughly half that of kerosine—means lower heat content per unit volume. In addition, completely new servicing and distribution methods would be required. Cost and availability would have to be determined.

Some other considerations involved in developing new fuels are those of economy, compatibility with engine and airframe materials, availability, and storageability. In addition, safety in storage might necessitate fuel tank inerting or filling the space on top of the fuel with an inert gas such as nitrogen, and thus precluding the likelihood of explosion.

REVIEW AND STUDY QUESTIONS

1 What is the source of gas turbine fuels?

2 List the steps in the refining process.

3 What is the military specification number with which gas turbine fuels must comply; the civil specification number?

4 List the JP series of fuels. Give a brief description of each.

5 Describe the two generally used fuels for civil aircraft.

6 Make a table of some major fuel tests. Tell why each test is performed.

7 Of what significance is the net heating value of a fuel?

8 Why is water such a problem in relation to gas turbine fuel? In what form may water exist in turbine fuel? How is the water problem solved?

9 What precautions should be taken while handling turbine fuels?

10 List some possible future developments for turbine fuels.

Chapter 12

Fuel systems
and components

FUEL CONTROLS

Introduction

Depending upon the type of engine and the performance expected of it, fuel controls may range in complexity from simple valves to automatic computing controls containing hundreds of intricate, highly machined parts.

Strictly speaking, a pilot of a gas turbine powered airplane does not directly control his engine. His relation to the power plant corresponds to that of the bridge officer on a ship who obtains engine response by relaying orders to an engineer below deck who, in turn, actually moves the throttle of the engine (Fig. 12-1). But before the engineer moves the throttle, he monitors certain operating factors which would not be apparent to the captain, such as pressures, temperatures, and rpm. He then refers to a chart and computes a fuel flow or throttle movement rate which will not allow the engine to exceed its operating limits.

Theory of operation

Fuel controls may sense some or all of the following engine operating variables.

1 Pilot's demands
2 Compressor inlet temperature
3 Compressor discharge pressure
4 Burner pressure
5 Compressor inlet pressure
6 Rpm
7 Turbine temperature

Modern fuel controls can be divided into two basic groups, hydromechanical and electronic. There are as many variations in controls as there are fuel control manufacturers. Although each type of fuel control has its particular advantage, most controls in use today are of the hydromechanical type. Regardless of type, all controls accomplish the same things, although some may sense more of the aforementioned variables than others. At best, fuel controls are extremely complex devices composed of speed governors, servo systems and feedback loops, valves, metering systems, and various sensing mechanisms. The electronic fuel controls contain thermocouples, amplifiers, relays, electrical servo systems, switches, and solenoids.

The discussion of fuel-control theory will limit itself mainly to the hydromechanical type, but included in this section (Fig. 12-2) is a schematic showing the general functions of the components used in an integrated electronic fuel control system. Also included is the electronic fuel trimming mechanism used on the Allison 501-D13 engine.

The simplest conceivable control would consist of a plain metering valve to regulate fuel flow to the engine. This type of control could be installed on an engine used for thrust or the generation of gas (Fig. 12-3).

Some refinements might include a:

1 Pump to pressurize the fuel
2 Shutoff valve to stop fuel flow
3 Relief valve to protect the control when the shutoff valve is closed
4 Minimum fuel control adjustment to prevent complete stoppage of fuel by the metering valve

A flow of fluid may be metered by keeping the pressure drop or difference across the metering valve a constant value while varying the valve orifice, or the valve orifice may be kept a constant size and the pressure difference varied. Most modern fuel controls meter fuel by using the first method, so an additional refinement would consist of a device to maintain a constant pressure drop across the metering valve re-

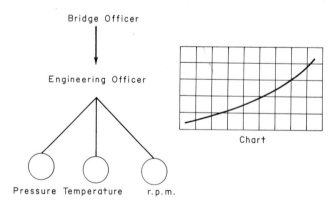

FIG. 12-1 *Boat power-plant control analogy to a fuel control.*

FIG. 12-2 *J47 integrated electronic fuel-control system.*

Cockpit control panel This panel provides various indicator lights and control switches including a starter switch.   A selector lever allows the pilot to transfer to hydromechanical control for comparison or as an emergency measure.

Pilot's control lever The pilot selects engine thrust by the position of this lever. Regardless of how far or how rapidly the lever is moved, automatic features ensure maximum rates of engine acceleration or deceleration, but within safe engine operating limits.

Main fuel-control amplifier The "thrust request" from the pilot's control lever is signaled electrically to this amplifier; also it receives sensor signals covering various engine operating conditions. From these a control signal is integrated and sent out to the metering unit.

Main fuel-metering unit The fuel-metering valve of this unit is electrically controlled from the main fuel-control amplifier.   In this way, fuel is metered to the engine spray nozzles in response to the integrated fuel demands, and within safe operating limits.

Afterburner fuel-control amplifier When the requested engine thrust calls for afterburner operation, this amplifier signals the afterburner fuel-metering unit, causing afterburner lightup. Following that it regulates fuel metering to the afterburner for the additional thrust.

Afterburner fuel-metering unit This fuel-metering unit controls lightup and fuel flow to the afterburner spray nozzles. It is electrically regulated from the afterburner fuel-control amplifier. The amplifier also senses and integrates suitable engine parameters.

Exhaust-nozzle area control amplifier This amplifier receives a signal from a thermocouple which senses the temperature of the exhaust gases. This signal is electronically compared with other engine operating conditions. A resulting working signal directs the nozzle area control.

Exhaust-nozzle area control unit This is a hydraulic unit which is under electrical control from the amplifier. It serves to position the exhaust-nozzle area mechanism through hydraulic actuating cylinders. Nozzle area is varied for optimum operating conditions.

gardless of the pressure level on either side of the valve, or the valve opening.

The fuel components discussed are important. It would take a very careful operator to run the engine without one or more of these refinements. Another component which is only slightly less essential is an acceleration limiter.   Since these engines are internally air cooled, much of the air pumped by the compressor is used to cool the combustion gases to the point where they can run the turbine without melting the blades.   In order to accelerate the engine, the fuel flow is increased, but only to the point where the limiting temperature is reached.   As the engine accelerates and increases the airflow, more fuel can be added.   This function can

be performed by the operator, but if it must be done often, it can probably be done better and more cheaply by an automatic device.   If turbine inlet temperature were the only engine limitation, a control sensing this temperature could be used, although such controls are generally complex and expensive.   In most cases it is also necessary to avoid the compressor surge and stall lines (Fig. 12-4).   (Refer to Chap. 5.)   Since a good incipient stall detector has not yet been developed, it is necessary to schedule the accelerating fuel in accordance with some engine parameter or combination of engine parameters.   When the shortest possible acceleration time is important, the control becomes rather involved.   This is the primary reason why aircraft gas

FIG. 12-3 *Some steps in the development of one type of hydromechanical fuel control.*
(a) Basic fuel control. *(b) Adding a shutoff.* *(c) Adding a high-pressure relief valve, a differential relief valve, and a minimum-flow valve.* *(d) Adding a governor and an acceleration scheduling valve.* *(e) Adding a droop control.* *(Woodward Governor Company)*

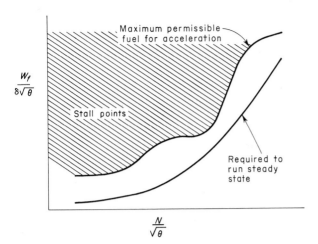

$\dfrac{W_f}{\delta\sqrt{\theta}}$

Maximum permissible fuel for acceleration

Stall points

Required to run steady state

$\dfrac{N}{\sqrt{\theta}}$

FIG. 12-4 *Typical acceleration limit curve.*

turbine controls are so complicated. For smaller engines with less critical compressors, or for applications where the cost and simplicity of the control are more important than optimum performance, a simpler control is used, giving equally effective engine protection, but with a longer acceleration time. Compressor discharge pressure or burner pressure is commonly used as the sensed variable for these simple controls, since they vary with both engine speed and inlet air conditions, and thus gives a fair indication of the amount of fuel which can be burned safely.

The amount of fuel required to run the engine at rated rpm varies with the inlet air conditions. For example, it requires less fuel to run the engine on a hot day than on a cold day. In order to relieve the operator of the necessity of resetting the power lever, the final refinement, a speed governor, is added to the simple fuel control. A speed governor becomes necessary when:

1 The turbojet is used in an airplane where air inlet conditions change drastically.

2 The simple machine delivers hot gases to another wheel, or is subject to variation in back pressure from any other source.

3 Any shaft power is taken from the machine so that the fuel flow required is a function of load as well as speed.

A simple governor consists of flyweights balanced by a spring. When the engine is running unloaded, at rated speed, the metering valve is open only far enough to supply the small fuel flow required. If a load is applied to the engine, the speed will decrease. This causes the flyweights to move in under the force of the spring, and the fuel valve to open wider and admit more fuel. With the additional fuel, the engine picks up speed again, and as the set speed is reached, the flyweights move the fuel valve in the closing direction until the proper steady-state fuel flow is reached. Note however, that since the engine now requires more fuel to carry the load, the fuel valve must be farther open than it was at no load. This causes the flyweights to

run slightly farther in, so that the spring is relaxed somewhat and exerts a little less force. This means that the system will come to equilibrium at a speed slightly lower than the unloaded speed. Thus, as load is progressively added to the engine, the speed will progressively decrease. If speed versus load is plotted, a drooping line would result (Fig. 12-5). Therefore, there is always this characteristic "speed droop," sometimes called *regulation* or *proportional control*. The droop characteristic is common to all mechanical governors. It is a good thing from the standpoint that it makes the engine-governor system stable, but it does mean that the engine is either running below rated speed when loaded or above rated speed when unloaded.

The problem of droop can be reduced in various ways.

1 Use a weaker spring which requires a lower force necessary for valve movement.

2 Make the metering port very wide radially so that a very small movement of the valve is required.

3 Increase the pressure differential across the metering valve to force the required fuel through a smaller opening of the valve.

All of these methods have limitations. The problem is solved in several different ways, some of which are discussed in the detailed examination of the following four fuel controls.

Many modern fuel controls will also incorporate:

1 Servo systems to boost weak input signals and thus make the control more sensitive.

2 Devices to prevent "undershooting" and "overshooting" by returning the metering valve to its desired position before the governor alone can do the job.

3 Auxiliary functions such as inlet guide vane positioning and nozzle, afterburner, and thrust reverser signals. Several other auxiliary functions are discussed on the following pages.

TYPES OF FUEL CONTROLS

The principle of operation of several fuel controls used on current jet engines is examined in this section. It would be difficult to include information on all of the fuel controls now used. The controls selected for

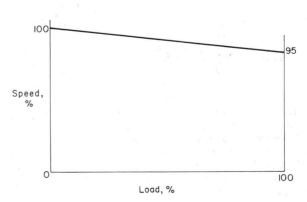

FIG. 12-5 *The effect of speed droop.*

discussion are those most commonly used and/or those illustrating certain fuel-metering principles. Included are the following controls:

1 TJ-A4 manufactured by Bendix and used on the J-33.

2 AP-B3 manufactured by Bendix and used on the 501-D13 (T-56) with electronic fuel trimming.

3 1307 manufactured by Woodward and used on the CJ805 (J-79).

4 JFC25-7 manufactured by Hamilton Standard and used on the JT-4. (This control with some change is similar to the JFC25-16 being used on the JT-3D fan engine.)

BENDIX TJ-A4 GAS TURBINE FUEL CONTROL
(Figs. 12-6 and 12-7)

General description

The function of this gas turbine fuel control is to maintain exhaust gas temperatures within specified limits during acceleration or deceleration, sustain combustion during deceleration, and maintain any fixed engine speed regardless of altitude as long as the speed is within the operating range of the engine.

The control unit meters fuel in response to variations in engine speed and compressor inlet air density, and provides an all-speed governor to maintain pilot-selected engine speed regardless of air density (altitude) or aircraft speed, except during the time the altitude idle bleed is controlling the fuel flow. The fuel control unit incorporates the following elements:

1 The bypass valve maintains a constant pressure drop between fuel inlet pressure and metered fuel pressure (manifold pressure) under normal operating conditions, and the relief valve provides a maximum pressure blowoff, preventing excessive pressure buildup in the system whenever the cutoff valve is closed to shut down the engine or in the event of an emergency shutoff at high engine speeds. The fuel not needed by the fuel-metering unit is bypassed through this bypass valve to the inlet side of the engine driven fuel pump.

2 The regulator valve, through the centrifugal force of the speed density weights and the metering head across the metering head diaphragm, tends to maintain a constant pressure drop across the governor valve which varies in proportion to engine speed for any given density.

3 The governor valve provides the engine with a governed speed for any constant throttle selection.

4 A density-compensating circuit corrects the fuel pressure differential across the governor valve for variations in air pressure and temperature.

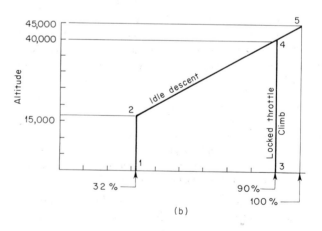

FIG. 12-6 **(a)** *Engine fuel requirements. Line 1-2: Governor wide open. Line 2-3: Governor wide open and regulator valve opening increasing. Point 3: Governor break point. Line 3-4: Governor slope (governor valve closing to required position). Line 4-5: Governor valve at minimum flow stop (high metering head). Line 5-6: Governor valve at minimum flow stop (regulator closing). Decreasing differential across governor valve (P2-P4). Line 6-1: Governor valve opening to balance position.* **(b)** *Locked throttle climb and idle descent. (Bendix Corporation)*

TO NO 7-14 NOZZLE

CUT OFF LEVER

CONTROL LEVER

P₀ FUEL PUMP INLET PRESSURE

P₁ MAIN FUEL PUMP DISCHARGE PRESSURE

P₂ UNMETERED FUEL PRESSURE

P₃ COMPENSATING FUEL PRESSURE

P₄ METERED FUEL MANIFOLD PRESSURE

COMPRESSOR INLET DENSITY

ENGINE LUBRICATING OIL

DRIVE SHAFT SEAL DRAIN

EMERGENCY FUEL PRESSURE

THROTTLE SWITCH ASSEMBLY

CUT OFF VALVE

FUEL OUTLET

GOVERNOR VALVE

DENSITY WEIGHT

OUTER GOV. LEVER

DRIVING SPLINE

ENGINE OIL FOR LUBRICATING BEARINGS

DRIVE SHAFT SEAL DRAIN

GOVERNOR WEIGHT

REVERSE REGULATOR SPRING

REGULATOR VALVE MAX. OPEN STOP

REVERSE REGULATOR SPRING ADJ.

ALTITUDE IDLE BLEED

RELIEF VALVE

BY-PASS ENTRANCE BLEED

FUEL BY-PASS VALVE

TO FUEL PUMP INLET

FUEL INLET STRAINER

FROM MAIN ELEMENT OF FUEL PUMP

FROM EMERGENCY ELEMENT OF DUAL FUEL PUMP

STARTING FUEL CONTROL UNIT

CHECK VALVE

MIN. FLOW ADJUSTING SCREW

GOV. VALVE SLEEVE ADJ. NUT

REGULATOR SPRING

DENSITY COMPENSATING NEEDLE

DENSITY ANEROID

ANEROID DRAIN

METERING HEAD DIAPHRAGM

DENSITY CIRCUIT CONTROL JETS

DOUBLE CHECK VALVE

TO EMERGENCY FUEL CONTROL

P₂

P₄

P₀

FIG. 12-7 *Schematic diagram of the Bendix TJ-A4 main fuel-control assembly. (Bendix Corporation)*

Principles of operation

The air supply to the combustion chambers of a turbo-jet engine will vary with engine speed, aircraft speed, and air density.   These variations are recognized by the main fuel control assembly, and the fuel is metered to the engine so as to prevent excessive temperatures during acceleration for any combination of these variations.   Fuel is supplied to the fuel control by a dual engine-driven fuel pump.   As fuel enters the unit, the pressure is regulated by the bypass valve.   The bypass valve maintains a specific pressure drop between fuel inlet pressure and metered fuel pressure.   This is accomplished by bypassing any excess fuel to the inlet side of the fuel pump.

The bypass valve is attached to a diaphragm. Metered fuel pressure plus a spring force is applied to one side of the diaphragm which tends to close the bypass valve. Fuel inlet pressure is applied to the opposite side of the diaphragm which tends to open the bypass valve.   The valve will be positioned, by the differential force acting on the diaphragm, to where the amount of fuel being bypassed will maintain the fuel inlet pressure in the correct relation to the metered fuel pressure.   The forces acting upon each side of the diaphragm will then be equal; therefore, the bypass valve will maintain a pressure drop across the control equal to the spring force (inlet pressure minus metered fuel pressure).   At any time the pressures applied to each side of the diaphragm become unbalanced, the bypass valve will be moved in the direction of the greatest force, until a position is reached where again the forces applied to the diaphragm are in balance, therefore, maintaining the correct drop across the control for all conditions. The bypass spring force may be adjusted by the amount of shims installed between the spring and bypass cover. The relief valve is a spring-loaded valve incorporated inside of the bypass valve.   The relief valve functions to provide a maximum pressure blowoff, preventing excessive pressure buildup in the control.

The fuel, at a pressure determined by the bypass valve, then flows to the regulator valve which regulates the unmetered fuel pressure so as to maintain the desired fuel metering head (unmetered fuel pressure minus metered fuel pressure) across the governor valve in proportion to engine speed and compressor inlet density.   The regulator valve is positioned by forces of the metering head diaphragm and the centrifugal head generating weights acting upon it.

The thrust from the centrifugal head generating weights, which sense changes in engine speed, is applied, through suitable linkage, to a shaft on which the regulator valve is mounted and to which the metering head diaphragm attaches.   The force of the centrifugal weights tending to open the regulator valve is opposed by the force of the pressure differential across the metering head diaphragm tending to close the regulator valve.   The pressure differential across the metering head diaphragm is created by unmetered fuel passing through two jets, incorporated in the diaphragm, into the altitude-compensating circuit, thus causing a pressure drop.   The unmetered fuel pressure, being the greater of the two pressures acting upon the diaphragm, will create a differential pressure which will tend to close the valve.   Some controls will incorporate a regulator spring on the altitude-compensating side of the diaphragm which will work in conjunction with the centrifugal head generating weights during the low range of the accelerating curve.   The two opposing forces (differential pressure across the diaphragm and centrifugal weight force) will control the position of the regulator valve, therefore maintaining the correct unmetered fuel pressure to furnish the required metering head across the governor valve.   The metering head will vary with engine speed, increasing with increased engine speed and decreasing with decreased engine speed at any given density.

At low rpm the centrifugal head generating weights (speed density) force is too great; therefore, it results in a fuel flow that would provide the engine with excessive fuel which may result in excessive acceleration temperatures.   A reverse regulator spring is incorporated to overcome the weight force and close the regulator valve. The regulator valve will remain closed until the weight force plus the regulator spring force overcomes the reverse regulator spring force plus the pressure differential across the metering head diaphragm.   The effect of the reverse regulator spring is minimized quickly as engine speed rises.

The fuel, at a pressure adjusted by the regulator valve, then passes through the governor valve, cutoff valve, and from there to the engine fuel manifold.   The governor valve performs the actual metering of the fuel. Because of the cutoff valve construction there is very little pressure drop through the valve; therefore, no metering is performed by this valve.

To meter the fuel there must be a metering orifice and a pressure differential (metering head) across the orifice.   In the fuel control the regulator valve establishes and maintains the required pressure differential across the metering orifice.   The governor-valve opening is the metering orifice, and its area is adjusted to obtain the required fuel flow.

The desired engine speed is selected by the pilot's throttle lever.   The throttle lever on the fuel control operates the cutoff valve and a forked lever which preloads the governor-valve spring.   A movement of the throttle lever will change the degree of opening of the cutoff valve, and will also set up a definite governor-valve spring force which tends to position the governor valve. The governor spring force tending to open the valve is opposed by the force of the centrifugal governor weights tending to close the governor valve. These two opposing forces will enable the governor valve to seek a position where the amount of fuel being metered and delivered to the engine will maintain an engine speed that will create a centrifugal governor weight force equal to the governor spring force set up by the pilot.

For any changes in engine speed, caused by the pilot moving the throttle, a corresponding change will take place in the various pressures within the fuel control. For example, if the engine speed is to be increased from point 1 to point 4 on Fig. 12-6a, the pilot moves the throttle toward the open position, thereby increasing the governor-valve spring force. This creates a state of unbalance between the governor-valve spring force and the governor weight force. The governor valve immediately moves into its wide open position. The metering head across the governor valve will drop, momentarily reducing the pressure differential across the metering head diaphragm. The centrifugal head generating weight force will then overcome the diaphragm force, moving the regulator valve toward the open position to provide the required increased metering head across the governor valve for the increased fuel flow needed for acceleration, as represented by line 1 to 2 in Fig. 12-6a. As the engine speed picks up, because of the increased fuel flow, the centrifugal head generating weight force increases in proportion to engine speed, therefore further moving the regulator valve toward the open position establishing the required metering head across the governor valve to maintain a predetermined acceleration schedule represented by line 2 to 3 on Fig. 12-6a. The fuel flow at point 3 (a speed slightly less than point 4) is somewhat greater than actually required to run the engine at point 4. When the increasing engine speed creates a governor weight force (which is proportional to engine speed) greater than governor spring force, the governor valve will be moved toward the closed position until a predetermined position is reached and a state of balance is established between the governor spring and governor weight forces. As the governor valve is moved toward the closed position, the unmetered fuel pressure ($P2$) will momentarily increase, therefore increasing the pressure differential across the metering head diaphragm and creating a state of unbalance between the diaphragm force and the centrifugal head generating weight force. The regulator valve will then move toward the closed position until a point is reached where again a state of balance between the diaphragm and weight forces exists and the required metering head is estab-

lished across the newly positioned governor valve to run the engine at point 4.

When the pilot moves the throttle to reduce engine speed, the governor valve will immediately move to its minimum flow stop because of the relieving of the governor-valve spring force. The unmetered fuel pressure ($P2$) will momentarily increase, therefore increasing the pressure differential across the metering head diaphragm. A state of unbalance is created between the diaphragm and centrifugal head generating weight forces. The regulator valve is moved toward the closed position establishing the required metering head across the governor valve to maintain a predetermined deceleration schedule, represented by line 5 to 6 on Fig. 12-6a. When the engine speed is decreased to a speed that creates a governor weight force which is very near to the governor spring force set up by the newly positioned throttle, the governor valve will move toward the open position until a predetermined position is reached and a state of balance exists between the governor spring and governor weight force. The unmetered fuel pressure ($P2$) will momentarily decrease, therefore decreasing the pressure differential across the metering head diaphragm creating a state of unbalance between the diaphragm and centrifugal head generating weight forces. The regulator valve will move towards the open position until the diaphragm and centrifugal head generating weight forces are again balanced and the required metering head is established across the governor valve to run the engine at the new throttle position. As metered fuel pressure ($P4$) increases or decreases, the fuel inlet pressure, as regulated by the bypass valve, increases or decreases proportionally, maintaining the correct drop across the control.

As the aircraft ascends or descends the regulator valve position must be varied, as the air pressure and temperature vary with altitude, to maintain the correct pressure drop across the governor valve. This is accomplished by the density-compensating circuit. The density-compensating circuit parallels the main fuel supply circuit and establishes the pressure differential across the governor valve. The small amount of fuel flowing through the density-compensating circuit passes through the jets in the metering head diaphragm, past the bellows controlled needle, bypassing the governor valve, and then to the engine fuel manifold. Movement of the needle will vary the pressure differential across the metering head diaphragm by varying the compensating fuel pressure ($P3$).

The gas-filled bellows is responsive to changes in air pressure and temperature, elongating as the air pressure decreases or temperature increases, and contracting as air pressure increases or temperature decreases. Decreasing air pressure or increasing temperatures will cause the bellows to elongate, moving the contoured needle farther out of its orifice. This will lower compensating fuel pressure ($P3$) and in turn momentarily increase the pressure differential across the metering head diaphragm. The increased differential pressure acting upon the diaphragm will move the regulator valve toward the closed position, lowering the unmetered fuel pressure with the resultant decrease in metering head across the governor valve. The decreased metering head across the governor valve will reduce the fuel flow sufficiently to maintain the engine speed as air pressure decreases or temperature increases. Therefore, during a lock-throttle climb, where a constant rpm is to be maintained, the governor valve theoretically, remains in one position forming a fixed orifice and the altitude-compensating circuit varies the metering head across the governor valve to maintain the correct fuel flow for that particular engine speed as air density varies. The reverse of this correction will occur with increasing pressure or decreasing temperature at which time an increase in fuel flow will be required to maintain the pilot-selected engine speed. As the aircraft ascends, an altitude will be reached where the altitude circuit will completely close the regulator valve in its effort to maintain the correct metering head across the governor valve as the air density decreases. To obtain fuel flow past the closed regulator valve for altitude idle, idle descents, or above the altitude where the regulator valve is closed, an adjustable altitude idle bleed is incorporated in the control.

For example, if a pilot were to make a lock-throttle climb at 90 percent rpm (point 3 on Fig. 12-6b) as long as the rpm remained constant the governor valve will remain in a fixed position. The altitude-compensating circuit will vary the pressure differential across the metering head diaphragm, as air density decreases, moving the regulator valve toward the closed position to maintain the correct metering head across the governor valve for 90 percent engine speed. The rpm will remain constant (line 3 to 4, Fig. 12-6b) and the governor valve will remain in one position as the aircraft ascends, whereas the regulator valve is able to maintain the metering head across the governor valve required to run the engine at 90 percent. An altitude will be reached where the altitude-compensating circuit will completely close the regulator valve (point 4, Fig. 12-6b) in its effort to maintain the required metering head. At this point the metering head across the governor valve is maintained by a fixed orifice which is composed of the altitude idle bleed plus the leakage past the now closed regulator valve. As the aircraft continues to ascend, the fuel supplied by the altitude idle bleed and leakage past the closed regulator valve will be greater than required to maintain the correct metering head across the governor valve, therefore, the fuel supplied to engine will be too great to maintain 90 percent rpm. The engine rpm

will therefore increase, increasing the centrifugal governor weight force which will overcome the governor spring force and immediately move the governor valve against its minimum flow stop. The aircraft may ascend to an altitude (point 5, Fig. 12-6b) where the amount of fuel supplied by the altitude bleed and regulator valve leakage will increase the engine rpm to 100 percent. Above this critical altitude the engine will overspeed.

When descending from high altitudes, the pilot may move the throttle lever into the IDLE position to increase the rate at which the aircraft is able to descend without the engine exceeding its maximum speed limitation. If the aircraft is at an altitude at which the metering of fuel is accomplished by the altitude idle bleed plus regulator leakage, the movement of the throttle to IDLE will have no immediate effect upon the governor valve or regulator valve as these valves will be in the closed position. If the aircraft is at an altitude where the governor valve is metering the fuel and the regulator valve is maintaining the metering head, when the pilot moves the throttle lever into the IDLE position, the governor-valve spring force will be reduced and then the governor weight force will overcome the spring force immediately moving the governor valve against its minimum flow stop. The unmetered fuel pressure will increase momentarily, increasing the pressure differential across the metering head diaphragm, therefore closing the regulator valve. With the governor and regulator valves closed the fuel will be metered to the engine by the altitude idle bleed and leakage past the regulator valve. Referring to Fig. 12-6b, the rpm will decrease along line 5 to 2 as the aircraft descends and the air density becomes greater. When the aircraft descends to an altitude where the quantity of fuel supplied by the altitude idle bleed and regulator leakage is not enough to maintain the idle rpm required by the throttle setting, the governor spring force will overcome the governor weight force and move the governor valve to an open position where the governor spring and weight forces become balanced. The unmetered fuel pressure, acting upon the metering head diaphragm, will momentarily decrease allowing the centrifugal head generating weight force to open the regulator valve to a position where the diaphragm and weight forces become balanced. The regulator valve will then maintain the required metering head across the governor valve. As the aircraft continues to descend, the governor valve opening will remain constant and the altitude-compensating circuit will vary the differential pressure across the metering head diaphragm, therefore allowing the regulator valve to move toward the open direction to maintain the correct metering head across the governor valve for the IDLE throttle setting (line 2 to 1, Fig. 12-6b).

A pressure switch which is a safety feature to automatically cut in the emergency fuel control system when the metered fuel pressure ($P4$) becomes too low for safe engine operation is incorporated on the TJ-A4 fuel control. The pressure switch is a normally closed switch and the contacts open under pressure. Metered fuel pressure (P4) is applied on a spring-loaded metal diaphragm in the pressure switch, compressing the spring and opening the switch. Whenever the metered fuel pressure falls below a predetermined value, the spring tension will move the diaphragm and close the switch which in turn cuts in the emergency control, thus preventing engine failure due to the main fuel control failing.

A separate control is required to meter fuel during the starting cycle.

BENDIX AP-B3 FUEL CONTROL (Fig. 12-8)

General description

The fuel control is a hydromechanical metering device used on the Allison 501-D13 (T-56) engine, and accomplishes the following:

1 Supplies a controlled fuel flow to initiate an engine fire-up.
2 Supplies a controlled fuel flow during acceleration from fire-up to the stabilized starting rpm (either low-speed taxi or high-speed taxi) to assist the 5th- and 10th-stage air-bleed system in the prevention of compressor surge.
3 Meters fuel flow in accordance with variations in air density caused by compressor inlet air temperature or pressure changes.
4 Permits pilot to vary fuel flow to the engine by movement of the throttle.
5 Meters approximately 20 percent more fuel than is required to operate the engine based upon rpm, air density, and throttle setting. This provides the temperature datum valve with a definite amount of fuel to trim.
6 Provides the means of completely stopping fuel flow to the engine at shutdown.
7 Limits the maximum possible fuel flow.
8 Provides overspeed protection for the engine.
9 Provides the means of selecting either low-speed or high-speed taxi operation.
10 Controls power available in maximum reverse.

The fuel control is only one part of the total fuel-metering system and operates in conjunction with a temperature datum valve and temperature amplifier. (See page 194.)

Principles of operation

The bypass valve assembly bypasses the excess fuel delivered to the fuel control, and establishes a pressure differential of fuel pump discharge pressure (P1) minus metered fuel pressure (P2) across the metering valve. This differential (P1 − P2) will remain practically constant during all operation. The position of the bypass valve is determined by the differential forces acting on the valve's flexible diaphragm. When the bypass valve is stabilized, the opening force of P1 equals the closing force of P2 plus spring force. Therefore, P1 − P2 equals spring force. The length of the spring is a function of bypass valve position, and spring force is a function of spring length. Thus, when the bypass valve moves to assume a new position, the spring length will vary, causing the spring force to change slightly.

The relief valve establishes the maximum fuel pressure within the fuel control, and thus establishes the maximum possible fuel flow from the fuel control. It is set to open when P1 exceeds P0 (low-pressure filtered fuel pressure) by a preset amount.

The metering valve meters all fuel flow to the temperature datum valve in accordance with variations in engine rpm, throttle setting, and compressor air inlet temperature and pressure. The metering valve also provides protection from overspeed by reducing the fuel flow when a certain overspeed rpm is exceeded. The size of the metering-valve orifice may be changed either by rotation or linear movement of the valve. The metering valve is rotated due to changes in compressor air inlet pressure. Changes in rpm, throttle settings, and compressor air inlet temperature actuate a cam assembly which results in linear movement of the metering valve. The metering valve linear opening force is a spring. The cam assembly establishes the linear position, and thus the orifice size of the metering valve during normal operation. The governor spring force is established by the governor setting lever which is controlled either by a cam and cam follower positioned by the throttle, or by the solenoid-operated governor reset mechanism. When the solenoid is energized, the governor reset mechanism positions the governor setting lever such that the governor spring is set for 10,000 (+300/−100) rpm low-speed taxi operation. When the solenoid of the governor reset solenoid assembly is deenergized, the reset mechanism positions the governor setting lever such that the governor spring is set for the overspeed rpm of the taxi and flight ranges. The solenoid of the reset solenoid assembly is controlled by the cockpit low-speed taxi switch. The force of the governor weights serves as a closing force for the metering valve. During low-speed taxi operation, the linear position of the metering valve is established by a balance of two forces—governor spring force and governor weight force. The cam assembly does not position the metering valve in low-speed taxi operation. During high-speed taxi and flight operation, the governor spring force is greater than the governor weight force. Thus, the governor spring tends to move the metering valve fully open. However, the maximum linear opening of the metering valve will be established by the cam assembly. In the event of overspeeding, the governor weight force increases with rpm. When governor weight force overcomes the governor spring force, the metering valve moves to decrease its linear opening, and thus reduce fuel flow from the fuel control. This limits the engine speed at a definite speed above 13,820 rpm. During

FIG. 12-8 *Fuel-control schematic of the Bendix AP-B3-7.* (*Allison Service School*)

an overspeed condition, the cam assembly has no control over the linear position of the metering valve because the governor weight force moves the metering valve away from the cam assembly. When the overspeed is corrected, the governor weight force decreases, and the governor spring begins moving the metering valve open. Then the cam assembly again determines the maximum linear opening of the metering valve.

The inlet pressure actuator assembly senses compressor air inlet pressure changes by means of a pressure probe in the left horizontal air inlet housing strut. The inlet pressure actuator initiates an action which causes the metering valve to rotate to provide a corrected fuel flow required by any air-pressure variation. A partially evacuated bellows, sensitive to air-pressure changes, repositions the pressure actuator servo valve by means of a lever action whenever compressor air inlet pressure changes. The position of the pressure actuator servo valve establishes servo pressure (Px') which, in turn, establishes the position of the pressure piston and the pressure actuator rack. When the air pressure changes, the pressure actuator servo valve causes Px' to change. This moves the pressure piston and pressure actuator rack, and results in the pressure actuator servo valve being moved to a stabilized position. When the pressure actuator rack moves, the metering valve drive gear causes the metering valve to rotate by means of a bevel gear. Any change in air pressure results in the rotational movement of the metering valve.

The speed servo control assembly senses rpm changes, and initiates an action which causes the metering valve to move linearly and monitor fuel flow to prevent compressor surges during engine accelerations. The position of the speed servo valve establishes servo pressure (Px) which, in turn, establishes the position of a speed piston and speed rack. When rpm increases, the speed weights actuate linkage to move the speed servo valve toward a closed position. This causes Px to increase. Thus, the speed piston moves the speed rack and linkage to stabilize the speed servo valve. Movement of the speed rack rotates the speed and temperature shaft which has two cams—an acceleration cam and a part throttle cam. Each of these cams has a follower—the acceleration cam follower and the part throttle cam follower. The acceleration and part throttle cams are designed such that, during rpm changes, the acceleration cam positions the acceleration cam follower; and when there is no rpm change, the part throttle cam positions the part throttle cam follower, its shaft, and the acceleration cam follower. The acceleration cam follower's position establishes the metering valve's linear position, and thus the flow of metered fuel from the fuel control. Any change in rpm results in linear movement of the metering valve.

The temperature compensation section senses compressor air inlet temperature changes by means of a probe inserted through the air inlet housing beneath the left horizontal strut. The temperature compensation section initiates an action which causes the metering valve to move linearly to provide a corrected fuel flow required by any air temperature variation. The probe and a bellows in this section are filled with alcohol. Any air temperature variation causes the alcohol's volume to change. Thus, the length of the bellows is dependent upon the sensed air temperature. When air temperature changes, the temperature compensation section causes the speed and temperature shaft, with the two cams on it, to move linearly. Either the acceleration or the part throttle cam, whichever is in control of the acceleration cam follower at the time of the air temperature change, will reposition the acceleration cam follower. This causes the metering valve to move linearly to provide a corrected fuel flow. A return spring always retains the speed and temperature shaft in contact with the bellcrank of the temperature compensation section. Another bellows in this section is used to prevent any change in $P0$ fuel temperature or pressure from moving the speed and temperature shaft. The fuel control only compensates for variations in air temperature, and never for fuel temperature changes.

The part throttle scheduling cam is positioned by the throttle. When the throttle is moved, the part throttle scheduling cam moves its follower. The part throttle scheduling cam follower moves the part throttle cam follower linearly on its shaft. This changes the relative position of the part throttle cam follower in relation to the part throttle cam. The contour of the part throttle cam causes the part throttle cam follower to pivot slightly. The shaft of the part throttle cam follower then moves the acceleration cam follower. The acceleration cam follower moves the metering valve linearly to schedule fuel flow as required by the throttle movement.

The servo pressure valve assembly establishes and maintains the regulated servo pressure (PR) at a predetermined value above $P0$. PR is used by the inlet pressure actuator assembly and the speed servo control assembly, along with servo valves to establish Px and Px' required by the assemblies. The position of the servo pressure valve is determined by PR, the closing force, and $P0$ plus a spring force, the opening force. The pressurizing valve causes metered pressure ($P2$) to build up to a predetermined value before it opens to allow metered fuel pressure ($P3$) to flow to the cutoff valve assembly. This causes $P1$ to build up before fuel can flow from the fuel control, and results in quicker stabilization of the fuel-control components during the initial phases of an engine start. The pressurizing valve is not designed to have any metering effect on the fuel, but there is a small decrease in pressure across the pressurizing valve. This is the reason for indicating a

P2 and *P3* metered fuel pressure. The opening force on the pressurizing valve is *P2*, and the closing force is *P0* plus spring force.

The cutoff valve assembly provides the means by which fuel flow to the engine is started or stopped. Electrical actuation of the cutoff valve is desirable for automatic engine starts and normal shutdowns. Since the possibility of an electrical failure exists, mechanical actuation of the cutoff valve is required for emergency shutdowns. Therefore, the cutoff valve may be moved to the closed position, either electrically or mechanically. The cutoff valve must be permitted to open both electrically and mechanically during an engine start.

The only time the cutoff valve will be mechanically held closed is when the emergency shutdown handle is pulled to the emergency position. Pulling the emergency handle causes the normal cutoff lever to move such that a bellcrank and lever move a plunger to compress a spring within the cutoff valve. When the force of this spring exceeds the force of an opposing spring, the cutoff valve moves against its seat to stop fuel flow. Energizing the cutoff valve actuator motor causes the cutoff cam to move the bellcrank, lever, and plunger to compress the spring and close the valve. When the cutoff valve is closed, *P3* is ported to *P0*. The cutoff valve is not designed to have any metering action, but a small decrease in pressure does occur across the cutoff valve. This is the reason for indicating a *P3* and *P4* metered pressure.

Engine lubricating oil is used to lubricate the drive bearings of the fuel control. This oil is supplied and scavenged by the power section's lubricating system. Internal components of the fuel control are lubricated by the fuel which flows through the fuel control.

Operating characteristics

The operating characteristics of the engine with respect to fuel flows furnished by the AP-B3 control are illustrated in Fig. 12-9. Disregarding for the moment any altitude or temperature corrections, this diagram may be assumed to represent engine operation at some average constant engine air inlet condition. The acceleration curve (*ABCD*) represents the fuel flow required at different speeds to develop maximum allowable turbine inlet temperatures for engine acceleration, except for those limitations imposed by the necessity of circumventing the compressor surge area. The minimum fuel-flow curve represents the minimum desired fuel flow to prevent loss of fire in the engine burners (flameout). At part throttle the governor slopes, as illustrated, serve two purposes.

1 To control engine speed outside the limits of the propeller governor setting, namely: start, flight idle on the ground, taxi, and reverse thrust.
2 To provide a measure of protection in overspeed conditions by reducing fuel flow and turbine temperature.

Fuel is metered in the control through one controlled orifice area. All the input variables are mechanically integrated and result in the creation of a specific orifice area. The fuel head across the orifice is maintained constant within close limits.

In Fig. 12-9 the acceleration curve represents acceleration during an engine start. The compressor surge area is avoided by action of the acceleration cam contour. Compressor inlet pressure and temperature change also contribute to the shape of this curve, and the combination of acceleration cam contour and compressor inlet pressure effect would continue to produce

FIG. 12-9 *Fuel curve at sea level.* (Bendix Corporation)

the acceleration curve *BCD*; however, during start, fuel flow is trimmed at *B* by the action of the part throttle cam, causing the curve to assume the lower level until the stabilized start point is reached, as illustrated in Fig. 12-9.

During an acceleration beyond point *B* to a maximum throttle opening of 90°, the curve is limited at point *C* by the part throttle scheduling cam (face cam) and the part throttle setting cam. The combination of the effect of both of these cams produces the curve *CE*. Temperature change will shift the plotted curves upward or downward as required to avoid a corresponding shift of the compressor surge area on a temperature basis, always avoiding the surge area but at the same time maintaining maximum permissible fuel flows and corresponding engine efficiency by following the upward shift of the surge area. The higher the temperature, the more the curve would shift away from the presently indicated surge area. At lower temperatures the fuel curve would follow the receding surge area within predetermined limits.

However, before engine speed reaches point *E*, propeller governor action (separate from the fuel control system) maintains a predetermined maximum engine speed at any throttle setting above a tentatively established position of 34°. If for any reason the propeller governor were ineffective or sluggish in its operation, maximum fuel flow from the control would be limited at point *E* at 90° throttle lever position, thus defining maximum engine speed by operation of the centrifugal governor weights. When the governor weight force overcomes the governor spring force, the metering valve is moved toward a closed position, thus limiting maximum engine speed.

Each of the represented curves preceding point *C* in Fig. 12-9 are part throttle curves determined by degrees of throttle opening below 90°; these curves are defined by cam contours and the effect of compressor inlet pressure. In each case the desirable engine speed is maintained by the propeller governor with the exception of points below a tentative point of approximately

FIG. 12-11 *Throttle angle effect. (Bendix Corporation)*

34° throttle opening. The overspeed governor cutoff curve *EF* represents return to the minimum fuel flow from a 90° throttle opening. Other curves originating at the governor break point (dotted line extending below point *E*) and connecting with the ends of the part throttle characteristics curves would terminate parallel to *EF*.

Figure 12-10 illustrates the result of governor scheduling cam operation. The cam rise begins at a tentative point of approximately 20° of throttle opening and reaches its maximum speed setting at approximately 37.5° of throttle opening. Beyond this point the governor speed is maintained relatively constant.

Below approximately 20° the governor break point is determined by the governor spring force versus the governor weight force. Taxi range propeller load limits illustrate fuel requirements and engine speeds during ground operation (forward or reverse thrust). Reverse thrust operation is at reduced speed on part throttle curve back-slopes; forward thrust is indicated at normal operating speeds, as illustrated in Fig. 12-9.

Referring to Fig. 12-11, which is a detailed enlargement of the part throttle characteristics portion of Fig. 12-9, the approximate fuel curves for various throttle angle positions are illustrated. Note that the 0- and 58° curves are similar, thus providing increased fuel flow for reverse thrust operation. Also, as lower fuel flows are selected (for instance, the idle and land band) the curves become somewhat sharper. Governing, provided by the propeller governor, ceases below ap-

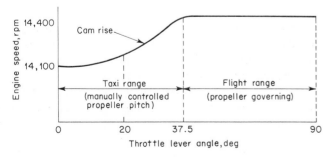

FIG. 12-10 *Governor cam effect. (Bendix Corporation)*

FIG. 12-12 *Fuel control and engine nozzle fuel flow comparison at sea level.* (Bendix Corporation)

proximately 34° of throttle opening. The significance of the slightly increasing increments of dip or hook in the lower fuel curves is to provide proportional increments of engine speed control for fixed pitch propeller operation, approaching the region of idle and start, by reduced fuel flow.

At altitude, the fuel curve will be similar to that illustrated in Fig. 12-9, except that fuel flow will be lessened as altitude increases, thus flattening out the curve.

It must be remembered that the operation of the AP-B3 gas turbine fuel control is allied with other components of the engine fuel system, and that the fuel flows provided by this control are not (as a result) necessarily the same fuel flows delivered to the engine burners. An example of this is illustrated in Fig. 12-12, wherein a relative comparison of these values is available at sea level standard conditions. A basic knowledge of the complete fuel system is helpful in order to fully understand the function performed by this fuel control. (See the following section on the Temperature Datum Valve.)

Temperature datum valve *(Fig. 12-13)*

The temperature datum valve is a part of the electronic fuel trimming system of the 501-D13 engine, and is located between the fuel control and the fuel manifold. It receives 120 percent of the engine fuel requirements from the fuel control. The extra 20 percent of fuel enables the fuel trimming system to adjust fuel flow to compensate for variations in density and Btu content of the fuel, manufacturing tolerances in the components of the fuel system, and turbine inlet temperature limitations (TIT). The amount of fuel bypassed by the temperature datum valve is controlled by the temperature datum control.

In describing the operation of the temperature datum valve, certain terms are used to indicate conditions of trimming or bypassing. *Null* is that condition during which the electronic trim system makes no correction to fuel flow; and the extra 20 percent of fuel delivered to the temperature datum valve is bypassed. *Take* is that condition during which more than 20 percent of the fuel is bypassed in order to prevent excessive temperature during acceleration, and to compensate for "rich" fuel schedules and high Btu content fuel. *Put* is that condition during which less than 20 percent of fuel is bypassed in order to compensate for "lean" fuel schedules and low Btu content fuel.

Components of the electronic fuel trimming system are:

1 Temperature datum valve (mounted on bottom of compressor housing)
2 Temperature datum control (engine furnished, but aircraft mounted)
3 Relay box (engine furnished, but aircraft mounted)
4 Coordinator control (mounted on fuel control)
5 Temperature trim light (in cockpit)
6 Temperature trim switch (in cockpit)
7 Temperature datum control switch (in cockpit)

The electronic fuel trimming system has two ranges of operation, *temperature limiting* and *temperature control*. Temperature-limiting operation is desirable during engine starts and accelerations where the "rich" mixtures, required for acceleration, could result in excessive turbine inlet temperatures. If the turbine inlet temperatures become excessive during temperature limiting, the temperature datum valve must take (bypass more) fuel. When rpm is constant, temperature-control operation is desirable. Therefore, turbine inlet temperature is scheduled. In order that the turbine inlet temperature remains as scheduled, it may be necessary for the temperature datum valve to take or put fuel.

The electronic fuel trimming system is in the temperature-limiting range of operation if one or more of the following conditions exist.

1 Engine rpm is less than 13,000 (temperature limit is 871°C).
2 Throttle setting is less than 65 deg (temperature limit is 977°C if rpm is above 13,000).
3 Temperature trim switch is in LOCKED (temperature limit is 977°C if rpm is above 13,000).

The temperature limit of 871°C is required when the bleed air valves on the fifth and tenth stages of the compressor are open. When these bleed valves are closed, a temperature limit of 977°C is possible.

The electronic fuel trimming system is in the temperature-control range of operation *only* if all three of the following conditions exist.

1 Engine rpm greater than 13,000
2 Throttle setting greater than 65 deg
3 Temperature trim switch is in CONTROLLED

FIG. 12-13 *Temperature datum valve schematic.* (Allison Division of General Motors)

The temperature datum control compares two input signals.

1 Temperature signal (from 18 thermocouples wired in parallel at the inlet of the turbine)
2 Reference signal (from one of three potentiometers, depending upon engine operation)

As a result of comparing these two signals, the temperature datum control may complete a circuit to the temperature datum valve motor. Energizing this motor will move the bypass control needle in the temperature datum valve either to put or take as required to establish the selected turbine inlet temperature, or limit the turbine inlet temperature.

During the starting cycle (engine rpm below 13,000), a "start" potentiometer (adjusted to 871°C) in the temperature datum control provides the reference signal.

When rpm exceeds 13,000, the speed-sensitive control initiates an action which causes the normal potentiometer (adjusted to 977°C) in the temperature datum control to provide the reference signal. If TIT exceeds the referenced temperature limit of either 871 or 977°C, a take signal is sent to the temperature datum valve motor which moves the bypass control needle to increase the amount of fuel bypassed. Bypassing more fuel results in a reduced fuel flow to the engine which limits the TIT to prevent excessive temperatures. When operating in the temperature-control range, the reference signal to the temperature datum control will be provided from the variable potentiometer in the coordinator. The intensity of this signal is controlled by throttle position. The voltage difference of the reference signal and the temperature signal, as compared by the temperature datum control, will determine the signal to be sent to the temperature datum valve motor. This will result in the bypass control needle being repositioned to change the amount of fuel being bypassed, and thus altering fuel flow to the engine as required to permit the temperature signal (turbine inlet temperature) to equal (balance) the reference signal.

Prior to a landing approach and with the throttle above 65 deg, the pilot may elect to *lock in* a fuel correction. This is done by placing the temperature trim switch in LOCKED when the turbine inlet temperature is stabilized. The solenoid of the temperature datum valve is deenergized when the fuel correction is locked in. This allows a spring to move the temperature datum valve brake to the APPLIED position, resulting in the bypass control needle being locked in a corrected fuel-flow position, which will provide for a fixed percentage correction of metered fuel flow during the approach and landing. It must be understood that locking in a fuel correction never locks in a specific volume of fuel flow to the engine, but does lock in a fixed percentage of any fuel metered by the datum valve. Locking in a fuel correction will permit a more accurate control of horsepower output during the approach and landing.

Fuel, delivered to the temperature datum valve from the fuel control, must flow through the venturi. The velocity of the fuel increases as it approaches the throat of the venturi, and decreases as it flows away from the venturi throat. As a result of the velocity changes, the static pressure ($P5$) at the venturi throat is lower than the static pressure ($P4'$) at the venturi outlet. Venturi outlet ($P4'$) fuel is delivered to the pressurizing valve and the bypass control needle.

The pressurizing valve is set to open whenever venturi outlet ($P4'$) fuel pressure exceeds bypass ($P0$) pressure by approximately 50 psi. The setting of the pressurizing valve is established by a spring. When the pressurizing valve opens during an engine start, fuel flow to the engine begins. At engine shutdown, the pressurizing valve prevents drainage of fuel out of the temperature datum valve. Restriction to the flow of fuel through the pressurizing valve and fuel nozzles is constant when the pressurizing valve is open, and the fuel nozzles' metering valves are fully open. Thus, venturi outlet ($P4'$) pressure will determine the volume of fuel which will flow to the fuel nozzles through the pressurizing valve.

The volume of fuel, which will flow through an orifice, is a function of restriction (orifice size) and the pressure differential across the orifice. Thus, the amount of fuel which will pass through the orifice established by the bypass control needle is a function of the difference in pressure between venturi outlet ($P4'$) and metered bypass ($P6$) pressure. The orifice, established by the bypass control needle, can be made larger or smaller by moving the needle out of or into the orifice opening. Movement of the bypass control needle is accomplished by means of the motor generator, which is controlled by the temperature datum control (amplifier). The rpm of the motor generator is lessened by the reduction gear and a spur gear train so that the bypass control needle may be moved very slowly when the motor rotates. The motor is reversible, and its direction of rotation is determined by the signal sent to the motor by the temperature datum control. The output of the generator, which is driven by the motor, is a function of motor rpm, and "tells" the temperature datum control how fast the fuel correction is being made by the bypass needle. The brake solenoid controls the position of a brake which acts on the shaft of the motor. The brake is spring-loaded to the LOCKED position, and is "released" when the brake solenoid is energized. When the brake is locked, the bypass control needle cannot move because the motor shaft and reduction gearing cannot rotate. A two-way compression spring is compressed whenever the bypass control needle is moved by the motor. This spring will return the bypass control needle to NULL if the brake is released and the motor has no torque.

The maximum "put" stop establishes how far the motor can move the bypass control needle into the orifice. As this orifice decreases in size, its restriction to the flow of venturi outlet ($P4'$) fuel through it increases. This results in a smaller percentage of fuel flow through the bypass control needle, and a greater percentage of fuel flow through the pressurizing valve and fuel nozzles. The 20 percent take stop and 50 percent take stop are used to establish how far the motor can move the bypass control needle out of its orifice. As the orifice size increases, its restriction to the flow of venturi outlet ($P4'$) fuel through it decreases. Thus, a greater percentage of fuel flows through the bypass control needle, and a smaller percentage flows through the pressurizing valve and fuel nozzles. The take reset solenoid valve is used to establish the take mechanism (rack and piston) against either the 20 percent stop or 50 percent stop. When the take reset solenoid is energized, metered bypass ($P6$) fuel is ported on both sides of the take mechanism piston, and bypass ($P0$) is on the end of the rack. The differential areas and forces act to position the take mechanism rack against the 50 percent take stop. When the solenoid is deenergized, one side of the take mechanism piston is ported to metered bypass ($P6$) fuel, and the other side is ported to bypass ($P0$) fuel. Since metered bypass ($P6$) fuel is the higher pressure, the take mechanism moves, and the piston contacts the 20 percent take stop. When the mechanism moves from the 50 percent stop to the 20 percent stop, the rack rotates a pinion. This rotation moves the pinion nearer to the end of the bypass control needle due to worm gear action. The take reset solenoid valve is deenergized at 13,000 rpm. Therefore, maximum possible take is 20 percent at all rpm in excess of 13,000. The null orifice adjustment has an eccentric projection on one end which fits into an opening of the sleeve surrounding the bypass control needle. When the null orifice adjustment is turned, the sleeve moves in relation to the bypass control needle, and the orifice size established by the bypass control needle is varied slightly. The restriction of this orifice is thus varied to cause a slight change in the percentage of venturi outlet ($P4'$) fuel which will flow through the bypass control needle. A null orifice adjustment should be made if the peak starting turbine inlet temperatures are too high or too low.

The regulator valve is a double-ported valve that is secured to a flexible diaphragm. It is double-ported to prevent the flow through the valve from having an effect upon the valve's position. The position of the regulator valve is determined by a balance of forces acting on the diaphragm. One side of the diaphragm is ported to venturi throat pressure ($P5$), while the other side is ported to metered bypass pressure ($P6$). When the regulator valve is stabilized, venturi throat pressure ($P5$) is equal to metered bypass pressure ($P6$). If either of these pressures exceed the other, the regulator valve moves to again establish their equality.

The one-way check valve will allow the temperature datum valve to bypass fuel with a common bypass line attached to the fuel control. The one-way check valve prevents fuel, bypassed by the fuel control, from flowing onto the temperature datum valve. Thus, during cranking up to 2200 rpm, any fuel bypassed by the fuel control cannot reverse flow into the temperature datum valve and through the pressurizing valve to the fuel nozzles.

The entire system is illustrated in Fig. 13-3.

HAMILTON STANDARD MODEL JFC25 FUEL CONTROL

General description

The JFC25 fuel control is designed to control the engine in either forward or reverse thrust operation under all operating conditions. Two control levers are provided. One to control the engine during forward or reverse operation, and the other to effect engine shutdown and starting by closing and opening a fuel shutoff valve. Provision has been made for future incorporation of an emergency system in the control.

The fuel control accurately governs the engine steady-state selected speed, acceleration, deceleration, maximum burner pressure, thrust reversal, and provides a number of auxiliary signals. The speed-governing

system is of the proportional or droop type (Figs. 12-14 and 12-15).

The JFC25 may be considered as consisting of a metering and a computing system. The metering system selects the rate of fuel flow to be applied to the engine burners in accordance with the amount of thrust demanded by the pilot, but subject to engine operating limitations as scheduled by the computing system as a result of its monitoring various operating parameters. The computing section senses and combines various engine operational parameters to control the output of the metering section of the fuel control during all regimes of engine and aircraft operation. This fuel control, with some modification, is similar to the ones used on the JT3 and JT4 turbojet engines.

Principles of operation (typical control) (Fig. 12-16)

The metering system operates in the following manner. High-pressure fuel is supplied to the control inlet from the engine-driven pump. This fuel initially encounters the filtration system which consists of a coarse filter and a fine filter. The coarse filter protects the metering section against damage by fuel contaminants. This filter will open when clogged to permit continued operation with unfiltered fuel. The fine filter protects the computing section against damage by fuel contaminants. This filter is self-cleaning, whereby trapped particles are removed and passed through the metering system. The fuel next encounters the *pressure-regulating valve*. This valve is designed to maintain a constant pressure differential across the throttle valve. All high-pressure fuel in excess of that required to maintain this pressure differential is bypassed to pump interstage pressure by the pressure-regulating valve. The valve is servo controlled, whereby the actual pressure drop is compared to a selected pressure drop and any error is hydraulically compensated. The error resets the pressure-regulating-valve spring on this valve so that suf-

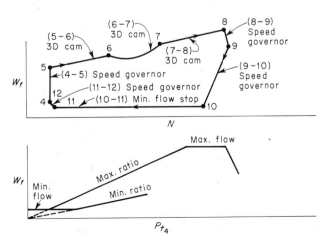

FIG. 12-14 *Characteristic fuel-flow curves.*

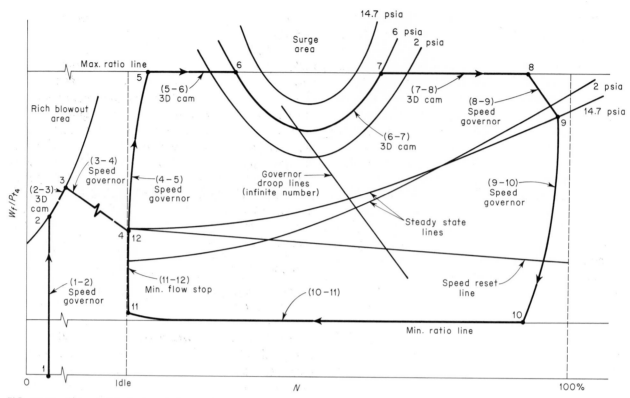

FIG. 12-15 *Characteristic fuel-control operating curves.*

ficient high-pressure fuel is bypassed to maintain the selected pressure drop. The high-pressure fuel, as altered by the pressure-regulating valve, then passes through the metering valve. This valve consists of a contoured plunger which is positioned by the computing section of the control within a sharp-edged orifice. By virtue of the constant pressure drop maintained across the valve, the fuel flow is proportional to the position of the plunger. An adjustable stop is provided to limit the motion of this plunger in the decrease fuel direction to permit selection of the proper minimum fuel flow.

The final component to act upon the metered flow prior to its entry into the fuel manifold is the minimum pressure and shutoff valve. This valve is designed to shut off the flow of metered fuel to the engine when the pilot moves his shutoff lever to the OFF position. This generates a high-pressure signal by means of the throttle operated pilot valve, which acts on the spring side of the shutoff valve, forcing it down against a seat, thus shutting off the flow of fuel to the engine. When the shutoff lever is moved into the ON position, the high-pressure signal is replaced by pump interstage pressure, and when metered fuel pressure has increased sufficiently to overcome the spring force, the valve opens and fuel flow to the engine is initiated. Thereafter, the valve will provide a minimum operating pressure within the fuel control, ensuring that adequate

pressure is always available for operation of the servos and valves at minimum flow conditions.

The computing system positions the throttle valve to control the steady-state engine speed, acceleration, and deceleration. This is accomplished by using the ratio W_f/P_B (the ratio of metered fuel flow to engine burner pressure) as a control parameter. This parameter has been pioneered by Hamilton Standard and is presently used on all of Hamilton Standard main fuel controls.

The positioning of the throttle valve by means of the W_f/P_B parameter is achieved through a multiplying system whereby the W_f/P_B signal for acceleration, deceleration, or steady-state speed control is multiplied by a signal proportional to P_B to provide the required fuel flow.

P_B is sensed as follows: A metallic bellows is internally exposed to P_B and the resulting force is opposed by an evacuated bellows of equal size. The net force, which is proportional to absolute burner pressure, is transmitted through a lever system to a set of rollers whose position is proportional to W_f/P_B. These rollers ride between the above lever and a second lever. Thus the force proportional to P_B is transmitted through the rollers to the second lever. Any change in the roller position (W_f/P_B) or the P_B signals causes the upsetting of the equilibrium of this lever which results in the opening or closing of a variable or metering orifice which is supplied with regulated high-pressure fuel

FIG. 12-16 *The Hamilton Standard JFC25. Similar controls are used on the JT3 and JT4 engines. (Hamilton Standard Division, United Aircraft Corporation. From J. V. Casamassa and R. D. Bent, "Jet Aircraft Power Systems," 3d ed., McGraw-Hill Book Company, New York, 1965.)*

through a fixed-bleed orifice. The opening or closing of the metering orifice modulates the fuel pressure between the two orifices, and this pressure is used to control the position of a piston attached to the throttle valve plunger. The motion of this piston compresses or relaxes a spring which will return the second lever to its equilibrium position.

Deceleration control is accomplished by placing a minimum stop on the W_f/P_B signal. This provides a linear relationship between W_f and P_B which results in blowout-free decelerations. This stop is adjustable.

Acceleration control is accomplished by placing a maximum stop on the W_f/P_B signal. This stop is positioned by a three-dimensional cam which is rotated by a signal proportional to engine speed and translated by a signal proportional to engine inlet pressure. The three-dimensional cam is so contoured as to define a schedule of W_f/P_B versus engine speed for each value of engine inlet pressure. This combination will permit engine accelerations which avoid the over-temperature and surge limits of the engine without compromising engine acceleration time.

Engine speed is sensed by an engine-driven flyweight governor of the centrifugal type which controls the movement of the speed servo piston through a pilot valve. When speed changes, the flyweight force varies and the pilot valve is positioned to meter high-pressure fuel to the speed servo piston or to allow it to drain. The motion of this piston repositions the pilot valve until the speed-sensing system returns to equilibrium. The position of the servo piston is indicative of actual engine speed. This piston incorporates a rack which meshes with a gear segment on the acceleration three-dimensional cam to provide the speed signal for acceleration limiting. The piston is also utilized to control selected engine speed as described below.

The compressor inlet pressure-sensing servo translates the speed set cam in proportion to expansion or contraction of the evacuated bellows for speed reset at altitude.

Decreased compressor inlet pressure will expand the sensing bellows allowing servo pressure to bleed at the flapper valve. Servo pressure decreasing, high pressure will move the servo to the left translating the cam to the right, causing the cam follower to rise in conformity to the contour of the cam, therefore decreasing the W_f/P_B ratio. The acceleration cam is simultaneously translated.

As the servo moves to the left, spring pressure is diminished, tending to close the flapper valve, thereby allowing sufficient servo pressure to accumulate so that a new position of equilibrium is established.

With increased CIP (compressor inlet pressure), the flapper valve will tend to close further, thereby causing servo pressure to overcome pump discharge pressure

acting on a smaller area, resulting in a reverse action to that effected by a decreased CIP.

Engine speed control is accomplished by comparing the actual speed as indicated by the speed servo piston to the desired speed as selected by the pilot through a power lever operated three-dimensional cam. This cam defines schedules of W_f/P_B versus power lever angle (selected speed) for each value of CIP. The deviation of desired speed from the actual speed, or the speed error, effects a change in the W_f/P_B signal in the multiplying linkage. This causes an increase or decrease in fuel flow to effect the necessary speed correction. The speed-setting three-dimensional cam is rotated by the pilot's power lever and translated by a signal proportional to CIP. The CIP signal is obtained from the CIP servo system previously described. The bias of selected engine speed by CIP is required to compensate for the speed governing error due to CIP variations which is normally encountered with proportional speed controls.

The engine thrust reversal mechanism consists of a cam-operated pilot valve which meters compressor discharge pressure bleed air to the thrust reversal actuators when the power lever is retarded to the REVERSE position. The speed-setting cam incorporates a reverse power regime to schedule higher engine speeds as the power lever is retarded beyond idle into reverse. The cam includes a flat or idle portion prior to the initiation of thrust reversal.

Auxiliary functions include a throttle-operated pilot valve which provides the shutoff signal to the shutoff and minimum pressure valve, and a pressure signal to the manifold drain valve. The valve is positioned by a shutoff lever operated cam so that the signals are generated at the desired lever positions. The pilot valve also provides a windmill bypass feature when the shutoff valve is closed. This feature bleeds the throttle valve downstream pressure to increase the throttle-valve pressure drop. This allows the pressure-regulating valve to continue to operate normally. Thus damage to the pumps due to excessive pressures is prevented during engine windmilling.

WOODWARD TYPE 1307 FUEL CONTROL
(Fig. 12-17)

General description

The Woodward main fuel control is used on the J79 and CJ805 series turbojet engines, and provides the following engine control functions:

1 Maintains engine speed (rpm) according to the throttle schedule.
2 Schedules maximum and minimum fuel rate limits.
3 Limits maximum compressor discharge pressure limit ($P3$) by limiting fuel flow.

4 Reduces maximum speed (rpm) limit in the low engine inlet temperature range.

5 Provides a pilot-actuated reset of minimum fuel, when required, for high-altitude starting.

6 Resets the flight idle speed as a function of compressor inlet air temperature.

7 Controls the position of the inlet guide vanes by providing control fuel for the inlet guide vane actuators.

8 Provides the exhaust-nozzle area control with an interlock signal when the engine is being accelerated at maximum fuel limit (J79 only).

9 Provides the afterburner pump with a pressure signal as a function of power-lever position and engine speed (J79 only).

To enable the control to perform the above objectives, there must be inputs in addition to the supply of fuel. The inputs include the compressor inlet temperature, the compressor discharge pressure ($P3$), and the speed of the main shaft. These three inputs, referred to as parameters, and a power-lever (throttle) setting determine the outputs of the control. The compressor inlet temperature is sensed by the compressor inlet temperature sensor which is a separate piece of equipment. The outputs of the control include a controlled fuel supply to the combustion chamber of the engine, a control fuel pressure signal for the inlet guide vane actuators, an interlock pressure signal to the exhaust-nozzle area control, and an afterburner pressure signal to the afterburner fuel control.

NOTE: Sections dealing with afterburning and nozzle area control apply to military J79 engines only.

The airframe boost pump supplies fuel to the main fuel pump from the fuel tank. The boost pump is a low-pressure pump with a discharge pressure ($P0$) that does not exceed 65 psia. Working with the airframe boost pump as a unit is another low-pressure pump, the engine boost pump. These two pumps supply the main fuel pump, which, in turn, supplies the main fuel control with a maximum fuel flow of about 20,000 lb/hr, at a pressure ($P1$) that ranges from 150 to about 900 psig. Fuel is bypassed from the regulator to the engine boost pump discharge line at case pressure (Pb). A line also bypasses fuel from the regulator to the airframe boost pump discharge line at $P0$ pressure.

Principles of operation

NOTE: All numbers refer to Fig. 12-17.

Maximum fuel is supplied to the control inlet port (107) from the main fuel pump discharge at pressure $P1$. The flow of fuel is divided at the metering valve, sending fuel to the engine at one pressure ($P2$) and a bypass flow to the pump inlet at a second pressure (Pb).

Fuel inlet pressure ($P1$) and outlet pressure ($P2$) are applied to opposite sides of a sensing land on the differential pilot valve plunger (110). Inlet pressure ($P1$) on the bottom side of the land is opposed by $P2$ plus the force of the pressure regulator reference spring (111). The controlling action of the valve plunger regulates pressure $P4$ until the bypass flow causes the force produced by $P1 - P2$ to be equal to the force of the spring. As $P2$ increases, or $P1$ decreases, the valve plunger is forced downward by $P2$, venting $P1$ to $P4$. This action forces the bypass valve plunger (109) to reduce the opening, increasing $P1$ enough to restore the $P1 - P2$ differential and recenter the differential pilot valve plunger. When $P1$ increases, or $P2$ decreases, the valve plunger is forced upward by $P1$, venting $P4$ to Pb. This action allows $P1$ pressure to force the bypass valve plunger to the left, thus opening the port and increasing bypass flow. This decreases $P1$, restoring the $P1 - P2$ differential. Therefore a constant differential pressure is maintained across the fuel valve plunger (108), resulting in a fuel-flow rate that is a function of valve position alone, and is substantially independent of pump delivery rate or pressure level in the system. Adjustment of the specific-gravity cam (112) sets the preload on the pressure regulator reference spring (111), allowing manual compensation for differences in the density of various fuels. The $P1 - P2$ differential increases as the spring preload is increased.

Fuel at $P1$ is supplied through a filter to the pressure-regulating valve (105), which regulates the servo pressure, Pc, for the pilot valves and servos. Fuel at Pc is opposed by the pressure-regulating-valve spring (106) and case reference pressure, which is the same as bypass pressure (Pb). The combined action of the pressure and spring positions the valve plunger so that $Pc - Pb$ is essentially constant.

Flow of fuel to the engine is determined by the position of the fuel valve plunger (108), which is normally positioned by the fuel valve servo piston (30), which is controlled by the speed control plunger (67) of the governor pilot valve assembly. The two fuel limit pistons (27 and 28) act as scheduled limit stops, so the plunger action cannot cause the rate of fuel flow to exceed scheduled maximum or minimum limits.

When the fuel rate is within the scheduled limits, the fuel limit pistons are vented to Pb, exerting no force on the fuel-valve plunger (108). When this condition exists, the fuel-valve plunger is positioned by the speed control plunger (67) acting to regulate pressure on the fuel-valve servo piston (30), which in turn acts to balance a counterforce produced by Pc on the return servo piston (26). Since the fuel-valve servo piston has a surface area twice that of the return servo piston, the speed-control plunger regulates the fuel-valve plunger position by varying the pressure on the fuel-valve servo piston between the limits of Pb and Pc.

1 P3 LEVEL ADJUSTMENT
   SCREW
2 P3 SENSOR ADJUSTMENT
   SPRING
3 P3 AUXILIARY BELLOWS
   ASSEMBLY
4 P3 AUXILIARY BELLOWS
   TRANSFER SPRING
5 P3 BELLOWS ORIFICE
   DIAPHRAGM
6 P3 BELLOWS ASSEMBLY
7 P3 SENSOR-VALVE SEAT
   ASSEMBLY
8 P3 SENSOR DAMPER
   PISTON
9 P3 FEEDBACK FULCRUM
   ADJUSTMENT
10 P3 FEEDBACK LEVER

11 P3 FEEDBACK SPRING
12 P3 SERVO PISTON
13 P3 PILOT VALVE PLUNGER
14 ORIFICE
15 P3 REFERENCE BELLOWS
   ASSEMBLY
16 STEM OF P3 REFERENCE
   VALVE
17 STEM OF EXTERNAL P3
   REFERENCE VALVE
18 EXTERNAL P3 REFERENCE
   BELLOWS ASSEMBLY
19 P3 REFERENCE-PRESSURE
   CHECK-VALVE ASSEMBLY
20 DRAIN TO AIRFRAME
   BOOST PUMP
21 TO OVERBOARD DRAIN
   (ATMOSPHERIC PRESSURE)
22 P3 REFERENCE PRESSURE
   RELIEF VALVE ASSEMBLY
23 UNDERSHOOT VALVE
   PLUNGER
24 UNDERSHOOT VALVE
   SPRING
25 ORIFICE
26 RETURN SERVO PISTON
27 FUEL LIMIT PISTON
28 FUEL LIMIT PISTON
29 FUEL SERVO LEVER
30 FUEL-VALVE SERVO PISTON
31 VARIABLE-COMPENSATION
   PLUNGER
32 BUFFER-VALVE PISTON
33 BUFFER SPRING
34 COMPRESSOR-INLET-
   TEMPERATURE SENSOR
35 COMPRESSOR-INLET-
   TEMPERATURE FEEDBACK
   LEVER

36 COMPRESSOR-INLET-
   TEMPERATURE PILOT
   VALVE PLUNGER
37 COMPRESSOR-INLET-
   TEMPERATURE PILOT
   VALVE SLEEVE
38 NOZZLE LOCK-VALVE
   PLUNGER

39 ON-OFF SPEED HIGH-
   POINT ADJUSTING SCREW
40 ON-OFF SPEED LOW-
   POINT ADJUSTMENT
   SCREW
41 ON-OFF SPEED ADJUSTING
   PISTON
42 PILOT VALVE PLUNGER

43 TACHOMETER SERVO
   PISTON
44 ON-OFF SPEED LEVER
45 RACK OF THE
   TACHOMETER SERVO
   PISTON ROD
46 GEAR
47 SPEED FEEDBACK CAM

48 TACHOMETER FEEDBACK
   FOLLOWER LEVER
49 TACHOMETER LINKAGE
   FULCRUM ADJUSTMENT
   SCREW
50 TACHOMETER SPEEDER
   SPRING ADJUSTING SCREW
51 TACHOMETER FEEDBACK
   LEVER

FIG. 12-17 Schematic diagram of the type 1307 fuel control. (Woodward Governor Company)

202

94 P3 SERVO IDLER GEAR
95 P3 CAM
96 DECELERATION ADJUSTMENT SCREW
97 DECAMMING PISTON
98 FUEL SUMMING LINK
99 CAM SUMMING LINK FORK
100 FUEL-LIMIT LEVER
101 FUEL-LIMIT-LEVER PIVOT POINT
102 FUEL CAM
103 FUEL-LIMIT PLUNGER
104 LINKAGE LOADING SPRING
105 PRESSURE-REGULATING VALVE
106 PRESSURE-REGULATING-VALVE SPRING
107 REGULATOR INLET PORT
108 FUEL-VALVE PLUNGER
109 BYPASS-VALVE PLUNGER
110 DIFFERENTIAL-PILOT-VALVE PLUNGER
111 PRESSURE-REGULATOR REFERENCE SPRING
112 SPECIFIC-GRAVITY CAM
113 INLET-GUIDE-VANE PLUNGER SPRING
114 INLET-GUIDE-VANE PLUNGER
115 INLET-GUIDE-VANE VALVE DISK
116 INLET-GUIDE-VANE VALVE STEM SPRING
117 INLET-GUIDE-VANE FEEDBACK GEAR SEGMENT
118 POWER-ACTUATOR PLUNGER
119 FEEDBACK GEAR
120 INLET-GUIDE-VANE-CAM FOLLOWER LEVER
121 INLET-GUIDE-VANE-CAM STYLUS
122 INLET-GUIDE-VANE CAM
123 INLET-GUIDE-VANE SHAFT ASSEMBLY
124 FEEDBACK CABLE
125 INLET-GUIDE-VANE SERVO

INCREASE RPM

52 TACHOMETER REFERENCE SPRING
53 TACHOMETER PILOT VALVE PLUNGER
54 FLYWEIGHTS OF THE TACHOMETER BALLHEAD ASSEMBLY
55 BIMETAL STRIP ASSEMBLY
56 IDLE SPEED ADJUSTMENT
57 HIGH-TEMPERATURE SPEED RESET LEVER SCREW
58 COMPRESSOR INLET TEMPERATURE SERVO PISTON
59 THREE-DIMENSIONAL CAM END PLATE
60 HIGH-TEMPERATURE SPEED RESET ARM

61 HIGH-TEMPERATURE SPEED RESET ADJUSTING SCREW
62 HIGH-TEMPERATURE SPEED RESET CAM
63 HIGH-TEMPERATURE SPEED RESET LEVER
64 GOVERNOR REFERENCE SPRING
65 BIMETAL STRIP ASSEMBLY
66 FLYWEIGHTS OF THE GOVERNOR BALLHEAD ASSEMBLY
67 SPEED-CONTROL PLUNGER

68 MILITARY SPEED ADJUSTMENT
69 SPEED-CONTROL LEVER
70 SPEED-CONTROL-LEVER LEAF SPRING
71 SPEED-CONTROL-LEVER BEARING ROLLER
72 MAXIMUM-SPEED RESET CRANK
73 MAXIMUM-SPEED RESET LEVER SCREW
74 MAXIMUM-SPEED RESET LEVER
75 POWER-LEVER SHAFT

76 SPEED-SETTING CAM
77 AFTERBURNER SIGNAL ADJUSTMENT SCREW
78 AFTERBURNER SIGNAL LEVER
79 AFTERBURNER VALVE PLUNGER
80 SHUTDOWN-BYPASS-VALVE PLUNGER
81 SHUTDOWN-VALVE PLUNGER
82 SHUTDOWN-BYPASS-VALVE LEVER
83 ORIFICE
84 SOLENOID RESET VALVE

85 MINIMUM-FUEL ADJUSTMENT SCREW
86 MINIMUM-FUEL RESET ADJUSTMENT PISTON
87 MINIMUM-FUEL RESET SPRING
88 MINIMUM-FUEL RESET ADJUSTMENT CAM
89 CAM SUMMING IDLER LEVER
90 CORRECTED FUEL CAM FOLLOWER
91 CORRECTED FUEL CAM
92 CAM SUMMING LEVER
93 PIVOT OF CAM SUMMING LEVER

When the speed governor is in transient condition, the following action takes place. The fuel-valve servo piston (30) is supplied with fuel at Pc at an underspeed signal or with fuel at Pb at an overspeed signal through the action of the governor pilot valve assembly. The flyweights of the governor ballhead assembly (66) act on the speed-control plunger. Their centrifugal force is translated to axial force at the toes of the flyweights; this force is opposed by the force of the governor reference spring (64). The position of the speed-setting cam (76) determines the compression of this spring and the speed that the engine must attain so that the flyweights will balance the force of the spring. The speed-setting cam is adjusted by rotation of the power-lever shaft (75). Uniform governor operation is accomplished through a compensating system consisting of a buffer valve piston (32) floating between two buffer springs (33), a compensating land on the speed control plunger, and a variable-compensation plunger (31). When the speed of the engine falls below its set value, the governor reference spring overcomes the reduced centrifugal force of the flyweights, and the speed control plunger moves downward. This downward movement uncovers the port at the upper end of the plunger, permitting fuel at Pc to enter the passage leading to the fuel valve servo piston (30) by displacing the buffer-valve piston. The change in pressure forces the servo piston downward, rotating the fuel servo lever (29) clockwise, opening the fuel-valve plunger (108). Displacement of the buffer-valve piston compresses one of the buffer springs (33) causing a pressure differential across the buffer-valve piston (32) which is transmitted to the compensating land of the speed-control plunger. The greater pressure on the lower side of this land acts to supplement the force of the flyweights, causing the speed-control plunger to close before the required speed has been attained. As fuel leaks across the variable-compensation plunger, this false speed signal is dissipated and the buffer-valve piston recenters; at the same rate the engine speed returns to normal. Action resulting from engine overspeed is similar but in the reverse direction. Increased centrifugal force of the flyweights, due to increased engine speed, overcomes the force of the governor reference spring, resulting in an upward movement of the speed-control plunger. This plunger movement opens the regulating port to Pb, thereby causing the return servo piston to move the fuel valve in the closed direction to decrease the flow of fuel. While this action is taking place, the decreased pressure on the left-hand end of the buffer-valve piston allows it to move to the right. The resulting pressure differential, caused by the buffer-valve piston compressing the spring on the right-hand end of the piston, acting on the compensating land of the speed-control plunger, recenters the plunger before the required speed

is attained. As fuel leaks across the variable-compensation plunger, the pressure differential due to this action is dissipated, at the same rate as the engine speed and flyweight force, to normal. The buffer-valve piston is designed to bypass fuel after a given displacement, in order to accommodate large flows of fuel either to or from the fuel-valve servo piston, resulting from abrupt changes in fuel requirements. The bypass ports of the buffer-valve piston are offset so that the piston must be displaced to a greater degree during a reduction in the flow of fuel, therefore reducing the undershoot when the speed is suddenly reduced to idle. To keep the buffer-valve piston displaced while the engine is decelerating, the undershoot-valve plunger (23) maintains a minimum pressure on the fuel-valve servo piston. This pressure balance is accomplished by the end of the plunger being exposed to the same pressure as the servo piston. When this pressure falls below a specified minimum, the undershoot-valve spring (24) overcomes the upward force of the plunger forcing it downward and allowing fuel at Pc to bleed through an orifice (25) of the plunger to the servo piston. This action maintains pressure in the line at a level sufficient to keep the buffer-valve piston displaced. As the pressure increases, the undershoot-valve plunger closes and the Pc supply is cut off. An orifice in the valve plunger drains valve leakage to Pb.

The maximum fuel limit, or the acceleration fuel limit, is determined by three inputs received by the regulator from the engine. The three inputs, compressor discharge pressure ($P3$), regulator speed, and compressor air inlet temperature, work together according to the relation: maximum fuel limit = $f(P3) \times f$(speed and compressor inlet temperature). This relation is established by a mechanical-hydraulic computer in the following manner.

The $P3$ transducer changes $P3$ pressure into an angular displacement of the $P3$ cam (95). Fuel at $P1$ flows through an orifice (14) at pressure $P5$ into the $P3$ bellows assembly (6). $P5$ pressure is opposed by $P3$ and the $P3$ sensor adjustment spring (2). The opposing forces regulate the flow through the port of the $P3$ sensor valve seat assembly (7) which acts as the $P5$ regulating valve to maintain a constant pressure differential, $P5 - P3$. The $P3$ auxiliary bellows assembly (3) normally has no differential pressure across it and is provided as an emergency substitute for the $P3$ bellows. Should the $P3$ bellows fail, $P5$ would in effect be vented to the $P3$ bellows orifice diaphragm (5). The pressure drop across the orifice causes the diaphragm to overcome the force of the $P3$ auxiliary bellows transfer spring (4), and move upward, closing the $P3$ connection to the $P3$ bellows (6). This results in continued normal operation through the $P3$ auxiliary bellows assembly (3). Pressure $P5$ on the right end of the $P3$ pilot-valve plunger (13) is balanced by the force of the P3 feedback spring (11) and P3 reference pressure on the left end of the plunger. The P3 pilot valve plunger regulates the supply of fuel to or from the P3 servo piston (12). The servo piston is opposed by Pc supplied to the left end of the piston and has half the surface area. As P3 increases, P5 also increases, applying more force on the right end of the P3 pilot valve plunger, moving it to the left. This movement vents Pc to the right end of the P3 servo piston, forcing it to the left. As the piston moves to the left, the P3 feedback spring is compressed, the P3 feedback lever (10) transmits this force to the pilot valve plunger, moving it to the right, closing the port, and stopping the Pc supply to the servo piston. As P3 decreases, the reverse action takes place, the pilot valve moves to the right, venting the servo piston to Pb (case pressure), allowing the servo to move to the right. This movement decreases the tension on the P3 feedback spring allowing it to recenter the pilot valve. Movement of the P3 servo piston (12) is transmitted to the P3 cam (95) through the P3 servo rack and the P3 servo idler gear (94), resulting in a rotation of the cam in proportion to P3. The cam is machined to produce a follower output proportional to the log f(P3) and moves one end of the cam summing lever (92) accordingly. Setting the P3 feedback fulcrum adjustment (9) sets the ratio of P3 servo piston travel to P3. The evacuated P3 reference bellows assembly (15) regulates the flow through the stem of the P3 reference valve (16) to produce a constant P3 reference pressure on the left end of the P3 pilot-valve plunger. This prevents random fluctuations in fuel pressure in the case from affecting calibration. Fuel passing the stem of the P3 reference valve drops to airframe boost pressure P0 and passes to the drain to airframe boost pump (20) through the P3 reference pressure check valve assembly (19). Should there be a surge of P0 between the airframe boost pump and the check valve assembly, the check valve assembly would close. Under these conditions, P0 pressure would rise between the stem of the P3 reference valve and the check valve until this slightly higher pressure would open the P3 reference pressure relief valve assembly (22) directing a small amount of fuel to the overboard drain (21). The external P3 reference bellows assembly (18) will remain inactive and the stem of the external P3 reference valve (17) will remain closed until there is a rupture or failure of the internal P3 reference bellows assembly (15). Such a failure of the internal bellows will cause the spring inside the bellows to close the valve stem, allowing the P3 reference pressure to rise. At the new higher pressure the external bellows will function, allowing fuel to pass the stem of the external P3 reference valve to the airframe boost pump or to the overboard drain.

The control speed and compressor inlet temperature

section works as follows. Rotation of the corrected fuel cam (91) and the inlet guide vane cam (122) is a function of speed and is accomplished by the tachometer ballhead assembly and an associated servo system. As engine speed increases, the centrifugal force of the flyweights of the tachometer ball head assembly (54) overcomes the opposing force of the tachometer reference spring (52), resulting in an upward movement of the tachometer pilot-valve plunger (53). This movement of the plunger vents Pc to the lower surface of the tachometer servo piston (43). Since the area on the lower surface of the piston is twice the area on the upper surface of the piston, the servo piston moves upward. The rack of the tachometer servo piston rod (45) rotates the corrected fuel cam and the inlet guide vane cam. The speed feedback cam (47) also rotates with the movement of the piston rod. This cam, in turn, depresses the tachometer feedback follower lever (48) and the tachometer feedback lever (51). This downward movement compresses the reference spring, and the tachometer pilot valve plunger is recentered, stopping the supply of Pc to the servo piston. When speed decreases, the reaction is the opposite; as the lower surface of the servo piston is vented to Pb, Pc on the upper surface forces the piston downward, and the pilot valve plunger is recentered. Movement of the servo piston (43) in relation to the speed feedback cam is set through the adjustment of the tachometer speeder spring adjusting screw (50) and the tachometer linkage fulcrum adjustment screw (49). The speeder spring adjusting screw adjusts the preload on the reference spring and has a greater effect at low speeds. Adjustment of the linkage fulcrum adjustment screw determines the feedback ratio. The corrected fuel cam and the inlet guide vane cam are positioned axially in relation to the compressor inlet temperature. Movement is initiated by the compressor inlet temperature sensor (34) and transferred to the two cams by the compressor inlet temperature servo piston (58), the compressor inlet temperature pilot valve plunger (36), and the compressor inlet temperature feedback lever (35). For each temperature input there is a unique horizontal position for the cams, resulting in a unique schedule of follower positions versus speed. The corrected fuel cam for each axial position produces a function of the controlled fuel supply over the compressor discharge pressure (P3) equal to a function of the speed as specified for the particular input temperature.

The cam summing lever (92) combines the final inputs from the corrected fuel cam (91) and the P3 cam (95), and transfers this movement through the fuel summing link (98) and cam summing link fork (99) to the fuel limit lever (100). This movement is proportional to log maximum fuel limit/P3 + log P3, which is equivalent to log maximum fuel limit/P3 × P3 or log maximum fuel limit.   The porting of the fuel-valve plunger (108) is accompanied by movement of the fuel supply fuel cam (102) so that cam follower displacement is proportional to log fuel supply.   Log maximum fuel limit and log fuel supply are compared and their difference results in a displacement of the fuel limit plunger (103). If the maximum fuel limit is greater than the fuel supply, the fuel limit lever (100) positions the fuel limit plunger so that the fuel limit piston (28) is vented to Pb.   This action permits the speed-control plunger (67) to regulate the fuel supply by controlling the pressure on the fuel-valve servo piston (30).   When the fuel supply reaches the maximum fuel limit, the fuel cam (102) has rotated clockwise, moving the left end of the fuel limit lever downward, forcing the fuel limit plunger to close the lower port.   Further movement of the fuel valve plunger is stopped since the return servo piston (26) and the fuel limit piston effectively overcome the force produced by the fuel-valve servo piston.   The accelerating fuel limit is thereafter determined as follows: The fuel limit lever (100) pivots on the summing link fork (99) and positions the fuel limit plunger (103).   This controls the fuel limit piston (28) until the governor speed matches the speed setting.   The speed control plunger (67) then rises, reducing the pressure on the fuel-valve servo piston to regulate fuel supply and maintain the set speed.

Deceleration fuel limit is established by the fuel limit plunger (103) moving upward, as a result of the rotation of the fuel cam (102) caused by a change in the speed or the speed setting.   The plunger covers the upper port leading to the deceleration fuel limit piston (27).   As the fuel-valve plunger (108) continues to close, pressure is exerted on the decamming piston (97), moving it upward.   When the piston stops, pressure builds up against the fuel limit piston (27), preventing further closing of the fuel-valve plunger until the computer output indicates a lower fuel limit.   During the upward movement of the decamming piston, it rotates the cam summing idler lever (89) counterclockwise by contacting the deceleration adjustment screw (96).   This movement moves the corrected fuel cam follower (90) away from the corrected fuel cam (91) to a position predetermined by the setting of the adjustment screw. The result is a deceleration fuel schedule equal to a constant fuel supply/$P3$, which corresponds to the deceleration fuel varying in direct proportion to $P3$.

When the fuel flow reaches the specified normal low limit, the fuel valve plunger (108) is stopped mechanically by the minimum fuel reset adjustment piston (86). The reset piston is held against the minimum fuel reset adjustment cam (88) as long as the solenoid reset valve (84) remains closed.   Switching action by the pilot opens the reset valve, venting the reset piston to overboard drain.   The solenoid reset valve is not part of the fuel regulator.   Fuel at Pc is metered to the reset piston through an orifice (83) with less capacity than the reset valve; therefore the minimum fuel reset spring (87) overcomes the force of the piston when the valve is open.   A lower minimum fuel limit is then established by the minimum fuel adjustment screw (85), limiting the travel of the fuel-valve plunger.

An auxiliary function of this control is the inlet guide vane mechanism.   The inlet guide vane cam (122) is mounted in tandem on the same shaft as the corrected fuel cam.   It produces a follower displacement proportional to a function of the engine speed and the compressor inlet temperature, expressed as a function of the speed and compressor inlet temperature.   Positioning of the inlet guide vane actuators is accomplished by a flow of fuel controlled by the inlet guide vane plunger (114).   The position of the inlet guide vane feedback gear segment (117) compares the computed position with the feedback position.   Movement of the actuator will persist until the feedback position corresponds to the schedule computed position.   This will occur when the inlet guide vane plunger is at a neutral position.   A change in speed or compressor inlet temperature repositions the inlet guide vane cam so the inlet guide vane cam stylus (121) may contact a different radius of the cam.   If the stylus is displaced to a larger radius, it rotates the inlet guide vane cam follower lever (120) and the feedback gear segment in a counterclockwise direction.   This movement forces the plunger assembly upward, venting $P1$ to the right surface of the inlet guide vane servo (125) and the left surface to the Pb.   The inlet guide vane servo (125) is not part of the control.   The servo moves toward the rod end, pulling the feedback cable (124) in the same direction. The cable turns the inlet guide vane shaft assembly (123) counterclockwise and the feedback gear segment clockwise, allowing the inlet guide vane plunger spring (113) to recenter the plunger assembly.   This action stops the servo at a position corresponding to the radius on the cam.   If the spring fails to recenter the plunger, the inlet guide vane valve stem spring (116) moves the power actuator plunger (118) and the inlet guide vane valve disk (115) downward.   This vents $P1$ to the top end of the inlet guide vane plunger, which forces the plunger down.

When speed reaches a specified maximum in relationship to compressor inlet temperature, a further decrease in compressor inlet temperature will start reducing the set maximum speed.   The three-dimensional cam end plate (59), actuated by the compressor inlet temperature servo piston (58), contacts the maximum speed reset crank (72).   This causes clockwise movement of the maximum speed reset lever (74).   The speed-control lever (69) moves in a decrease speed direction overriding the speed setting cam (76). This is done by the speed-control lever leaf spring (70) yielding, allowing the speed-control lever to shift downward in relation to the speed-control lever bearing roller (71). The point that compressor inlet temperature will start limiting maximum speed is set by the adjustment of the maximum speed reset lever screw (73).

When speed decreases to a specified minimum in relationship to compressor inlet temperature, a further increase in compressor inlet temperature will start increasing the set idle speed. The three-dimensional cam end plate (59), actuated by the compressor inlet temperature servo piston, contacts the high-temperature speed reset arm (60) turning it and the high-temperature speed reset cam (62) in a clockwise direction. The cam forces the high-temperature speed reset lever (63) to rotate in a counterclockwise direction. This depresses the governor reference spring (64), resulting in a higher speed setting. The temperature at which the idle speed setting begins to increase is set by the adjustment of the high-temperature speed reset adjusting screw (61). The maximum idle limit is adjusted by the high-temperature speed reset lever screw (57).

The speed signals function as follows. If the engine has not exceeded the specified speed value, the pilot valve plunger (42) will supply P1 to the nozzle lock valve plunger (38). If the specified speed value is exceeded, the ON–OFF speed lever (44) will raise the pilot valve plunger, venting the nozzle lock plunger to Pb. The same action will supply P1 to the afterburner valve plunger (79). As P1 is supplied to the afterburner valve plunger, P1 also acts on the ON–OFF speed adjusting piston (41), raising it. This changes the fulcrum of the ON–OFF speed lever from the ON–OFF speed high-point adjusting screw (39) to the ON–OFF speed low-point adjustment screw (40). Under this condition the pilot-valve plunger will continue to supply P1 to the afterburner valve plunger and the ON–OFF speed adjusting piston until the speed falls below a lower specified value. When the speed falls below the lower specified value, the pilot valve plunger moves downward, venting the afterburner valve plunger to Pb. This action allows the ON–OFF speed-adjusting piston to drop the fulcrum of the ON–OFF speed lever to the specified speed value adjusting screw. With the pilot-valve plunger down, P1 is again vented to the nozzle lock valve plunger.

The nozzle lock signal, another auxiliary function, operates as follows. The nozzle lock valve plunger (38), supplied with P1 from the pilot-valve plunger, is also subject to the same pressure applied to the acceleration fuel limit piston (28). When fuel is being scheduled at the maximum acceleration rate, the pressure applied to the fuel limit piston acts on the bottom of the nozzle lock plunger, forcing it upward. This action vents the P1 pressure to the exhaust-nozzle area control.

The power-lever shaft (75) rotates to provide four scheduled inputs received by the main fuel control.

1 *Speed setting*—The position of the speed setting cam (76) determines the load on the governor reference spring (64) by positioning the speed control lever (69). The military speed adjustment (68) adjusts the fulcrum of the speed control lever to the military speed setting. The idle speed adjustment (56) acts as a stop for the speed control lever to set the idle speed.

2 *Stopcock operation*—If the power-lever shaft is rotated to an extreme counterclockwise position, the shutdown valve plunger (81) will be forced upward to a closed position. This action stops the flow of fuel to the engine regardless of the position of the fuel-valve plunger (108).

3 *Shutdown bypass valve operation*—When the shutdown valve plunger closes, it forces the shutdown bypass valve lever (82) to open the shutdown bypass valve plunger (80). This reduces P2 by venting it to Pb, allowing the differential pilot valve plunger (110) to continue regulating P1 − P2 and to maintain P1 to operate the inlet guide vane servo while unloading the supply pump.

4 *Afterburner pressure signal*—When the afterburner signal lever (78) rotates with the power-lever shaft in the increase speed direction, it depresses the afterburner valve plunger. This action opens the port to the afterburner pump at a predetermined power-lever setting, adjusted by the afterburner signal adjustment screw (77).

To compensate for the effect of changes in fuel temperature, bimetal strip assemblies (55 and 65) are used in parallel with the reference springs on the speed control plunger (67) and the tachometer pilot valve plunger (53).

FUEL PUMPS

Fuel pumps for gas turbine engines generally employ one or two gear-type pumping elements. Some pumps also incorporate an integral centrifugal boost stage. If the pump contains two gear stages, they may be connected in series as on the JT3C and D engine, in parallel as on the CJ805 engine, or either way as is the case with the 501-D13.

The Chandler Evans Corporation is one of the principal manufacturers of fuel pumps, which, like fuel controls, are produced in a wide variety of designs. Described and pictured in this section are several representative examples of this unit as used on the JT4, JT3C and D, CJ805-23, and 501-D13.

SINGLE-GEAR ELEMENT WITH CENTRIFUGAL BOOST (JT4) *(Fig. 12-18)*

Fuel enters the pump at the fuel INLET port, flows across the centrifugal boost element, out the INTRCLR

PUMP DISCHARGE
PRESSURE TAP (P₄)

"SEAL DRAIN"

GEAR ELEMENT

DISCHARGE TO
FUEL CONTROL

AFTER FILTER
PRESSURE TAP (P₃)

FILTER

FUEL CONTROL
"BYPASS" RETURN
PORT

RELIEF VALVE

"INTRCLR RET"
FUEL PORT

"INTRCLR OUT"
FUEL PORT

IMPELLER

IMPELLER DISCHARGE
PRESSURE TAP (P₂)

CHECK
VALVE

TO GEAR
LUBRICATION
AREA

INLET PRESSURE TAP (P₁)

FUEL FROM FUEL
CONTROL AT BODY
PRESSURE

"INLET" FUEL

	INLET FUEL
	INTERSTAGE FUEL
	DISCHARGE FUEL
	SEAL DRAIN

FIG. 12-18 *Single-gear-element pump with centrifugal boost stage.* (Chandler Evans Corporation)

OUT (intercooler out) port to the fuel deicing heat exchanger, returning to the pump through the INTRCLR RET port. The fuel then passes through the inlet screen assembly, the main gear stage, and out the DISCHARGE port to the engine main fuel control. Fuel not required by the main fuel control is returned to the pump through the BYPASS port, located schematically between the impeller and the inlet screen assembly. Fuel leakage from the main fuel control is returned to the pump via the low-pressure return port.

Fuel entering the pump at the INLET port is boosted by the centrifugal pumping element (gear driven centrifugal impeller) prior to entering the single positive-displacement gear-type pumping element. The pressure rise across the centrifugal boost element (boost discharge pressure minus inlet pressure) is a function of impeller rpm and fuel flow and reaches a maximum of approximately 70 psi at 3710 pump rpm. Fuel pressure is further increased across the gear-type pumping element, with gear stage discharge pressure which is controlled by main fuel control pressure regulation, reaching a maximum of 765 psig at rated conditions.

Additional pump components and their functions are as follows:

1 *High-pressure relief valve*—The piston-type spring-loaded valve

is designed to limit the pressure rise across the main gear stage (discharge minus after filter pressure) and begins relieving at approximately 825 psi rise, bypassing the full output of the pump internally to the inlet side of the inlet screen assembly without exceeding a pressure rise of 900 psi.

2 *Slippage check valve*—The spring-loaded ball check valve is designed to insure positive pump lubrication pressures at high altitude in the event of pump operation with negative inlet pressures, such as might be experienced with failure of the aircraft tank-mounted boost pumps. The pressure differential across this valve ranges from 10 to 19 psi.

3 *Self-relieving inlet screen assembly*—The inlet screen assembly, fabricated from 40 by 40 mesh stainless steel wire with a perforated outer stainless steel shell reinforcement, is designed to limit the pressure drop across the screen element in the presence of ice or contaminant, to a maximum of 10 psi.

4 Several pressure measuring taps are provided in the pump for use on the flow bench.

DOUBLE-GEAR ELEMENTS (SERIES) WITH NO CENTRIFUGAL STAGE (JT3C AND JT3D)
(Fig. 12-19)

This pump includes the following basic components: inlet fuel filter with self-relieving valve, two positive-displacement gear-type pumping elements, two relief valves, one check valve, one control valve, and one drive shaft equipped with a rotary seal.

Two positive-displacement gear-type pump elements (boost stage and main stage) operate in series to supply fuel to the engine fuel control. The boost stage acts as a pressure boost for the main stage, which supplies the fuel to the engine fuel control. Control of internal fuel pressures and main stage discharge pressure is maintained by a group of three valves. The pump is installed on the engine and functions as follows.

Power to drive the pump is supplied by the engine through a mounting pad which accommodates the main drive shaft spline. Exterior plumbing brings fuel to:

1 Inlet port, FUEL IN

2 Fuel from the engine fuel regulator at case pressure to the bypass return port, BY PS RET

3 Engine fuel controller main bypass fuel to the main stage return port, PRIM RET

4 Fuel from the boost stage discharge port, SEC OUT through the engine fuel deicer system to the boost stage return port, SEC RET

5 Fuel from the main stage discharge port, PRIM OUT to the engine fuel controller

Under normal operating conditions, fuel flows through the pump from the FUEL IN port and the inlet fuel filter element and self-relieving valve to the boost stage, out the SEC OUT port to the SEC RET port, to the main stage and out of the PRIM OUT port to the engine fuel controller. Fuel not required by the engine is returned to the pump by the fuel control through the PRIM RET and BY PS RET ports.

INLET FUEL
PRESSURE TAP
(AFTER FILTER)

FUEL CONTROL
BY-PASS FUEL
RETURN PORT
"BY PS RET"

INLET FILTER
ELEMENT COVER

BOOST STAGE
DISCHARGE PORT
"SEC OUT"

BOOST STAGE
RETURN PORT
"SEC RET"

MAIN STAGE
DISCHARGE PORT
"PRIM OUT"

MAIN STAGE
RETURN PORT
"PRIM RET"

INLET FUEL
PORT
"FUEL IN"

MAIN STAGE
INLET
CHECK VALVE "B"

MAIN STAGE
DISCHARGE
PRESSURE TAP

MAIN STAGE
RETURN
PRESSURE TAP

NOTE:

MAIN STAGE PRESSURE RELIEF VALVE "A",
BOOST STAGE PRESSURE REGULATING VALVE "D",
AND BOOST STAGE
DISCHARGE PRESSURE TAP
ARE LOCATED ON BACK SIDE OF PUMP AND
DO NOT SHOW IN THIS VIEW.

SEAL DRAIN

(a)

FROM

AIRCRAFT
FUEL
TANK

A RELIEF VALVE
B RELIEF VALVE
C CHECK VALVE
D SECOND STAGE
E MAIN-FUEL-SYSTEM RELIEF
  VALVE
F SEAL OVERBOARD DRAIN
G FIRST STAGE

(b)

FIG. 12.19 (a) *This pump is composed of two gear elements connected to flow fuel in series.*
There is no centrifugal stage. NOTE: *The letter references in the text refer to Fig. 12-19a.* (b)
Schematic of Chandler Evans pump used on Pratt & Whitney JT3 engines.

MAIN STAGE PRESSURE-RELIEF VALVE A This valve controls the maximum value of pump discharge pressure, and is set to open when main stage discharge pressure reaches approximately 1050 psi. When the valve is open, fuel flow is bypassed internally to the inlet side of the main stage pumping element. The *A* valve is normally closed during operation.

MAIN STAGE INLET CHECK VALVE B If the boost element fails, this valve will open, providing a fuel supply to the main element. The *B* valve is normally closed during operation.

BOOST STAGE PRESSURE-REGULATING VALVE D This regulating valve controls the pressure of the fuel delivered to the engine fuel deicer system, and therefore, the pressure of fuel delivered to the main stage inlet. The valve is set to open at between 45 and 65 psi above pump inlet pressure. When the valve is open, fuel is recirculated internally to the pump inlet.

DOUBLE-GEAR ELEMENTS (PARALLEL) WITH CENTRIFUGAL BOOST (CJ805-23) *(Fig. 12-20)*

In this pump fuel first enters at the centrifugal-type boost element. The boost element, which is driven at a greater speed than the high-pressure elements, increases the pressure of the fuel 15 to 45 psi, depending upon engine speed. The fuel is discharged from the boost element to the two gear-type positive-displacement, high-pressure elements. Each of these elements discharges fuel through a check valve to a common dis-

charge port. At a discharge pressure of 850 psig, the high-pressure elements deliver approximately 51 gpm.

Shear sections are incorporated in the drive systems of each element. Thus, if one element fails, the remaining element remains operative, and the check valves prevent recirculation through the inoperative element. One element can supply sufficient fuel for moderate aircraft speeds.

A relief valve in the discharge port of the pump opens at approximately 900 psi and is capable of bypassing the total flow at 960 psi. This permits fuel at pump discharge pressure to be recirculated as a protection against "dead-heading" the pump. The bypass fuel is routed to the inlet side of the two high-pressure elements.

The pump always supplies more fuel than is needed in the system. The fuel control determines the amount of fuel required for engine operation and bypasses the remainder back to the pump. This bypass flow is routed to the intake side of the high-pressure elements.

The fuel pump is mounted at 7 o'clock on the rear face of the transfer gearbox and requires a power input of 48 hp maximum. Pump speed is 3960 rpm at 100 percent engine speed. Four ports on the pump are for attaching pressure-measuring instruments. Two ports, located between the boost and gear elements, may be used to measure pressure at the inlet of the gear elements (engine boost). The two other ports, located downstream of each gear element, may be used to measure discharge pressure of each element. A port on the pump mounting flange provides for drainage of the interstage shaft seal area.

FIG. 12-20 *Parallel arrangement of double-gear element pump with booster stage. (General Electric)*

DOUBLE-GEAR ELEMENTS (SERIES OR PARALLEL) WITH CENTRIFUGAL BOOST STAGE (501-D13) *(Fig. 12-21)*

This fuel pump is engine-driven and is attached to the rear of the accessory case. It incorporates two gear-type pressure elements supplied by one centrifugal boost pump. The design of the pump is such that the capacity of the primary gear-type element is 10 percent greater than that of the secondary element. This feature allows series operation with the primary element taking the full load without the need for a bleed valve bypassing the secondary element during normal operation. The fuel pump operates in conjunction with the high-pressure fuel filter which is mounted on the bottom of the fuel pump.

During an engine start the pump elements are in parallel operation, and the paralleling valve in the fuel filter is energized closed. The pressure switch in the fuel filter is closed, causing a cockpit-mounted warning light to illuminate and indicate that the secondary element is operating properly (2200 to 9000 rpm). If the primary element fails (indicated by a warning light being lit) while the engine is running, the secondary element provides sufficient fuel flow and pressure to operate the power unit in flight. During a start, if a primary element has failed, fuel flow may not be sufficient for a satisfactory start. The primary fuel pump failure warning light is cockpit mounted. It goes on when the primary element of the fuel pump has failed. The light also goes on during the engine starting cycle when the fuel pump elements are operating in parallel (2200 to 9000 rpm).

The fuel pump and filter assembly consists of two castings which may be separated. The upper portion is the fuel pump which contains the boost pump and the two pump elements. The lower portion is the filter assembly and contains the removable high-pressure filter, the check valves, the paralleling valve, and the pressure switch.

FUEL NOZZLES

On most gas turbine engines, fuel is introduced into the combustion chamber through a fuel nozzle whose function is to create a highly atomized, accurately shaped spray of fuel suitable for rapid mixing and combustion with the primary airstream under varying conditions of fuel and airflow. Most engines use either the single (simplex), or the dual (duplex) nozzle.

THE SIMPLEX NOZZLE

Figure 12-22 illustrates a typical simplex nozzle. This nozzle, as its name implies, has the advantage of being simpler in design than the duplex nozzle. Its chief disadvantage lies in the fact that it is unable to provide a satisfactory spray pattern with the large changes in fuel pressures and airflows encountered in bigger engines.

THE DUPLEX NOZZLE

At starting and low rpm, and at low airflow, the spray angle needs to be fairly wide in order to increase the chances of ignition and to provide good mixing of fuel and air, but at higher rpm and airflow, a narrow pattern is required to keep the flame of combustion away from the walls of the combustion chamber (Fig. 12-23). The small fuel flow that is used in idling is broken up into a fine spray by being forced through a small outlet formed by the primary holes. The secondary holes are larger, but still provide a fine spray at higher rpm because of the higher fuel pressure. The chief advantage then, of the duplex nozzle, is its ability to provide good fuel atomization and proper spray pattern at all rates of fuel delivery and airflow without the necessity of utilizing abnormally high fuel pressures.

In order for the duplex nozzle to function, there must be a device to separate the fuel into low (primary) and high (secondary) pressure supplies. This flow divider may be incorporated in each nozzle, as is the case with the single-entry duplex type, as shown in Fig. 12-24a and b, or a single-flow divider may be used with the entire system (Fig. 12-25).

Single-entry duplex nozzles incorporating an internal flow divider require only a single fuel manifold, while, as shown in Fig. 12-25, dual-entry fuel nozzles require a double fuel manifold. Some dual fuel manifolds may not be apparent as such. For example, the Pratt & Whitney JT3 and JT4 series engines utilize a concentric manifold system (Fig. 12-26).

The flow divider, whether self-contained in each nozzle, or installed in the manifold, is usually a spring-loaded (Fig. 12-27) valve set to open at a specific fuel pressure. When the pressure is below this value, the flow divider directs fuel to the primary manifold and/or nozzle orifice. Pressures above this value cause the valve to open and fuel is allowed to flow in both manifolds and/or nozzle orifices.

Most modern nozzles have their passages drilled at an angle so that the fuel is discharged with a swirling motion in order to provide low axial air velocity and high flame speed. In addition, an air shroud surrounding the nozzle cools the nozzle tip and improves combustion by retarding the accumulation of carbon deposits on the face. The shroud also provides some air for combustion and helps to contain the flame in the center of the liner (Fig. 12-28).

Extreme care must be exercised when cleaning, re-

SERIES OPERATION
0-2200 R.P.M. AND 9000-UP R.P.M.

LOW PRESSURE
FUEL FILTER
BY-PASS VALVE

BOOST PUMP
BY-PASS VALVE

SECONDARY PUMP

PRIMARY PUMP

BOOST PUMP

FUEL IN

**BOOST PUMP
DISCHARGE**

PRESSURE
SWITCH

PARALLELING VALVE

LOW PRESSURE
FUEL FILTER

CHECK VALVE

CHECK VALVE

HIGH PRESSURE FILTER

HIGH PRESSURE FILTER
BY-PASS VALVE

OFF

LOW PRESSURE FILTERED FUEL

BY-PASS FROM FUEL CONTROL
AND TEMPERATURE DATUM VALVE

NOT ENERGIZED

PRIMARY FUEL PUMP
FAILURE WARNING LIGHT

NOT ENERGIZED

**HIGH PRESSURE
FILTERED FUEL**

PARALLEL OPERATION
2200-9000 R.P.M.

ON

ENERGIZED   ENERGIZED

PRIMARY FAILURE
AT ANY R.P.M.

ON

ENERGIZED

SAME EVENTS OCCUR
ENERGIZED OR NOT ENERGIZED

FIG. 12-21   *Fuel pump and high-pressure filter flow schematic.   (Allison Division of General
Motors)*

FIG. 12-22 *A simple nozzle.*

FIG. 12-23 *The spray angle changes when fuel flows in the primary or primary and secondary manifolds.*

Small Slot Only

Large and Small Slot

FUEL INLET

FUEL DISCHARGE

FILTER

FUEL INLET

FLOW DIVIDER

FUEL DISCHARGE

SPIN CHAMBER

PRIMARY FLOW
SECONDARY FLOW
CDP AIR

SPIN CHAMBER

(a)

NOZZLE BODY

FILTER ASSY.

VALVE SEAT

VALVE

ADJUSTING SCREW

DIRECTOR

SPRAY TIP

(b)

FIG. 12-24 (**a**) *The CJ-805 (J79) single-entry duplex nozzle. The spray angle of this nozzle is 80 to 100° with primary flow, and 80 to 90° with combined primary and secondary flows. The angle varies inversely with pressure.* (**b**) *Single-entry duplex nozzle used on the Allison J33.*

1	A/C FUEL CELL	11	FLOW DIVIDER
2	A/C BOOST PUMP	12	FUEL MANIFOLDS
3	A/C FUEL SHUT OFF	13	FUEL NOZZLE
4	A/C LOW PRESSURE FILTER	14	COMBUSTION STARTER
5	BOOST FUEL PUMP	15	MANUAL DRAIN
6	MAIN FUEL PUMP	16	SEAL DRAIN
7	HIGH-PRESSURE FILTER	17	FUEL PRIMING SOLENOID
8	PE 3A FUEL REGULATOR	18	CHECK VALVE
9	FLOW METER	19	DRIP DRAIN VALVE
10	OIL COOLER		

High pressure
Low pressure

FIG. 12-25 *Fuel system of the General Electric J73 showing the flow divider and the required double fuel manifold.*

1	SPRING	9	OUTER SECONDARY- STRAINER SNAP RING
2	LOWER PRIMARY FERRULE	10	SECONDARY STRAINER
3	UPPER PRIMARY FERRULE	11	NOZZLE BODY INSERT
4	SPRING SEAT	12	PRIMARY PLUG
5	PRIMARY-STRAINER SNAP RING	13	NOZZLE BODY
6	PRIMARY STRAINER	14	INSERT SNAP RING
7	SPRING SEAT SNAP RING	15	RETAINING NUT
8	INNER SECONDARY- STRAINER SNAP RING		

FIG. 12-26 *A double-entry nozzle with a concentric fuel manifold used on the Pratt & Whitney JT3D engine.*

FIG. 12-27 *The flow divider and the nozzle are an integral unit on the General Electric J85 (CJ610).*

FIG. 12-28 *The Allison 501-D13 engine uses a single-entry duplex nozzle incorporating an air shroud.*

FIG. 12-29 *Vaporizer tube used on the Wright J65 engine.*

pairing, or handling the nozzles, since even fingerprints on the metering parts may produce a fuel flow which is out of tolerance.

Engines such as the Wright J65 and some models of the Lycoming T-53 and T-55 use devices called vaporizing tubes (Fig. 12-29) instead of injector nozzles. The vaporizing tube is essentially a U-shaped pipe whose exit faces upstream to the compressor airflow. Excellent mixing of the fuel and air results from this arrangement.

OTHER FUEL SYSTEM COMPONENTS

FUEL FILTERS

All gas turbine engines will have several fuel filters installed at various points along the system. It is common practice to use at least one filter before the fuel pump and one on the high-pressure side of the pump. (See Chap. 13 on the complete fuel system for the location of the filters in some commonly used engines.) In most cases the filter will incorporate a relief valve set to open at a specified pressure differential in order to provide a bypass for fuel when filter contamination becomes excessive.

Types of filters

1 *Paper cartridge type* (*Fig. 12-30*)—This type of filter is usually used on the low-pressure side of the pump. It incorporates a replaceable paper filter element which is capable of filtering out particles larger than 50 to 100 μ, or the size of a human hair.

(One micron equals 0.000039 inch, or 25,400 microns equal one inch.) Its function is to protect the fuel pump from being damaged due to fuel contamination.

2 *Screen disk type* (*Fig. 12-31*)—Located on the outlet side of the pump, this filter is composed of a stack of removable fine wire mesh screen disks which must be disassembled and cleaned periodically in an approved solvent.

3 *Screen type* (*Fig. 12-32*)—Generally used as a low-pressure fuel filter, some of these filter screens are constructed of sinter-bonded stainless steel wire cloth and are capable of filtering out particles larger than 40 μ.

In addition to the main-line filters, most fuel systems will incorporate several other filtering elements, locating them in the fuel tank, fuel control, fuel nozzles, and in any other place deemed desirable by the designer. (See Figs. 13-1 to 13-7 for the location of the filtering elements in some typical fuel systems.)

PRESSURIZING AND DRAIN (DUMP) VALVES
(*Fig. 12-33*)

The purpose of the pressurizing and drain valve on the CJ805 and the CJ610 engines (see Figs. 13-1 and 13-4) is to prevent flow to the fuel nozzles until sufficient pressure is attained in the main fuel control to operate the servo assemblies which are used to compute the fuel-flow schedules. It also drains the fuel manifold at engine shutdown to prevent post-shutdown fires, but keeps the upstream portion of the system primed to permit faster starts.

Body   Paper filter element

Bypass valve

Cover

FIG. 12-30 *A typical low-pressure filter with a paper element.*

FIG. 12-31 *A typical mesh-screen disk-type filter.*

1	VALVE STEM	**7**	FILTER HEAD
2	SPRING RETAINER	**8**	TUBE ASSY
3	SPRING	**9**	FILTER PACK ASSY
4	RELIEF VALVE	**10**	PACK SPACER
5	VALVE SEAT	**11**	RETAINER CUP
6	RELIEF-VALVE ASSY	**12**	SUMP

The pressurizing and dump valve used on the Pratt & Whitney JT3 engines (Fig. 12-34) has a somewhat different function. In addition to the draining or dumping function, this unit also serves as a flow divider. At the beginning of an engine "start" the fuel control supplies a pressure signal to the pressurizing and dump valve, causing the valve to close the manifold drain and open a passage for fuel flow to the engine. On engine shutdown, fuel flow is cut off immediately by a valve in the fuel control. The pressure signal drops and the dump valve will open, allowing fuel to drain from the manifold. The flow divider allows fuel to flow to the primary and secondary manifolds depending on fuel pressure. (See Fig. 13-2.)

The Allison J33 and 501-D13 engines incorporate an electrically actuated drain valve (which Allison calls a drip valve), activated through the ignition switch on the J33, or automatically at a specific rpm on the 501-D13 (Fig. 12-35) to assure a clean cutoff and prevent fuel from dripping into the combustion chambers at low fuel pressures. In this way gum and carbon deposits are prevented, and the fire hazard is reduced. The General Electric CJ610 fuel manifold drain valve performs the same function, but works when fuel pressure drops below a specified minimum. (See Figs. 13-1, 13-3, and 13-5.)

Some manufacturers, such as Allison and Pratt & Whitney, install a pressure-operated valve in the com-

FIG. 12-32 *A typical screen-type filter.*

FIG. 12-33 *Pressurizing and drain valve for the General Electric CJ805 (J79) engine.*

FIG. 12-34 *Pratt & Whitney pressurizing and dump valve schematic.*

To manifold

From manifold

Drain ←

Energized

Deenergized

FIG. 12-35 *Drip valve used on the Allison 501-D13 engine.*

bustion-chamber section. When the pressure in the burners drops below a specified minimum, usually a few pounds per square inch, this valve will open and drain any residual fuel remaining after a false start or normal shutdown. (Refer to Fig. 13-2 to see where this drain valve fits into the system.)

FLOW METERS

Most fuel systems will incorporate a flow meter as a measure of fuel consumption in pounds per hour. While the flow meter is usually an airframe-supplied accessory, it is included here to show its location in the system, which is generally after the fuel control. (Figures 13-1, 13-2, 13-4, and 13-5 show the placement of this unit.)

FUEL-OIL COOLERS

Some engines use fuel as a cooling medium for the oil. (Refer to Figs. 13-1 and 13-4. For a more detailed look at fuel-oil coolers refer to Fig. 15-8.)

FUEL HEATERS

The General Electric CJ805-23, CJ610, some models of the Pratt & Whitney JT3 engines, and others may incorporate an additional unit to reduce the possibility of ice crystals forming in the fuel. The fuel heater consists basically of an air-to-liquid heat exchanger and a thermostatically controlled valve to regulate airflow. The thermostatic valve is responsive to the temperature of the outgoing liquid. The liquid is turbojet engine fuel and the air is compressor bleed air supplied by the engine. (See Fig. 13-4.)

The need for the fuel heater has been reduced because of the increasing use of PFA 55MB, an anti-icing inhibitor and biocidal agent. See Chap. 11, page 177.

REVIEW AND STUDY QUESTIONS

1 What is the relationship between the operator, fuel control, and engine in the control of power?
2 List the basic inputs to a fuel control.
3 Name two groups (types) of fuel controls.
4 Discuss the essential requirements of any fuel control.
5 What is the purpose of the servo system used in many modern fuel controls?
6 Why is an acceleration limit system needed on the fuel control?
7 What are two ways to meter fuel?
8 Explain briefly the operation of the following fuel controls: TJ-A4, AP-B3, 1307, and JFC25.
9 What type of fuel pump is used on most turbine engines?
10 Describe the operation of a typical double-element fuel pump with integral booster impeller.
11 Explain what is meant by "series" and "parallel" pump operation.
12 Why is it necessary to use duplex fuel nozzles on many engines?
13 What is a flow divider? Where may it be located?
14 What device is used in place of the fuel nozzle? Tell how it works.
15 Name three types of fuel filters.
16 What is the purpose of the pressurizing and drain valve?
17 What is the purpose of the fuel heater used on some engines?

Chapter 13

Typical fuel systems

The fuel system must supply clean, accurately metered fuel to the combustion chambers. Although the systems will differ in many respects, they all have certain elements in common. For example, all fuel systems must have a fuel pump, fuel control, pressurizing valve or its equivalent, fuel manifold, and fuel nozzles (or vaporizers). How these specific units do their jobs differs radically from one engine to another. Some systems incorporate features that are not, strictly speaking, necessary to the metering of fuel. Examples of this can be found in the use of fuel as a cooling medium for the oil, and in the use of fuel to operate variable inlet guide vanes, stators, and compressor bleed mechanisms.

It is the purpose of this section to illustrate typical fuel systems so that the reader will obtain some idea of fuel flows and the location of the several parts that constitute the system.

THE GENERAL ELECTRIC CJ610 FUEL SYSTEM
(Fig. 13-1)

This fuel and control system meters fuel to the engine and provides actuation pressure for the variable inlet geometry (VG) system. It consists of the following engine-mounted components:

Fuel pump
Fuel control
Overspeed governor
Fuel-oil cooler
Fuel pressurizing valve
Fuel manifolds
Fuel manifold drain valve
Fuel nozzles (with integral flow divider)
Actuator assembly (VG)
Bleed valves
Fuel flowmeter (airframe-furnished equipment)

220

Control system

The control system schedules the rate of engine fuel flow for variations in air density, air temperature, and engine speed.

Fuel pump

The fuel pump comprises a single-element positive-displacement pump, centrifugal boost pump, filter, and bypass circuit with a pressure-relief valve. The pump supplies fuel to the fuel control and is mounted on and driven by the accessory gearbox.

Fuel control

The fuel control is mounted on and driven by the fuel pump. The control incorporates a hydromechanical computer section and fuel-regulating section to operate the control servos. Parameters of engine speed, power-lever setting, compressor inlet temperature, and compressor discharge pressure are used in the computer section to schedule the operation of the fuel-metering valve and the VG servo valve. The fuel-regulating section meters fuel to the engine under all operating conditions.

Overspeed governor

The isochronus overspeed governor is mounted on and driven by the accessory gearbox. Fuel is supplied to the governor bypass section from the fuel control, and to the governing section from the fuel pump. Overspeed governing is controlled by bypassing the fuel, when it is in excess of engine maximum limiting speed requirements, to the fuel pump inlet port.

Fuel-oil cooler

For a description of the fuel-oil cooler, refer to Chap. 15.

Fuel pressurizing valve

The pressurizing valve is mounted on the fuel-oil cooler and connects to the fuel manifolds, manifold drain valve, and fuel pump interstage reference pressure line. During starting, boost pressure and spring force close the pressurizing valve to prevent low-pressure fuel flow to the fuel nozzles, and to allow the fuel control to build up sufficient pressure to operate the control servos and (VG) actuators. The control pressure then opens the pressurizing valve and closes the manifold drain valve. Fuel is then distributed to the fuel nozzles at sufficient pressure for satisfactory atomization.

Fuel manifolds

Two fuel manifold tubes are located around the mainframe casing. Each manifold tube connects to six

FIG. 13-1 *General Electric CJ610 fuel system schematic.*

fuel nozzles. Fuel is supplied from the pressurizing valve, through the manifold tubes, to the fuel nozzles.

Fuel manifold drain valve

The fuel manifold drain valve drains the fuel manifolds at engine shutdown to prevent residual fuel from dribbling out the fuel nozzles, thus creating a fire hazard. It also prevents the formation of gum and carbon deposits in the manifold and nozzles. The valve consists of a piston, which is spring-loaded, to open the manifold drain passage at shutdown, and a fuel filter with a bypass valve that opens if the filter becomes clogged. During engine operation, the pressurizing valve actuates to close the manifold drain passage of the valve and admit fuel to the fuel manifolds.

Fuel nozzles

Twelve fuel nozzles, mounted on the main frame, spray atomized fuel into the combustion chamber. The fuel nozzle incorporates a flow divider, a primary and secondary flow passage, and an air-shrouded spin-chamber-type orifice. During starting, low-pressure fuel in the primary passage sprays a mixture adequate for ignition. As the engine accelerates, increased fuel

pressure opens the flow divider and additional fuel flows into the secondary passage to the spin chamber where it merges with the primary passage fuel flow. The air shroud sweeps air across the nozzle orifice to prevent carbon formation. (See Fig. 12-27.)

Actuator assembly (VG)

Two variable-geometry actuators, mounted on the compressor casing, position the inlet guide vanes and interstage bleed valves. They are linear-travel, piston-type actuators, hydraulically actuated by high-pressure fuel from a servo valve in the fuel control. The actuator piston rods are connected to bellcranks which position the inlet guide vanes and interstage bleed valves. A feedback cable is connected from the bellcrank assembly to the fuel control and supplies the fuel-control servo valve with a position signal.

Bleed valves

Two bleed valves are mounted on each side of the compressor stator casing. During transient engine speeds, the valves bleed air from the third, fourth, and fifth stages of the compressor according to a bleed schedule, which is a function of compressor speed and inlet air temperature, prescribed by the fuel control. The valves are actuated by the fuel control and two VG actuators through a bellcrank-linkage arrangement. A synchronizing cable synchronizes the bleed-valve positions and, in case of malfunction in either VG actuator, transmits the motion of the functioning VG actuator to the other.

THE PRATT & WHITNEY JT3 FUEL SYSTEM
(*Fig. 13-2*)

The principal function of this fuel system is to deliver fuel to the engine at such pressures and flow rates as are required to achieve the engine power output desired. A secondary function is the automatic compensations for the variations in altitude encountered in flight. As pointed out earlier in this book, technical limitations in engine design impose a third function, that of limiting acceleration fuel flows so as to prevent surge and excessive engine pressures and temperatures. The final function of the fuel system is the establishment of a minimum fuel flow to prevent "lean die-out" of the flame of combustion during deceleration.

These four essential functions are accomplished by the fuel system largely through the intricate workings of its major component, the engine-driven fuel control. The fuel control acts as a kind of intermediary between the pilot and his engine. It translates his power-lever signals to increase or decrease fuel flows, and it monitors certain flight variables of which the pilot may not be aware, thereby relieving the pilot of the chore of continual power-setting adjustments.

The operation of the fuel system employed in the engine and the functions of its various components may be described by tracing the passage of fuel from the inlet connection of the fuel pump to its ultimate discharge through the fuel nozzles in the engine combustion chambers.

The system consists of the following components:

Fuel pump
Fuel deicing heater (optional)
Fuel deicing filter assembly (optional)
Fuel control
Fuel-oil cooler (optional)
Fuel pressurizing and dump valve
Fuel manifold
Fuel nozzles
Water-injection system (optional)
Fuel tubes
Drain connections

Fuel pump

The first component to be considered in the engine fuel system is the fuel pump. The pump is a two-stage, engine-driven, bypass-equipped unit which receives fuel from the aircraft fuel tank system and discharges it at predetermined pressures and quantities through a fuel deicing system (optional) to the fuel control. The two, positive displacement, gear-type, pumping stages operate in series: the boost stage discharging to the fuel deicing system (through a heater and filter), which in turn discharges into the main stage and from there to the fuel control. (See Fig. 12-19.)

Fuel deicing heater (*optional*)

The fuel deicing heater is an air-fuel heat exchanger attached to a filter assembly which is mounted at the bottom of the engine just aft of the fuel pump. It consists of an air chamber surrounded by a fuel jacket. Sixteenth-stage air is circulated through the air chamber. The heat from this air is transferred to the fuel circulating in the fuel jacket. The heater has a boss to which a temperature bulb may be attached.

Fuel deicing filter assembly (*optional*)

The fuel deicing filter assembly consists of a 40-μ filter element encased in a cylindrical housing. This housing is attached to the heater as described above. The filter assembly is fitted with a pressure-drop warning switch, a bypass valve, and a water drain plug.

Fuel control

The fuel control is a hydromechanical fuel-metering unit designed to schedule fuel flow to control engine speed, thus governing thrust output. It provides the correct flow of fuel to the engine to establish and maintain the engine speed selected by the pilot. It accomplishes this by varying the fuel flow in response to changes in combustion-chamber pressure, and in the difference between the desired speed and the actual engine speed. Fuel from the control is discharged into the fuel-oil cooler (optional) and then to the fuel-pressurizing and dump valve. (See Figs. 12-15 and 12-16.)

Fuel-oil cooler (*optional*)

Metered fuel from the fuel control enters the fuel-oil cooler. This unit will be discussed under the lubrication system since its prime function is to help cool the oil in conjunction with the airframe-supplied air-oil cooler. It consists of a cylindrical oil chamber surrounded by a jacket through which the fuel passes. Heat from the oil is transferred to the fuel via radiation.

Fuel pressurizing and dump valves

Discharge fuel from the control via the fuel-oil cooler passes into the fuel-pressurizing and dump valve. The purpose of this valve is to provide the division of flow between the primary and secondary nozzle orifices to

FIG. 13-2 *Typical Pratt & Whitney fuel system.   Note the provisions for water injection.*
(See Chap. 9.)

ensure the proper spray pattern for efficient fuel combustion. Also incorporated in the fuel-pressurizing and dump valve body is a fuel dump valve which drains the fuel manifolds at shutdown. (See Fig. 12-34.)

Fuel manifold

Fuel from the fuel-pressurizing and dump valve enters the engine fuel manifold which provides separate paths for primary and secondary fuel flow.

Fuel nozzles

Installed in the manifold are 48 dual orifice nozzles which spray fuel into the combustion chambers. (See Fig. 12-26.)

Water-injection system *(optional)*

Because of the functional interrelationship of the water-injection system with the engine fuel system, they should be discussed together. A detailed description of one form of this system is covered in Chap. 9. It must be mentioned, however, that, in conjunction with the fuel control, a switch is operated which passes electrical power for opening or closing the airframe-supplied water-injection shutoff valve. Also, a sensing line from the water-injection control is attached to the fuel control for resetting the fuel control's maximum speed adjustment to a higher setting during water injection.

Fuel tubes

Aircraft fuel tubing will bring fuel to the main fuel pump inlet. With the Pratt & Whitney aircraft fuel deicing system (optional), a large tube from the pump carries fuel to the fuel deicing fuel-heater buildup just aft of the pump. Another tube returns the fuel to the pump from the filter. If the fuel deicing system is not installed, the mounting holes in the pump are blanked off. Two large tubes are mounted on the bottom between the fuel pump and the fuel control. The forward tube is the fuel return tube (high pressure), and the rearward tube between the pump and the control is the fuel supply tube. The rearmost tube between the pump and the control is the bypass tube (low pressure). From the right side of the fuel control to the right side of the fuel pressurizing and dump valve, a large tube supplies fuel to the valve.

Drain connections

Plugged drain connections are provided on the fuel components as well as in the combustion chamber case. The pressurizing and dump valve drain line, the combustion chamber drain line, and the fuel component drain lines are airplane installations.

THE ALLISON 501-D13 FUEL SYSTEM *(Fig. 13-3)*

The system consists of the following components:

Engine-driven fuel-pump assembly
Paralleling valve
High-pressure fuel-filter assembly
Low-pressure fuel-filter assembly
Pressure switch
Fuel control
Primer valve
Temperature datum valve
Fuel manifold
Fuel nozzles
Drip valve
Primer valve

Fuel pump

Fuel is supplied by the aircraft fuel system to the inlet of the engine-driven fuel-pump assembly. The fuel-pump assembly consists of a boost pump and two spur gear-type pumps. The gear-type pumps may be placed in either series or parallel by an electrically operated paralleling valve located in the high-pressure fuel-filter assembly. The boost pump output is delivered to the low-pressure fuel-filter assembly which filters the fuel and delivers it to the high-pressure fuel-filter assembly, where it is directed to the inlets of the two gear-type pumps. The output of the two gear pumps is filtered by the high-pressure fuel filter. A pressure switch, in the high-pressure fuel-filter assembly, completes an electrical circuit to the fuel-pump light in the cockpit to give a warning of a primary gear pump failure. (See Fig. 12-21.)

Fuel, leaving the high-pressure fuel filter, may take two paths. One path enters the fuel control and flows through the fuel-metering section. Here the fuel volume is corrected to 120 percent of engine demand. This correction is for rpm, throttle, and air-density variations. The second path enters the fuel control through the primer valve and bypasses the metering section. The latter path is utilized only during the initial phase of the starting cycle when the use of the primer system is selected by a manually positioned cockpit primer switch.

Fuel control

The fuel control delivers metered fuel to the temperature datum valve which provides further correction to the fuel flow. The temperature datum valve is part of the electronic fuel trimming system, and the fuel-flow correction made by the temperature datum valve is established by the temperature datum control (not pictured). The electronic fuel trimming system compensates for variations in fuel density and Btu content. The temperature datum valve receives more fuel from

FIG. 13-3 *501-D13 fuel system schematic.* *(Allison Service School)*

the fuel control than it delivers to the fuel manifold, and is always bypassing fuel. The amount of fuel bypassed is determined by the position of a bypass control needle which varies in response to an electrical signal from the temperature datum control (amplifier). The amplifier determines this electrical signal by comparing a desired turbine inlet temperature signal to the actual turbine inlet temperature signal provided by a parallel circuit of 18 thermocouples located in the turbine inlet. (See Fig. 12-8.)

Fuel manifold

Fuel flow from the temperature datum valve is delivered to the fuel manifold through an aircraft-furnished flowmeter. The fuel manifold distributes the fuel to six fuel nozzles which atomize and inject the fuel into the forward end of the six combustion liners. A drip valve, located at the lowest point of the fuel manifold, is used to drain the fuel manifold at engine shutdown. During the starting cycle, a solenoid is energized to close the drip valve, and fuel pressure holds the drip valve closed during normal operation. At shutdown, a spring opens the drip valve.

Fuel, bypassed by the fuel control and temperature

datum valve, is returned to the fuel-pump assembly by way of the high-pressure fuel-filter assembly. Any fuel leakage past the seals of the fuel-pump assembly and fuel control is drained overboard through a common manifold.

Primer system

During an engine start, it is desirable to fill the fuel manifold rapidly so that an initial high pressure to the fuel nozzles will allow the nozzles to better atomize the fuel. This ensures a better light-off during engine starts. The secondary and primary fuel pumps are placed in parallel during a start to ensure sufficient fuel flow to fill the fuel manifold rapidly. If a starting attempt is not successful, additional fuel can be delivered to the fuel manifold on the next starting attempt by using the primer system. The primer system must be "armed" by the cockpit primer switch. If the primer system is armed, the primer valve will open at 2200 rpm due to speed-sensitive control and ignition relay operation. When the pressure in the fuel manifold exceeds approximately 50 psi, a pressure switch, connected to the fuel manifold, opens an electrical circuit which will cause the primer valve to close. When the primer

FIG. 13-4 *Typical CJ805-23 fuel system.* (*General Electric*)

valve is open, fuel will flow through the primer valve to the upstream side of the fuel control cutoff valve. Functionally, the primer valve is in parallel with the metering section of the fuel control.

THE GENERAL ELECTRIC CJ805-23 FUEL SYSTEM *(Fig. 13-4)*

This fuel system consists of the following components:

Fuel filter
Fuel heater
Fuel pump
Fuel nozzle
Pressurizing and drain valve
Inlet guide vane actuator
Fuel control
Inlet guide vane mechanical feedback assembly
CIT sensor
Variable stator reset mechanism

Fuel pump

The pump consists of three elements, two gear type and one boost type arranged in tandem. All three pumping elements are driven by coaxial shafts and incorporate individual shear sections so that failure of one pumping element will not adversely effect the operation of the remaining two pumping elements. A gear train is also provided in the pump to drive the boost pump at a higher speed than the gear pumping elements. In addition to the pumping elements, the housing also contains a check valve, located at the outlet of both gear elements and serves to prevent counterflow through a sheared gear pump element. A pressure-relief valve is also incorporated in the housing and is set to open at 900 to 1000 psig discharge pressure. Four ports are provided in the pump. These are inlet, boost bleed, bypass, and outlet. Three pressure taps are incorporated in the pump to measure pressure. (See Fig. 12-20.)

Fuel heater

The fuel heater is an air-to-liquid heat exchanger, incorporating a thermostatically controlled valve to regulate airflow. The thermostatic valve is responsive to the temperature of the outgoing liquid. The liquid is turbojet engine fuel and the air is compressor bleed air supplied by the engine.

Fuel filter

The fuel filter, which is in the fuel line between the fuel heater and the fuel control, protects the fuel controller from contaminants in the fuel. Fuel enters the filter and surrounds the filter screen. The fuel passes through the screen into an inner chamber, then flows out the discharge port. If the filter becomes clogged, fuel is bypassed through the relief valve. The filter

screen is constructed of sinter-bonded, stainless steel wire cloth and filters out 98 percent of all particles larger than 43 μ. At the base of the filter is a drain port to facilitate draining the filter prior to removal for cleaning or replacement.

Fuel control

The fuel control maintains engine rpm according to the throttle schedule, schedules maximum and minimum fuel rate limits, reduces maximum rpm limit in the low engine inlet temperature region, controls the position of the inlet guide vanes (IGV) by providing control fuel for the inlet guide vane actuators, and provides fuel shutoff that is separate from the throttle schedule. To enable the control to perform the above objectives, there must be inputs in addition to the supply of fuel. The inputs include the air inlet temperature (CIT), the compressor discharge pressure (P3), and the speed of the main shaft. These three inputs, referred to as parameters, and a power-lever (throttle) setting determine the outputs of the control. The air inlet temperature is sensed by the compressor inlet temperature sensor. The outputs of the control include a controlled fuel supply (W_f) to the combustion chamber of the engine and control fuel pressure signal for the inlet guide vane actuators.

Compressor inlet temperature sensor

The compressor inlet temperature (CIT) sensor is a temperature sensor and transducer unit for the fuel regulator. It responds to the air inlet temperature of CJ805 turbojet engines and positions the temperature transducer differential servo of the main regulator.

Variable stator reset mechanism

The variable stator reset mechanism is a feedback bias mechanism used to alter the schedule of the inlet guide vanes and variable stator vanes of the engine during certain operating conditions.

Inlet guide vane actuator and inlet guide vane mechanism feedback assembly

The vane actuator assembly is a valve-operated fuel piston-type actuator with a fixed cooling flow orifice across the piston. This actuator controls the position of the inlet guide vanes of the engine through a fuel signal from the fuel control. The mechanical feedback assembly informs the fuel control where the guide vanes are positioned.

Pressurizing and drain valve

This valve is a pressure-operated valve designed to prevent flow to the engine fuel nozzles until sufficient pressure is attained in the fuel control. The valve operates to drain the fuel manifold at engine shutdown, but will maintain pressure between the fuel control and the fuel nozzles. There are five ports on the valve: reference pressure, two (2) fuel outlets, fuel inlet, and drain port.   (See Fig. 12-33.)

Fuel nozzle

The fuel nozzle is a fuel-metering device.   It produces a conical fuel spray of fine droplets, uniform density, and uniform thickness over its entire range of operating pressures.   (See Fig. 12-24a.)

THE ALLISON J33 FUEL SYSTEM   (*Fig. 13-5*)

The principal components of this fuel system are:

Boost pump
Dual-element parallel main fuel pump
Fuel filters—low and high pressure
Drain cock valve
Differential pressure switch
Main fuel control
Drip valve
Double-check valve
Fuel nozzles
Combustion-chamber drain valve

The boost pump

The boost pump is an engine-driven centrifugal-type pump which is used to assure a positive head of fuel to the main fuel pump.

Dual fuel pump

The engine-driven gear-type fuel pump incorporates an emergency fuel element in addition to the main-fuel-pump gears.   The two sets of gears are driven by concentric shafts with the shear section on each shaft located so that, if foreign material lodges in either of the pump gears, the shear section of that pump will fail without interfering in the operation of the drive shaft of the alternate pump.

Fuel filters

The low-pressure fuel filter contains a removable filter element and a single relief valve, set at 9 psi, incorporated to bypass fuel around the filter element should it become clogged.   The high-pressure filter is an Air-Maze type filter in which the filter element is composed of a stack of removable screen disks (filter packs).   A single relief valve, set at 65 to 80 psi differential pressure, is incorporated in the filter body to bypass fuel around the filter element should the element become clogged.

Drain cock valve

The drain cock valve is a manually operated valve located at the bottom of the low-pressure fuel filter to provide a means for filter drainage.

Fuel differential pressure switch

The differential pressure switch is mounted on the main fuel pump; it senses a drop in pressure whenever either side of the pump fails, and turns on an aircraft-furnished warning light.

Main fuel control

The main fuel control maintains exhaust gas temperatures within specified limits during accelerations and decelerations, sustains combustion during deceleration, and maintains any fixed engine speed regardless of altitude as long as the speed is within the operating range of the engine.   The control meters fuel in response to variations in engine speed and compressor inlet air density.   This control provides an all-speed governor to maintain pilot-selected engine speed regardless of air density (altitude) or aircraft speed, except during the time the altitude idle bleed is controlling the fuel flow.   (See Fig. 12-7.)

Solenoid drip valve

The solenoid drip valve is a spring-loaded, normally open fuel valve which drains the fuel manifold when the pressure in the manifold drops below 6 to 10 psig. This action ensures a clean cutoff and prevents fuel from dripping into the combustion chambers at extremely low fuel pressures.   The solenoid is actuated to close the valve during starting operation, thus preventing loss of fuel.

Double-check valve

The double-check valve prevents reverse flow of fuel back to the two fuel supplies.

Fuel nozzles

The fuel nozzles are of the duplex type and utilize a single manifold.   Fuel enters each nozzle through a fine wire mesh filter and, at low pressures, flows only through a small drilled passage to the spray tip assembly. An annular channel around the swirl chamber carries the fuel to two small holes drilled tangentially into the chamber wall.   A swirl action is established and the fuel then passes through the spray tip orifice.   With increasing fuel pressure, the spring-loaded pop valve opens and additional fuel is directed to the swirl chamber through a larger central passage.   This fuel enters the chamber through four additional holes also located on a tangent to the wall.   The combined fuel is then ejected through the spray tip orifice into the combustion chamber.   (See Fig. 12-24b.)

Combustion-chamber drain valve

The combustion-chamber drain valve is a spring-loaded, piston-type valve that seats on a neoprene ring and is used to drain any unburned fuel from the com-

FIG. 13-5 Allison J33 fuel system schematic showing arrangement of the various components.

bustion chambers. It is located under the adapter for combustion chamber number 8. It is connected to a drain manifold which, in turn, is connected to the seven lowest combustion chambers, namely, numbers 5 to 11 inclusive. The combustion-chamber drain valve is designed to open and allow fuel to drain to the atmosphere when fuel pressure within the combustion chamber falls below 2 psig pressure. When raw fuel collects in the air adapters during a false start or on stopping the unit, it must be drained away before another start is attempted. The chamber drain manifold and combustion-chamber drain valve automatically perform this draining function, thereby preventing a hot start.

THE LYCOMING T53 FUEL SYSTEM (Fig. 13-6)

The fuel system consists of the following components:

Fuel regulator
Overspeed governor
Starting fuel solenoid shutoff valve
Main and starting fuel manifolds
Igniter nozzles
Fuel vaporizers
Combustion-chamber drain valve

System Operation

Fuel enters the engine fuel regulator and after metering goes to the starting and main discharge ports. The starting fuel flows to a solenoid shutoff valve, wired in conjunction with the ignition system. Energizing the ignition system activates the solenoid valve, allowing starting fuel to enter the starting fuel manifold and combustion chamber through five igniter nozzles. Two igniter plugs initiate the flame. Main fuel is delivered from the fuel regulator to the main fuel system when the engine rpm is great enough to deliver minimum fuel pressure. After combustion occurs and ignition is de-energized, the solenoid valve shuts off the flow of starting fuel. The igniter nozzles are self-purging and remove excess fuel automatically. Main fuel flow is maintained as the engine flame is propagated. An electrical cable is connected to the starting fuel solenoid shutoff valve and to the engine fuel regulator. After engine shutdown, the pressure-actuated combustion-chamber drain valve opens automatically and drains unburned fuel from the combustion chamber. The engine is designed to use JP4 fuel.

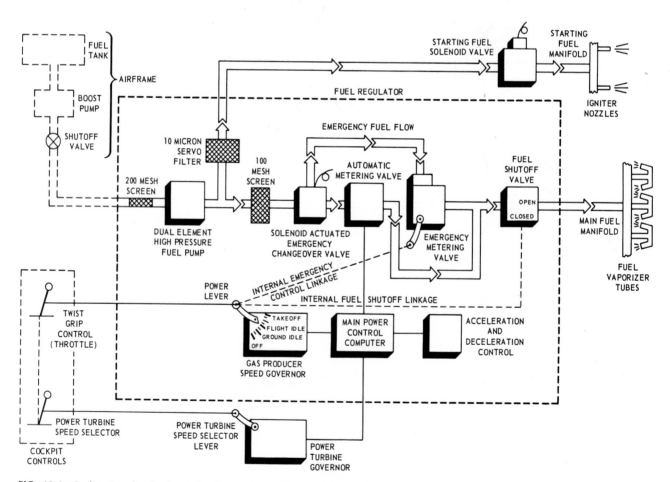

FIG. 13-6 *Fuel system for the Lycoming T53 incorporating separate controls for the gas producer and power turbines of the engine.*

Fuel control

The fuel control itself consists of a fuel regulator for the gas producer section and an overspeed governor for the power turbine section. An integral dual fuel pump and an emergency control system are incorporated into the fuel regulator. For emergency fuel system operation, a special emergency valve is connected to the power-lever control.

The fuel regulator is of the hydromechanical type incorporating an all-speed flyball governor for acceleration and deceleration control and a droop-type governor for a steady-state speed control.

Inputs to the regulator consist of a speed selector lever, compressor inlet pressure and temperature, and gas producer speed. The compressor pressure and temperature sensors act to limit fuel flow to prevent the

FIG. 13-7 *The Continental J69 fuel system utilizes a rotating main fuel distributor supplied with fuel through the shaft, and a stationary starting fuel nozzle.*

turbine inlet temperature from exceeding the limits under all operating conditions. The inlet pressure sensor biases the fuel flow at the main metering valve through a multiplying linkage. The inlet temperature sensor biases the fuel flow for acceleration, deceleration, and maximum permissible steady-state speed through the rotation of a three-dimensional cam which is translated as a function of gas producer speed. The control in sensing these parameters monitors fuel flow, preventing temperature limits from being exceeded.

The overspeed governor is a flyball droop-type governor. This governor acts as a topping device by limiting fuel flow in the event the power turbine tends to exceed the power turbine rpm selected.

THE CONTINENTAL J69 FUEL SYSTEM (*Fig. 13-7*)

The final system to be discussed contains the following units:

Fuel pump
Fuel filter
Fuel control consisting of a starting fuel system and a main fuel system

Fuel pump

The engine fuel system starts with the fuel pump. This pump, driven off the accessory gear train, has a centrifugal booster stage which is intended to provide boost pressure if the boost provisions in the aircraft system should fail. It also reduces vapor effects by raising total boost pressure. The centrifugal booster stage feeds two gear-pump pressure sections operating in parallel. Either section will provide full pressure and flow for the engine and each section is independent of the other.

Fuel filter

From the main fuel pump, fuel is carried by a hose to the fuel filter built into the fuel control unit. This filter incorporates two separate filtering elements with provisions to bypass the fuel if the elements should become clogged. A manually operated flushing valve permits closing off the rest of the fuel system when reverse flushing of the filter is accomplished. This valve is at the filter outlet.

Fuel control

Within the fuel control there are two separate fuel paths. From the flushing valve outlet, starting fuel is led through a starting fuel filter to a pressure regulator, then to the starting fuel solenoid valve. From this valve, starting fuel passes through adjustable bleed valves to the external piping that leads the fuel to the starting fuel nozzles.

The main fuel path feeds to the acceleration control,

to the governor valve, then to the cutoff valve from which flow is to the pressurizing valve and thence into the engine fuel tube. The acceleration control is designed to influence fuel input during acceleration and also to compensate for changes of altitude or other ambient air conditions. The governor valve influences flow to hold the speed called for by the throttle lever setting. The governor valve is servo operated and responds to pressure signals developed in the "speed sensing" element. The latter also sends pressure signals to the bypass valve. The function of the bypass valve is to maintain a design pressure differential across the metering elements (which are the acceleration control and the governor valve). This pressure differential is maintained by bypassing fuel back to the fuel-pump inlet. Since the design pressure differential must change with speed, the bypass valve is made responsive to a signal from the speed-sensing element. The pressurizing valve is designed to open only above a minimum pressure and so prevents "dribble" of fuel or drainage of the control unit when the engine comes to a stop.

The fuel control also contains check valves, "trim" provisions, and passages for return of fuel bleed-off or seepage.

The fuel control is the key element affecting engine control. Provided the proper volume and pressure of fuel are fed into the fuel control unit, it regulates and meters engine fuel input to cover all operating conditions automatically. During starting the separate starting fuel path sets up fuel flow to the starting fuel nozzles. The fuel control starting fuel solenoid valve opens this path and closes it in response to signals from a control element not supplied with the engine. Then the acceleration control sets up fuel flow to the main fuel distributor such as to speed the engine up from starting speed to idle without surge or overtemperature. As the engine reaches the speed set by the throttle lever position, the governor valve will come into action to hold the speed as set. After the engine has reached idle, the acceleration control is designed to control fuel input for all changing conditions for all operation from idle up to full speed without allowing surge or overtemperature. It compensates for acceleration, for change of altitude, and for other change of ambient air characteristics. The governor valve, in all cases, acts to hold engine speed to the value set by throttle lever position.

REVIEW AND STUDY QUESTIONS

1 What is the purpose of any fuel system?
2 Very briefly describe the fuel systems used on the CJ610, JT3, 501-D13, CJ805-23, J33, T53, and J69.

Chapter 14

Lubricating oils

GAS TURBINE OILS

Lubricants now must perform under environmental and mechanical conditions much more severe than a few years ago. Early aircraft gas turbine engines operated on light mineral oils, and some engines requiring such oils are still in service. But the low-temperature requirements imposed by high-altitude flight, coupled with the higher engine operating temperatures are not met by existing petroleum-based oils. Inasmuch as a mineral oil is generally not capable of giving satisfactory performance at both very low and very high temperatures, most modern turbojet and turboprop engines are lubricated with synthetic oils. Synthetic oils are also used in some accessories on the engine such as starters and constant-speed drives to preclude using the wrong oil in these units. These oils can also be found in modern airplane hydraulic systems and in some instruments.

The characteristics of both the natural petroleum oil and the synthetic oil have been outlined in Military Specifications MIL-O-6081 and MIL-L-7808, respectively.

MIL-O-6081

MIL-O-6081 is a narrow cut (see the section on fuels) light mineral oil containing additives to enhance oxidation resistance and improve viscosity-temperature properties. (See page 234 for a more complete list of oil additives.) It generally has a low pour point, low viscosity at low temperatures, reasonable stability in the presence of heat, and is noncorrosive to metals commonly used in engines. It is used in applications where the bearing temperatures are about 300°F or less. At elevated temperatures this oil suffers large evaporation losses, inadequate viscosity, and causes large coking deposits. The lubricant is processed from crude oil obtained from various parts of the world. The crude oil can be broadly separated into two groups—paraffinic oils and naphthenic oils. The division is based on the way the hydrogen and carbon atoms are linked together. The paraffinic oils are relatively stable at high temperatures, have a high viscosity index (see the following section for a definition of terms), and contain a high percentage of dissolved wax. Naphthenic oils are less stable at elevated temperatures, but have little or no wax, and therefore tend to remain liquid at low temperatures. Their viscosity index is poor. Most natural petroleum jet engine oils employ a mixed base stock.

MIL-L-7808

This oil is the most widespread synthetic lubricant used in the United States. The specifications for both the natural and synthetic oils list −65°F for starting requirements, but the synthetic lubricant is rated for temperatures up to 400°F. Although there are many synthetic lubricants on the market, the one most commonly used is classified as a dibasic-acid ester. It can be made by using animal tallow or vegetable oils (castor bean) as the raw material in a reaction with alcohol, or, from petroleum hydrocarbon synthesis. The exact identities of the compounds used in the construction of these oils is kept under proprietary secrecy. Since the processing required for a synthetic oil is complex, its current price of approximately $7.00 per gallon as compared to $2.50 per gallon for natural oil can be readily understood. Oils meeting the MIL-L-7808 specification are sometimes called type I oils (Table 14-1). A newer type II oil is described on page 236.

CHARACTERISTICS OF LUBRICATING OILS

Lubricants for jet engines must exhibit certain physical and performance properties in order to perform satisfactorily. The following is a list of tests performed on gas turbine oils to determine their physical and performance properties.

Physical properties

1 *Viscosity index*—This refers to the effect of temperature on viscosity. All petroleum products thin with a temperature increase and thicken with a temperature decrease. A high viscosity index number indicates a comparatively low rate of change.

2 *Viscosity*—This is the measure of the ability of an oil to flow at a specific temperature.

3 *Pour point*—This refers to the effect of low temperatures on the pourability of the oil.

4 *Flash point*—This is the lowest temperature at which the oil gives off vapors that will ignite when a small flame is periodically passed over the surface of the oil.

TABLE 14-1
Synthetic lubricant MIL-L-7808 specification

Viscosity, centistokes:	
210°F	3.0 min
100°F	11.0 min
−65°F	13,000 max
Viscosity change, −65°F, % at 3 hr	±6.0 max
Pour point, °F	−75 max
Flash point, °F	400 min
Neutralization no.	−
SOD lead corrosion, 325°F, mg/sq in. in 1 hr	6.0 max
450°F corrosion, mg/sq in.:	
Copper	3.0 max
Silver	3.0 max
347°F corrosion and oxidation stability, mg/sq cm:	
Copper	±0.4
Magnesium	±0.2
Iron	±0.2
Aluminum	±0.2
Silver	±0.2
% viscosity change, 100°F	−5 to +15
Neutralization no. increase	2.0 max
Evaporation loss, 400°F, %	35 max
"H" rubber swell, %	12 to 35
Panel coke, 600°F, mg	80 max
Deposition no.	5.0 max
Foam test	Pass
72-hr low-temperature stability, −65°F, centistokes	17,000 max
Compatibility with MIL-L-7808 oils	Pass
Ryder gear test, relative rating, %	68 min

5   *Fire point*—This is the lowest temperature at which an oil ignites and continues to burn for at least 5 sec.

6   *Volatility*—This is the measure of the ease with which a liquid is converted to a vaporous state.

7   *Acidity*—This test indicates the corrosive tendencies of the oil.

Performance factors

1   *Oil foaming*—This is the measure of the ability of the oil to separate from entrained air.

2   *Rubber swell*—This is the measure of how much the oil will cause swelling in a particular rubber compound.

3   *Oxidation and thermal stability*—This is a measure of how well an oil can resist the formation of hard carbon and sludge at high temperatures.

4   *Corrosivity to metals*—This is a test to determine the corrosivity of the oil by its effect on a small strip of polished copper. Other metals may also be used.

5   *Gear or pressure tests*—This shows the ability of the oil to carry a load.

6   *Carbon residue or coking tests*—This measures the amount of carbon residue remaining in an oil after subjecting it to extreme heating in the absence of air.

7   *Engine tests*—This demonstrates the characteristics of the oil in an actual engine.

Additional tests such as the water emulsion test, compatibility test, storage stability test, interfacial tension test, and several others may be performed to determine several other physical and performance properties of an oil.

In many cases suitable chemical substances are mixed with the oil to impart desirable characteristics. These additives include such materials as detergents, rust preventatives, dyes, anticorrosives, antioxidants, foam inhibitors, viscosity index improvers, pour point depressants, and a host of other additives for improving performance and imparting new properties to the lubricant. Much of the research in lubricants is concentrated in this area.

REQUIREMENTS OF A GAS TURBINE LUBRICANT

As mentioned elsewhere in this book, jet engine temperatures may vary from a −60 to over 400°F. Since oil must be fluid enough at the low-temperature extreme to permit rapid starting and prompt flow of oil to the parts to be lubricated, the jet engine oils must have a fairly low viscosity and pour point. On the other hand, the viscosity index must be as high as possible or the oil will become too thin to support the bearing and gear loads when the engine comes up to operating temperatures.

The flash point, fire point, oxidation resistance, thermal stability, and volatility of an oil are also very important in view of the high operating temperatures in the hot section of the engine and the high-altitude, low ambient pressure in which the engine normally operates. Temperatures of the hotter bearings of some gas turbine engines reach from 400 to 500°F or higher during operation. The relatively few gallons of oil in the system are circulated at a high rate from the tank through the coolers, to bearings and gears, and then back to the tank. Bulk oil temperatures in some engines may run to slightly less than 300°F, with some oil being heated locally to the much higher temperatures of bearing surfaces. These extreme conditions coupled with the fact that scavenge oil is very thoroughly mixed with air used to pressurize the bearing sumps (see Chap. 15 on oil systems), promotes thermal decomposition, oxidation, and volatilization of the lubricating medium. Results of these harmful processes include the formation of sludge, corrosive materials, and other deposits. They also increase viscosity and high oil consumption. In addition, excess deposits can increase bearing friction and temperatures, clog filters and oil jets, interfere with oil flow and cause increased seal wear. Sludge deposits may coat tube surfaces in oil coolers and prevent normal removal of heat from the oil.

Resistance to foaming is also a very important property of an oil. In the preceding paragraph it was noted that a large quantity of air is put into the system by the scavenge pumps and bearing sumps. This air-oil mixture is carried to the oil supply tank or special air-oil separator, where, with a good oil, rapid separation occurs and excess air can be vented off harmlessly. On the other hand, an oil unsuitable in this respect will foam, and much of the air-oil mixture will be vented overboard. A substantial amount of oil can be lost this way. Furthermore, an air-oil mixture supplied to the bearings will not remove heat nor lubricate as efficiently as a solid oil flow.

HANDLING SYNTHETIC LUBRICANTS

Synthetic oils are not as storage stable as conventional petroleum oils. Temperature extremes should be avoided, oil stock should be used as soon as possible, and partial withdrawals should be avoided. In general, most commercial engine operators either limit or entirely prohibit mixing different brands of oil, although the oil specifications require that every oil shall be compatible with previously approved oils. Military services routinely mix oil brands with no gross ill effects noted.

Synthetic lubricants have a deleterious effect on some types of paints, electrical insulation, and elastomer materials used in seals, although in some cases a slight swelling of rubber seals is desirable to prevent leakage of oil. It has been found that some people show a skin sensitivity to this type of lubricant, but in general, synthetic oils may be classed in the same category as mineral oils, both in liquid and vapor states, with regard to toxicity. As in the case of mineral oil, ingestion and prolonged skin contact are to be avoided.

FUTURE DEVELOPMENTS

Higher temperatures will necessitate oils with improved thermal stability. Experiments are under way looking into the possibility of using liquid metals, solid lubricants, and gases or vapors containing various additives. Figure 14-1 shows the lubrication potential of some other lubricating mediums. Several companies

(a)

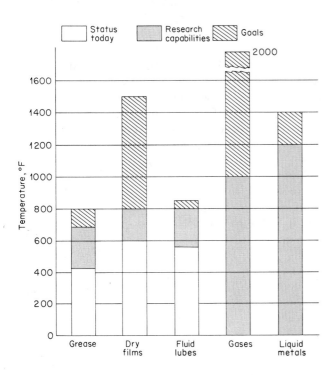

FIG. 14-1 *Potentials of high-temperature lubricants.*

(b)

FIG. 14-2 *The high thermal stability of Type II oils results in reduced deposits.* (**a**) *Type I oil.* (**b**) *Type II oil.*

have developed a Type II lubricant meeting the Military Specification No. MIL-L-23699. It uses a new synthetic base and new additive combinations to cope with the more severe operating conditions of the second and third generations of jet engines (Fig. 14-2) and is being widely adopted by military and civilian operators. The new oil's chief advantage lies in the higher viscosity and temperature ratings.

The effort to find a suitable lubricant for high- and low-temperature applications may come full circle with the adoption of a superrefined petroleum oil which shows promise of having all of the properties of the best synthetics, but at a lower cost.

REVIEW AND STUDY QUESTIONS

1 Name two types of lubricating oils now in use for gas turbine engines. Describe the properties of each.
2 Make a table of the characteristics of lubricating oils.
3 Why are additives placed in the oil?
4 Discuss the requirements for an oil to be used in gas turbine engines.
5 What precautions are necessary when handling synthetic lubricants?
6 What can be expected in the future in relation to lubricants for gas turbines?

Chapter 15

Lubricating systems

Although the oil system of the modern gas turbine engine is quite varied in design and plumbing, most have units which are called upon to perform similar functions. In a great majority of cases a pressure pump or system furnishes oil to the several parts of the engine to be lubricated and cooled, after which, the oil having done its job, a scavenging system returns the oil to the tank for reuse. It is interesting to note, in relation to the cooling function of the oil, that the problem of overheating is more severe after the engine has stopped than while it is running. Oil flow which would normally have cooled the bearings has stopped, and the heat stored in the turbine wheel will raise the bearing temperature to a much higher degree than that reached during operation. Most systems will include a heat exchanger to cool the oil. Many are designed with pressurized sumps, the function of which will be discussed more fully in the following pages. Some systems incorporate a pressurized oil tank which will ensure a constant head pressure to the pressure lubrication pump to prevent pump cavitation at high altitude.

Oil consumption in a gas turbine engine is rather low compared to that of a reciprocating engine of equal power. For example, the large J-79 jet engine has a maximum oil consumption of 2.0 lb (approximately one quart) per hour as compared to the R-3350 engine which may consume as much as 50 lb (approximately 26 quarts) per hour. Oil consumption on the turbine engine is primarily a function of the efficiency of the seals. However, oil can be lost through internal leakage, and on some engines by malfunction of the pressurizing or venting system. Oil sealing is very important in a jet engine because any wetting of the blades or vanes by oil vapor will encourage the accumulation of dust and dirt. A dirty blade or vane represents high friction to airflow, thus decreasing engine efficiency, and resulting in a noticeable decrease in thrust or increase in fuel consumption. Since oil consumption is so low, oil tanks can be made relatively small with a corresponding decrease in weight and storage problems. Tanks may have capacities ranging from ½ to 8 gal. System pressures may vary from 15 psig at idle, to 200 psig during cold starts. Normal operating pressures and bulk temperatures are about 50 to 100 psig and 200°F, respectively.

In general, the parts to be lubricated and cooled include the main bearings and accessory drive gears, and in the turboprop, the propeller gearing. This represents a gain in gas turbine engine lubrication simplicity over the complex oil system of the reciprocating engine. The main rotating unit can be carried by only a few bearings, while in a piston power plant there are hundreds more moving parts to be lubricated. On some turbine engines the oil may also be used to operate the servo mechanism of some fuel controls, to control the position of the variable area exhaust nozzle vanes, and to operate the thrust reverser.

Because each bearing in the engine receives its oil from a metered or calibrated orifice, the system is generally known as the *calibrated* type. With a few exceptions the lubricating system used on the modern jet engine is of the *dry-sump* variety. In this design the bulk of the oil is carried in an airframe or engine-supplied separate oil tank, as opposed to the *wet-sump* system in which the oil is carried in the engine itself. Although our discussion will limit itself to dry-sump systems, an example of the wet-sump design can be seen in the Allison J-33 engine, Fig. 15-12. In this engine, the oil reservoir is an integral part of the accessory drive gear case.

OIL-SYSTEM COMPONENTS

The oil-system components used on gas turbine engines are as follows:

Tank(s)
Pressure pump(s)
Scavenger pumps
Filters
Oil coolers
Relief valves
Breathers and pressurizing components
Pressure and temperature gages
Temperature regulating valves
Oil jet nozzles
Fittings, valves, and plumbing

It should be noted that not all of the units will necessarily be found in the oil system of any one engine, but a majority of the parts listed will be found in most engines.

Oil tanks *(Fig. 15-1)*

Tanks can be either an airframe or engine manufacturer supplied unit. Usually constructed of welded sheet aluminum or steel, it provides a storage place for the oil, and in most engines is pressurized to ensure a constant supply of oil to the pressure pump. The tank can contain a venting system, a de-aerator to separate entrained air from the oil, an oil level transmitter and/or dipstick, a rigid or flexible oil pickup, coarse mesh screens, and various oil and air inlets and outlets.

Pressure pumps *(Fig. 15-2)*

Both the gear- and gerotor-type pumps are used in the lubricating system of the turbine engine. The gear-type pump consists of a driving and driven gear.

The rotation of the pump, which is driven from the engine accessory section, causes the oil to pass around the outside of the gears in pockets formed by the gear teeth and the pump casing. The pressure developed is proportional to engine rpm up to the time the relief valve opens, after which any further increase in engine speed will not result in an oil-pressure increase. Although Fig. 15-2a shows the relief valve in the pump housing, it may be located elsewhere in the pressure system for both types of pumps. Figure 15-13 and others show the relief valve in the system instead of the pump.

The gerotor pump has two moving parts, an inner toothed element meshing with an outer toothed element. The inner element has one less tooth than the

FIG. 15-1 *This tank, used on the General Electric CJ805 engine, incorporates a separate oil supply for the constant-speed drive (CSD). The CSD is needed to enable the alternator to produce a constant electrical frequency regardless of engine rpm within the limits of the drive. NOTE: Electronic constant frequency controlling devices are being tested to eliminate the need for the CSD.*

FIG. 15-2 *The two basic types of oil pumps used on gas turbine engines.* (**a**) *Gear oil pump.*
(**b**) *Gerotor oil pump.*

outer, and the "missing tooth" provides a chamber to move the fluid from the intake to the discharge port. Both elements are mounted eccentricly to each other on the same shaft.

Scavenger pumps

These pumps are similar to the pressure pumps but are of much larger total capacity. An engine is generally provided with several scavenger pumps to drain oil from various parts of the engine. Often one or two of the scavenger elements are incorporated in the same housing as the pressure pump (Fig. 15-3). Different capacities can be provided for each system despite the common driving shaft speed, by varying the diameter or thickness of the gears to vary the volume of the tooth chamber. A vane-type pump may sometimes be used.

Filters *(Figs. 15-4 to 15-7)*

The three basic types of oil filters for the jet engine are the cartridge, screen-disk, and screen types shown in Figs. 15-4, 15-5, and 15-6, respectively. The cartridge filter must be replaced periodically, while the other two can be cleaned and reused. In the screen-disk filter shown in Fig. 15-7, there are a series of circular screen-type filters, with each filter being comprised of two layers of mesh so as to form a chamber between the

mesh layers. The filters are mounted on a common tube and arranged in a manner to provide a space between each circular element. Lube oil passes through the circular mesh elements and into the chamber between the two layers of mesh. This chamber is ported to the center of a common tube which directs oil out of the filter.

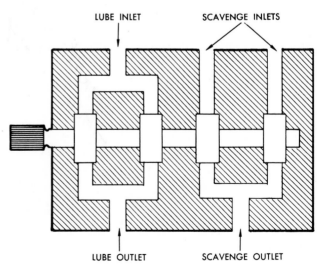

FIG. 15-3 *Schematic of a double-element pressure and scavenger lube pump in a common housing.*

PRESSURE RELIEF VALVE

OIL OUT

OIL IN

FILTER HEAD

FILTER BOWL

FILTER ELEMENT

FIG. 15-4 *Cartridge-type oil filter. The valve will open if the element becomes clogged.*

All of the various types of filters will incorporate a bypass or relief valve, either as an integral part of the filter, or in the oil passages of the system, to allow a flow of oil in the event of filter blockage. When the pressure differential reaches a specified value (about 15 to 20 psi), the valve will open and allow oil to bypass the filter. Some filters incorporate a check valve (Figs. 15-5 and 15-7) which will prevent either reverse flow, or flow through the system when the engine is stopped. Filtering characteristics vary, but most filters will stop particles of approximately 50 μ.

Oil coolers *(Fig. 15-8)*

The oil cooler is used to reduce the temperature of the oil by transmitting heat from the oil to another fluid. The fluid is usually fuel, although air-oil coolers have been used. Since the fuel flow through the cooler is much greater than the oil flow, the fuel is able to absorb a considerable amount of heat from the oil, thus reducing the size of the cooler greatly, as shown in Fig. 15-8b, as well as the weight. Thermostatic or pressure-sensitive valves control the temperature of the oil by determining whether the oil shall pass through or bypass the cooler.

Breathers and pressurizing systems *(Fig. 15-9)*

In many modern engines internal oil leakage is kept to a minimum by pressurizing the bearing sump areas with air that is bled off the compressor. The airflow into the sumps minimizes oil leakage across the seals in the reverse direction. The system operates as follows.

The oil scavenge pumps exceed the capacity of the lubrication pressure pump(s) and are therefore capable of handling considerably more oil than actually exists in the bearing sumps and gearboxes. Because the pumps are a constant-displacement type, they make up for the lack of oil by pumping air from the sumps. Thus, large quantities of air are delivered to the oil tank. Sump and tank pressures are maintained close to each other by a line which connects the two. If the sump pressure exceeds the tank pressure, the sump vent check valve opens, allowing the excess sump air to enter the oil tank. The valve allows flows only into the tank, so oil or tank vapors cannot back up into the sump areas. Tank pressure is maintained a small amount above ambient.

Functioning of the scavenge pumps and sump vent check valve results in a relatively low air pressure in the sumps and gearboxes. These low internal sump pressures allow air to flow across the oil seals into the sumps. This airflow minimizes lube oil leakage across the seals. For this reason, it is necessary to maintain sump pressures low enough to ensure seal air leakage into the sumps. But under some conditions the ability of the scavenge pumps to pump air forms a pressure low enough to cavitate the pumps or cause the collapse of the sump, while under other conditions too much air can enter the sump because of excessive quantities of air entering through worn seals.

Cover

O-ring

Spacer

Filter disk assembly

Check valve assembly

Filter disk

Perforated tube

FIG. 15-5 *In this disk-type filter, installed in the 501-D13 (see Fig. 15-10), a check valve prevents oil from flowing from the tank into the accessories section when the engine is stopped. The bypass valve is located elsewhere in the system.*

1	RELIEF-VALVE RETAINING PLUG AND SEAL	6	PLASTIC SEAL
2	RELIEF-VALVE SPRING	7	SEAL
3	RELIEF-VALVE POPPET	8	FILTER ELEMENT
4	FILTER HEAD	9	FILTER BOWL
5	SEAL	10	SEAL
		11	DRAIN PLUG

FIG. 15-6 *A screen-type filter with a bypass (relief) valve.*

If the seal leakage is not sufficient to maintain proper internal pressure, check valves in the sump and tank pressurizing valves open and allow ambient air to enter the system. If the seal leakage exceeds that required to maintain proper internal sump and gearbox pressure, air flows from the sumps, through the sump vent check valve, the oil tank, the tank and sump pressurizing valves, and then to the atmosphere. Tank pressure is always maintained a few pounds above ambient pressure by the sump and tank pressurizing valve.

TYPICAL OIL SYSTEMS

The Allison 501-D13 *(Fig. 15-10)*

This system incorporates a low-pressure, independent dry sump oil system which includes one combination main pressure and scavenge oil pump assembly, three separate scavenge pumps, a pressure-regulating valve, an oil filter and check valve, a filter bypass valve, and a scavenge pressure-relief valve. Oil is supplied to the power unit by an aircraft-furnished tank and cooled by an aircraft-furnished cooler.

The main oil pump is located on the center of the front face of the accessory drive housing cover. Oil, supplied to the pressure pump from the aircraft-furnished tank, is pumped through a disk-type filter and check valve, through drilled and cored passages and internal and external lines to those parts of the power

1	OUTLET PORT	6	FILTER TUBE
2	CHECK VALVE	7	FILTER TUBE OIL INLET SLOTS
3	PRESSURE RELIEF VALVE	8	DRAIN PLUG
4	INLET PORT		
5	FILTER DISK		

FIG. 15-7 *Oil flow through a typical screen disk filter.*

(a)

(b)

FIG. 15-8 (**a**) *Diagram of a typical fuel-oil cooler.* (**b**) *An actual fuel-oil cooler.*

FIG. 15-9 *Tank and sump pressurizing system.*

1 TANK PRESSURIZING VALVE
2 SUMP VACUUM VALVE
3 SUMP AND TANK PRESSUR-
    IZING VALVE
4 NINTH- OR SEVENTH-STAGE
    AIR
5 BEARING AIR-OIL SEALS
6 SCAVENGE PUMPS
7 SUMP VENT CHECK VALVE
8 DEAERATOR

unit which require lubrication. A pressure-regulating valve located in the main oil pump regulates the oil pressure delivered by the pump. A filter check valve is included in the system to prevent oil from seeping into the power unit after shutdown.

Scavenge oil is returned to the aircraft tank by the rear turbine scavenge pump, the front turbine scavenge pump, the diffuser scavenge pump, and the main scavenge pump. Scavenge oil is carried by drilled passages, and internal and external lines.

Two magnetic drain plugs are provided on the accessory drive housing; one at the bottom of the housing and one in the scavenge oil outlet connection.

The power section breather is located on top of the air inlet housing. It is a cyclonic separator of air and oil, in that oil-saturated air coming through the vent line from the diffuser enters the breather and is rotated by the spiral passageway in the breather. Movement of the air through this passageway imparts a centrifugal force on the air that separates the air and oil. The air is vented overboard, and the oil flows through passages to the scavenge oil sump in the accessory drive housing. (See Chap. 23.)

The General Electric CJ610 *(Fig. 15-11)*

The engine has a pressurized closed-circuit lube system designed to furnish oil to parts which require lubrication during engine operation. After oil has been supplied to these parts it flows to the sumps; here it is recovered and recirculated throughout the system. All

system components are engine-furnished and engine-mounted except the oil pressure transducer, which is airframe-furnished equipment but also engine-mounted. The main components of the lube system are located beneath the compressor section. They include: a lube and scavenge pump mounted on the rear right-hand pad of the accessory gearbox; an oil tank, secured to the lube and scavenge pump; an oil cooler, mounted on the oil tank; and an oil filter, contained within the lube and scavenge pump casing; a scavenge oil temperature tap, located at the gearbox on the left-hand scavenge tube; and the oil pressure transducer (airframe-supplied).

The pressure element of the lube pump pumps oil from the tank, through the oil cooler, through the oil filter, and into the accessory gearbox. Part of the oil services the gearbox; the remainder flows through the gearbox to two OUT ports on the left-side of the gearbox. Oil flows from one OUT port through an external line to the number 1 bearing. It flows from the second OUT port through an external line which is branched to service the transfer gearbox. The main line connects to the main frame. This line services, through internal tubing, the internal bearings, seals, and gears of the engine. The five scavenge elements of the lube and scavenge pump pick up the oil which collects in the engine sumps and return it to the oil tank.

A closed vent circuit provides for pressurization of all parts of the lube system, including the oil tank, sumps, and gearboxes. This ensures pressurization to the inlets of the pump service element and scavenge elements.

FIG. 15-10 *The Allison 501-D13 lubrication system.*

FIG. 15-11 *The General Electric CJ610 oil system. The weighted oil pickup prevents the pump from drawing air.*

The sumps are pressurized by seal-leakage air that enters the sumps. Vent lines and check valves between the engine sumps, gearboxes, and oil tank maintain a balanced pressure between the sumps, gearboxes, and oil tank. These vent lines and check valves also prevent overpressurization of the sumps by venting air (in excess of what the scavenge elements can handle) directly to the oil tank. A pressure-relief valve on the outboard side of the oil tank controls the pressure in the entire system by venting overboard any air in excess of 2.5 (±0.5) psig. A small orifice through the center of this valve provides for depressurization of the system at engine shutdown.

The lube and scavenge pump is mounted on three studs at the right rear pad of the accessory gearbox. It is a positive-displacement pump consisting of six guided-vane-type elements mounted along a common drive shaft and contained within the same housing.

Five of the elements scavenge oil from the engine sumps; one element is the pressure element which supplies oil to the engine. The operating elements extend aft into the oil tank from the pump flange on which the oil tank is mounted. Scavenge oil passes from the sumps, through the accessory gearbox, through one of five scavenge ports on the face of the pump mounting flange, through the sump scavenge element, and into the oil-tank dwell chamber through a common discharge port. Oil from the tank enters the pressure element through a pendulum-type swivel pickup tube that extends out from the aft right-hand side of the pump body. The oil is pumped by the pressure element directly to the oil cooler, through the oil filter, and into the gearbox; from here it is then distributed throughout the system.

A pressure-relief valve, mounted in parallel with the lube discharge passage, is included to prevent damage that might result from excessive oil pressure due to cold starting or restriction of normal oil flow. The relief valve is factory-adjusted to open at a differential pressure of 90 (±5) psi across the valve. If this pressure differential is exceeded, the relief valve opens and oil from the pressure element is discharged back into the oil tank.

The rear pad of the pump is a drive capable of driving the tachometer-generator.

Lube pump discharge pressure is transmitted from a pressure tap located on the lube pump housing, to the cockpit lube pump pressure indicator (airframe-furnished equipment). Pressure readings indicate lube filter condition and lube pump operation.

Scavenge oil temperature is transmitted from a temperature tap in the left-hand scavenge tube to the cockpit scavenge oil temperature indicator (airframe-furnished equipment). Temperature readings indicate the operating conditions of the lube pump, lube filters, oil cooler, and engine bearings.

The oil filter assembly is mounted within the lube pump housing at the bottom, and is accessible for removal. It is a full-flow, in-line-type filter with a screen element of corrugated corrosion-resistant steel. The screen filters out contaminants over 40 μ in size. A filter bypass valve is included in the core of the filter element. If a pressure difference between oil entering the filter and oil leaving the filter exceeds 20 to 24 psi, the valve opens to permit a direct flow of oil through the unit without filtration.

The fabricated-steel oil tank is mounted on the rear flange of the lube and scavenge pump. Included within the tank is a separate air chamber, a dwell chamber, and a system of vent tubes. The filler port is located on the rear face of the tank, and the oil level in the tank is indicated by a dipstick graduated in pints to be added. A remote-fill line (airframe-furnished) connection is available on the rear face of the tank. When it is used, a vent line is required from the oil tank to the remote filler assembly. Oil that overflows during filling is collected in a scupper and may be drained overboard through the scupper drain port. The oil tank, when FULL is read on the dipstick, has a total capacity of 4.0 quarts of which 3.0 quarts are usable. There is adequate space allowed for expansion. The bottom of the tank is formed into a concave well which provides a recess for mounting the tachometer-generator unit.

The oil cooler is a shell and tube heat exchanger mounted on the front face of the oil tank at the right-hand side. Fuel flows through the tubing and absorbs heat from the hot engine oil flowing over the tube bundle. Oil enters and leaves the cooler through ports located in the housing. A pressure bypass valve is designed to bypass oil around the cooler in response to overpressure. If the cooler clogs, the pressure valve control bypasses the oil when the pressure differential across the valve exceeds 20 (±4) psi.

The Allison J33   *(Fig. 15-12)*

This unit is lubricated by a simple wet sump system which furnishes oil under pressure to the accessory drive coupling, turbine rotor coupling, and the bearings of the rotor shafts. In addition, pressure oil is supplied to the mounting pads for the fuel pump, hydraulic pump, fuel control, and afterburner pump. All of the bearings

FIG. 15-12   *Wet-sump oil system schematic for the Allison J33.*

in the accessories drive casing are lubricated by means of a splash system and the oil mist created by spraying a stream of oil against the gear train.

The supply reservoir for the system is an integral part of the accessories drive gear casing. The operating capacity of the reservoir is 12 quarts and the minimum supply allowable is 6 quarts. Oil level in the reservoir may be determined with a quick-disconnect-type bayonet gage located on the right-hand front side of the accessories drive gear casing.

Scavenge oil is returned to the reservoir by gravity and pump suction. Oil from the front compressor bearing and the accessories drive coupling shaft drains

by gravity directly into the reservoir. The oil from the turbine coupling and the three remaining rotor shaft bearings drains into a sump from which the oil is pumped, by the scavenge element of the pump, through a finger-type screen into the reservoir.

The General Electric CJ805-23 aft fan *(Fig. 15-13)*

In this system the main lube and scavenge pump supplies high-pressure oil from the engine-mounted tank to the areas requiring positive lubrication, and four scavenge pumps return the oil to the tank. Filters remove foreign material from the oil, and coolers prevent the oil from rising to destructive temperatures. Air

1 SUMP VENT INLET PRESSURE VALVE	10 SUMP AND TANK PRESSURIZING VALVE	20 DOWNCOMER TUBE	31 ORIFICE BLOCK
2 TO OVERBOARD VENT	11 ANTI-G BAFFLES	21 SUMP PRESSURE REFERENCE TAP	32 CHECK VALVE
3 CSD AND THRUST-REVERSER RETURN	12 FUEL OIL COOLER	22 FAN-SPEED TACHOMETER	33 SUPPLY OIL FILTER
4 TANK PRESSURIZING VENT	13 ENGINE OIL DRAIN	23 NO. 1 BEARING AND FRONT GEARBOX	34 REAR-GEARBOX SCAVENGE PUMP
5 DEAERATOR	14 THRUST-REVERSER SUPPLY	24 PRESSURE-RELIEF VALVE	35 EDUCTOR
6 TEMPERATURE REFERENCE TAP	15 OIL LEVEL	25 OIL-PRESSURE TAP	36 EDUCTOR
7 DEAERATORS	16 OIL SUPPLY	26 NO. 2 BEARING	37 NO. 5 BEARING SCAVENGE PUMP
8 CSD AND THRUST REVERSER COMPARTMENT	17 CSD SUPPLY	27 NO. 3 BEARING	38 TRANSFER GEARBOX
9 SCAVENGE-OIL FILTER	18 SCUPPER DRAIN	28 NO. 4 BEARING	39 TRANSFER-GEARBOX SCAVENGE PUMP
	19 CSD AND THRUST-REVERSER COMPARTMENT DRAIN	29 NO. 5 BEARING	40 DAMPER BEARING
		30 BYPASS FLOW	41 REAR GEARBOX
			42 LUBE AND SCAVENGE PUMP

FIG. 15-13 *The General Electric CJ805-23 lubrication system.*

valves in the system maintain the correct pressure balance. The system supplies oil to lubricate the five rotor support bearings and the gears and bearings in the gearboxes. It scavenges, filters, and cools the used oil to prepare it for recirculation through the system, and regulates air pressure in the system to maintain a positive head of oil pressure at the inlet to the lube and scavenge pumps. It also establishes a pressure differential across the bearing seals, thus controlling oil consumption. The components required to perform the above tasks are divided into three functional subsystems: the oil supply, the scavenge, and the sump and tank pressurization subsystems.

The oil tank is a two-compartment tank. Oil in one compartment is for the oil supply subsystem. Oil in the other compartment is used for the hydraulic fluid used in the thrust reverser and constant-speed drive systems. One element of the lube and scavenge pump receives oil at tank pressure and discharges oil at higher pressures to the lube oil filter. The two other elements scavenge oil from the numbers 3 and 4 bearing sumps. This oil is discharged to the scavenge oil filter. The oil lube filter prevents the oil jet nozzles from clogging by filtering the oil flowing from the lube pump. The oil-pressure tap lube distribution manifold contains two calibrated orifices which work with a pressure-relief valve to protect the oil-pressure transducer from extreme pressure surges. The pressure-relief valve limits the maximum pressure sensed by the transducer, and bypasses extreme oil pressure surges from the lube pump discharge back to the lube pump inlet. Supplied by the airframe manufacturer, the oil-pressure transducer senses oil pressure and generates an electrical signal for the cockpit indicator. The last parts in the oil supply subsystem are the oil jet nozzles which spray lubricating oil over the engine bearings, gears, and seals.

The scavenge subsystem begins with the transfer-gearbox scavenge pump which scavenges used oil from the number 1 bearing front gearbox, damper bearing, and transfer gearbox and discharges oil to the scavenge oil filter. The rear-gearbox scavenge pump scavenges oil from the number 2 bearing and rear gearbox, and discharges this oil to the scavenge oil filter. The number 5 bearing scavenge pump scavenges used oil from the number 5 bearing and aft fan tachometer-generator and discharges this oil to the scavenge oil filter. The used oil received from the four scavenge pumps is filtered by the scavenge oil filter and delivered to the engine fuel-oil cooler. The engine fuel-oil cooler cools used oil received from the scavenge-oil filter by using engine fuel as the coolant. Oil discharged from the cooler returns to the oil tank. An optional fuel-oil cooler supplied by the engine manufacturer cools the return oil from the constant-speed drive. Engine fuel is the coolant. Another optional air-oil cooler, supplied by the

airframe manufacturer, may also be used to cool used oil returning from the constant-speed drive.

The final subsystem contains the sump and tank pressurizing valve which regulates pressure in the bearing sumps, oil tank, gearboxes, and connecting pipes. Also incorporated in this subsystem is the sump vent check valve which vents sump air pressure to the tank, yet prevents reverse oil flow. (See page 240.)

The Continental J69 *(Fig. 15-14)*

Oil from the engine oil tank (not supplied with the engine) is led to the main oil pump where the pressure section develops main oil pressure. The output of the pressure pump is led through an antileak valve to the main oil filter. This filter system incorporates a pressure-regulating arrangement as well as bypass provisions to pass oil beyond the filter element if it should become clogged. From the oil filter output, oil for the rear bearing is carried by an external hose. Another external hose picks up return oil from the rear bearing to carry this oil to the rear-bearing scavenge section of the oil pump. The rear-bearing housing incorporates a vent passage as well as passages to feed the oil to and from the rear bearing. At the front of the engine, oil is led from the main oil filter output through passages to the front bearings and front-end gears. Oil is also fed to the accessory gear train that fans out across the lower part of the compressor housing. Oil from the front bearings and upper gears drains down to the accessory case from which one scavenge section of the oil pump pulls return oil. All scavenge sections of the oil pump lead return oil back to the engine oil tank. The front-end section is vented by a passage to the top of the upper gear housing. (See Chap. 24.)

The Lycoming T53 *(Fig. 15-15)*

Engine lubricating oil supplied from the aircraft oil tank enters the oil pump located on the accessory gearbox. The two-element, gear-type oil pump is driven by a single, splined drive shaft. One element is used to supply main lubricating oil pressure, the other element is used to return scavenge oil to the aircraft oil tank. A pressure-relief valve in the oil pump is adjusted to deliver between 60 and 80 psi oil pressure. This setting is rated for a maximum inlet oil temperature of 93°C (200°F) and an oil flow of 3300 lb/hr at sea level and 3000 lb/hr at 25,000 ft. Pump pressure is directly proportional to compressor rotor speed at pressures below the relief-valve setting. From the oil pump, the engine oil flows through internal passages to the oil filter. The oil filter is a wafer-disk type. A bypass valve, set at a differential pressure of between 15 and 20 psi, allows oil flow to bypass the filter elements and to supply emergency lubrication to the engine in the event

FIG. 15-14 *The Continental J69 oil system schematic.*

the filter becomes clogged. Filtered oil is directed into two flow paths. One path flows internally through passages in the accessory drive gearbox to the inlet housing to lubricate the output reduction carrier and gear assembly, torque-meter, overspeed governor, and tachometer drive support and gear assembly, accessory drive carrier assembly, sun gearshaft, and number 1 main bearing. The second path flows externally and leads to the numbers 2, 3, and 4 main bearings. Scavenge oil is drained by paddle pumps through various internal passages and external lines to the accessory drive gearbox where the main scavenge pump picks up the oil and sends it first to the oil cooler, and then to the tank. A more detailed examination of this system and its components is given in Chap. 22.

The Pratt & Whitney JT3D *(Fig. 15-16)*

The JT3D engine lubrication system is a self-contained, high-pressure design consisting of a pressure system which supplies oil to the main engine bearings and to the accessory drives, and a scavenge system which scavenges the bearing compartments and acces-

sory drives. The oil is cooled by passing through a fuel-oil cooler. A breather system, interconnecting the individual bearing compartments and the oil tank, completes the engine lubricating system. The engine requires a synthetic lubricant.

The engine oil tank on most models is mounted in the upper right quadrant of the intermediate case, by being fastened with two straps attached to brackets on the front and rear flanges of the intermediate case. On some models the oil tank is supplied by the airframe manufacturer. Strips of resilient material serving as vibration isolators are installed between the tank and the engine, and the tank and the straps. The tank has a capacity of 6.0 gal with a minimum usable quantity under all operating attitudes of 3.25 gal. Internally, the tank incorporates a flow de-aerator, which is so located that the outlet is submerged even at low tank levels to prevent re-aeration of the oil. Various holes in the tank permit the tank to breathe and the oil to enter and leave. There are also other holes for draining, cleaning, and inspection.

Oil is supplied to the inlet of the spur gear pressure

FIG. 15-15 The Lycoming T53 lubrication system with centrifugal-type paddle pumps.

250

OIL TANK

GEARBOX

P&WA
FUEL-OIL
COOLER
BOEING
ONLY

AIRFRAME
SUPPLIED
COOLER
DOUGLAS
ONLY

CROSS HATCH INDICATES
PORTION AIRFRAME SUPPLIED

PUMP INLET
PRESSURE OIL
SCAVENGE OIL
BREATHER
SUMP

A MAIN OIL PUMP
B PRESSURE-RELIEF VALVE
C OIL FILTER WITH CHECK
    VALVE
D FILTER BYPASS VALVE
E SCAVENGE PUMP (VENTED
    INTO GEARBOX)
F CENTRIFUGAL AIR-OIL
    SEPARATOR

G PRESSURE-RELIEF VALVE
H TEMPERATURE BYPASS
    VALVE
I VENT TO NO. 4 AND NO.
    5 BEARING CAVITY
J OIL-PRESSURE TRANSMITTER
    (VENTED INTO GEARBOX)
K SCAVENGE PUMPS

FIG. 15-16 The Pratt & Whitney JT3D oil system.

251

pump. This pump is a duplex unit having a single gear stage for the pressure and scavenge section, separated by a center body. The pump forces the oil through the oil filter into an adapter and through external tubing, to the engine components requiring lubrication and cooling. Proper distribution of the total oil flow among the various locations is maintained by metering orifices and clearances. Oil-pressure differential is controlled by an oil-pressure relief valve.

An oil filter assembly, equipped with a bypass relief valve assembly and located forward of the accessory and component drive gearbox, assures a clean supply of oil to the lubrication system. The valve permits the oil to bypass the filter element in the event the screens become clogged. The filter assembly is composed of a series of screens in disk form, separated alternately by stamped inlet and outlet spacers, assembled around an inner filter element. The filter assembly is easily accessible for removal for disassembly and cleaning. Connections are provided for an oil-pressure transmitter and a differential pressure switch to activate with the buildup of screen contaminants.

The scavenge oil system contains five gear-type pumps located throughout the engine. They are located in the front accessory section for scavenging the number 1 bearing compartment and front accessory section; the accessory and component drive gearbox for scavenging the numbers 2, 2½, and 3 bearing compartments through a common adapter; then through external tubing to the accessory and component drive gearbox; the dual scavenge pump in the diffuser case for scavenging the numbers 4, 4½, and 5 bearing compartments through the oil tube heat shields; and the turbine rear pump for scavenging the number 6 bearing

compartment. (Figure 20-27 shows the location of the various bearings.) The numbers 1 and 6 bearing scavenge oil flows through external tubing to the gearbox to join the scavenge oil from the numbers 4, 4½, and 5 bearing areas on its way to the tank. The oil handling capacity of the combined scavenge-oil pumps is approximately three times the quantity output of the pressure oil pump. All scavenge oil is routed through the fuel-oil cooler and to the oil tank by means of external tubing. The scavenge oil contains a considerable amount of entrapped air which must be vented overboard. This entrapped air is handled and dissipated by the engine breather system through the breather centrifuge.

Each of the separate scavenge areas are vented through external tubing and inner passages to a breather chamber formed by the compressor intermediate case annulus and then to a cavity in the accessory and component drive gearbox. The common overboard vent is from this cavity through a rotary breather which prevents the majority of oil particles from being carried overboard in the breather airflow. (See Chap. 20.)

REVIEW AND STUDY QUESTIONS

1 Compare the oil system requirements of the reciprocating and gas turbine engines.

2 Other than lubricating, what jobs can the oil do?

3 List the several components contained in a typical gas turbine lubricating system. Discuss each unit in some detail.

4 Very briefly describe the lubricating system of the 501-D13, CJ610, J33, CJ805-23, J69, T53, and JT3D engines.

Chapter 16

Ignition systems

Jet engine ignition systems fall into two general classifications: first, the induction type, producing high-tension sparks by conventional induction coils, and, second, the capacitor type, or those that cause ignition by means of high-energy and very-high-temperature sparks produced by a condenser discharge. A third kind of ignition system not widely adopted, but incorporated on the Pratt-Whitney PT6A, utilizes a glow plug.

REQUIREMENTS FOR THE GAS TURBINE IGNITION SYSTEM

The advent of various types of jet engines toward the end of World War II created an entirely new set of problems for the manufacturers of ignition equipment.

In conventional reciprocating engines, accurately timed sparks occur between the spark-plug electrode when the fuel-air mixture has been subjected to a pressure of about 5 to 10 atm. Furthermore, the mixture has been heated by rapid compression and remains somewhat turbulent, although it is ignited when the piston velocity is nearly zero. Under these conditions ignition is relatively easy.

The nearly ideal fuel/air ratios and essentially stable conditions within the combustion chamber have been replaced by a very cold and considerably overlean (too much air in relation to fuel) fuel-air mixture that rushes past the igniter plugs at a high velocity. This causes difficulty because, in order to start a fire, a mixture, in spite of its low temperature and excessive air content, must be brought to a high temperature in the brief instant that it is adjacent to the igniter plugs.

In addition, spark-plug fouling is a major problem. Since jet engine combustion is a self-sustaining process, ignition systems are required to operate only during the starting cycle. The spark plug or igniter is not able to keep itself clean by continuous arcing across its gap, as is the case with reciprocating engine spark plugs.

The lower volatility of jet fuels, coupled with the extremely high altitudes and correspondingly low temperatures in which the gas turbine engine operates, makes the conditions for an in-flight relight in the event of a flameout even more difficult.

EARLY INDUCTION-TYPE IGNITION SYSTEMS
(Fig. 16-1)

Early jet engine ignition systems evolved using the tried principles that were developed for the reciprocating engine. Some of these early systems employed a vibrator and transformer combination somewhat similar to the booster coils used for starting purposes on reciprocating engines. Other units substituted a small electric motor driving a cam to provide the necessary pulsating magnetic field to the primary coil of the transformer. Several variations appeared, all using the same basic principle of high-voltage induction by means of a transformer in order to reach the necessary voltage capable of causing an arc across the wide-gap jet igniter plug. A typical unit of this kind is illustrated in Fig. 16-1. An interesting variation of this transformer type of ignition system is the opposite-polarity system used on some models of the General Electric J-47 (Fig. 16-2). In this circuit two electrodes extend into the

FIG. 16-1 *Early type of induction ignition system. (Bendix Corporation)*

FIG. 16-2 *Opposite-polarity ignition system.*

combustion chamber. Each electrode alternately becomes highly positively and negatively charged, thus causing a very high potential difference to exist across the electrodes.

MODERN CAPACITOR-TYPE IGNITION SYSTEMS

In modern engines it is necessary to have not only a high voltage to jump a wide-gap igniter plug, but also a spark of high heat intensity for the reasons mentioned in the section dealing with ignition-system requirements. The high-energy, capacitor-type ignition system has been universally accepted for gas turbine engines, because it provides both high voltage and an exceptionally hot spark which covers a large area. Excellent chances of igniting the fuel-air mixture are assured at reasonably high altitudes.

The term "high energy" has been used throughout this section to describe the capacitor type of ignition system. Strictly speaking, the amount of energy produced is very small. The intense spark is obtained by expending a small amount of electric energy in a very small amount of time.

Energy is the capacity for doing work. It can be expressed as the product of the electrical power (watt)

and time. Gas turbine ignition systems are rated in *joules*. The joule is also an expression of electric energy, being equal to the amount of energy expended in one second by an electric current of one ampere through a resistance of one ohm. The relationship between these terms can be expressed by the formula:

$$W = \frac{J}{t}$$

where W = watts (power)
J = joules
t = time, sec

All other factors being equal, the temperature of the spark is determined by the power level reached. It can be seen from the formula that a high-temperature spark can result from increasing the energy level (J), or by shortening the duration (t) of the spark. Increasing the energy level will result in a heavier, more bulky ignition unit, since the energy delivered to the spark plug is only about 30 to 40 percent of the total energy stored in the capacitor. Higher erosion rates on the igniter plug electrodes would also occur because of the heavy current flowing for such a comparatively long time. Furthermore, much of the spark would be wasted, since ignition takes place in a matter of microseconds. On the other hand, since heat is lost to the igniter plug electrodes, and since the fuel-air mixture is never completely gaseous, the duration of the spark cannot be too short.

An example of the relationship between watts and time is shown in the following table for a 4-joule ignition unit (4 joules appearing at the plug).

TIME, SEC	POWER, WATTS
1	4
0.01 (hundredths)	400
0.001 (thousandths)	4,000
0.0001 (ten-thousandths)	40,000
0.00001 (hundred-thousandths)	400,000
0.000001 (millionths)	4,000,000

In an actual capacitor discharge ignition system, most of the total energy available to the igniter plug is dissipated in 10 to 100 μsec (0.000010 to 0.000100 sec), so the system described above would actually deliver 80,000 watts if the spark duration was 50 μsec.

$$W = \frac{J}{t}$$
$$= \frac{4}{0.000050}$$
$$= 80,000$$

To review, the spark temperature (a function of the watts value) is the most important characteristic of any ignition system, but all three factors—watts, energy, and time—must be considered before the effectiveness of any ignition system can be determined.

TWO TYPES OF HIGH-ENERGY IGNITION SYSTEMS

Just as ignition systems for jet engines are divided into induction and capacitor discharge types, the capacitor discharge type can be further divided into two basic categories.

1 High-voltage capacitor ignition system with dc or ac input
2 Low-voltage capacitor ignition system with dc or ac input

High-voltage capacitor system—dc input
(Fig. 16-3)

As the cycle of operation begins, the power source delivers 28-volt-dc input to the system at the exciter. Dual ignition is provided on the engine by twin circuits throughout the exciter as shown in Fig. 16-4, or by two separately mounted exciters, depending on engine configuration, as shown in Fig. 16-5. In either case, each triggering circuit is connected to a spark igniter. The operation described here takes place in each individual circuit and is essentially the same in both units, with the exception of the mechanical features of the armature. Figure 16-6 shows a unit with two exciters and a separate ignition transformer. The operation is the same as the devices shown in Figs. 16-4 and 16-5.

The following description of a typical dc input ignition unit, refers to Fig. 16-5. In this system the direct current supply, after passing through a radio noise filter (1) to prevent high-frequency feedback into the aircraft electrical system, is fed to the primary of the transformer, which is an integral part of the vibrator assembly (2). From the primary this current is passed through a pair of breaker contacts, normally closed, to ground. A primary capacitor is connected across these contacts to damp excessive arcing.

The action of the vibrator is produced by the transformer, which has a laminated core. With the contacts in a closed position, the flow of current through the

(a)

(b)

FIG. 16-4 (**a**) *General Laboratories Associates, Inc., ignition unit used on the Allison 501-D13 engine.* (**b**) *Capacitor-discharge electronic ignition exciter; a dc input is used on this unit. (General Laboratories Associates, Inc.)*

FIG. 16-3 *Bendix dual high-voltage system with dc input.*

coil produces a magnetic field. This field exerts a force against the armature, which is mounted on a pivot.

The armature is pulled downward, and after a certain degree of travel to acquire momentum, strikes the end of the contact spring. With further movement the contacts are separated, the flow of current stops, and

Low voltage
Alternating intermediate voltage
Direct intermediate voltage
High voltage

1	FILTER ASSEMBLY	5	TRIGGER TRANSFORMER
2	EXCITER ASSEMBLY	6	TRIGGER CAPACITOR
3	STORAGE CAPACITOR	7	SPARK IGNITER
4	SPARK GAP	8	RECTIFIER

(a)

(b)

FIG. 16-5 (a) *This schematic is typical of the type used on the Pratt & Whitney JT3 and JT4 series engines. It is one of two separate units with a dc input and a high-voltage output. (General Laboratories Associates, Inc.)* (b) *External appearance of the GLA high-energy unit.*

the magnetic field collapses. With the cessation of magnetic force against the underside of the armature, its movement slows to a halt, and it is positively returned to its original position, first by the tension of the contact spring, and finally by the pull of the permanent magnet mounted above it. The spring meanwhile returns the lower contact to a closed position, and the vibrating cycle resumes.

The collapse of the magnetic field in the transformer causes a high alternating voltage to be induced in the secondary. This produces successive pulses flowing into the storage capacitor (3) through the gas-charged rectifier tube (8), which limits the flow to a single direction. With repeated pulses the capacitor assumes a greater and greater charge, at a constantly increasing voltage.

When this intermediate voltage reaches the predetermined level for which the spark gap has been set (4), the gap breaks down, allowing a portion of the ac-

cumulated charge to flow through the primary of the triggering transformer (5) and the trigger capacitor (6) connected in series with it.

The surge of the current through the primary induces a very high voltage in the secondary of the triggering transformer, which is connected to the spark igniter (7). This voltage is sufficient to ionize the gap, and produces a trigger spark.

When the gap at the spark igniter is thus made conductive, the storage capacitor discharges the remainder of its accumulated energy through it, together with the charge from the trigger capacitor. This results in a capacitive spark of very high energy, capable of vaporizing globules of fuel and overcoming carbonaceous deposits.

The bleeder resistor is provided in the discharge circuit to dissipate the residual charge on the trigger capacitor between the completion of one discharge at the spark igniter and the succession of the next cycle.

The spark rate will vary depending on the value of the input voltage. At lower voltage values, more time will be required to raise the intermediate voltage on the storage capacitor to the level necessary to break down the spark gap. Since that level remains constant, however, being established by the physical properties of the gap, the full normal store of energy will always be accumulated by the storage capacitor before discharge.

Typical specifications for this system are as follows:

Input voltage:	Normal: 24 volts dc
	Operating limits: 14 to 30 volts dc
Spark rate:	4 to 8 per sec at each plug, depending on input voltage
Designed to fire:	2 igniter plugs
Accumulated energy:	3 joules
Duty cycle:	2 min on, 3 min off, 2 min on, 23 min off

(a)

FIG. 16-6 (**a**) *High-energy ignition system with separate transformer and dc input.* (Continued on following page.)

IGNITION TRANSFORMER

HIGH TENSION LEAD

IGNITION EXCITER

INTERMEDIATE VOLTAGE LEAD

(b)

FIG. 16-6 (continued) (**b**) *External appearance of the ignition system with the separate transformer.*

FIG. 16-7 *A high-energy system with cam-operated breaker points.*

Two igniter plugs are mounted in the combustion section outer case. The spark igniters are generally located in two diametrically opposite combustion liners. The igniters receive the electrical output from the ignition exciter unit and discharge the electric energy during engine starting to ignite the fuel-air mixture in the combustion liners.

Figure 16-7 shows a typical high-voltage, high-energy, capacitor-type ignition system using a motor-driven cam to operate the breaker points instead of a vibrator, and a motor-driven single-lobe cam instead of a sealed spark gap tube (Fig. 16-7).

High-voltage capacitor system—ac input
(*Fig. 16-8*)

As shown in Fig. 16-8, power is supplied to the input connector of the unit from the 115-volt, 400-cycle source in the aircraft, and is first led through a filter which serves to block conducted noise voltage from feeding back into the airplane electrical system. From the filter, the circuit is completed through the primary of the power transformer to ground.

In the secondary of the power transformer an alternat-

FIG. 16-8 *High-energy, high-voltage system with an ac input.*

ing voltage is generated at a level of approximately 1700 volts. During the first half-cycle this follows a circuit through the doubler capacitor and rectifier *A* to ground, leaving the capacitor charged. During the second half-cycle, when the polarity reverses, this circuit is blocked by rectifier *A*; the flow of this pulse is then through ground to the storage capacitor, through rectifier *B*, the resistor, and the doubler capacitor back to the power transformer.

With each pulse the storage capacitor thus assumes a greater and greater charge, which by virtue of the action of the doubler capacitor approaches a voltage approximately twice that generated in the power transformer. When this voltage reaches the predetermined level for which the spark gap in the discharge tube *X* (the control gap) has been calibrated, this gap breaks down, allowing a portion of the accumulated charge to flow through the primary of the high-tension transformer and the trigger capacitor in series with it. This surge of current induces a very high voltage in the secondary of the high-tension transformer, sufficient to ionize the gap in dis-

charge tube *Y*. The storage capacitor immediately discharges the remainder of its accumulated energy through the spark igniter. This produces a capacitive spark of very high energy.

The bleeder resistors are provided to dissipate the residual charge on the trigger capacitor between the completion of one discharge at the spark igniter and the succession of the next cycle.

Typical specifications for this system are as follows:

Input voltage:	Normal: 115-volts 400-cycle ac
	Operating limits: 90 to 120 volts
Spark rate:	Normal: 1.50 to 2.75 per sec
	Operating limits: 0.75 to 5.00 per sec
Designed to ignite:	One spark igniter
Accumulated energy:	14 to 17 joules
Duty cycle:	2 min on, 3 min off,
	2 min on, 23 min off

Low-voltage capacitor system—dc input (less than 1000 volts to the plug) (*Fig. 16-9*)

The basis of operation upon which the low-voltage, high-energy ignition system is built is the self-ionizing

FIG. 16-9 *Two complete Bendix Scintilla high-energy, low-voltage systems in one case.*

feature of the igniter plug. In the high-voltage system a double spark is produced; the first part consisting of a high-voltage component to ionize (make conductive) the gap between the igniter plug electrodes in order that the second high-energy low-voltage portion may follow. The low-voltage, high-energy spark is similar to the above except that ionization is effected by the self-ionizing igniter plug discussed above.

The explanation refers to Fig. 16-10, which shows one of two separate and independent low-tension, high-energy ignition units used on some models of the General Electric J-79 engine.

The main ignition unit changes the amplitude and the frequency characteristics of aircraft power into pulsating dc. To do this the components in the ignition unit are grouped in stages to filter, amplify, rectify, and store an electric charge.

A pi-type filter ($C1$, $L1$, $C2$), located in the input stage, grounds out radio interference entering or leaving the unit. This prevents the ignition unit from disrupting the operation of other aircraft electronic equipment and stabilizes the output of the unit itself.

At radio frequencies the choke coil ($L1$) blocks current flow in either direction. Capacitors $C1$ and $C2$ act as short circuits to ground. Radio-frequency noise pulses, approaching the filter from either direction are blocked by the coil and shunted to ground through the capacitors.

The choke coil ($L1$) passes aircraft dc easily, and the capacitors ($C1$ and $C2$) now act as blocking devices to prevent grounding out the current. Current flows through the filter to the primary of the step-up transformer ($L2$).

The opposition to current flow varies because of the change in reactance (resistance) of the choke and capac-

FIG. 16-10 *High-energy, low-voltage system with a vibrator. This system is used on the General Electric J79.*

itor when frequency changes. At radio frequencies, inductive reactance (resistance) of the coil is high and capacitive reactance of the capacitors is low.

When power is applied to the unit, current flows from ground through the normally closed contacts of the vibrator, through the transformer primary winding (L2), the radio-frequency filter, and back to the power source.

Current through the primary winding causes the normally closed contacts of the vibrator to open, momentarily halting any further current flow. This action changes the dc to a pulsating dc in the primary. The pulsating dc induces a high-voltage ac across the transformer secondary.

Capacitor C3, wired across the vibrator contacts, can be referred to as a buffer capacitor. It protects or buffers the contacts against a voltage arc which might occur during normal operation. Such an arc develops carbon deposits and pit marks on the contacts, and reduces the service life of the vibrator. The ac voltage developed across the transformer secondary winding (L3) is next applied across the half-wave rectifier formed by two diode gas rectifier tubes (V1, V2). The rectifier circuit converts the ac voltage to a pulsating dc. The rectifying action of this circuit depends on the cathode to plate polarity of diode tube V1. When the top of the secondary winding (L3) is positive, the plate of V1 becomes positive with respect to its cathode. Diode V1 is ionized by this potential and starts to conduct. At this point diode V2 is ionized and also conducts. On the opposite half-cycle of the ac voltage across the transformer secondary (L3), the voltage at the top of the winding is negative. The plate of diode V1 becomes negative with respect to its cathode, and neither rectifier conducts.

The output of the half-wave rectifier is a pulsating direct current that flows from the tubes, down the transformer secondary winding (L3) to ground, and up from ground to the lower side of the tank capacitor (C4).

The current supplying the diodes is derived from electrons leaving the top side of C4 because of capacitor reaction to the charge building up on the lower side.

As the rectified current flows to the tank capacitor (C4), a charge of energy is built up across C4. Each time the tank capacitor is ready to discharge, its voltage has reached the ionizing potential of the sealed air gap.

The function of the sealed air gap G1 is similar to that of an automatic switch. While the gap is deionized, the switch is open and no ignition voltage can appear across the spark plug. Once ionized, the gap allows the tank capacitor voltage to ionize the spark-plug gap. With both gaps ionized, the tank capacitor has a complete current path and discharges instantly across the spark-plug electrodes.

A bleed resistor (R1) is wired across the output circuit to act as a dummy load in the event the ignition unit is energized while the spark plug is disconnected. This eliminates the possibility of damaging the ignition unit.

As stated previously, the spark plugs used in this ignition system are the shunted-gap type, which are self-ionizing and designed for low-tension (relatively low voltage) applications. See Figs. 16-14b and 16-15.

Although the spark plug fires at relatively low voltage, a high-temperature spark is obtained from the speed at which the energy is discharged across the gap. The spark is of very short duration (40 μsec), but momentarily expends a great amount of power. Tank capacitor discharge current from the main ignition unit surges to the spark-plug electrodes, building a potential between the center electrode and ground electrode. The semiconducting material shunts the electrodes. When the potential between electrodes reaches approximately 800 volts, it forces enough current through the semiconductor to ionize the air gap between the electrodes. The full tank capacitor current arcs instantly across the ionized gap, emitting a high-energy spark. Figure 16-11 shows a typical low-tension system with ac input.

FIG. 16-11 *High-energy, low-voltage system without a vibrator. This system is used on some models of the General Electric J79.*

Combination or dual-duty ignition system used on the JT3D engine *(Fig. 16-12)*

This ignition system includes one intermittent-duty exciter, one continuous-duty exciter, one intermediate voltage lead, and two high-tension leads. It is designed to fire two spark igniters during ground starts by means of the 20-joule intermittent-duty exciter, or one spark igniter during flight by means of the 4-joule continuous-duty exciter. This functional description covers the operation of the complete system.

When intermittent operation is to be employed, dc power is supplied to the input of the intermittent-duty exciter from the 24-volt aircraft electrical system. It is first passed through a radio noise filter to prevent high-frequency feedback.

From the filter, input voltage is fed to the primary of the transformer in the vibrator, which is an integral part of the vibrator assembly. From the primary a current thus flows through a pair of breaker contacts, normally closed, to ground. A capacitor is connected across these contacts to damp excessive arcing.

With the contacts closed, the flow of current through the coil produces a magnetic field. The force exerted by this field pulls the armature free from the permanent magnet above it. Rapid acceleration builds up kinetic energy in the armature for a brief period before it strikes the contact spring. This opens the contact points quickly, the flow of current stops, and the magnetic field collapses. The armature is returned by the tension of the contact spring, and is positively held in its original position by the permanent magnet. The spring having meanwhile closed the contacts, the vibrating cycle recommences.

Each collapse of the magnetic field induces a high voltage in the secondary of the transformer. This produces successive pulses flowing through the gas-charged rectifier, which limits the flow to a single direction, into the storage capacitors, which thus assume a greater and greater charge, at a constantly increasing voltage.

When this intermediate voltage reaches the predetermined level for which discharge tube X has been calibrated, this tube breaks down. A small portion of the accumulated charge, flowing through the primary of transformer A, induces a high voltage in the secondary. This voltage triggers the threepoint, discriminating discharge tube Y, which breaks down and permits a surge of current to flow from the storage capacitors through the primary of the trigger transformers and trigger capacitor number 2.

The very high voltage thus induced in the secondary of the trigger transformers is sufficient to ionize the gaps at the spark igniters, producing a trigger spark.

The remainder of the energy in the storage capacitors is immediately discharged, following a path through the secondary of the trigger transformer and the high-tension lead to spark igniter number 1, through ground to spark igniter number 2, and back through the other high-tension lead and trigger transformer secondary to the storage capacitors.

The inductance in the inductors is high enough that the current shunted through them is not significant, but after completion of the spark cycle they provide a return path to bleed off any residual charge on the trigger capacitors.

If one spark igniter is shorted, the operation is the same, producing only one spark. If the circuit to one spark igniter is open, the operation is the same, producing only one spark; the path from the operating spark igniter returns through ground and the inductor on the opposite side of the exciter circuit to the storage capacitors.

When continuous operation is to be employed, power is supplied to the input of the continuous-duty exciter from the 115-volt, 400-cycle-ac source in the aircraft.

It is first led through a filter which serves to block conducted noise voltage from feeding back into the aircraft electrical system. From the filter the circuit is completed through the primary of the power transformer to ground.

In the secondary of the power transformer an alternating voltage is generated at a level of approximately 1500 volts. During the first half-cycle this follows a circuit through the doubler capacitor and rectifier A to ground, leaving the capacitor charged. During the second half-cycle, when the polarity reverses, this circuit is blocked by rectifier A; the flow of this pulse is then through ground and the resistors to the storage capacitor, through rectifier B and the doubler capacitor back to the power transformer.

With each pulse the storage capacitor thus assumes a greater and greater charge, which by virtue of the action of the doubler capacitor approaches a voltage approximately twice that generated in the power transformer. When this voltage reaches the predetermined level for which the spark gap in the discharge tube has been calibrated, this gap breaks down, and the accumulated charge on the storage capacitor reaches the output terminal of this exciter.

From the output terminal it is carried to the intermittent-duty exciter by the intermediate voltage lead. Being prevented from reaching the storage capacitors in this unit by the discriminating discharge tube Y, a portion of the charge flows through the primary of trigger transformer number 1 and associated trigger capacitor number 1.

This surge of current induces a very high voltage in the secondary of the trigger transformer, sufficient to ionize the gap at spark igniter number 1.

FIG. 16-12 *Dual system used on the Pratt & Whitney JT3D engine.*

Porcelain insulator

Constrained gap

(a)

Porcelain insulator

Annular gap

(b)

FIG. 16-13 *Two types of igniter gaps.* **(a)** *Constrained gap.* **(b)** *Annular gap.*

(a)

1	GASKET	**6**	COUPLING THREAD
2	LOWER SHELL	**7**	TERMINAL SCREW
3	UPPER SHELL	**8**	SEALING WIRE
4	GASKET	**9**	CEMENT
5	INSULATOR	**10**	CENTER ELECTRODE

INSULATOR
HOT ELECTRODE
GROUND ELECTRODE
SEMI-CONDUCTOR

(b)

FIG. 16-14 **(a)** *Typical igniter plug used on Pratt & Whitney JT3 series engines.* **(b)** *Igniter plug for the General Electric J85.*

FIG. 16-15 *The tip of an igniter plug used with low-voltage systems.* *(General Electric)*

The remainder of the charge is immediately dissipated as a spark at the spark igniter, the return circuit being completed through ground to the continuous-duty exciter.

The inductor in the intermittent-duty exciter serves to bleed off any residual charge on trigger capacitor number 1 between spark cycles.

JET-ENGINE IGNITERS

Jet-engine igniters come in many sizes and shapes depending upon the type of duty they will be subjected to. The electrodes of the plugs used with high-energy ignition systems must be able to accommodate a current of much higher energy than the electrodes of conventional spark plugs are capable of handling. Although the high-energy current causes more rapid igniter-electrode erosion than that encountered in reciprocat-

HIGH-VOLTAGE AIR GAP

HIGH-VOLTAGE SURFACE GAP

HIGH-VOLTAGE AIR-SURFACE GAP

LOW-VOLTAGE SHUNTED-SURFACE GAP

HIGH-VOLTAGE SHUNTED-SURFACE GAP

FIG. 16-16 **(a)** *Types of igniter tips.* *(Continued on following page.)*

AA15S   AA27S (J52, JT8)   AA30S-5   AA37S (JT8)   AA42S (JT3)

AA50S (JT4)   AA63S   AA72S   AGF2-5 (glow plug)   FHE151

FHE19-6L (CR104-2)   FS89-1

FIG. 16-16   (*continued*)   (**b**) *Sectional views of a number of currently used igniters.*

CHAMPION
AA16S

P & W
JT 4

AA16S

CHAMPION
AA37S

P 8 W
JT3–D

AA37S

AiReseach

FHE-118-1

Cont.
J69

FHE-60

GE
CJ805-23

AA-30S-1

AiReseach

AA-34S-1

P 8 W
JT 12

FHE-137A

GE
CT-58

FHE-24-6

Allison
501-D13

FS-89-1

AiReseach

FHE-53-5

GE
CJ805-3

FHE-100-6

CHAMPION
HE-7

HE-7

FIG. 16-17 *A great variety of igniter plug types are used today. An application of each is indicated next to the igniter. (Champion Spark Plug Company)* ing-engine spark plugs, it is not of large consequence because of the relatively short time that a turbine engine ignition system is in operation. It does, however, constitute one of the reasons for not operating the gas turbine ignition system any longer than necessary. Igniter plug gaps are large in comparison with those of conventional spark plugs, because the operating pressure at which the plug is fired is much lower than that of a reciprocating engine.

Most igniter plugs are of the annular-gap type shown in Fig. 16-13*b*, although constrained gaps as shown in Fig. 16-13*a* are used in some engines. Normally, the annular-gap plug projects slightly into the combustion chamber liner in order to provide an effective spark. The spark of the constrained-gap plug does not closely follow the face of the plug; instead it tends to jump in an arc which carries it beyond the face of the chamber liner. The constrained-gap plug need not project into the liner, with the result that the electrode operates at a cooler temperature than that of the annular-gap plug. Figures 16-14, 16-15, 16-16, and 16-17 illustrate some of the varieties of gas turbine igniters.

The turbojet ignition system, designed for severe altitude conditions common to the military form of operation is rarely, if ever, taxed to its full capabilities by transport use. Flameout is much less common than it was, and flight relight is not normally required of the ignition system. Ignition problems in general are of a minor nature in comparison to the constant attention required by the piston engine system. Airborne ignition analysis equipment is unnecessary. Spark igniter plug replacement is greatly minimized. Only two plugs per engine are used, compared to the three dozen used in some reciprocating engines.

The trends that are taking place in the gas turbine ignition area are:

1 Use of ac power inputs, thus eliminating the vibrator, a major source of trouble.

2 Use of solid-state rectifiers.

3 Use of two discharge tubes permits the level of the stored energy per spark to be more consistent throughout the life of the exciter.

4 Sealed units.

5 Longer time between overhauls.

6 The advent of short-range jets has increased the ratio of ignition "on" time to engine operation. This has led to the development of dual systems, one of which was described in this section.

REVIEW AND STUDY QUESTIONS

1 List the requirements for a gas turbine ignition system. How does this compare to a reciprocating engine's requirements?

2 Describe a typical induction-type ignition system. Describe the variations of this system.

3 Discuss the general operating principle behind the modern gas turbine ignition system.

4 Make a list of the input and output variations possible with capacitor discharge ignition systems.

5 What is the relationship between joules, watts, and time? Of what significance is this in the design of a gas turbine ignition system?

6 Briefly describe the operation of the following capacitor discharge gas turbine ignition systems: high-voltage dc; high-voltage ac; low-voltage dc; low-voltage ac.

7 Discuss the trends that are taking place in the gas turbine ignition field.

Chapter 17

Starting systems

The purpose of any starter system is to accelerate the engine to the point where the turbine is producing enough power to continue the engine's acceleration. This is called the *self-accelerating* speed. The proliferation of gas turbine starter types seems to indicate that no one starter shows a definite superiority, for all situations, over other types. The choice of a starting system depends upon several factors.

1 *Length of starting cycle*—For military equipment, starting time may be of primary importance. In addition, the speed with which the starter can accelerate the engine to idle speed will influence not only peak exhaust gas temperatures, but also the length of time the engine spends at these high starting temperatures (Fig. 17-1). Unlike the reciprocating engine starter, the gas turbine starter must continue to accelerate the engine even after "light-off." Slower than normal accelerations or starters which "drop out" too soon may cause "hot" or "hung" starts. (See Chap. 18.) A hung start is a situation where the engine accelerates to some intermediate rpm below idle, and stays there. Hot starts are, of course, what the name implies: a start where turbine or exhaust gas temperature limits are exceeded.

2 *Availability of starting power*—Even small gas turbine engines require large amounts of either electric or pressure energy. Large engines require correspondingly more. Some starting systems are completely self-contained, while others require power from external sources. Many airplanes carry their own energy source in the form of a self-contained small auxiliary gas turbine engine which produces electric and/or pressure energy. Power may also be taken from a running engine in multiengine installations. In such a situation, one engine might be started using a starter requiring no external source of power such as a solid propellant, or fuel-air combustion starter. The other engine(s) can then be started in turn with power taken from the running engine. Starting power requirements for gas turbine engines differ from those of reciprocating engines. In the reciprocating engine, the peak load to the starter is applied in the first moments of starter engagement, but because of the increasing compressor load, the load on the turbine starter is actually increasing during engine acceleration prior to "light-off."

3 *Design features*—Included in this area are such things as specific weight (pounds of starter weight per foot-pound of torque produced), simplicity, reliability, cost, and maintainability.

The following is a list of the various forms of gas turbine starters.

1 Electric motor starter
2 Electric motor-generator (starter-generator)
3 Pneumatic or air turbine starter
4 Cartridge or solid propellant starter
5 Fuel-air combustion starter
6 Gas turbine starter (jet fuel starter)
7 Hydraulic motor starter
8 Liquid monopropellant starter
9 Air-impingement starter
10 Hand-crank starter

ELECTRIC MOTOR STARTER (*Fig. 17-2*)

These starters are 28-volt, series-wound electric motors, designed to provide high starting torque. Their use is limited to starting smaller engines because of the very large current drain (over 1000 amp for some models) and because they are relatively heavy for the amount of torque they produce. The starter includes an automatic jaw meshing mechanism, a set of reduction gears, and a clutch. The straight electric motor starter as a means for starting gas turbine engines has generally given way to the starter-generator in order to save weight and simplify accessory gear arrangements. A typical electric motor starting system is illustrated in Fig. 17-3. It may have provisions for automatically engaging the ignition units when the starter switch is thrown. If the circuit is so arranged, the ignition system is constructed so that it may be separately energized for air restarts. The starter system may also be equipped with a relay to "drop" the starter out when a specified rpm has been reached or the starter load reduced. Some systems incorporate a timing switch to permit a gradual voltage buildup as the starter gains speed.

ELECTRIC MOTOR-GENERATOR (STARTER-GENERATOR) (*Fig. 17-4*)

Most small gas turbine engines such as the General Electric CJ610, Pratt & Whitney JT12 and PT6, Allison T63, Continental J69, and the Lycoming T53 utilize a starter-generator. This system has the advantage of being lighter than a separate starter and generator since a common armature is used and it requires no engaging or reduction gear mechanism. The engine accessory section also requires one less gear.

As shown in Fig. 17-4, a splined drive, which usually incorporates a torsional vibration dampener to protect the drive quill against engine torsional vibration, con-

FIG. 17-1 *Exhaust-gas temperature versus starting time using a cartridge and pneumatic starter.*

FIG. 17-2 *Typical electric motor starter.*

FIG. 17-3 *Early electric motor starting and electrical system.*

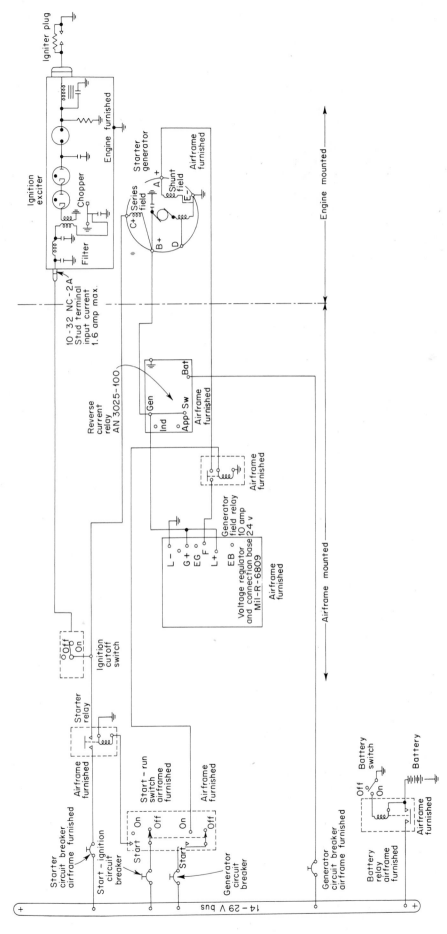

FIG. 17-4 *Simple starter-generator system (Allison T63).*

FIG. 17-5 *Typical starter-generator.*

nects the starter-generator to the engine (Fig. 17-5). The unit incorporates two field windings. The series winding is used to develop the low-speed, high starting torque necessary to crank the engine, while the shunt or parallel winding functions when the unit is acting as a generator. There are four external connections (A+ or shunt field connection; B+ or armature positive; C or series field connection; and E− or armature negative). The starting electrical load is very high. To limit the tremendous battery drain, some airplane electrical systems are arranged so that their two 28-volt batteries can be placed in series for starting and in parallel operation for normal generator functions. This has the effect of providing the same amount of power (volts × amperes) to the starter with a reduced current flow.

AIR TURBINE STARTER (*Figs. 17-6 and 17-7*)

Models of this starter are installed in the Boeing 707, 720, KC135, and B52, Douglas DC8 and DC9, Convair 880 and 990, Lockheed Electra, General Dynamics F111, and others. Its primary advantage is its light weight (about 20 to 25 lb) to torque ratio when compared to the electric motor starter and starter-generator. The principal disadvantage is that it requires a supply of high volume airflow of approximately 40 lb/min at a pressure of about 50 psi. Sources include compressed air from an auxiliary gas turbine engine carried on board the aircraft or maintained as a part of the airport facilities, compressed air bled from the other running engine(s), or compressed air from an air storage system, as shown in Fig. 17-8. Very often one engine of a multiengine airplane will be equipped with a cartridge, fuel-air combustion, or gas turbine starter, having self-start capabilities. Air bled from the running engine can

then be supplied to the air turbine starters installed on the other engines.

This starter and other types may be supplied with a quick-attach-detach (QAD) coupling, V band, or key-hold-type pad that attaches to a mounting flange which, in turn, is designed for direct attachment to a standard engine accessory drive.

The air turbine starter converts energy from compressed air to shaft power. To start the system, an air valve is opened by the "start" switch, after which the operation of the valve and starter is automatic. The same switch is used as a "stop" switch in emergencies. As air enters the starter inlet, the radial- or axial-flow turbine wheel assembly rotates. The reduction gears contained within the starter convert the high speed and low torque of the turbine wheel to a relatively low speed and high output torque. The reduction gears are lubricated with Mil-L-7808 oil, the same type used in the engine, by a splash-type oil system. Engagement of the starter is usually accomplished through a jaw or pawl and ratchet clutch. When a predetermined speed is reached, an internal governor assembly, through a switch, deactivates an electric circuit which closes the valve in the air supply line. The starter rotating assembly automatically disengages from the permanently engaged splined output shaft when the starter drive speed exceeds the starter output shaft speed.

For self-contained starting, independent of ground support equipment, some systems use air supplied from storage bottles installed in the airplane. A line combustor may heat the air to 700°F. To minimize air consumption, water is injected during the starting cycle. (Refer to Fig. 17-8.)

An interesting variation of this form of starter, produced by the Garrett AiResearch Manufacturing Company, is the Constant Speed Drive Starter. The unit, installed in the British Aircraft Corporation (BAC) One-Eleven Transport, combines in one unit an air turbine starter plus constant-speed shaft power to drive the ac generator.

CARTRIDGE OR SOLID PROPELLANT STARTER (*Fig. 17-9*)

Originally, starters of this type were constructed to operate solely by means of high-pressure, high-temperature gas generated by the burning of a solid propellant charge. Changes in the cartridge-type starter have added the additional capability of starting with compressed air from an external source.

A charge, a little larger than a coffee can, is inserted in the breech and ignited electrically. The relatively slow burning propellant produces gases at approximately 2000°F and 1200 psi to turn the starter for about 15 sec.

FIG. 17-6 *Three Garrett AiResearch Air Turbine starters.* **(a)** *This pneumatic starter is for the Boeing 727. Note the keyhole-type QAD flange.* **(b)** *High (500 psig) or low (35 psig) pressure may be applied to this ATS100-129 pneumatic starter used on many JT3D engines.* **(c)** *ATS-50 pneumatic starter for small gas turbine engines.*

In recent years the pneumatic-cartridge starter has achieved considerable use in the U.S. Air Force, primarily because of its inherent characteristics of a lightweight, self-contained system with the extremely high torque value of over 600 ft-lb, plus the option of quick starts from the high-pressure, high-temperature cartridge gases, or from low pressure supplied from a running engine, conventional ground support equipment, or airborne starting units (Fig. 17-10).

A more detailed examination of one make of pneumatic-cartridge jet engine starter used in the McDonnell-Douglas F4C follows. (Refer to Fig. 17-11.)

For a cartridge start, a standard Air Force type MXU-4 cartridge (Fig. 17-11) is first placed in the breech cap (2). Next, the breech cap is closed down on the breech chamber by means of the breech handle (3) and rotated a part-turn to engage the lugs between the two breech sections. This rotation allows the lower section of the breech handle to drop into a socket and completes the cartridge ignition circuit. (Up to this point, it would have been impossible to fire the cartridge.) As shown in Fig. 17-11, the cartridge is then ignited by applying voltage to the connector (4) at the base of the handle. This energizes the insulated ignition contact (5) at the

FIG. 17-7 *The Hamilton Standard Model PS700-1 starter designed for use on the Pratt & Whitney JT9D installed in the Boeing 747.*

top of the breech cap, which touches a point on the cartridge itself. The circuit is completed to ground by the ground clip (6) (a part of the cartridge) which contacts the inner wall of the breech cap. Upon ignition, the cartridge begins to generate gas. The gas is forced out of the breech to the hot gas nozzles (7), which are directed toward the buckets on the turbine rotor (8), and rotation is produced. Gas emerging from the opposite side of the wheel enters an exhaust ring (9), in the exhaust duct, is collected, and passes out of the starter via the overboard exhaust connector (10). However, before it reaches the nozzle, the hot gas passes an outlet leading to the relief valve (12). This valve ports hot gas directly to the turbine, bypassing the hot gas nozzle, as the pressure rises above the preset maximum. Therefore, the pressure of the gas within the hot gas circuit is maintained at the optimum level.

FIG. 17-8 *Simplified schematics showing several air sources.*

FIG. 17-9 *AiResearch air/cartridge starter.*

FIG. 17-10 *Cutaway view of the Sundstrand Cartridge/Pneumatic starter.*

For a pneumatic start, compressed air from a ground cart is led by ducting on the aircraft to the compressed air inlet (13). It passes into the compressed air nozzle ring and is directed against the buckets of the turbine rotor by vanes placed around the ring. Rotation is thus produced in essentially the same manner as in the cartridge start. Compressed air leaving the turbine rotor collects in the same exhaust ring and is ported overboard via the overboard exhaust connector.

Whether starting is accomplished by cartridge or compressed air, some opposing force is required to keep turbine speed within safe limits. This opposing force is provided by the aerodynamic braking fan (14). The fan is connected directly to the turbine shaft. It is supplied with air from the aircraft nacelle and its output is carried off by an exhaust ring (16) concentric with, and located within, the turbine exhaust ring. Hot gas (or compressed air) exhaust, and aerodynamic braking fan output are kept separate up to the overboard exhaust connector. At this point, they merge, the cool air from the fan cooling the hot exhaust gas.

The gearshaft (17) is part of a two-stage reduction which reduces the maximum turbine speed of 67,500 rpm to an output of approximately 4000 rpm.

The large gear of the final output turns the output spline shaft (24) through an overrunning clutch (18).

The clutch is situated in the output area between the gear shaft, on which the final drive gear is located, and the output spline shaft. It is a pawl or sprag type, one-way overrunning clutch, and its purpose is to prevent the engine, once operating under its own power, from driving the starter, thereby possibly driving the turbine rotor at a speed above its safe limit. The nature of a pawl or sprag clutch is such that it can transmit torque in only one direction. That is, the driving member will operate through the clutch, delivering full torque to the driven member. But the driven member cannot become the driver—even though revolving in the same direction—and transmit torque back into the original driver. Any tendency for it to do so would disengage the clutch. When the engine has been started and the starter has finished its cycle and stopped, only the output spline shaft and the outer (driven) part of the clutch will be revolving. The balance of the starter will be at rest.

The starter is equipped with an output spline shaft having a shear section that permits the shaft to shear if torque to the engine during the starting cycle is excessive. When the shaft shears, torque to the engine is stopped, thus preventing damage to the aircraft engine gearbox. The output spline shaft will also shear during the overrunning cycle (engine started and operating) if the starter malfunctions in such a manner as to develop a frictional resistance to torque from the aircraft engine gearbox.

In the event the clutch and spline shaft fail to operate

1	CARTRIDGE	9	TURBINE EXHAUST RING	15	AIR INLET FOR BRAKING	
2	BREECH CAP	10	OVERBOARD EXHAUST		FAN	
3	BREECH HANDLE		CONNECTOR	16	FAN EXHAUST RING	
4	CONNECTOR	11	EXHAUST FROM TURBINE	17	GEARSHAFT	
5	IGNITION CONTACT		AND FAN	18	OVERRUNNING SPRAG	
6	GROUND CLIP	12	RELIEF VALVE		CLUTCH	
7	HOT-GAS NOZZLES	13	COMPRESSED AIR INLET	19	FLYWEIGHT	
8	TURBINE ROTOR	14	AERODYNAMIC BRAKING FAN	20	SWITCH ACTUATING ROD	

21	SWITCH
22	ADJUSTING SCREW
23	GEARBOX VENT
24	SPLINE SHAFT
25	OIL SLINGER
26	OIL SUMP
27	MAGNETIC PLUG

FIG. 17-11 *Sundstrand Cartridge/Pneumatic starter schematic.*

and the turbine is driven beyond burst rpm by the aircraft engine, the containment clamp shown in Fig. 17-10 provides additional strength to the starter turbine area preventing damage to the aircraft.

A vent (23) through the clutch and output shaft eliminates internal pressure buildup. Centrifugal force caused by output rotation prevents oil leakage through the vent.

The starter is lubricated by a splash system. Oil slingers (25) attached to the clutch output race pick up oil from the sump (26) and distribute it throughout the interior of the starter as the output spline revolves. A catching cup construction in the housing carries the oil

into the overrunning clutch and other difficult-to-reach areas. Since the part to which the slingers are attached is constantly spinning, even after the starter has completed its cycle, starter lubrication continues as long as the aircraft engine is operating. The oil sump contains a magnetic plug (27) to collect contaminants.

FUEL-AIR COMBUSTION STARTER *(Fig. 17-12)*

The fuel-air combustion starter is essentially a small gas turbine engine, minus its' compressor. It is completely self-contained, as is the cartridge starter system, but unlike the preceding system, requires no additional components to function. All fuel, air, and electric power needed for operation are carried on board the aircraft.

In addition to the turbine, the system consists of an air storage bottle, fuel storage bottle, and a combustion chamber, together with the necessary ignition and control components. During flight, an engine-driven compressor maintains 3000 lb of air pressure in an airborne bottle. This permits engine starts without the necessity of recharging the air system from an external source. The usual high-pressure bottle will provide enough air for two restarts without recharging. Provision is also made to connect an external 600-psi air supply. In either case, the starter receives a reduced air pressure of 350 psi.

In a typical system shown in Fig. 17-12, the starter is activated by a ground start switch in the cockpit. When the ground start switch is pressed, the starter air solenoid valve opens, admitting air from the storage bottle or from the external 600-psi connection into the combus-

tion chamber. At the same time, the fuel valve opens to admit fuel from the accumulator, and the starter ignition system is momentarily energized, igniting the fuel-air mixture. This action causes a rapid expansion of air, which spins the starter turbine, which in turn accelerates the engine through the reduction gearing and clutch. When engine speed reaches about 21 percent rpm, starter fuel is exhausted, resulting in a dropoff of burner pressure. The pressure switch actuates, opening the air duct to the fuel and air valves. If starter speed exceeds 22.6 percent engine rpm before fuel is exhausted, the centrifugal switch will open, shutting off the fuel and air valves. Exhaust from the starter combustion chamber is directed through an exhaust duct at the lower side of the starter and into the engine air-guide section. A pressure reducer and an air control valve in the starter reduce the supply air pressure to about 330 psi before it enters the fuel accumulator and the combustion chamber. The fuel accumulator contains enough fuel obtained from the

FIG. 17-12 *Fuel-air combustion system.*

airplane fuel system through a takeoff line at the engine fuel flow divider to operate the starter for about 4 sec. The accumulator is pressurized with about 330-psi air pressure to ensure fuel flow to the combustion chamber. The starter has a safety clutch, which automatically disengages the starter drive shaft from the engine drive spline to prevent the engine from driving the starter turbine to destructive overspeed. In case of failure of the starter clutch, the safety clutch must be manually reset which necessitates removing the starter from the engine. An air motoring switch allows the air solenoid valve to open while bypassing the fuel solenoid valve and starter ignition circuits for the purpose of motoring the engine to 4 to 6 percent.

THE GAS TURBINE STARTER (Fig. 17-13)

This is another of the completely self sufficient starting systems. Relatively high power output is available for a comparatively low weight. The starter is actually a small free turbine engine complete with a gas generator section containing a centrifugal compressor, combustion chamber, and turbine to drive the compressor. It also contains its own fuel control, starter, lubrication pump and system, and ignition system. The gases flowing through the gas generator section drive the free turbine, which in turn, drives the main engine through a reduction gear and clutch mechanism to automatically engage and disengage the starter's free turbine from the engine. The starter is itself started by using a small electric motor, compressed air, or hydraulic power from the aircraft system. Typical specifications are:

Type:	Free turbine engine
Weight:	70 to 80 lb
Shaft speed:	0 to 8000 rpm
Performance:	20 to 30 sec engine starting time
Fuel:	Same as used in aircraft
Oil:	Same as used in aircraft
Mounting:	QAD

Inherent inefficiencies of transferring starting energy to the main engines through pneumatic, hydraulic, or electrical means are eliminated. The pilot has complete control of engine starting from the cockpit and the gradual application of starting torque extends the life of the main engine components. A further advantage of this system is that it can "cold crank" or "motor" the main engines for 10 min at a time to permit checking fuel, hydraulic, and electrical systems.

HYDRAULIC STARTERS

Hydraulic starting systems fall into two categories:

1 Energy limited
2 Power limited

(a)

(b)

(c)

FIG. 17-13 *Garrett AiResearch and Solar gas turbine starters.* **(a)** *Garrett AiResearch jet fuel or gas turbine starter JFS100.* **(b)** *Solar gas turbine self-contained starter (GTSS).* **(c)** *Schematic of the Solar GTSS.*

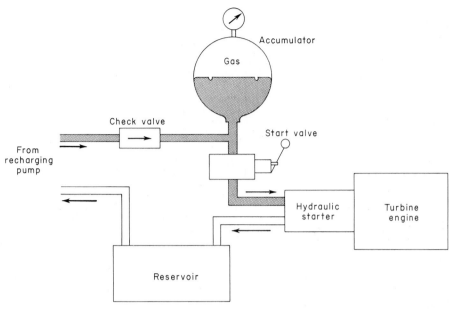

FIG. 17-14 *Energy-limited or accumulator starting system.*

The energy-limited system (Fig. 17-14) uses a highly pressurized accumulator and a large positive displacement motor. Examples of other starting systems that are also energy-limited are the electric motor, when supplied from a battery, and the cartridge starter. The energy-limited system is designed to complete the start in as short a time as possible in order to minimize the amount of stored energy required. The accumulator system is best suited to small engines up to 150 hp.

A power-limited system (Fig. 17-15) uses an auxiliary power unit (sometimes a small gas turbine engine, which is itself started by an energy-limited system) to drive a pump which supplies the correct amount of flow and pressure to a variable-displacement hydraulic starter motor. The variable-displacement motor permits high torque to be applied without exceeding the power limits of the main engine at starter cutoff speed.

It is possible to adapt the hydraulic starter as a pump, but since the starter cutout speed is less than 50 percent of the normal engine operating speed, a two-ratio gearbox is necessary to provide proper speed for both pumping and starting. The hydraulic pump on the auxiliary power unit can also be used to supply power to the aircraft.

FIG. 17-15 *Power-limited starting system.*

(a)   (b)

FIG. 17-16   (a) *Vickers Corporation hydraulic starting system for the Sikorsky CH53A heli-copter.* (b) *Vickers Corporation hydraulic starting system for the Vertol CH47A (Chinook) helicopter.*

Figure 17-16 shows two typical hydraulic starter installations in current use.

The APU in the Sikorsky CH53A (Fig. 17-16a) is started hydraulically by means of stored energy in a 250 cu in. accumulator (4000 psi maximum). The main engines receive their starting power from a pump mounted on the main accessory gearbox which is shaft driven by the Solar T-62T-12APU. (See Fig. 17-20a.) The accessory pump also provides power for the winch and other utility functions. The T-64 main engine starters deliver 50 ft-lb of torque at 3500 psi and 21.5 gpm. Maximum starter speed is 7300 rpm; and cutout is accomplished by a mechanically actuated switch that senses motor displacement.

The starting system used in the Vertol CH47A (Fig. 17-16b) is somewhat similar to the one described above in that the Solar APU is started by means of stored energy in a 200-cu in., 3000-psi hydraulic accumulator, and the main engines receive their starting power from a pump mounted on the main accessory gearbox. It is different in that the gearbox is driven by hydraulic power from the APU starter operating as a pump, driving a fixed-displacement motor mounted on the gearbox. During main engine operation an overrunning clutch isolates the accessory gearbox drive motor until the APU is again started for main engine starting or a system checkout. The accessory-gearbox-mounted dual-pressure pump supplies 9 gpm at 4000 psi for starting the Lycoming T-55 main engines on the ground, and 3000 psi for air restarts. The variable displacement maximum starter speed is 2800 rpm, and cutout is accomplished by a tachometer signal from the engine.

LIQUID MONOPROPELLANT STARTER

In this system a charge of liquid monopropellant (a monopropellant fuel is one which requires no separate air supply to sustain combustion) is decomposed to produce the high-energy gas needed for turbine operation. Monopropellants which can be used include highly concentrated hydrogen peroxide, isopropyl nitrate, and hydrazine. All are difficult materials to handle, and principally because of this there has been no operational installation of such equipment in this country.

THE AIR-IMPINGEMENT STARTER   (Fig. 17-17)

In many ways this starter system is the simplest of all starter types, consisting essentially of nothing more than a duct. An air supply from either a running engine or a ground power unit is directed through a check valve onto the turbine blades (most common) or the centrifugal compressor. Engines using this starting system are the Fairchild J44, on which the air is fed to the compressor, and some models of the General Electric J85 and J79. (See Chap. 2.) In the latter two engines, air is directed onto the rear or middle turbine wheel stages. (See Fig. 21-9.) Obviously, the advantage of this system is manifested in its extreme simplicity and light weight. It is best suited to smaller engines because of the high-volume air supply necessary for larger engines.

NOTE: Starter air input

1	FRONT FRAME	**5**	COMBUSTION SECTION
2	COMPRESSOR STATOR	**6**	TURBINE STATOR
3	COMPRESSOR ROTOR	**7**	TURBINE ROTOR
4	MAIN FRAME—ACCESSORY DRIVE	**8**	AFTERBURNER ASSEMBLY

FIG. 17-17 *General Electric J85 equipped with an air-impingement starting system* [*See* (6)].

(a)

(b)

(c)

FIG. 17-18 *Some examples of engines equipped with hand-crank starters.* (**a**) *German engine.* (**b**) *Japanese engine.* (**c**) *British engine.*

THE HAND-CRANK STARTER *(Fig. 17-18)*

This method of starting gas turbine engines is, of course, limited to very small units, on the order of 50 to 100 hp. As the name implies, starting is accomplished by turning a hand crank which, through a series of gears, turns the engine to the self-sustaining rpm. Hand crank to engine shaft speed ratios are in the order of 100 : 1.

(c)

(a)

FIG. 17-19 *These engines are installed in the widely used MA-1A U.S.A.F. starting cart.*
(**a**) *AiResearch GTC85-70-1.* (**b**) *MA-1A starting cart.* (*Continued on following page.*)

GROUND OR AUXILIARY POWER UNITS
(*Fig. 17-19*)

The ground or auxiliary power unit, while not an integral part of the primary aircraft engine, is nevertheless an important adjunct to it.

These units are small, light-weight, trouble-free gas turbine engines, completely automatic in their operation (Fig. 17-20). They are generally constructed with centrifugal compressors and axial- or radial-inflow turbines. Starting the APU or GPU is accomplished by means of a small electric or hydraulic motor, or by a hand crank. Typical of these units is the AiResearch gas turbine compressor GTC85, an electrically started, self-sufficient unit with a two-stage radial compressor and a turbine driven by the exhaust products of a single, tangentially located burner. Air is bled off from the compressor section and supplied to the main engine starter from this unit at a pressure ratio of approximately 3:1 and a temperature of 350°F. The unit is approximately 38 in. long, 18 in. in diameter, and weighs 275 lb. Although these engines can operate on a wide variety of fuels, the units generally use the same fuel as the main engines.

Auxiliary power units have been used to drive ac and dc generators, hydraulic pumps and motors, other fluid pumps, and air compressors. The airborne units on conventional aircraft are usually located toward the rear, but, as shown in Fig. 17-21, can be installed in any location.

RADIAL DIFFUSER AXIAL DIFFUSER FUEL DISTRIBUTOR COMPRESSED AIR DISCHARGE

EXHAUST DIFFUSER

CONTROL ISLAND

INDUCER

COMPRESSOR

1st STAGE NOZZLE 1st STAGE TURBINE

2nd STAGE NOZZLE

2nd STAGE TURBINE

(c)

FIG. 17-19 (continued). (c) *Continental 141 external and cutaway views.*

TABLE 17-1
Summary of the advantages and disadvantages of the starter types

TYPE	ADVANTAGES	DISADVANTAGES	TYPE	ADVANTAGES	DISADVANTAGES
Electric motor starter	1 Self-contained starts possible for small engines 2 Engine may be motored for short periods without starter overheating	1 Limited to starting small engines 2 Relatively heavy for torque produced 3 Reduction gears necessary 4 Engaging mechanism necessary	Gas turbine starter	1 Completely self-contained starts possible 2 High torque-to-weight ratio 3 Long periods of engine motoring possible	1 One of the most complex of starter types in that it requires all of the systems of the main engine plus an over-running clutch
Starter-generator	1 One less accessory drive necessary 2 No overrunning clutch, gearbox, or engaging mechanism necessary 3 Lighter than a single starter and generator 4 Self-contained starts possible for small engines	1 Limited to small engines 2 Relatively heavy for torque produced when operating as a starter	Hydraulic starter	1 Compact in size 2 Can be self-contained for smaller engines 3 Can be adapted to function as a pump 4 Relatively uncomplicated	1 Requires external power for large engines or for continuous cranking (internal APU may be used)
Air turbine starter	1 High torque to weight ratio (5 to 10 times higher than electric motor) 2 Engine may be motored at low or high speed 3 Can use air from a running engine	1 High-volume air supply required 2 Gearbox needed with self-contained oil supply 3 Electrical connections needed for speed control	Monopropellant starter	1 High starting torque-to-weight ratio	1 Dangerous fuels 2 Complex system required
Cartridge starter	1 Self-contained starts possible for large engines 2 Very high torque-to-weight ratio 3 Quick starts possible for military 4 Automatic starts possible	1 Cartridge needed for each start 2 Gearbox, clutch, and oil system necessary 3 No motoring possible for systems checkout	Air-impingement starter	1 Simplest of all types 2 Can be used to motor engine, but only with continuous air supply 3 Extremely light 4 Can use air from another running main engine	1 Requires a high-volume air supply (3 to 5 times the pneumatic energy requirements of the air turbine starter)
Fuel-air combustion starter	1 Completely self-contained 2 High torque-to-weight ratio 3 Automatic starts possible 4 Engine may be motored for short periods on internal air supply at low rpm	1 Relatively complex 2 Only two self-contained starts possible	Hand-crank starter	1 Very reliable 2 Independent of external power systems, except muscle power 3 Lightweight	1 Limited to very small engines 2 Cranking handle must be stored

(a)

(b)

(c)

FIG. 17-20 *Some auxiliary gas turbine units.* (**a**) *Solar T-62 Titan auxiliary gas turbine engine schematic and external view, used in several Sikorsky helicopters. Weight is 70 lb.* (**b**) *AiResearch GTCP 85-98D used in the Douglas DC-9.* (**c**) *AiResearch GTCP 85-98, used in the Boeing 727.*

FIG. 17-21 *Various locations for the Solar T-62 auxiliary engine.*

REVIEW AND STUDY QUESTIONS

1 Compare the starting requirements for the reciprocating and gas turbine engines.

2 What are some of the factors which influence the choice of the starting system?

3 List 10 types of starters. Very briefly describe each starter type.

4 Make a table listing the advantages and disadvantages of each starter type.

5 What form does the auxiliary, or ground power unit take? How can this engine be utilized?

PART 4

Testing and maintenance

1   Fuel and oil inlet temperature
2   Starter air temperature
3   Scavenge oil temperature
4   Compressor inlet temperature
5   Exhaust gas or turbine inlet temperature
6   Wet and dry bulb temperature
7   Ambient air temperature

and pressure gages and/or manometers to measure

1   Fuel inlet pressure
2   Lubrication-system pressure
3   Main and afterburner fuel-pump pressure
4   Nozzle pump inlet and rod end pressure (J-79 engine)
5   Starter air pressure
6   Barometric or ambient air pressure
7   Sump or breather pressure
8   Turbine pressure or engine pressure ratio (EPR)
9   Water pressure
10 Turbine cooling air pressure

Additional instruments and controls include

1   Power lever and various control switches
2   Vibration pickup and gage (usually taken at compressor and turbine planes)
3   Clock and stopwatch

Chapter 18

Engine testing and operation

All manufacturers run their engines in test cells before sending them to the users. After the test (green run), the manufacturer will usually disassemble one engine in several to ensure quality control. If an engine fails during a test run, that engine and a specific number of prior engines are disassembled to check for faults.

THE TEST CELL *(Fig. 18-1)*

Testing is done in a test cell or house, fully equipped to measure all of the desired operating parameters. Some of the larger installations cost over a million dollars. The building is usually of concrete construction and contains both the control and engine room, although in some installations only the control or instrumentation room is enclosed. Most cells have silencers installed in the inlet stack for noise suppression and a water spray rig in the exhaust section for cooling. Many modern test cells incorporate computers to automatically record all instrument readings and correct them (see pages 291 to 293) to standard day conditions.

Testing of large modern engines has become a very real problem in that the amount of air required by the engine or its components was not readily available with existing equipment. New facilities have had to be built to simulate conditions encountered at very high Mach numbers and very high altitudes, and, in many cases, this has been as difficult as the development of the engine itself.

Test-cell instrumentation usually includes temperature gages to measure

FIG. 18-1 *Typical test cell and control room.*

4 Tachometer-generator and readout device

5 Fuel-flow transmitter and meter

6 Thrust measuring electronic or hydraulic load cell and readout

When the engine is installed in the cell, a bellmouth inlet (Fig. 18-2) and screen are attached. The bellmouth inlet is a funnel-shaped tube having rounded shoulders which offers so little air resistance that the duct loss can be considered zero. The screen itself does offer some resistance and must be taken into account when extremely accurate data must be collected. Twenty-four-volt electric power is provided to operate the ignition system and any solenoid valves on the engine. One hundred fifteen volts, four hundred cycles may also be provided for some ignition systems and valves.

Test schedules vary with different model engines and manufacturers, but usually includes instrument observations during starting and acceleration, and at the several thrust settings of idle, maximum cruise, maximum climb, and maximum continuous takeoff. Acceleration time may also be recorded.

Most manufacturers will have an *engine log sheet* on which is recorded the following data in addition to the instrument readings (Fig. 18-3):

1 Date of run

2 Engine model and serial number

3 Serial number of components

4 Grade and specific gravity of fuel

5 Grade or specification of oil

6 Test-cell depression (pressure drop due to test-cell inlet restrictions)

7 Total time of test-cell runs

8 Reasons for unscheduled shutdowns

9 Repairs made to engine during test

10 Reasons for engine rejection (if applicable)

11 Oil consumption

12 Jet nozzle area

13 Overhaul agency (if applicable)

14 Test operator's and inspector's signatures

Correct engine performance is indicated by comparing corrected values (see Performance Testing that follows) with charts and graphs computed and drawn by the manufacturer guaranteeing minimum performance and values for his engine.

PERFORMANCE TESTING

As indicated earlier in this book, the performance of any engine is considerably influenced by changes in ambient temperature and pressure because of the way these parameters effect the weight of the air entering the engine. In order to compare the performance of similar engines on different days, under different atmospheric conditions, it is necessary to "correct" a given engine's performance to the standard day conditions of 29.92 in. of mercury and 59°F (519°R).

For example, the following conditions are known about a running engine:

1 rpm = 9465

2 EGT = 510°C (950°F or 1410°R). See note that follows.

3 W_f = 4000 lb/hr

4 W_a = 200 lb/sec. (Although airflow is listed here, it is difficult, if not impossible, to measure the weight of airflow directly. Airflow can be determined indirectly through pressure measurements in the engine.)

5 F_n = 10,000 lb

6 TSFC = 0.400

    Barometric pressure   = 30.3 in. Hg
    Standard day pressure = 29.92 in. Hg
    Ambient temperature   = 82°F
    Standard day temperature = 59°F + 460° (519°R)

NOTE: To convert degrees Fahrenheit to degrees Rankine, add 460 to the Fahrenheit reading.

Since these are all "observed" measurements, they must be "corrected" in order that valid comparisons can be made between engines. To change the observed operating parameters to the corrected values, i.e., the rpm, EGT, *F/F*, *A/F*, F_n, and TSFC that the engine would have if it were running under standard day conditions, it is necessary to apply a pressure correction factor, delta (δ), and a temperature correction factor, theta (θ).

$$\delta = \frac{\text{observed pressure (in. Hg)}}{\text{standard day pressure in. Hg}}$$

$$\theta = \frac{\text{observed temp. (°R)}}{\text{standard day temp. (°R)}}$$

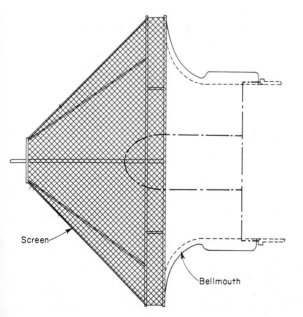

Screen

Bellmouth

FIG. 18-2 *Bellmouth inlet and screen.*

ROUTINE ENGINE INSPECTION TEST LOG

CONTRACT NO. _____

Field	Value
MFG. MODEL	LE-00000
MFG. NO.	T-53-L11
CUST. MODEL	T-53-L11
CUST. NO.	
MIL. RATED H.P. AT S.L.	1100
TEST SPEC.	TM55-1520-211-34
CUST. TEST SPEC.	—
FUEL SPEC.	—
CUST. FUEL SPEC.	MIL-J-5824
GRADE	
OIL SPEC.	—
CUST. OIL SPEC.	MIL-L-7808
GRADE	
TEST STAND NO.	—
TEST STAND TYPE	LTC T-744
FUEL CONTROL MFG'R	CELO
FUEL CONTROL MODEL	TA2G
PARTS LIST NO.	81700 C2
FUEL CONTROL NO.	222AF-480
PRESS. REQ'D.	5# MIN
OVERSPEED GOV. NO.	612 A6/94
PARTS LIST NO.	81800 A1
FLOW METER NO.	JEAN SIEGLER
STARTER MFG'R	JEAN SIEGLER
STARTER NO.	1440

TIME	26.946	27.946
	2200	0700
CORR. BARO.	30.14	30.13

SHEET NO. _____   DATE _____

1ST STAGE NOZZLE E.F.A. 9.18
2ND STAGE NOZZLE E.F.A. 25.65
ANTI-ICE PR @MRP 4/ HG
OIL CONS _____ N.R.P. @ 0.2 #/HR

NOTES: FUEL AND OIL LEAKS, ETC.

ACCELERATIONS OK
WAVE-OFFS OK @ 20" H2O
O/S GOV. CHECK OK
O/S GOV. CUT-IN 101.3% N
MAIN P.R.V. SETTING 2.5

NORMAL RATED

TESTER Smith
OBSERVER Dale Brown
TYPE OF TEST REPAIR FINAL   ENGINE WEIGHT 472.53

ACCEPTED
LYCOMING
LBS. AIR FORCE

TIME THIS TEST 3:12   HRS. No fuel or oil leaks

BEGIN CHECK-OUT PROCEDURE
IGNITORS OFF @ 25% N - STARTER OFF @ 35% N
BLEED BAND CLOSES @ 77% - OK
600# W.F. VS 320 PSI. MANIFOLD PRESSURE
INC. 770 TRIM 1/8 TURN
3.8 SEC. G.I.T. 1095
WAVE-OFFS - OK
FUEL MANIFOLD PRESSURE LINE CAPPED FOR ACCL CHECK F.I.
DISCONNECT RAM AIR TUBE - CONNECT P-1 BELLOWS FOR WAVE-OFFS
O/S GOV. CHECK - OK
DISCONNECT P-1 BELLOWS - RECONNECT RAM TUBE
CDT-483 sec.   CDI - 56 SEC
BEGIN FINAL RUN
IGNITORS OFF AT 25% N - STARTER OFF AT 35% N
ALL TEMPERATURES OK
CDI-56 SEC
IGNITORS OFF @ 25% N - STARTER OFF @ 35% N
SWITCH TO EMERGENCY @ T.O. 650 # WF
CHECK FOR LEAKS
ENGINE PRESERVED

FIG. 18-3 Lycoming T53 engine test log.

For the atmospheric conditions stated above, delta and theta will be

$$\delta = \frac{30.3}{29.92} = 1.013$$

$$\theta = \frac{82 + 460}{59 + 460} = \frac{542}{519} = 1.045$$

$$\sqrt{\theta} = 1.022$$

See Appendixes E-14 and E-15 for tables listing the values of delta and theta for various pressures and temperatures.

To correct the observed data gathered for the above engine, the following formulas are used.

1 Corrected rpm = $\dfrac{\text{observed rpm}}{\sqrt{\text{temperature correction factor}}}$

or

$$\text{rpm}_\text{corr} = \frac{\text{rpm}_\text{obs}}{\sqrt{\theta}}$$

2 Corrected EGT = $\dfrac{\text{observed EGT (°R)}}{\text{temperature correction factor}}$

or

$$\text{EGT}_\text{corr} = \frac{\text{EGT}_\text{obs}}{\theta}$$

3 Corrected fuel flow,

$$= \frac{\text{observed fuel flow}}{\text{pressure correction factor} \times \sqrt{\text{temperature correction factor}}}$$

or

$$W_\text{f,corr} = \frac{W_\text{f,obs}}{\delta \sqrt{\theta}}$$

4 Corrected airflow

$$= \frac{\text{observed airflow} \times \sqrt{\text{temperature correction factor}}}{\text{pressure correction factor}}$$

or

$$W_\text{a,corr} = \frac{W_\text{a,obs} \sqrt{\theta}}{\delta}$$

5 Corrected thrust = $\dfrac{\text{observed thrust}}{\text{pressure correction factor}}$

or

$$F_\text{n,corr} = \frac{F_\text{n,obs}}{\delta}$$

6 Corrected TSFC

$$= \frac{\text{observed fuel flow}}{\text{observed thrust} \times \sqrt{\text{temperature correction factor}}}$$

or

$$\text{TSFC}_\text{corr} = \frac{W_\text{f,obs}}{F_\text{n,obs} \sqrt{\theta}}$$

$$= \frac{\text{TSFC}_\text{obs}}{\sqrt{\theta}}$$

$$= \frac{W_\text{f,corr}}{F_\text{n,corr}}$$

Additional corrections for humidity and variable specific heat fuels are also made on some engines.

Using the observed operating parameters given above, we find the corrected values to be

1 $\text{rpm}_\text{corr} = \dfrac{\text{rpm}_\text{obs}}{\sqrt{\theta}} = \dfrac{9465}{1.022} = 9261$ rpm

2 $\text{EGT}_\text{corr} = \dfrac{\text{EGT}_\text{obs}}{\theta} = \dfrac{1410}{1.045} = 1349°\text{R} = 889°\text{F} = 476°\text{C}$

3 $W_\text{f,corr} = \dfrac{W_\text{f,obs}}{\delta \sqrt{\theta}} = \dfrac{4000}{1.013 \times 1.022} = 3864$ lb/hr

4 $W_\text{a,corr} = \dfrac{W_\text{a,obs} \sqrt{\theta}}{\delta} = \dfrac{200 \times 1.022}{1.013} = 202$ lb/sec

5 $F_\text{n,corr} = \dfrac{F_\text{n,obs}}{\delta} = \dfrac{10,000}{1.013} = 9872$ lb

6 $\text{TSFC}_\text{corr} = \dfrac{W_\text{f,obs}}{F_\text{n,obs} \sqrt{\theta}} = \dfrac{4000}{10,000 \times 1.022} = 0.391$

If one knows the corrected values (given in the manufacturer's performance specifications), engine operating parameters for *any* pressure and temperature can be computed as follows:

1 $\text{rpm}_\text{obs} = \text{rpm}_\text{corr} \sqrt{\theta}$

2 $\text{EGT}_\text{obs} = \text{EGT}_\text{corr} \theta$

3 $W_\text{f,obs} = W_\text{f,corr} \delta \sqrt{\theta}$

4 $W_\text{a,obs} = \dfrac{W_\text{a,corr} \delta}{\sqrt{\theta}}$

5 $F_\text{n,obs} = F_\text{n,corr} \delta$

6 $\text{TSFC}_\text{obs} = \text{TSFC}_\text{corr} F_\text{n,obs} \sqrt{\theta}$

GROUND OPERATING PROCEDURES (*Fig. 18-4*)

Although operation of the gas turbine engine has been greatly simplified as a result of automated starting sequence starting systems and more sophisticated fuel controls, it is still possible to seriously damage an engine or surrounding equipment through mismanagement of the engine's controls and improper positioning of the aircraft. Before starting any gas turbine engine, the operator must be familiar with the manufacturer's starting, operating, and stopping procedures and engine limitations. Turbine temperatures are especially important in this respect and are more fully discussed on page 298. Specific danger zones exist at the front and rear of the engine (Fig. 18-5). From a safety standpoint, gas turbine operation is somewhat more hazardous than reciprocating engine operation. The whirling propeller at the front of the reciprocating engine is a clear and familiar hazard compared to the high-velocity airstream present at the front of an operating gas turbine engine. Several deaths and injuries have resulted from personnel being drawn into the inlet duct of an operating engine. Loose articles of clothing and other materials such as glasses, wipe-rags, caps, etc., have been snatched from people near an operating engine, causing severe damage to the engine.

The high velocity and temperature exhaust gases at the rear present a somewhat more obvious danger. They exit with a speed of over 1000 mph, and can do

GENERAL SIGNALS

AFFIRMATIVE; CONDITION SATISFACTORY; OK; TRIM GOOD, ETC.

Hold up thumb and forefinger, touching at the tips, to form the letter "O."

NEGATIVE; CONDITION UNSATISFACTORY; NO GOOD, ETC.

With the fingers curled and thumb extended, point thumb downward toward the ground.

ADJUST UP (higher)

With the fingers extended and palm facing up, move hand up (and down), vertically, as if coaxing upward.

ADJUST DOWN (lower)

With the fingers extended and palm facing down, move hand down (and up), vertically, as if coaxing downward.

SLIGHT ADJUSTMENT

Hold up thumb and forefinger, slightly apart (either simultaneously with the other hand when calling for an up or down adjustment, or with the same hand, immediately following the adjustment signal).

SHORTEN ADJUSTMENT (as when adjusting a linkage)

Hold up thumb and forefinger somewhat apart (other fingers curled), then bring thumb and forefinger together in a slow, closing motion.

LENGTHEN ADJUSTMENT (as when adjusting a linkage)

Hold up thumb and forefinger pressed together (other fingers curled), then separate thumb and forefinger in a slow, opening motion.

NUMERICAL READING (of an instrument or to report a numerical value of any type)

Hold up appropriate number of fingers of either one or both hands, as necessary, in numerical sequence (i.e., 5, then 7 = 57).

NUMERICAL READING (of an instrument)

Same as "Numerical Reading," under General Signals

INCREASE TRIM SETTING (or other adjustment)

Same as "Adjust Up (higher)," under General Signals

DECREASE TRIM SETTING (or other adjustment)

Same as "Adjust Down (lower)," under General Signals

SLIGHT ADJUSTMENT

Same as "Slight Adjustment," under General Signals

TRIM GOOD

Same as "Affirmative," under General Signals

READ EXHAUST GAS TEMPERATURE (EGT)

Make a motion with the hand, as if wiping perspiration from the brow.

CONNECT EXTERNAL POWER SOURCE

Insert extended forefinger of right hand into cupped fist of left hand.

DISCONNECT EXTERNAL POWER SOURCE

Withdraw extended forefinger of right hand from cupped fist of left hand.

START ENGINE

Circular motion with right hand and arm extended over the head. When necessary for multiengine aircraft, use a numerical finger signal (or point) with the left hand to designate which engine should be started. ✱

✱ NOTE: To use as an "all clear to start" signal, pilot or engine operator initiates the signal from the aircraft cockpit. Ground crewman repeats the signal to indicate "all clear to start engine."

FIG. 18-4 *Hand signals used for safer operation of turbine aircraft.   (Continued on following page.)*

READ TURBINE DISCHARGE PRESSURE (P$_{t7}$) OR ENGINE PRESSURE RATIO (EPR) INDICATOR
Hold the palms of both hands together, with the fingers extended and pointing up, in front of the body. With the right hand, push the left hand back.

READ N$_1$ OR N$_2$ TACHOMETER
Point to nose with forefinger of right hand. When required, hold up one (1) or two (2) fingers of left hand to designate whether N$_1$ or N$_2$ is desired.

READ FUEL FLOW INDICATOR AT IDLE THRUST
(A) Point to eye with forefinger.
(B) With the fingers cupped and held close to the lips, make a drinking motion by tilting the head back.

READ FUEL FLOW INDICATOR AT MILITARY (OR TAKE-OFF) THRUST
(A) Starting at shoulder level, make circular motion upward with one hand, followed by full arm stretch.
(B) With the fingers cupped and held close to the lips, make a drinking motion by tilting the head back.

READ FUEL FLOW INDICATOR IN MANUAL OR EMERGENCY AT IDLE (fighter aircraft)
(A) Clasp the left wrist with the right hand.
(B) Point to eye with forefinger.
(C) With the fingers cupped and held close to the lips, make a drinking motion by tilting the head back.

READ FUEL FLOW INDICATOR IN MANUAL OR EMERGENCY AT MILITARY (fighter aircraft)
(A) With the right hand clasped over the left wrist, move clenched left fist forward, as if moving a throttle.
(B) With the fingers cupped and held close to the lips, make a drinking motion by tilting the head back.

READ OIL PRESSURE INDICATOR
Place hand on top of head, palm down.

CHECK OIL LEVEL
With the fingers of both hands extended, palms facing each other, place one palm a few inches above the other.

CHECK AFTERBURNER NOZZLE POSITION (fighter aircraft)

(A) REQUEST: Hold the palms of both hands together, with the fingers extended. Using the heels of the palms as a hinge, open and close the hands several times, in a flapping motion.

REPLY:
(B) AFTERBURNER NOZZLE OPEN: With both arms extended horizontally in front of the body, move the arms apart.
(C) AFTERBURNER NOZZLE CLOSED: With both arms extended horizontally to the sides of the body, bring the arms together in front of the body.

CHECK OVERBOARD AIRBLEED VALVE POSITION
(A) REQUEST: Hold out clenched fist, then open and close the fingers several times.

REPLY:
(B) VALVE CLOSED (OR CLOSING): With the fingers extended, slowly close the hand to form a "fist."
(C) VALVE OPEN (OR OPENING): With the fingers forming a "fist," slowly open the hand.

CHECK ANTI-ICING SYSTEM
REQUEST: Cover nose with cupped hand, as if to protect it from cold.
REPLY: Affirmative or negative signal, as applicable (refer to General Signals).

CHECK FOR FUEL OR OIL LEAK
Cup hand over an eye, telescope fashion, moving the head as if looking for something.

PULL CIRCUIT BREAKER
With fingers of one hand cupped upward, draw hand down sharply, as if removing a plug.

REPLACE CIRCUIT BREAKER
With fingers of one hand cupped upward, push hand up sharply, as if replacing a plug.

FIG. 18-4 *Hand signals used for safer operation of turbine aircraft.* *(Continued on following page.)*

**PERSONNEL IN DANGER (for any reason).
REDUCE THRUST & SHUT DOWN ENGINE(S).**
(A) Draw right forefinger across throat. When necessary for multiengine aircraft, use a numerical finger signal (or point) with the left hand to designate which engine should be shut down.
(B) As soon as the signal is observed, cross both arms high above the face. The sequence of signals may be reversed, if more expedient.

**FIRE IN TAILPIPE.
TURN ENGINE OVER WITH STARTER.**
(A) With the fingers of both hands curled and both thumbs extended up, make a gesture pointing upward.
(B) As soon as the signal is observed, use circular motion with right hand and arm extended over the head (as for an engine start). When necessary for multiengine aircraft, use a numerial finger signal (or point) with the left hand to designate the affected engine.

**FIRE IN ACCESSORY SECTION.
SHUT DOWN ENGINE AND EVACUATE THE AIRCRAFT.**
(A) Draw right forefinger across throat. When necessary for multiengine aircraft, use a numerical finger signal (or point) with the left hand to designate which engine should be shut down.
(B) As soon as the signal is observed, extend both thumbs upward, then out. Repeat, if necessary.

IDLE RPM

Point to eye with forefinger. When tachometer reading is needed, engine operator holds up appropriate number of fingers in sequence to indicate numerical value.

ADVANCE THROTTLE TO MILITARY (OR TAKE-OFF) THRUST

Starting at shoulder level, make circular motion upward with one hand, followed by full arm stretch.

JAM ACCELERATION
Short jab with clenched fist, as in boxing.

SLOW ACCELERATION
Same as for jam acceleration, except in slow motion.

**REVERSE THRUST
(commercial aircraft)**

Swing out-stretched arm as far as possible behind the body and rotate in a circular motion.

**ACTUATE THE EXHAUST SILENCER
(commercial aircraft)**

Place both hands over the ears, as if to protect them from noise.

**RETRACT THE EXHAUST SILENCER
(commercial aircraft)**

With both hands placed over the ears, withdraw them outward, sharply.

**OPERATE IN MANUAL OR EMERGENCY
(fighter aircraft)**

With the right hand clasped over the left wrist, move clenched left fist forward, as if moving a throttle.

**RETURN TO NORMAL
(fighter aircraft)**

With the clenched left fist held forward, clasp the left wrist with the right hand, and draw left fist back toward the body.

**START AFTERBURNER
(fighter aircraft)**

(A) Short, quick jab from the body with the left fist, as in boxing, followed by a pronounced movement of the fist to the left (outboard) (B).

**STOP AFTERBURNER
(fighter aircraft)**

(A) Holding the left hand closed and arm horizontal, in front but slightly away from the side of the body, move the arm sharply to the right (inboard), then draw it quickly back, toward the body (B).

**ACTUATE POP-OPEN NOZZLE
(some fighter aircraft)**

With the palms of both hands together and the fingers extended, open hands at the base, using finger tips as a hinge.

SHUT DOWN ENGINE

Draw right forefinger across throat. When necessary for multiengine aircraft, use a numerical finger signal (or point) with the left hand to designate which engine should be shut down.

FIG. 18-4 *Hand signals used for safer operation of turbine aircraft (continued).*

Distance in feet

FIG. 18-5 *Engine intake and exhaust hazard areas (typical).*

EGT limits are not exceeded, but it does point up the need to keep the area to the rear of the engine clear of flammable material. The airplane should face into the wind to reduce the dangers of starting overtemperatures and to obtain faster, smoother accelerations. Facing the airplane into the wind is a necessity if any adjustments are to be made.

Damage caused by foreign objects has been one of the principal reasons for premature engine removal. The axial-flow compressor is particularly sensitive to this type of injury. Foreign object damage (FOD) has cost the U.S. Air Force over fifty million dollars per year. Because FOD has been such a problem, military and civil airport operators have had to retrain their personnel to establish new working habits. It is no longer satisfactory to allow the end of a cotter pin or safety wire to remain where it falls. Special cleaners (Fig. 18-6) have been developed to continually vacuum ramps and runways. Some of these machines can pick up 1-lb chunks of steel while traveling at 25 mph.

Other dangers associated with the operation of the gas turbine are those resulting from noise (see Chap. 8), and the ignition system (see Chap. 16). No work should be performed on the ignition system while the engine is in operation. If the system must be worked on soon after it has been in operation, touch the end of the lead wire to the shell of the igniter to dissipate any residual energy. Caution must be exercised to avoid the chance of injury or death. Many ignition systems

serious damage to both personnel and equipment. To cite an example from one airline safety report, "A cart was blown over a ten foot fence, cleared the fence by another ten feet, and landed seventy-five feet beyond. The cart weighed seven hundred fifty pounds." The jet blast can also pick up and blow loose dirt, sizable rocks, and other debris a distance of several hundred feet and with considerable force.

The heat of the exhaust stream is serious only if the engine is operating at low rpm. The velocity of the jet blast at higher power settings is so great that a person entering the gas stream would be hurled a considerable distance without being burned. Of course breathing the hot exhaust gases can have an irritating effect on lungs and eyes.

It is very important to correctly locate and position the airplane during ground operation. The aircraft should be run on concrete surfaces, since fuel and oil spillage will severely damage asphalt-type surfaces. The hot exhaust gas will also deteriorate the asphalt, especially if the engines are equipped with thrust reversers. An engine may occasionally *torch*. This is a condition where excess fuel accumulates during a starting attempt. It is not harmful to the engine if

FIG. 18-6 *Two types of runway and ramp vacuum cleaners.*

incorporate radioactive discharge tubes, which should be disposed of in a special manner. No work or inspection should be done in the area of the tailpipe for about ½ hr or longer to reduce the chances of injury from hot metal parts or from the flashing of residual fuel in the combustion chambers or tailpipe. Spilled fuels and oils present a fire hazard, and direct contact may cause skin drying or other irritations on some people. Fuel and oil should be removed from the skin with soap and water as soon as possible.

Many engines are equipped with compressor bleed valves (Chap. 5). When checking bleed-valve operation or doing other work on or near the compressor bleed while the engine is running, care should be taken to stand clear during the period the bleeds are open. When the bleed valves open, high-pressure air at high velocity is dumped overboard.

STARTING A GAS TURBINE ENGINE

Starting procedures will, of course, vary, depending upon engine type and installation. Listed below is the starting procedure for the Pratt & Whitney JT3D commercial turbofan engine equipped with a pneumatic starter.

1 *Throttle:*—IDLE
2 *Fuel shutoff lever:*—CLOSED
   CAUTION: Do not open the fuel valve before turning on the starter and ignition switches.
3 *Engine master switch:*—ON
4 *Fuel system shutoff switch:*—OPEN
5 *Fuel boost pump switch:*—ON
6 *Fuel inlet pressure indicator* (if the aircraft is so equipped):— 5 PSI MIN (to ensure that fuel is being delivered to the engine fuel pump inlet)
7 *Engine starter switch*—ON. Check for oil pressure rise
8 *Ignition switch*—ON.
   CAUTION: The ignition switch should not be turned on until the compressor begins to rotate.

When the N_2 tachometer indicates at least 10 percent rpm:

9 *Fuel shutoff lever*—OPEN. An engine "light up" will be noted by a rise in EGT. The engine should light up within 20 sec or less, after it is pressurized by turning on the fuel.
   CAUTION: Insufficient air pressure to either a pneumatic starter or a combustion starter that is being used as a pneumatic starter may not supply enough starter torque to start the engine properly, resulting in a hot, hung, or torching start. Such a condition is highly undesirable and may normally be avoided. When air bleed from another engine is used to operate the starter, caution is necessary to ensure that the operating engine is turning over fast enough to provide an adequate supply of pressurized air to the engine being started. An engine should never be permitted to take longer than two minutes to accelerate to IDLE rpm. In the event of torching, higher than usual exhaust gas starting temperature, too long an acceleration time, or other abnormalities, discontinue the starting attempt and investigate.

10 **Monitor the engine instruments** (See page 299)—until the engine stabilizes at IDLE, to ascertain that the start is satisfactory and that none of the limits stipulated in the Engine Check Chart are exceeded.

When the engine attains IDLE rpm (if some means of automatic cutoff is not provided):

11 *Engine starter switch*—OFF
12 *Ignition switch*—OFF
   CAUTION: If the fuel is shut off inadvertently by closing the fuel-shutoff lever, do not reopen the fuel valve again in an attempt to regain the "light." Whenever the engine fails to light, shut off the fuel and ignition and continue turning the compressor over with the starter for 10 to 15 sec to clear out trapped fuel or vapor. If this is not done, allow a 30-sec fuel draining period before attempting another start. Observe any starter cooling period or ignition cycle limitation that may be required. The starter may be reengaged at any time after the compressor has decelerated to 40 percent rpm or less.

Unsatisfactory starts can be categorized within the following three areas.

1 *Hot start*—The EGT goes above the manufacturer's specified limits as a result of a rich fuel/air ratio. Improper ratios can result from a malfunctioning fuel control, or ice, or other restrictions at the front of the compressor. Most manufacturers will list degrees of overtemperature in terms of time and temperature, rather than stating one specific overtemperature point. Figure 18-7 shows the starting overtemperature and time limits for the Pratt & Whitney JT12 (J60) engine installed in the Lockheed Jet Star and North American Sabreliner. Hot starts can very often be anticipated through experience by observing a greater than normal fuel flow or a faster than normal EGT rise. The operator should be prepared to abort the start, although some manufacturers recommend that the engine be run for a five minute cool down period unless it is obvious that the engine will be damaged by continued operation. A hot start may also be caused by a false or hung start.

2 *False or hung start*—After "light up" has occurred, the rpm does not increase to that of IDLE, but remains at some lower value. The EGT may continue to rise and again the operator should be prepared to abort before temperature limits are exceeded. A hung start could be the result of the starter receiving insufficient power or dropping out too soon.

3 *No start*—The engine does not light up within the specified time limit, indicated by no increase in rpm or EGT. Insufficient electric power, no fuel to the engine, problems in the ignition system, or a malfunctioning fuel control, all might lead to starting difficulties.

ENGINE OPERATION AND CHECKS

Just as starting procedures will vary with engine types, so will controls and instrumentation vary with airplane types.

Almost all gas turbine engine equipped airplanes will have the following levers, switches, and instruments to control and indicate engine operation:

1 Power lever
2 Fuel shutoff valve or switch
3 Engine pressure ratio (EPR) gage
4 Percent rpm gage

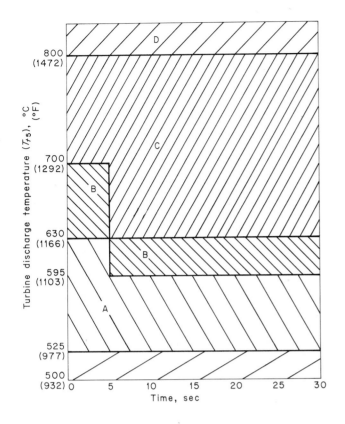

OVERTEMPERATURE PROCEDURES

A Shutdown. Check engine and determine cause of overtemperature.
B Perform visual inspection of all hot-section parts.
  (1) Inspect exhaust duct for foreign particles.
  (2) Inspect rear of the turbine for apparent damage.
  (3) Inspect combustion section, turbine vanes, and front of turbine section for excessive distortion or damage.
C Perform teardown inspection of all hot-section parts.
  (1) Inspect all turbine vanes for bowing, bend, and twist.
  (2) Fluorescent penetrant inspect all turbine blades.
  (3) Inspect all turbine blades for stretch.
  (4) Inspect turbine disks for growth and hardness. (First- and second-stage disk hardness must be at least 66 on Rockwell A scale.)
D Perform complete overhaul inspection of all hot-section parts.
  (1) Scrap all turbine blades.
  (2) Fluorescent penetrant inspect all turbine vanes.
  (3) Inspect all turbine vanes for bowing, bend, and twist.
  (4) Inspect turbine disks for growth and hardness. (First- and second-stage disk hardness must be at least 66 on Rockwell A scale.)

FIG. 18-7 *Engine starting overtemperature limits for the Pratt & Whitney JT12A-8 engine.*

 5 EGT or TIT gage
 6 Fuel-flow gage
 7 Oil pressure and temperature gage
 8 Torquemeter gage (turboprop or turboshaft only)
 9 Starter switch
10 Engine master switch
11 Fuel boost pump switch, pressure gage, and light
12 Ignition switch (may be activated as a function of power-lever position)

Depending upon the engine type, system, and aircraft, additional controls and instrumentation might be installed.

13 Water pump and injection switches
14 Anti-icing lights and switches
15 Nozzle area position indicator
16 Oil quantity gage
17 Feathering switches (turboprop only)
18 Emergency shutdown lever(s)
19 Free air temperature gage
20 Vibration indicator

Checking the gas turbine engine for proper operation consists primarily of reading engine instruments and then comparing the observed values with those given by the manufacturer for specific engine operating conditions, atmospheric pressure, and temperature.

Early model gas turbines usually used rpm as the sole engine operating parameter to establish thrust, while many present-day engines use engine pressure ratio (EPR) as the primary thrust indicator. On a hot day, compressor rpm for a given thrust will be higher than on a cold day. Furthermore, a dirty or damaged compressor will reduce thrust for a given rpm. EPR is used because it varies directly with thrust. It is the ratio of the total pressure at the front of the compressor to the total pressure at the rear of the turbine. The exhaust gas temperature is never used for setting thrust, although it must be monitored to see that temperature limits are not exceeded. Using EPR as the thrust indicator means that on a hot day it is quite possible for the engine rpm to exceed 100 percent, and on a cold day, desired thrust ratings may be reached at something less than 100 percent. Generally, thrust is set by adjusting the throttle to obtain a predetermined EPR reading on the aircraft instrument. The EPR value for given thrust settings will vary with ambient pressure and temperature.

Operational engines must occasionally be adjusted to compensate, within limits, for thrust deterioration caused by compressor blade deposits of dirt or scale. This process is called *trimming.* The word comes from the old practice of adjusting the engine's temperature and thrust by cutting, or trimming the exhaust nozzle to

FIG. 18-8 *Cleaning turbojet and turboprop engines by grit-blasting.*

size. Although the nozzle size on some engines can be varied by the insertion or removal of metal tabs called *mice*, the trimming process generally involves a fuel-control adjustment to bring the engine to a specific temperature, fuel flow, thrust, and engine pressure ratio. Manufacturer's instructions must be followed when performing trimming operations on any specific engine.

When the rated thrust cannot be restored without exceeding other engine limitations, the engine must either be field cleaned or removed and sent to overhaul (Fig. 18-8).

Field cleaning is accomplished by introducing a lignocellulose material into the air inlet duct while the engine is operating. The cleaning material known as Carboblast-Jet Engine Type is made by crushing apricot pits or walnut hulls. Specific steps to follow in cleaning any particular engine are to be found in the maintenance instructions for that engine. These steps generally include blocking some lines and ports and removing any equipment in the inlet duct that might be damaged by the cleaning material. The engine is then run at different speeds for stipulated periods of time while the Carboblast compound is fed into the inlet duct. After cleaning, the installation must be returned to its original configuration and the engine must be retrimmed.

REVIEW AND STUDY QUESTIONS

1 Describe the construction of a typical gas turbine test cell.

2 List the instrumentation and controls necessary for the proper testing of the gas turbine engine.

3 What is the purpose of a bellmouth inlet?

4 What is the purpose of the engine log sheet? List some of the major items included on this log sheet.

5 What is the definition of the correction factors delta and theta? Why are these correction factors used?

6 Make a list of the precautions to observe before starting any gas turbine engine. Discuss the specific problems of the exhaust jet and of foreign objects.

7 Give the starting procedures and precautions to observe when starting the JT3D engine.

8 Describe a hot start; hung start; no start.

9 List the instruments and controls to be found in most gas turbine equipped airplanes.

10 What engine operating parameter is used as a primary indication of thrust? Why isn't rpm indication a good method of setting thrust?

11 What is engine trimming? How is it accomplished on most gas turbine engines?

12 What is meant by field cleaning? How is field cleaning accomplished?

Chapter 19

Maintenance and overhaul procedures

The length of time between overhauls (TBO) has increased from 10 hr for the German Jumo 109-004B manufactured in 1945, to over 6000 hr for the Pratt & Whitney JT3D engine currently being produced. It should be kept in mind that between these major overhaul periods most engines are required to go through an intermediate "hot-section" inspection. This large improvement in TBO has been accomplished in the main through significant improvements in engine design, metallurgy, manufacturing, overhaul, inspection, and maintenance procedures.

Previous chapters in this book have dealt mainly with the design, metallurgical, and manufacturing aspects of the engine. The other three factors, overhaul, inspection, and maintenance procedures, will be discussed in this chapter.

OVERHAUL

The TBO varies considerably between engine types. It is generally established for civil aircraft by the equipment operator and the engine manufacturer, working in conjunction with the Federal Aviation Agency (FAA). With the exception of the FAA, the overhaul times for military aircraft are established in essentially the same manner. Taken into account are such factors as the type of operation and utilization, the servicing facilities and experience of maintenance personnel, and the total experience gained with the particular engine. As a specific model engine builds up operating time, and is sent to the overhaul agency, the parts are inspected for wear and/or signs of impending failure. If the critical parts seem to be wearing well, an extension of TBO may be approved. One of the most important factors in determining time between overhauls is the use to which the engine is put. Frequent starts and stops, or power changes (cycle changes) necessary on short haul aircraft, result in rapid temperature changes which, in turn, will affect the TBO. Most manufacturers have adopted a system of permanently marking critical parts of the engine such as turbine disks and blades, which are subject to deterioration through cycle changes or time limits. A part must be removed from service when either the number of cycles or the time reaches the maximum limit.

Modern gas turbine engines are expensive, with some versions costing over 500,000 dollars. It is essential that the operators in the overhaul shops keep complete and accurate records to guarantee that a component be removed or modified when required, and, on the other hand, that parts are not discarded prematurely. In order to do this, most engine parts must be identifiable. The marking methods take several forms, determined by the desired permanency, the type of material being marked, and the location of the part. Temporary marking methods include:

1. Several brands of marking pencils. It is extremely important to *not* use any material that would leave a deposit of lead, copper, zinc, or similar material on any hot section part, as this might cause premature failure due to carburization or intergranular attack. (This includes grease and lead pencils.)
2. Chalk.
3. Several brands of ink.

Permanent marks may be accomplished by:

1. Electrolytic etch applied through a stencil or with a special electrolytic pen. This is not the same as electric arc scribing which has been found unsuitable for the gas turbine engine. Electrolytic etch should not be used on anodized surfaces.
2. Metal stamping using a hammer, press, or roll. This method is limited to parts having less than a specific hardness.
3. Vibration peening produces characters by a vibrating radius-tipped tool.
4. Engraving with a rotating cutter or grinder.
5. Drag impression using a freely rotating radius-tipped conical tool.
6. Blasting with an abrasive substance through a stencil.
7. Branding used on nonmetallic parts such as plastic, bakelite, etc.

In all cases the manufacturer's recommendations must be followed.

The actual overhaul of the engine can be divided into:

1. Disassembly
2. Cleaning
3. Inspection
4. Repair
5. Reassembly
6. Testing
7. Storage

Disassembly

Disassembly can be accomplished on a vertical or horizontal disassembly stand (Fig. 19-1). Some engines can be disassembled by using either method, while others lend themselves to a particular procedure. After the engine is broken down into its major components, many of the subassemblies are then mounted on individual stands (Fig. 19-2) for further work. A large number of specialized tools are necessary to ensure dismantling without damage to the closely machined, highly stressed parts. A set of these tools often may cost as much as the engine.

Every manufacturer issues a complete and detailed overhaul manual which gives a step-by-step disassembly procedure and also shows where and how to use the special tools. Appropriate warnings and cautions where necessary to minimize possible injury to the worker and damage to the engine are included. Special instructions are given for the many parts such as the bearings and carbon seals which require special handling. Other parts must be reassembled in their original position, so they must be tagged and marked accordingly. Seals, other than the carbon rubbing types, are not reused. Metal-type seals will have been crushed, and many rubber-type seals are made to expand in contact with fuel or oil. Once this type of rubber seal has been removed, it will not fit back into its original groove.

FIG. 19-2 *Continental J69 accessories section disassembly stand.*

Combustion section lift fixture

(a)

(b)

FIG. 19-1 *Two methods of disassembling a gas turbine engine.* **(a)** *Vertical disassembly of a General Electric J79.* **(b)** *Horizontal disassembly of a Pratt & Whitney JT3.*

Reproduced in Fig. 19-3 are two pages removed from the overhaul manual for an early General Electric J85-GE-5 engine. The pages are typical of those found in a majority of these publications.

Cleaning

Engine cleaning is designed to accomplish several things.

1 Permit a thorough examination of components for the presence of service flaws and for changes in dimension through abrasion and wear.

2 Remove deposits which adversely affect the efficient functioning of the engine parts.

3 Prepare surfaces for applications of repair and salvage processes, such as plating, welding, and painting.

4 Remove various organic and inorganic coatings which require replacement either for inspection of the underlying surfaces, or to remove deteriorated coatings unsuitable for another engine run.

The selection of the cleaning materials and the processes used for each part are determined by the nature of the soil, type of metal, type of coating, and the degree of cleanliness necessary for a thorough inspection and the subsequent repair process. Not all parts need to be stripped down to the base metal, nor do all stains need to be removed from the plated parts. Furthermore, some cleaning solutions and/or procedures will strip or attack plated parts or cause undesirable reactions with the base metal. For example, titanium should not be cleaned with trichlorethylene in order to avoid the possibility of stress corrosion associated with the entrapment of chlorine-containing materials in tight-fitting areas.

Cleaning solutions range from commonly used organic solvents such as petroleum washes and sprays for degreasing and general cleaning, vapor degreasing solutions such as trichlorethylene, and carbon solvents for hard carbon deposits, to less familiar cleaning materials. Steam cleaning can be used on parts not requiring mechanical or chemical cleaning and where paint and surface finishes need not be removed. Cleaning by tumbling is also an approved method for use on parts that are to be magnetically inspected. The tumbling process tends to obscure defects if the dye penetrant method of inspection is used. Most of these materials and methods are generally suitable for use on the cold section of the engine.

Hot-section cleaning requires processes involving a series of controlled acid or alkali baths and water rinses in various combinations. Grit blasting, wet or dry, is another method commonly used on both hot and cold sections of the engine.

Some parts such as ball and roller bearings require special handling. The bearing can become magnetized in service and may have to be demagnetized in order to properly clean it of magnetic particles. The bearing must not be allowed to spin during cleaning, and split bearings must be kept as units.

Since many of the solutions will attack the skin as readily as the part being cleaned, protective clothing and devices such as goggles, gloves, aprons, hand creams, etc., must be used while working with these products.

In all cases it is imperative to follow the manufacturer's recommendations in relation to materials and procedures used when cleaning gas turbine parts.

Inspection

When the engine is being manufactured, and during the overhaul process, it is, of course, necessary to check the quality of the various parts. The inspection section of the overhaul manual includes specific and detailed information, much of it gained through operating experience, outlining whether or not and the extent to which a part can be repaired and a table of minimum and maximum dimensional limits with which each part must comply. Special critical areas are called to the attention of overhaul personnel. Time and/or cycle limits are compared to the life limits of such parts as compressor and turbine blades and disks, and accurate records are kept of all work performed.

The inspection process can be divided into two broad groups.

NONDIMENSIONAL INSPECTION These methods include the use of fluorescent and nonfluorescent particles for those parts that can be magnetized, and fluorescent and nonfluorescent dye penetrants for those that cannot. Gages utilizing ultrasonic vibrations (Fig. 19-4) can be used to detect hidden flaws, and for critical parts x-rays are employed (Fig. 19-5). Included in this method is simple visual inspection for general condition (Fig. 19-6).

DIMENSIONAL INSPECTION This process includes the use of mechanical measuring tools such as micrometers, dial indicators, and other specialized gages and plugs, and tools using light, sound, and air pressure as the measuring medium.

Magnetic-particle inspection (Fig. 19-7) is a nondestructive method of testing magnetizable ferrous materials for surface or subsurface cracks. When a part is magnetized by passing a current through it, or by placing it in a magnetic field, the two walls of any crack in the piece being tested will become weak secondary poles. If the part is immersed in a solution containing finely divided iron oxide magnetic particles, or if this solution is made to flow over the part, the suspended particles will tend to collect along the walls of the crack. The crack will be indicated by a dark red line or, if the suspension also contains fluorescent particles, as a bright line when viewed under an ultraviolet lamp. Each part

1 UPPER-HALF COMPRESSOR
   STATOR CASING
2 LOCKING KEY
3 LOWER-HALF COMPRESSOR
   STATOR CASING
4 LOCKNUT
5 BOLT
6 CUSHION CLAMP
7 LOCKNUT
8 BOLT

9   CUSHION CLAMP
10 DIFFUSER SUBASSEMBLY
11 UPPER-HALF TURBINE
    STATOR CASING
12 LOWER-HALF TURBINE
    STATOR CASING
13 FRONT FRAME
14 COMPRESSOR STATOR
    HALF VERTICAL SUPPORT
    (PT NO. 21C677)

15 MAIN FRAME
16 THERMOCOUPLE HARNESS
17 THERMOCOUPLE BRACKET
18 MAIN FUEL MANIFOLD
19 MANIFOLD SUPPORT
20 OUTER COMBUSTION
    CASING
21 RETAINER

B-2261

FIG. 19-3 *Typical disassembly instructions taken from a General Electric J85 overhaul manual. (Continued on following page.)*

c. Seventeen bolts (16) and 16 locknuts (17) secure the forward flange of the upper-half compressor casing to the front frame aft flange.

Note

Five of the bolts were removed when the inlet-guide vane actuator ring was removed. Two locknuts were removed with the spark generator forward bracket. Two locknuts were removed with the anti-icing valve. One bolt hole under the right-hand actuator is not used. Remove the remaining bolts, locknuts, the junction box forward bracket (20) and the T_5 amplifier forward bracket (21).

d. Install the stator casing lifting device and remove the upper-half compressor casing (28). Remove the 4 retainers (22) for the compressor vane segments. Position the compressor stator-half vertical support at the 12 o'clock position and secure the support to the flange of both the mainframe and the front frame with 2 bolts and locknuts.

4–131. REMOVAL OF UPPER-HALF COMPRESSOR STATOR CASING, J85-GE-5. (See figure 4–48A.)

Note

For special tools, see figure 3–1, group 10.

a. Remove 6 locknuts and 6 washers from the body-bound bolts located in bolt holes 1, 5, and 11 in the horizontal flanges of the compressor stator casing.

b. Remove the 6 body-bound bolts and 4 washers by using a plastic drift pin to drive the bolts out of the holes.

CAUTION

Do not turn the bolt in the hole during removal; this would enlarge the hole and impair the alignment function.

c. Remove the remaining 16 bolts and 16 locknuts from the horizontal flanges of the compressor stator casing.

d. Remove the 2 supports and washers for the synchronizing cable conduit.

e. Seventeen bolts and 16 locknuts secure the forward flange of the upper-half compressor casing (1) to the front frame (13). Nine of the bolts were removed with the inlet guide vane actuator ring. Four locknuts were removed with the T_5 amplifier forward brackets. Three locknuts were removed with the anti-icing valve and stand-off bracket. One locknut was removed with the T_5 amplifier lead clamp. One bolt hole under the right-hand actuator is not used.

f. Remove the remaining locknuts and bolts, the junction box forward bracket, and the 2 offset brackets from the upper-half compressor casing forward flange.

g. Remove 26 locknuts and 26 bolts from the aft flange of the upper-half compressor stator casing.

h. Remove the junction box aft bracket, the afterburner control temperature (T_5) amplifier aft bracket, the 4 forward mounts and the 4 brackets.

i. Install the stator casing lifting device and remove the upper-half compressor casing. On J85-GE-5A engines, remove the 2 locking keys (2) for the compressor vane segments. On J85-GE-5 engines that have not been retrofitted to the J85-GE-5A configuration, remove the 4 retainers (21) for the compressor vane segments. Position the compressor stator half vertical support (14) at the 12 o'clock position and secure the support to the flange of both the mainframe (15) and front frame (13) with 2 bolts and nuts.

4–132. REMOVAL OF LOWER-HALF COMPRESSOR STATOR CASING, YJ85-GE-5. (See figure 4–49.)

Note

For special tools, see figure 3–1, group 10.

a. Twenty-six bolts (1) and 18 locknuts (2) secure the aft flange of the lower-half compressor casing (3) to the mainframe. Four bolts and locknuts, used for securing the trunnion brackets during shipping, were removed when the engine was removed from the shipping container. One bolt, locknut, and clamp were removed with the feedback cable. The 8 bolts that secure the forward end of the 2 gearbox mounting brackets were removed with the gearbox. Remove the remaining bolts, locknuts, 2 offset brackets (4, 5), and the fuel drain valve bracket (6).

b. Seventeen bolts (7) and 16 locknuts (8) secure the forward flange of the lower-half compressor casing to the front frame. Three of the bolts were removed when the inlet-guide vane actuator ring was removed. One locknut and 2 cushion clamps were removed with the actuator fuel lines. One locknut was removed with the left-hand actuator. One bolt under the left-hand actuator is not used. Remove the remaining bolts, locknuts, fuel filter support (10) and the check valve bracket (11).

c. Install the stator casing lifting device and remove the lower-half compressor casing. Position the compressor stator half vertical support at the 6 o'clock position and secure the support to the flange of both the mainframe and the front frame with 2 bolts and nuts.

4–133. REMOVAL OF LOWER-HALF COMPRESSOR STATOR CASING, J85-GE-5. (See figure 4–48A.)

Note

For special tools, see figure 3–1, group 10.

a. Seventeen bolts and 16 locknuts secure the forward flange of the lower-half compressor casing (3) to the front frame (13). Three of the bolts were removed with the inlet-guide vane actuator ring. One locknut was removed with the left-hand actuator. One locknut was removed with the afterburner high pressure filter clamp. One bolt hole under the left-hand actuator is not used. Remove the remaining bolts, locknuts and fuel hose bracket from the lower compressor casing forward flange.

FIG. 19-3 *Typical disassembly instructions taken from a General Electric J85 overhaul manual (continued).*

FIG. 19-4 *Magnatest SR-200; a sonic testing machine.* (Magnaflux Corporation)

to be tested must be magnetized using a current of correct magnitude applied in a specific direction (a process called circular or longitudinal magnetization) so that the magnetic lines of flux are likely to pass across a suspected crack at right angles (Fig. 19-8). Particular attention is paid to bosses, flanges, lugs, shoulders, splines, teeth, or other intricate areas. Some skill is necessary to properly interpret indications. After testing, the part must be completely demagnetized by passing it slowly through a coil in which alternating current is flowing. Complete demagnetization is important and may be tested by using a field-strength indicator or a good quality compass. Specific procedures are generally outlined in the overhaul manual.

Dye penetrant inspection is a nondestructive method of testing nonmagnetizable materials such as aluminum and magnesium for *surface* cracks or imperfections only (Fig. 19-9). Although this process was developed for nonferrous materials, it can also be used to good advantage on products made of iron. Since this is a surface treatment, it is essential to have the surface absolutely clean and free of paint. A penetrating dye which may or may not fluoresce, is painted or sprayed on the part. The surface is then washed and a wet or dry developer is applied which will draw the penetrant from the defect. Cracks will appear as dark lines, or bright lines from the fluorescent material when viewed under the ultraviolet light. Again as with magnetic inspection, some degree of skill is necessary to interpret and evaluate the indications.

Visual inspection plays a most important part in the

overhaul of the gas turbine engine. Some conditions likely to be found, and their causes, are listed below. (Fig. 19-10)

1 *Abrasion*—A roughened area. Varying degrees of abrasion can be described as light or heavy, depending upon the extent of reconditioning required to restore surface. Usual cause is presence of fine foreign material between moving surfaces.

2 *Bend (bow)*—General distortion in structure as distinguished from a local change in conformation. Usual causes are uneven application of heat, excessive heat or pressure, or forces defined under stresses.

3 *Blistering*—Raised areas indicating separation of surface from base. Usually found on plated or painted surfaces. Associated with flaking or peeling. Usual cause is imperfect bond with base, usually aggravated by presence of moisture, gas, heat, or pressure.

4 *Break*—Complete separation by force into two or more pieces. Usual causes are fatigue, or sudden overload.

5 *Brinelling*—Indentations sometimes found on surface of ball or

FIG. 19-5 *One million volt x-ray machine.*

1 CONDUCTING CORD   5 SMALL BORESCOPE
2 TRANSFORMER   6 VIEWING PROBES
3 LIGHT CARRIER   7 ADAPTER 6795875
4 LARGE BORESCOPE

FIG. 19-6 *Borescope components used to visually examine internal engine parts.*

roller bearing parts. Usual causes are improper assembly or disassembly technique of the roller or ball bearings, by the application of force on the free race.

NOTE: Bearings which do not have full, constant rotation and are subject to sudden loading have brinelling tendencies.

6 *Bulge*—An outward bending or swelling. Usual cause is excessive pressure or weakening due to excessive heat.

7 *Burning*—Injury to parts by excessive heat. Evidenced by char-

acteristic discoloration or in severe cases, by a loss or flow of material. Usual causes are excessive heat due to lack of lubrication, improper clearance, or abnormal flame pattern.

8 *Burnishing*—Mechanical smoothing of a metal surface by rubbing, not accompanied by removal of material, but sometimes by discoloration around outer edges of area. Operational burnishing is not detrimental if it covers approximately the area carrying the load, and provided there is no evidence of pileup or burning. Usual cause is normal operation of the parts.

9 *Burr*—A sharp projection or rough edge. Usual causes are excessive wear, peening, or machining operation.

10 *Chafing*—A rubbing action between parts having limited relative motion. To be interpreted as an action which produces a surface condition rather than as a description of the injury.

11 *Chipping*—Breaking out of small pieces of metal. Do not con-

FIG. 19-7 *A modern magnetic-particle testing machine—Magnaflux Testing. (Magnaflux Corporation)*

Defects shown by longitudinal field. Part magnetized in coil.

PATH OF MAGNETIZING CURRENT   MAY BE PERMANENT OR FLEXIBLE CABLE   MAGNETIC LINES OF FORCE

LONGITUDINAL CRACK WILL NOT SHOW   45° CRACK WILL SHOW   TRANSVERSE CRACK WILL SHOW

Defects shown by circular field

CURRENT   CURRENT

MAGNETIC FIELD   LONGITUDINAL CRACK WILL SHOW   CRACK AT 45° WILL SHOW   TRANSVERSE CRACK WILL NOT SHOW

FIG. 19-8 *Cracks will show best when in line with the current flow and at right angles to the magnetic field. (Magnaflux Corporation. Copyright 1941, 1952, and 1957)*

FIG. 19-9 *A crack found by using a dye penetrant will save time, money, and lives.* (Magnaflux Corporation)

fuse with flaking. Usual cause is a concentration of stress due to nicks, scratches, inclusions, peening, or careless handling of parts.

12 *Corrosion*—Breakdown of surface by chemical action. Usual cause is presence of corrosive agents.

13 *Cracks*—A partial fracture. Usual cause is excessive stress due to sudden overloading, extension of a nick or scratch, or overheating.

14 *Dent*—Small, smoothly rounded hollow in the surface. Usual causes are concentrated overloading resulting from peening, or presence of chips between loaded surfaces, or the striking of a part.

15 *Electrolytic action*—Breakdown of surfaces by electrical action between parts made of dissimilar metals. Usual cause is galvanic action between dissimilar metals.

16 *Erosion*—Carrying away of material by flow of hot gases, grit, or chemicals. See guttering. Usual causes are flow of corroding liquids, hot gases, or grit-laden oil.

17 *Fatigue failure*—Progressive yielding of one or more local areas of weakness such as tool marks, sharp indentations, minute cracks, or inclusions, under repeated stress. As working stress on the piece is repeated, cracks develop, at ends of which there are high concentrations of stress. Cracks spread, usually from the surface, or near the surface, of the area. After a time, there is so little sound metal left, the normal stress is higher than the strength of the remaining material, and it snaps. Failure is not due to crystallization of metal, as many mechanics believe. Appearance of a typical fatigue failure is easily explained. As failure proceeds, severed surfaces rub and batter each other, crushing grains of material and producing a dull or smooth appearance; the remaining unfractured portion preserves normal grain structure up to the moment of failure. The progressive nature of the failure is usually indicated by several more or less concentric lines, the center, or *focus*, of which discloses original point or line of failure. Usual causes are tool marks, sharp corners, nicks, cracks, inclusions, galling, corrosion, or insufficient tightening of studs or bolts to obtain proper stretch.

18 *Flaking*—Breaking away of pieces of a plated or painted surface. Usual causes are incomplete bonding, excessive loading, or blistering.

19 *Flowing*—Spreading of a plated or painted surface. Usually accompanied by flaking. Usual causes are incomplete bonding, excessive loading, or blistering.

20 *Fracture*—See break and chafing.

21 *Fretting corrosion*—Discoloration may occur on surfaces which are pressed or bolted together under high pressure. On steel parts the color is reddish brown and is sometimes called "cocoa" or "blood." On aluminum or magnesium, the oxide is black. Usual cause is rubbing off of fine particles of metal by slight movement between parts and subsequent oxidizing of these particles.

22 *Galling*—A transfer of metal from one surface to another. Usual cause is severe chafing or fretting action caused during engine operation by a slight relative movement of two surfaces under high contact pressure.
NOTE: Do not confuse with pickup, scoring, gouging, or scuffing.

23 *Glazing*—Development of a hard, glossy surface on bearing surfaces. An often beneficial condition. Usual cause is a combination of pressure, oil, and heat.

24 *Gouging*—Displacement of material from a surface by a cutting or tearing action. Usual cause is presence of a comparatively large foreign body between moving parts.

25 *Grooving*—Smooth, rounded furrows, such as tear marks whose sharp edges have been polished off. Usual causes are concentrated wear, abnormal relative motion of parts, or parts out of alignment.

26 *Guttering*—Deep, concentrated erosion. Usual cause is enlargement of a crack or defect by burning due to flame or hot gases.

27 *Inclusion*—Foreign material in metal. Surface inclusions are indicated by dark spots or lines. Usual cause is a discontinuity in the material.
NOTE: Both surface inclusions and those near the surface may be detected during magnetic inspection by grouping of magnetic particles. Examination of a fatigue fracture may reveal an inclusion at the focal point.

28 *Nick*—A sharp indentation caused by striking a part against another metal object. Usual causes are carelessness in handling of parts or tools prior to, or during assembly, or sand or fine foreign particles in the engine during operation.

29 *Peening*—Deformation of surface. Usual cause is impact of a foreign object such as occurs in repeated blows of a hammer on a part.

30 *Pickup*—Rolling up of metal, or transfer of metal from one surface to another. Usual causes are rubbing of two surfaces without sufficient lubrication, presence of grit between surfaces under pressure during assembly, unbroken edges of press fitted parts, or incipient seizure of rotating parts during operation.

31 *Pileup*—Displacement of particles of a surface from one point to another. Distinguished from pickup by the presence of depressions at the point from which the material has been displaced.

32 *Pitting*—Small, irregularly shaped cavities in a surface from which material has been removed by corrosion or chipping. Corrosive pitting is usually accompanied by a deposit formed by a corrosive agent on base material. Usual causes of corrosive pitting are breakdown of the surface by oxidation or some other chemical, or by electrolytic action. Usual causes of mechanical pitting are chipping of loaded surfaces because of overloading or improper clearance, or presence of foreign particles.

Blistering   Brinelling   Buckling   Burning

Burning   Chipping   Corrosion   Crack

Crack   Deformation   Erosion   Fatigue failure

Flaking   Flowing   Fracture   Fretting corrosion

FIG. 19-10 *Typical defects discoverable through visual inspection.* *(Continued on following page.)*

Galling

Gouging

Grooving

Guttering

Nick

Pickup

Pileup

Pitting

Scoring

Spalling

FIG. 19-10 *Typical defects discoverable through visual inspection (continued).*

33 *Scoring*—Deep scratches made during engine operation by sharp edges or foreign particles; elongated gouges. Usual cause is presence of chips between loaded surfaces having relative motion.

34 *Scratches*—Narrow, shallow marks caused by movement of a sharp object or particles across a surface. Usual causes are carelessness in handling of parts or tools prior to, or during, assembly, or sand or fine foreign particles in the engine during operation.

35 *Spalling*—Sharply roughened area characteristic of progressive chipping or peeling of surface material. Do not confuse with flaking. Usual causes are surface cracks, inclusions, or any similar surface injury causing a progressive breaking away of surface under load.

36 *Stresses*—When used in describing the cause of failure of machine parts, stresses are generally divided into three groups—compression, tension, and shear. These forces are described as follows:

Compression—Action of two directly opposed forces which tend to squeeze a part together.

Tension—Action of two directly opposed forces which tend to pull apart.

Shear—Action between two opposed parallel forces.

Inspection is a vital part of engine overhaul. Without a quality inspection, the other overhaul procedures are essentially meaningless.

Repair

All serviceable engine parts must be repaired using methods approved by the manufacturer. Repair techniques vary widely. Welding is used extensively and is discussed in Chap. 10. Repairs on combustion chambers and many other parts of the engine are often made this way. After welding, it may be necessary to heat treat the part in order to remove the stress induced through welding and to restore the original properties of the metal.

Other parts can be restored to their original dimensions by plating. This is also discussed in Chap. 10. Replating by electrochemical means or hard facing by plasma-sprayed coatings or by detonation flame coatings is used to build up hubs and disks, and to repair and protect parts of the engine that chafe on each other. For example, combustion-chamber outlet ducts on many engines are permitted limited movement to compensate for engine growth as the engine temperature changes. Repair methods involve operations of all kinds, including grinding, blending, and other abrasive processes, lathe work, boring, straightening, painting, etc. (Fig. 19-11). If the engine contains rivets, these are repaired or replaced as required. The bushings to be found in the accessories section and other parts of the engine are replaced if necessary. If any threaded holes are stripped, they are repaired at this time by drilling and tapping and installing a threaded bushing, an oversize stud, or a helicoil insert.

Once again, the overhaul manual gives a detailed and approved repair procedure which must be followed to assure a reasonable service life or TBO.

Reassembly

Reassembly is accomplished on the same horizontal or vertical stand that was used for disassembly. At this time all gaskets, packings, and rubber parts are replaced from fresh stock. Specific clearance and limits, for example, radial and axial position of the rotating turbine and compressor assemblies, blade-tip movement, or wear patterns on gear teeth, etc., are checked as reassembly continues.

Extreme care must be taken to prevent dirt, hardware, lockwire, or other foreign materials from entering the engine. If anything is dropped, all work must be stopped until the foreign object can be located and removed. All parts must be safetied in some manner.

Standard safetying devices include lock or safety wire, plain and specialized lock washers, cotter pins used with castellated nuts, and fiber, nylon, or metal locknuts (Fig. 19-12). Some locknuts have a deformed section at the top to achieve the locking action. Lockwire, lockwashers, and cotter pins are never reused, but locknuts can be reused if they cannot be turned all the way on by hand. Standard and special torque values can be found in the overhaul manual and must be adhered to. (See Appendix E-1 for a typical table of torque values.)

Bearings require special handling. Gloves must be worn to prevent contamination from skin oil and acid. Rubber or lint-free gloves are recommended. Carbon rubbing seals are also quite fragile and must be treated accordingly.

Synthetic lubricants can have an adverse effect on skin, and protective gloves or hand creams should be used if needed.

Accurate balancing of the rotating assemblies is most important because of the high rotational speeds involved. The two methods for determining out of balance are static and dynamic balancing. Static balancing, as the name implies, is done while the part is stationary. But it is quite possible to have a part in static balance and still experience considerable out of balance while rotating. Dynamic balancing is achieved while the assembly is rotating. Often the individual stages of the compressor and turbine are balanced separately and then rebalanced as assembled components. Other rotating parts such as shafts, couplings, etc., are also balanced.

Balancing is achieved by (see Chap. 5):

1 The addition or movement of weights riveted, pressed, or pinned, in place near the rim of the compressor or turbine rotor.

2 Balancing bolts.

3 Careful grinding or drilling in specified areas.

4 Shifting blades in the compressor. Each blade will have a coded letter or number indicating that a blade falls within a specified range of weights.

Many manufacturers will mark turbine blades with a *moment-weight* number to permit balancing during assembly. Turbine blades may also be weighed at the time of reassembly and assembled in the disk in the manner outlined.

The performance of the engine is strongly influenced by the area formed by the turbine nozzle vanes. On those engines in which the vanes are removable, the entire nozzle assembly must be built up out of vanes that will cause the turbine nozzle flow area to be within stated limits. On one model engine having fixed nozzle vanes, the nozzle area can be adjusted by bending the vanes with a special tool. The area is then checked with a gage.

MAXIMUM ALLOWABLE
REPAIR LIMITS — INCHES

BLADE AREA		STAGES 1 AND 2
	A	3/4 R
	B	1/32 RB
	C	3/8 D
	D	NONE
	E	1/4 D
	F	1/16 D

R — RADIUS   D — DEPTH
RB — ROUND BOTTOM

DAMAGE TO THE LEADING EDGE OF THE
BLADES WITHIN TWO INCHES OF THE TIP
MAY BE BLENDED TO A MAXIMUM DEPTH OF
⅝ INCH FOR A MAXIMUM OF SEVEN BLADES
PER ENGINE.

THESE DIMENSIONS
CONTROLLED BY
DEPTH LIMIT

AREA C

CROSS SECTION OF
FAN BLADE ABOVE
PART SPAN SHROUD

THESE DIMENSIONS
CONTROLLED BY
DEPTH LIMIT

AREA E

CROSS SECTION OF
FAN BLADE BELOW
PART SPAN SHROUD

{ CAUTION }

THE LIMITS REFERRED TO IN THIS FIGURE IN
AREAS "C", "E" AND "F" PERTAIN TO LOCAL,
ISOLATED, DAMAGED AREAS ONLY AND
MUST NOT BE INTERPRETED AS AUTHORITY
FOR REMOVAL OF MATERIAL ALL ACROSS THE
TIP AND LEADING OR TRAILING EDGES AS
MIGHT BE DONE IN A SINGLE MACHINING
CUT.

FIG. 19-11 *Typical repair-section illustration showing repair limits for the JT3D fan blades.*

1. LOCKWIRE HOLES PARALLEL 2. INSERTING WIRE 3. BENDING WIRE AROUND BOLT 4. TWISTING WIRE 5. PULLING WIRE

6. BENDING WIRE AROUND BOLT 7. TWISTING WIRE 8. BENDING TWISTED WIRE 9. CUTTING EXCESS WIRE

(a)

(b)

FIG. 19-12 (a) *Steps in applying safety wire.* (b) *Typical safety wire patterns.*

Instructions for all phases of reassembly are set forth in the overhaul manual.

Testing

To ensure that the engine's performance meets that guaranteed to the customer, all engines are test run to an established schedule before being shipped, stored, or used in an aircraft. Fuel and oil consumption is checked, pressure and temperature measurements are taken at several points, and thrust or horsepower is accurately measured. A more detailed discussion of engine testing will be found in Chap. 18.

Storage

The degree of preservation is determined by the anticipated length of time the engine is expected to be inactive. In order to protect the engine for long term storage (usually three months or more), the following items are usually accomplished (Fig. 19-13):

1 All external openings in the engine are sealed with plugs and cover plates.
2 A dehydrating agent, usually bags of silica gel (Mil-D-3464), is placed in the engine inlet and exhaust duct.
3 The oil system is drained, and may or may not be flushed with a preservative oil (Mil-C-8188).
4 The fuel system is drained and flushed with the preservative oil by motoring the engine.

5 Some manufacturers recommend spraying oil into the compressor and turbine ends while motoring the engine, whereas others specifically caution against this practice on the grounds that dirt particles collecting on the blades will alter the airfoil shape and adversely affect compressor efficiency.
6 The engine is placed in a metal shipping container, and several bags of the dessicant are placed in a wire basket located within the shipping can. The container is then sealed and pressurized with approximately 5 psi of dry air or nitrogen to exclude moisture. An observation port in the can allows an internal humidity indicator to be seen. A safe humidity level is indicated by a blue color. The unsafe color is pink.
7 If a shipping can is not used, the engine is generally wrapped in a protective vapor-proof storage bag made of foil, cloth, and plastic, and carefully sealed against moisture.

MAINTENANCE

Maintenance practices for gas turbine engines differ little from those used on reciprocating engines. It is important to see that the engine compartment be kept as clean as possible because the high-velocity airflow through the engine will tend to draw any foreign objects into the compressor. All small parts, such as loose lockwire, nuts, bolts, etc., should be removed immediately.

The exterior of the engine should be inspected to see that all parts of the engine are secure and that there are no broken safety wires. Tubing should be checked for security, nicks, chafing, dents, and leaks. Controls should be checked for proper operation to ensure that they do not bind and that there is cushion in the flight deck controls. *Cushion* is obtained when the control lever on the unit hits its stop before the control lever in the cabin hits its stop.

Inspection of the gas turbine engine is made somewhat easier than that of a reciprocating engine because of the gas turbine's inherent cleanliness and the ready accessibility of many parts to visual inspection. The first several stages of most compressors can be inspected for cracks with the aid of a strong light. Also readily open to visual inspection for heat damage is the exhaust duct and the last stage or two of the turbine. The thermocouples and pressure probes are also available for inspection in this area, and in the case of the thermocouples, can be checked electrically and operationally with the proper equipment.

The oil system should be checked daily for proper oil level. It is recommended that different brands of oil are not mixed when adding or changing oil. Oil filters are cleaned and fuel filters are replaced periodically. Since the engine fuel pumping elements are lubricated by the fuel itself, water or ice in the fuel may damage the fuel-system components and cause erratic engine operation. Therefore, the aircraft's fuel sumps should be checked daily for water. On those engines equipped with magnetic chip detectors, there should be no continuity through the detector. If continuity is

1	SERVICE RECEPTACLE COVER	7	HUMIDITY INDICATOR
2	AIR RELEASE VALVE	8	CONTAINER LIFTING POINTS
3	SERVICE RECEPTACLE	9	PINS, WASHERS, AND COTTER PINS
4	DESICCANT	10	CONTAINER GASKET
5	RECORD RECEPTACLE		
6	CONTAINER LOCATING PIN		

FIG. 19-13 *Typical gas turbine shipping can.*

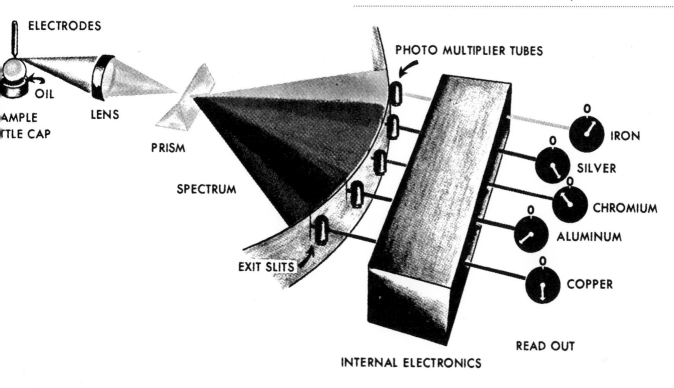

ELECTRODES

OIL

SAMPLE
BOTTLE CAP

LENS

PRISM

SPECTRUM

EXIT SLITS

PHOTO MULTIPLIER TUBES

IRON

SILVER

CHROMIUM

ALUMINUM

COPPER

READ OUT

INTERNAL ELECTRONICS

FIG. 19-14 *Spectrometric oil analysis.*

found, the chip detector must be removed, and the source of metal contamination determined. Spectrometric oil analysis is proving to be a reliable aid to preventing in-flight power-plant failures. In this process, periodic samples of used oil are taken and sent to an oil-analysis laboratory where the oil is burned by an electric arc. The light emitted is passed through a slit which is precisely positioned to the wavelength for the particular wear metal being monitored. Trends are observed and abnormal concentrations of metal are sought (Fig. 19-14).

An additional daily check should be made during coastdown after engine shutdown. Coastdown should be accomplished with no rubbing or abnormal noises. Some manufacturers will give a specific coastdown time.

Proper maintenance and overhaul are essential to safe, efficient operation, and reasonable service life.

REVIEW AND STUDY QUESTIONS

1 Who determines the time between overhauls? What factors are taken into consideration in determining the TBO?

2 What is meant by a hot-section inspection?

3 Why is it necessary to mark gas turbine parts? List some temporary and permanent marking methods.

4 List the seven steps in the overhaul of any gas turbine engine.

5 What is contained in the overhaul manual that makes it so important to the overhaul process?

6 Briefly outline the disassembly process.

7 What disposition is made of all seals except the carbon rubbing types?

8 Why must engine parts be cleaned?

9 List some cleaning materials and processes for cleaning the cold section of the engine; the hot section. What protective measures should be taken while using some kinds of cleaning solutions?

10 What special precautions must be observed when cleaning and handling gas turbine bearings?

11 List some nondimensional inspection methods; dimensional inspection methods.

12 Describe the magnetic-particle inspection process; the dye-penetrant inspection process.

13 Make a list of some of the major conditions to be found by visual inspection. List the causes of these conditions.

14 Briefly discuss several methods of repair to gas turbine parts.

15 What is the purpose of safetying? List some safetying devices.

16 What precautions must be observed when working with synthetic lubricants?

17 What is meant by static and dynamic balance? How are rotating parts of the gas turbine balanced?

18 What marking systems are used to denote turbine blade weights?

19 What influence does the nozzle area have on engine performance?   How is the nozzle area adjusted?

20 Briefly describe the tests performed on a gas turbine engine.

21 Describe the steps required to place an engine in storage.

22 What is the relationship between engine maintenance and engine cleanliness?

23 In what ways is the inspection of a gas turbine engine easier than that of a reciprocating engine?

24 Briefly describe some of the jobs to do when maintaining the gas turbine engine.

25 What is spectrometric oil analysis?   How is this process used in the maintenance of the gas turbine engine?

PART 5

Modern engines

Chapter 20

Pratt & Whitney JT3D

The limited nature of this book does not allow a comprehensive treatment of all of the current gas turbine engines in use today. As a result, several engines which have gained wide use in either civil or military aircraft, have been selected for a somewhat more detailed examination of their construction. The Pratt & Whitney JT3D engine is shown in Fig. 20-1.

SPECIFICATIONS

Number of compressor stages:	15
Number of turbine stages:	4
Number of combustors:	8
Maximum power at sea level:	17,000 lb
Specific fuel consumption at maximum power:	0.52
Compression ratio at maximum rpm:	13:1
Maximum diameter:	53 in.
Maximum length:	134 in. (approx.)
Maximum dry weight:	4150 lb (approx.)

The JT3D is an axial-flow turbofan engine having a 15-stage split compressor, an 8-can can-annular combustion chamber, and a 4-stage split turbine. Several models are available, differing only in minor details. In this engine the first two front-fan compressor stages are considerably larger than the remaining compressor stages. The fan provides two separate airstreams. (See Fig. 2-15.) The primary, or inner, airstream travels through the engine to generate pressures in the exhaust nozzle and thereby provide the propulsive force. The secondary, or outer, airstream is mechanically compressed by the fan and is ducted to the outside of the engine a short distance from the fan. This secondary airstream adds to the propulsive force and increases the propulsive efficiency, a process which is described in more detail in Chap. 3. Although the fan has the effect of a geared propeller, it is attached to and driven at the same speed as the front compressor.

OPERATION (Fig. 20-2)

The air enters the engine through the compressor inlet case assembly. The airframe inlet duct is attached to the front of the inlet case. This inlet case assembly is provided with vane-type multipurpose struts which transmit number 1 bearing loads to the outer case structure, conduct anti-icing air and lubricating oil to the inner diameter of the engine, and direct air to the front-compressor section.

The compressor section is of the split type and consists of two rotor assemblies. Each rotor assembly is driven by an independent turbine, and each rotor is free to rotate at its best speed. Since it is necessary to rotate only one of these units during the starting operation, the selection of the small (rear) compressor permits the use of a smaller starter.

Primary air from the inlet case enters the front compressor, which consists of eight rotor stages and seven vane stages. The gas path of this compressor has a constant inside diameter and a decreasing outside diameter. This compressor is the larger of the two, and provides the initial compression of air. The rotating parts are connected by a drive shaft which passes through the inside of the rear-compressor rotor and drive shaft to the second-, third-, and fourth-stage turbines.

Between the front and rear compressors (and around the rear-compressor rotor and case) is the intermediate case. It has an automatic arrangement for bleeding front-compressor air. This is to improve the acceleration characteristics of the engine. (See Chap. 5.) The inlet vanes (9th stage) transmit number 2 and number 3 bearing loads to the outer case, conduct supply and return oil to bearings, and direct the compressed air from the front compressor to the rear compressor.

The rear compressor has 7 rotor stages (10 through 16) and 6 vane stages (10 through 15). It has a constant outside diameter and an increasing inside diameter, and is driven by the first-stage turbine through an independent shaft concentric with the front-compressor drive shaft. Just aft of the rear compressor is the diffusor case.

Compressor exit guide vanes (16th stage) at the front of the diffuser case straighten the air which is then expanded for entry into the combustion chambers. Struts in the case transmit the number 4 and number 5 bearing loads to the outer portion of the case. Also, these struts conduct bearing oil pressure and suction lines and provide high-pressure air for such engine functions as anti-icing. They also provide a source of clean air for aircraft pressure needs. On engines so equipped, the water injection manifold is mounted on the front flange. The water is dispersed through 16 curled tubes mounted on the periphery of the diffuser case, through mating holes in the case and injected into the airstream. The outside contours of the com-

FIG. 20-1 *The Pratt & Whitney JT3D turbofan engine.*

pressor and diffuser sections give the engine its "wasp waist" and at the same time provide a convenient location for the accessory section.

The fuel manifold, which consists of eight circular clusters of six fuel nozzles, is located in the diffuser case annulus and injects the fuel into the airstream in governed proportions. At this point, the air is channeled into eight portions for burning with the fuel in the eight combustion chambers.

The combustion section consists of eight separate cans arranged annularly. These chambers are connected by crossover tubes. The compressed air, its velocity increased, and with fuel injected, is lighted by spark igniters installed in two bottom combustion chambers. After lightup, the flame is perpetuated by the construction of the combustion chamber and the heat generated by previous combustion. The exhaust gases pass through the combustion-chamber outlet duct into the turbine nozzle case.

The turbine nozzle case houses the front stages of

FIG. 20-2 *Typical JT3D turbofan engine gas flow.*

the four-stage turbine and is aft of the combustion section. The first stage drives the rear compressor, and the second, third, and fourth stages drive the front compressor. The turbine nozzle case also contains the four turbine exhaust nozzles. The nozzles are made up of a series of stationary vanes which direct the exhaust gases through the turbine blades and into the turbine exhaust case.

To the rear of the turbine nozzle case is the turbine exhaust case which houses the fourth-stage turbine disk and blades and through which the exhaust gases are ejected from the engine. The turbine exhaust case also supports the number 6 bearing and the number 6 bearing oil sump.

FRONT ACCESSORY SECTION (Fig. 20-3)

The front accessory section consists of one assembly and related parts, the front accessory drive support. The case of this assembly is made of magnesium. Sixteen nuts secure the front accessory support to the number 1 bearing support. The front accessory support has two mount pads on its front face. Only one is used. This is the mounting and drive for the compressor bleed-valve control. The other opening has provisions for mounting and driving a tachometer.

The number 1 bearing scavenge pump is mounted

FIG. 20-3 *Front accessories section (some models) showing (**1**) tachometer drive pad, (**2**) compressor bleed control mounting pad, and (**3**) oil scavenge pump area.*

on the lower rear face of the support. Air and oil for the bleed control are brought out of the number 1 bearing support and tubed to the control. The front accessory drive gear, which is externally splined, is inserted, with an O-ring seal around it, into the front compressor front hub engaging the internal spline in the hub. It is retained by the same nut that holds the number 1 bearing inner race in position. The front accessory drive gear meshes with and drives the tachometer drive gear, the number 1 bearing scavenge pump drive gear, and the compressor bleed-control drive gear.

NUMBER 1 BEARING SUPPORTS AND INLET CASE ASSEMBLY

These assemblies are discussed together since the supports are mounted in the inner diameter of the inlet case assembly, the vanes of which carry the structural load of the number 1 bearing (front compressor front) from the inner shroud to the outer shroud.

The inlet case assembly consists of 23 (or 28) hollow vanes incorporating foam-rubber stiffeners in the center bays, that are welded between hollow, double-walled titanium inner and outer shrouds. Each vane extends from the inner wall of the inner shroud to the outer wall of each shroud. There are holes in the side walls of the vanes that are between the shroud walls, and this forms a passage for the flow of anti-icing air. The left and right anti-icing tubes feed heated air, when desired, into the case and vane assembly, then forward into the inlet case.

Some of the vanes have tubes inside. These are for oil, breather, and bleed-valve control air lines. The number 1 bearing oil pressure and oil return tubes are located in the seven o'clock and five o'clock struts, respectively. The purpose of these vanes is to cause the air to enter the compressor rotor blades at the best angle for best compressor operation and to transport the structural load as discussed above.

The inner shroud, being of double-wall construction, provides for the passage of anti-icing air that has flowed inward through the guide vanes. The oil and air tubes that pass through the vanes have fittings mounted on the inner wall of the inner shroud.

On the front edge of the inner shroud, holes are drilled and tapped to hold the bolts that secure the number 1 bearing front support and the compressor inlet airseal assembly. The number 1 bearing housing holds the number 1 bearing outer race and rollers in its inside diameter. The front accessory front support is bolted to its forward face. Anti-icing air outlet holes are also on the front edge of the shrouds. The number 1 bearing rear support, the inner section of which houses the number 1 bearing oil seal, is bolted at its outer diameter to the compressor inlet vane inner-shroud rear flange.

The outer shroud, being also of double-wall construction, provides for the passage of anti-icing air. The outer wall of the outer shroud forms the support for the outer fittings of the tubes that pass through some of the vanes. A pressure probe fitting passes through both walls of the shroud to protrude into the airstream between the vanes. They are bolted to the outer walls.

The front rim of the outer shroud is drilled and tapped to receive the bolts which will hold the airframe air inlet duct. The rear rim of the outer shroud is drilled and tapped to receive the bolts that hold the shroud to the front-compressor case.

THE FRONT COMPRESSOR (*Fig. 20-4*)

The front compressor, which is housed in the front-compressor front case (and vane assembly) and rear case, consists of a rotor composed of eight rows of blades, with stators made up of seven rows of vane and shroud assemblies located between successive stages of blades. There is no second-stage stator, numbered as such, and there is no third-stage row of blades, designated as such. The first two rows of blades are considerably larger than the rest and are referred to as *fan* blades.

The airstream is separated into primary and secondary streams. The separation is achieved with the use of a spacer between the second- and fourth-stage blades. The primary airstream is directed internally by the third-stage stator while the secondary airstream is exhausted through the exit struts of the fan discharge case. The numbering of the blade stages from front to rear is 1, 2, and 4 through 9, and the numbering of the stator stages is 1 and 3 through 8. The ninth-stage stator vanes are incorporated in the intermediate case and will be discussed later.

The third-stage vane and shroud assembly is of single-piece construction, whereas the fourth through eighth stage are of the split type. The spacers of the fourth through eighth stage are integral on most models. The inner shrouds form a seal ring for the two airseals on the outer diameter of each rotor disk spacer.

The compressor is driven by a shaft from the second-, third-, and fourth-stage turbines. Its rotational speed is roughly two-thirds the speed of the rear or high-speed compressor. It provides the initial compression to the air that passes through the engine and transmits this air to the rear or high-speed compressor. The stator vanes and rotor blades diminish in size and increase in quantity from the front to the rear of the compressor. This matches the decreasing volume of the air as the pressure of the air rises.

The front accessories are driven by a gear attached to the front hub of the front-compressor rotor. The rear hub of the front compressor contains the front-compressor drive turbine shaft coupling.

The rear hub of the front-compressor rotor is supported by a double ball bearing (number 2). The two halves of the number 2 bearing (front compressor rear) are separated by an oil baffle in which drilled holes direct oil to the forward and aft sections of the double bearing. The number 3 bearing (rear compressor front) inner race and rollers are mounted on the end of the rear hub. An oil seal on the rear end seals the bearing compartment from the engine airstream.

On the front hub, the rotor is supported by a roller bearing (number 1), the liner of which is in the number 1 bearing front support. An oil seal on the front end seals the bearing compartment from the engine airstream. The bearing support is secured to the inlet case assembly.

FRONT-COMPRESSOR CASES

There are three front-compressor cases, namely: the front-compressor case and vane assembly, the fan discharge case assembly, and the front-compressor rear case assembly. These will be discussed individually below. The front-compressor cases carry the structural load of the front of the engine. These cases decrease in diameter from front to rear to match the decreasing diameters of the stator rings. The front-compressor case and vane assembly and the fan discharge case are part of the front-compressor rotor and case assembly.

FRONT-COMPRESSOR CASE AND VANE ASSEMBLY

The front-compressor case and vane assembly attaches to the rear flange of the compressor inlet case and the front flange of the fan discharge case. In the approximate center of the case, riveted to internal flanges are 55 (or 38) titanium first-stage stator vanes. At the titanium inner shroud of the vanes, a steel first-stage air-sealing ring is riveted. From the forward internal flange to the inlet case, a front airflow duct is inserted. Anti-icing air comes into the case through the reinforced openings and the outer wall, circulates, and flows forward into the inlet case. From the rearward internal flange to the fan discharge case forward flange, a rear airflow duct is inserted.

FAN DISCHARGE CASE ASSEMBLY

Attached to the rear flange of the front-compressor case and vane assembly by bolts and pinned to the rear airflow duct, previously discussed, is the fan discharge case. This case is constructed of stainless steel and consists of an outer shroud and an inner case with 38 steel ducts between them. The struts are secured in the inner case by a riveted locking plate at the rearward end and wired to the fairing retaining screws at the forward end.

FRONT COMPRESSOR

COMPRESSOR INLET CASE

FIRST STAGE BLADES (FAN)

FRONT COMPRESSOR EXIT VANES

4TH STAGE VANES

FRONT COMPRESSOR ROTOR

SECOND STAGE BLADES (FAN)

FRONT COMPRESSOR FRONT CASE

FRONT COMPRESSOR REAR CASE

ANTI-ICING AIR VALVE & ACTUATOR

FIG. 20-4 *Front-compressor section.*

FRONT-COMPRESSOR ROTOR AND CASE ASSEMBLY *(Fig. 20-5)*

The front-compressor rotor and case assembly consists of the front-compressor rotor, as described below, assembled to include the front-compressor case and vane assembly, the airflow ducts, the fan discharge case, and the third-stage vane and shroud assembly.

FRONT-COMPRESSOR ROTOR

The front-compressor rotor consists of 2 hubs, 7 disks, 7 spacer assemblies, 8 rows of blades, 2 sets (16 each) of tierods and associated hardware. Each row of blades is inserted into undercut slots in its disk. They are held in place by locks inserted under the blades and bent to secure. The blades do not have a tight fit, but rather are seated by centrifugal force during engine operation. The front hub forms the disk for the first row of blades, but the rear hub is a separate unit that is held fast to the rear face of the seventh-stage disk, or, on some models, to the forward face of the eighth-stage disk, by the tiebolts. The spacers between the disks are internally reinforced with tubes. The tiebolts run through these tubes and through the disks. These spacers have 2 knife-edges on their outside diameter, which run against the seal platforms on the stator vane inner shroud which was previously described. The exception to the above is the large spacer between the second- and fourth-stage compressor blades. This serves as a means of joining the fan section to the remainder of the compressor, and in so doing provides the needed space in that area. Each disk has 24 holes in its flange: 16 are for tierods and 8 are for balancing weights when needed. The front hub has 2 lips on its forward face and the second-stage disk has a similar lip on its rearward face to which balance weights can be added as required. The entire assembly is held together by the 2 sets of tiebolts. The smaller set holds the first 2 stages of blades together, while the longer set

FIG. 20-5 *Front-compressor case, vane assembly, and rotor.*

holds the third through eighth stages together. Both sections are joined together by the spacer, as previously mentioned. The rotor blades decrease in size from front to rear. The first 2 stages of blades (fan) are considerably larger than the rest. The angle of each row of blades is set to give the best efficiency at operating speed. The rear hub flange has large holes to allow some ninth-stage air into the compressor rotor. This air serves a dual purpose of providing bearing seal pressurizing and cooling. The front hub and the disks of the front-compressor rotor are titanium or steel. Most rear hubs are steel. The blades of the first 2 stages of all models are titanium. The remaining stages are of steel or titanium, depending on the engine model.

COMPRESSOR INTERMEDIATE SECTION
(Fig. 20-6)

The forward mounting points are on the compressor intermediate case which is attached to the rear flange of the front-compressor case. A locating pin is used at top center between the two flanges. The intermediate case surrounds the rear compressor, but is not considered as part of it. It serves to separate the low-pressure front compressor from the high-pressure rear compressor and serves a structural function of joining the external cases. The intermediate case is of steel construction and has a double wall on the forward end. Guide vanes are welded from the outer wall, through

FIG. 20-6 *Compressor intermediate case.*

the inner wall, and extended into a shroud ring. The double-mounting lugs are machined from rings. The case is welded to the rings. The front flange of the case is drilled and tapped for bolts that attach it to the front-compressor case, and the rear flange is drilled.

An oil breather pad is located between the mounting flanges at approximately the two o'clock position. An oil tube fitting is at the six o'clock position between the mounting flanges. Toward the rear of the case a hole is provided for air bleeding and the air-bleed valve mounting. The 30 vanes that are on the inside front of the case serve as air inlet guide vanes to the rear compressor. They are hollow steel vanes with openings in their side walls at the outer end. These openings, together with the double wall of the case, form the breather passage from the upper breather connections on the case to the lower opening. The lower opening connects directly to the main accessory case. Breather and oil tubes for the bearings located in the center of the case are through the hollow guide vanes. On many engines the inlet vanes are welded to the number 2 bearing front support whose outer configuration is shaped to form an inner-shroud ring for these vanes. At the front (inner) and rear (outer) ends of this support, bolt circles are provided to receive bolts to hold the diagonal and rear bearing supports. On one model the number 2 bearing front support is held in place with bolts. A hollow tubular seal is used at the rear (outer) bolt circle. On some model engines, the center support is part of the number 2 bearing housing. On others, the center support is separate.

On some engines, in order to reduce absorption of heat by engine oil, heat shielding and thermal-blanket insulation is provided for the number 2 bearing compartment. The bolts that secure the compressor intermediate front bearing housing to the rear face of the front bearing inner support also secure the compressor intermediate front bearing front heat shield to the front face of the support.

The compressor intermediate rear bearing heat shield consists of a front and rear heat shield, both of which are secured together and in turn are secured as a unit to the rear face at the inner bolt circle and outer bolt circle of the compressor intermediate bearing rear support.

The thermal-blanket insulation is contained within the heat shield.

The rear support holds the number 3 bearing seal assembly and the rear of the number 2 bearing housing and is bolted to the rear of the center support and the vane inner shroud. A stepped-edge seal ring is bolted to the support at the outer diameter of the rear support plate. This ring, together with its mating knife-edge seal minimizes air leakage out of the front end of the rear compressor. The area inside the ring and behind the rear support plate is exposed to high-pressure air extracted from the 12th stage of compression. The air pressure outside the seal ring is from the ninth stage.

FRONT-COMPRESSOR REAR CASE ASSEMBLY

Attached to the rear innermost flange of the fan discharge case and to the forward flange of the intermediate case is the front-compressor rear case assembly. The front-compressor rear case assembly is of welded construction. Welded to it internally are the supports for the vane and shroud assemblies. A center external flange serves as a reinforcement and is also used to support the brackets that carry external items.

FRONT-COMPRESSOR VANE AND SHROUD ASSEMBLIES

The first-stage stator vanes were discussed under the front-compressor case and vane assembly. There is no second-stage stator. The third- and fourth-stage rows or stators are made of aluminum except the fourth stage of one model engine, which is steel. The fifth through eighth stator vanes are made of stainless steel and are welded into steel shroud rings. The stators are pinned to inner shrouds to which are riveted inner airseal platforms. The third-stage stator vanes and shroud are built into a single circular assembly which is held stationary by a flange inserted between the fan discharge case and front-compressor rear flanges. The fourth- through eighth- stage stator vanes and shrouds are split and are prevented from rotating by being pinned to each other and to the third-stage vane and shroud. When assembled, the rings are held in the engine by shoulders on the inside of the front-compressor rear case.

The angle at which the vanes are mounted in the shrouds is set to feed air into the following row of rotor blades to give the best compressor efficiency at operating speed. Stator vanes decrease in size from front to rear to match the decreasing volume of air and the decreasing size of the rotor blades.

REAR COMPRESSOR (*Fig. 20-7*)

The rear, or high, compressor is driven by a hollow shaft from the first-stage turbine. Its function is to compress further the air delivered by the front compressor and then feed this air into the diffuser case and burners.

The rear compressor consists of a stator having 6 rows of vanes (stages 10 through 15) and a rotor having 7 rows of blades, stages 10 through 16. The exit guide vanes, stage 16, are mounted in the diffuser section. In function, these are part of the compressor, but because of their structural location, we will discuss them under the diffuser.

REAR-COMPRESSOR VANE AND SHROUD ASSEMBLIES

There are six vane and shroud assemblies in the rear compressor. The vanes reduce in height from front to rear of the compressor. The outer-side diameter of the air passage formed by these assemblies is constant; the decreasing size of the vanes is accomplished by increasing the diameter of the inner shroud rings. The vanes are steel and are brazed to the inner shroud and pierced through the outer shrouds. On some engines the 10th- through 14th-stage vane and shroud assemblies and the spacers separating the assemblies are integral. The 15th stage does not provide spacing. However, this is furnished by the 16th stage located in the diffuser case. Between each shroud, dowel pins are used to lock the series of shrouds together. The rear shroud is pinned to the outer shroud to prevent rotation. An edge of each spacer rests against a case shoulder to center the assembly.

AIRSEALS

The inside shroud of each row of vanes has a steel ring, with a small step on its inside face, riveted to it. Two knife-edge seals on each rotor spacer ride free of the steps forming an airseal between the compressor stages.

REAR-COMPRESSOR ROTOR (*Fig. 20-8*)

The rear-compressor rotor has 7 rows of blades on disks; 2 hubs, 6 spacer assemblies, and 16 tierods with nuts and washers. A knife-edge seal ring is riveted to a lip on the forward face of the 10th-stage disk. This seal ring rides free of the platformed seal which was referred to in the compressor intermediate case discussion. Each row of blades is inserted into undercut slots in its disk. They are held in place by locks inserted under the blades and bent to secure. The blades do not have a tight fit, but rather are seated by centrifugal force during engine operation.

Every disk has 32 holes in its flange: 16 are for tiebolts, and 16 are for balancing weights when needed. The entire assembly is held together by tiebolt heads on one end and a nut and washer on the other end.

The spacers between the disks are internally reinforced with tubes. The tiebolts run through the tubes and the spacer internal flanges as well as the disk flanges.

Neither the front nor rear hub is integral with a disk.

REAR COMPRESSOR

FIG. 20-7   *Rear-compressor section.*

FIG. 20-8 *Rear-compressor rotor showing (1) front hub, (2) spacer assembly, and (3) rear hub.*

On some models, the front hub is attached to the front face of the 12th-stage disk and the rear hub to the rear face of the 16th-stage disk. On others, the front hub is attached to the rear of the 11th-stage disk and the rear hub to the rear face of the 16th-stage disk. The hubs are secured to the rotor assembly by the steel tiebolts mentioned above. A steel tube runs from one hub to the other inside the rotor.

The tube is a force fit into the inside diameter of both hubs and permits breathing within its inside and keeps 12th-stage pressure air from the number 3 and number 4½ bearings.

The front seal was mentioned previously. If required, a balance weight may be riveted to it.

The third spacer from the front has holes drilled in it. Through these holes 12th-stage air is bled into the rotor center where it is bled through holes in the front hub. The air is directed forward to the space just behind the number 3 bearing rear support plate and pressurizes the number 3 bearing oil seal. Since there are no holes in the rear hub disk, the pressure of the air against this disk counteracts part of the rotor forward thrust.

The rear compressor case carries no structural bearing loads and is thus made of relatively thin sheet metal. Its purpose is to hold the stator parts of the compressor and act as an air separator. The air pressure increases from front to rear and finally becomes 16th-stage pressure. Between this case and the intermediate case which envelops it, the pressure is ninth-stage air. The case has a flange at its rear end to which the screws that attach the case to the diffuser section are secured. Also, bolt holes are provided to hold the immediate intermediate case to the diffuser section.

DIFFUSER CASE *(Figs. 20-9 and 20-10)*

The velocity of the air as it leaves the rear compressor is very high. This motion is both rearward and tangential around the engine. Exit guide vanes at the forward end of the diffuser case convert the tangential whirl into pressure energy. After the vanes, the high-pressure air will have a large rearward velocity. The gradual increasing area of the airflow passages provided by the diffuser case configuration decreases the airflow velocity to a suitable burning speed and increases the pressure.

The diffuser case shown in Fig. 20-10 is of welded corrosion- and heat-resistant steel construction with drilled flanges at both ends for bolting to the rear compressor and intermediate cases in the front and the combustion-chamber case in the rear.

The pad at the top center of the case is used for a breather connection. This leads to the bearing area through a strut. Airbleed outlet pads are on the outside of the case. An opening with mounting bosses at the bottom of the case provides for the angled accessory drives system and the accessory drive adapter which transmits high rotor motivation to the accessory drives gearbox assembly. The rearmost pad at the bottom center of the diffuser case is for mounting the fuel pressurizing and dump valve, which is attached outside the case. The fuel manifolds attach to the inside of the case at this pad. The fuel manifold inlet distributor which connects to the fuel pressurizing and dump valve passes through a hole in the case at this location.

Two forward-facing and one rearward-facing bolt rings are mounted on the struts from the outer case. Sheet metal between these bolt rings and on the inside and outer case add to the strength and form the gradually increasing cross section of the diffuser. A slightly tapered diffuser inner inlet duct is bolted between an inside flange on the inlet guide vane inner shroud and the outer, forward-facing, bolt circle inside the diffuser case. This piece forms a part of the diffuser ducting. The rivet circle that holds the diffuser inner inlet duct to the inlet vane ring extends forward to ride over two knife-edges that are on the rear disk of the rear compressor. This forms the airseal between the rear compressor and the bearing housing area at the center of the diffuser case. The outer shroud flange is clamped between the diffuser case and the rear compressor case when these units are assembled.

The optional water injection nozzles used on some engines are mounted around the periphery of the diffuser case. The nozzles permit the entry of water into the highly compressed airstream, thereby increasing its density and lowering its temperature prior to injection of the fuel from the fuel nozzle.

DIFFUSER

Gas generator — piston of a gas turbine engine

COMPRESSOR EXIT GUIDE VANES

COMBUSTION CHAMBER

NO. 4 BEARING

ACCESSORY DRIVE GEAR

DIFFUSER CASE

FUEL NOZZLE

FIG. 20-9 *Diffuser section.*

FIG. 20-10 *Diffuser case.*

NUMBER 4 AND NUMBER 5 BEARING OIL SUCTION PUMP

The number 4 and number 5 bearing oil suction pump and the accessory drive gears are in the lower rear of the diffuser.

BRACKETS

A quantity of brackets are attached to the external bolt circles for mounting external tubing and units.

FUEL MANIFOLD ATTACHMENT

As viewed from the rear, 16 brackets are welded to the inner structure of the diffuser. These brackets, and brackets that are welded to the inside rear of the diffuser outer case, support the fuel manifold.

FUEL MANIFOLD (Fig. 20-11)

The fuel manifold is split at the inner flange and between the number 1 and 8 clusters. The manifold

WATER INJECTION MANIFOLD (optional, on some models)

The water injection manifold is the split type which is mounted on the diffuser case front flange. The water is dispersed through the 16 curled tubes mounted on the periphery of the diffuser case. The elbows of the tubes are aligned to the 16 holes in the diffuser case. Water is metered from the water injection control through a supply tube to the tee fitting on the diffuser case front flange. Water then flows through the manifold into the airstream in the diffuser case.

NUMBER 4 BEARING HOUSING

The number 4 bearing is in the diffuser section. This supports the rear-compressor rear hub. The bearing housing and its seal are fastened to the forward-facing inner bolt ring with studs and nuts. A synthetic rubber gasket is used just inside of the stud circle.

The number 4 bearing housing has a heat-shield assembly bolted to it. The compressor rear bearing heat-shield assembly consists of several individual heat shields welded together. The complete unit is bolted to the compressor rear bearing housing and extends over the bearing housing, the breather tube, and the oil-pressure and scavenge tubes and along the tower shaft.

The thermal-blanket insulation is contained within the heat shield.

FIG. 20-11 *Fuel manifold.*

assembly consists of a primary and secondary fuel manifold and eight clusters of fuel nozzles. There are six fuel nozzles in each cluster. The fuel manifold incorporates mounting lugs in the inner and outer diameter which are secured to the rear face of the diffuser case. Eight combustion-chamber positioning brackets are mounted on the outer-diameter mounting lug locations.

FUEL NOZZLES *(See Fig. 12-26.)*

There are 24 nozzles mounted in each manifold, making a total of 48 per engine. There are two fuel outlets in each nozzle, a small center hole and a ring around the center hole. The ring sprays secondary fuel. This is done so that the small fuel flow that is used in idling will be broken up into a fine spray by being forced through a small outlet. The relatively larger outlet formed by the ring will generate a fine spray on the large flow of secondary fuel. Two screens are mounted in the rear of each nozzle, one for primary fuel and the other for secondary fuel. The primary screen is a small cylindrical type, whereas the secondary is a flat round type. Transfer of fuel from the tubes in the nozzle clusters is done by the nozzle body which contains internal passages that connect the nozzle center passage to the outer fuel tube and the nozzle outer passage to the inner fuel tube. Fuel nozzle seals, held under each nozzle, prevent leakage between passages and leakage to exterior. Each nozzle is held in place in the cluster by a threaded nozzle cap and a tab washer. There are holes around the nozzle cap wall to admit air for cooling and to aid in fuel vaporization.

Fuel is supplied to the primary and secondary orifices through separate manifold paths. The nozzle may be operated with spray from the primary orifice or with spray from both primary and secondary orifices as is the case at higher fuel flow. When both orifices are delivering fuel, their output is blended into a single spray.

The dual orifice nozzles are designed to discharge a predetermined amount of fuel when specified pressure heads are maintained across the primary and secondary stages. Extremely accurate calibration of each fuel nozzle minimizes flow variations between nozzles. Since the nozzle acts both as an atomizing and as a metering device, each nozzle must deliver a uniform spray pattern free from streaks and with an angle of spray which is held within close tolerances.

COMBUSTION SECTION *(Fig. 20-12)*

The combustion-chamber outer case is secured at the front flange to the rear flange of the diffuser case and at the rear flange to the turbine nozzle case. Eight combustion chambers, often called burner cans, the com-

bustion-chamber inner case, the number 5 bearing support, and the number 5 bearing housing are located inside the combustion-chamber outer cases.

COMBUSTION-CHAMBER OUTER CASES

There are two combustion-chamber outer cases, the front and the rear. They are constructed of corrosion- and heat-resistant steel. The front flange of the combustion-chamber outer front case is bolted to the rear flange of the diffuser case. The front flange of the combustion-chamber outer rear case is bolted to the rear flange of the outer front case and to the front flange of the turbine nozzle case. The outer rear-case rear flange is internal. It lies behind the forward external flange of the turbine nozzle case and bolts to it. Thus, the outer cases (if bolted together) or the rear outer case can be slid rearward over the turbine nozzle case to give access to the combustion chambers. The outer front case has interlocking lips on its flanges to provide sealing when joined.

COMBUSTION CHAMBERS *(Fig. 20-13)*

The combustion chambers are radially housed inside the combustion-chamber outer case. The forward face of each combustion chamber presents six apertures which align the six nozzles of the corresponding fuel nozzle cluster.

There are three basic types of combustion chambers in service. Combustion chambers type I and type II are interchangeable. However, type I and type II chambers are *not* functionally interchangeable with type III chambers. Within type I and type II, chambers number 1, 3, and 7 are interchangeable and numbers 2, 6, and 8 are interchangeable. In type III, numbers 2 and 3 are interchangeable, and numbers 6, 7, and 8 are interchangeable. Numbering is clockwise, as viewed from the rear, and starts with the one o'clock position chamber. Numbers 4 and 5 have spark-igniter sleeves and guides, and chamber number 4 has an air-pressure transfer tube in it. Interconnecting flame tubes join all the chambers around the circle. The tubes on the odd-numbered type I and II chambers are female and have an air shield on the upstream side that overlaps the mating male flame tube. In type III chambers, number 1 has female interconnecting flame tubes; number 5 has male tubes; and numbers 2, 3, 4, 6, 7, and 8 have one male and one female flame tube. When removing types I and II, the even-numbered chambers must be removed first. The removal sequence for type III is numbers 5, 6, 4, 3, 7, 2, 8, and 1.

The combustion chambers are a welded assembly. At the head of each chamber are six swirl vanes through which six fuel nozzles fit. The holes in the walls of

COMBUSTION

1 FUEL NOZZLES
2 INNER COMBUSTION CASE
3 COMBUSTION CHAMBER
4 OUTER COMBUSTION CASE

FIG. 20-12 *Combustion section.*

FIG. 20-13 *Combustion chamber.*

FIG. 20-15 *Combustion-chamber inner case and No. 5 bearing support.*

the chamber meter the entering air. Near the head of the chamber most of the air is used as combustion air. Further down the chamber the entering air is used to cool the hot gases to safe temperature for the chambers. The rows of smaller holes admit air that cools the can itself.

Each chamber is held in place by a positioning bracket and a clamp. The clamp holds the open end of the chambers to an outlet duct assembly which is fastened to the turbine case. Each positioning bracket is secured by two outer fuel manifold retaining bolts. The bracket hooks onto a retaining lug on the combustion chamber. The fuel nozzle inside the air-swirl guide holds the chamber in lateral movement.

FIG. 20-14 *Fireseal, narrow-band type.*

THE FIRESEAL (Fig. 20-14)

The fireseal is held by the bolts that join the front and rear combustion-chamber outer cases. The outer rim of the fireseal fits tightly against the engine pod. Some engines use the narrow-band-type fireseal, while the others use the offset lip type.

COMBUSTION-CHAMBER INNER CASE AND NUMBER 5 BEARING SUPPORT (Fig. 20-15)

The combustion-chamber inner case has reinforcements welded to its inside surface. Its prime function is to form the inner surface of the combustion section, but together with the number 5 bearing support, it provides an inner passage for the 16th-stage air which will help cool the radiant heat from the combustion chambers. Holes in its forward flange, the diffuser, and the number 5 bearing support permit this air to flow. A flange on the rear end attaches to the turbine nozzle inner case. This unit differs somewhat on different model engines.

TURBINE SECTION (Fig. 20-16)

The turbine section consists of a four-stage gas turbine. The first-stage rotor, also called the high-speed turbine, drives the rear compressor. The second-, third-, and fourth-stage rotors, also called the low-speed turbines, are mounted on a single shaft which drives the front compressor.

TURBINE NOZZLE CASE (Fig. 20-17)

The turbine nozzle case is constructed of corrosion- and heat-resistant steel. On its front flange, gang bolt assemblies are attached, and this flange bolts to the combustion-chamber outer case. The rear flange bolts to the turbine exhaust case using a spacer ring. Inside

TURBINE

FOURTH STAGE TURBINE DISK & BLADES
THIRD STAGE TURBINE DISK & BLADES
SECOND STAGE TURBINE DISK & BLADES

TURBINE EXHAUST CASE

FIRST STAGE TURBINE DISK & BLADES

FIRST STAGE TURBINE VANES

FOURTH STAGE TURBINE VANES
THIRD STAGE TURBINE VANES
SECOND STAGE TURBINE VANES

TURBINE NOZZLE CASE

COMBUSTION CHAMBER REAR OUTER CASE

FIG. 20-16 *Turbine section.*

FIG. 20-17 *Turbine nozzle outer case.*

the turbine case, slots and ridges are machined and stator vanes and seals are inserted in these locations.

TURBINE NOZZLE INNER CASE

On some engines, the front end of the turbine inner case is attached to the rear flange of the combustion-chamber inner case. On others, the front end is attached to the rear flange of the number 5 bearing support. At the outer rear end, two shoulders hold the inner end of the first-stage turbine vanes. The front

FIG. 20-18 *Combustion-chamber outlet duct.*

(largest) shoulder has pins for securing the vanes. On the inside diameter of the inner case, there are two knife-edged airseals. The innermost seal is riveted to a support welded to the approximate middle of the inner case. It rides free of an inner platform on the first-stage turbine disk. The outer airseal is riveted to the rear of the inner case. It rides free of an outer platform on the first-stage turbine disk.

COMBUSTION-CHAMBER OUTLET DUCT
(Fig. 20-18)

This duct guides the hot gases to the first-stage nozzle. It is retained to the number 5 bearing support. The duct is a welded assembly that is held in place by the combustion-chamber outer case-to-turbine nozzle case bolt circle. The forward flanges of the duct ports carry the rear edge of the clamps that hold the combustion chambers in place.

TURBINE VANES, SHROUDS, AND SEALS

First-stage vanes are cast from corrosion- and heat-resistant alloy with chromalize protective coating on all internal and external cast surfaces. Second-stage vanes are cast nickel base; third-stage vanes are cast cobalt base; and fourth-stage vanes are cast nickel base. First-stage vanes are held by pins between the recesses in the outer turbine case and are snapped onto their pins in the turbine nozzle inner case assembly to seat on the shoulders of the case.

A seal and a spacer are placed in the outer case just to the rear of the first-stage vanes. One knife-edge on the first-stage turbine blade shroud runs between the seal's two knife-edges.

Second-stage turbine vanes fit into the outer case just behind the first seal spacer. Extensions on the root platform of each vane hold them in place on their forward edges and a lock ring is used at the outer rear edge. The inner end of these vanes slip into slots in the shroud ring. The inside edge of the shroud ring has a turbine inner seal riveted to it. The seal ring carries four knife-edges on its inside flange. One of these knife-edges runs free against the shoulder on the rear-compressor drive turbine disk and the remaining three (rearmost) against flange face of the front-compressor drive turbine hub. This forms a seal between the front and second-stage rotors to force the working gases to pass through the second-stage vanes. A lock ring, a stepped seal, and a seal spacer are in the outer case following the second-stage vanes. The two knife-edges of the second-stage blade run free against the stepped seal. Mounting of the third-stage turbine vanes is the same as the second stage. The inner seal ring, however, instead of having knife-edges has a stepped platform.

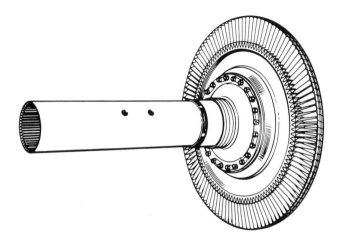

FIG. 20-19 *Rear-compressor drive turbine rotor.*

The knife-edges are on the spacer between the second- and third-stage turbine disks.   There are six of them set in pairs.   Mounting of the fourth-stage turbine vanes is identical to the third stage.   The outer seal is stepped and extends into the turbine exhaust case.   There is no locking ring, but the fourth-stage vanes are held in the rear by the stepped seal, which is held by its flange that fits between the turbine nozzle case and the turbine exhaust case flanges.

REAR-COMPRESSOR DRIVE TURBINE ROTOR
(Fig. 20-19)

The rear-compressor drive turbine rotor consists of a disk, blades, and a shaft.   The number 5 bearing inner race and seal assembly are located forward of the disk and secured on the shaft by a nut, a tab washer, and a lock ring during assembly.   The turbine shaft splines

into the rear-compressor rotor and is secured to the rotor hub by the rear-compressor drive turbine shaft coupling. The outer race of the number 4½ bearing is located inside the turbine shaft.

TURBINE BLADES (FIRST STAGE) (Fig. 20-20)

The first-stage blades are made of forged nickel alloy. The blades have "fir tree" serrations as their roots.   The blades can only be inserted by a forward and rear movement and are held in place by a rivet at the bottom of the "fir tree."   The working part of the blade is a curved surface that changes the direction of the swiftly moving gases that pass over it.   The reaction of these gases to change in direction of travel produces the force that turns the turbine rotor.

At the outward end of each blade is a wide flat section called a shroud.   This shroud prevents gas leakage at the blade ends.   Each blade has a stepped arrangement by which they lock to each other, and this forms a complete shroud ring when assembled.   This ring gives the rotor greater strength as well as making up a gas seal. Because of the particular construction, it is impossible to remove one turbine blade only, and at least half of the blades at 90 deg on either side must be removed. A staggered movement of all these blades must be made before the center blade fir tree will clear the disk.   There are 130 blades in the first-stage turbine rotor.

TURBINE DISK

The disk is made of corrosion- and heat-resistant nickel alloy.   A drilled flange on the front face of the disk is bolted to the rear end of the rear-compressor drive turbine shaft.   Balance holes in the disk flange are also provided.   Fir tree serrations are cut in the rim matching the serrations in the turbine blades.

TURBINE SHAFT

The shaft is hollow with internal splines at its front end which mate with external splines of the rear-compressor rear hub.   Turbine position in the turbine nozzle case is determined by a spacer ring that is between the end of the compressor hub shaft and an internal shoulder in the turbine shaft.

RIVET

FIG. 20-20 *First-stage turbine blades.*

FIG. 20-21 *Rear-compressor drive turbine shaft coupling.*

REAR-COMPRESSOR DRIVE TURBINE SHAFT COUPLING (Fig. 20-21)

A coupling holds the turbine shaft and the compressor rear hub together. Outside threads on the forward end of the coupling mate with threads on the inside of the compressor hub shaft, and a shoulder on the outside of the coupling butts against an internal shoulder in the turbine drive shaft. An internal spline at the rear of the coupling is used for wrenching. The coupling is locked in with a jam-nut having a left-hand thread, or by the number 4½ bearing outer race and liner.

FRONT-COMPRESSOR DRIVE TURBINE ROTOR (Fig. 20-22)

Three disks with turbine blades, a rear hub, a spacer, and a drive shaft make up the rotor. The second-stage disk is bolted to the drive shaft and the rear hub. The third- and fourth-stage disks are held together and to the second-stage disks by 10 tierods.

TURBINE BLADES

The second- and third-stage turbine blades are cast from stainless steel. Fourth-stage blades are forged from nickel alloy material. They are assembled in the manner previously described under the Rear-compressor Drive Turbine Rotor—Turbine Blades. The second-stage blades are larger in height than those of the first stage, the third-stage blades are even larger, and the fourth-stage blades are the largest. The reason for this is to match the blade size to the increase in volume of gas as it expands while passing through the turbine. There are 114 blades in the second-stage disk and blade assembly, 108 blades in the third stage, and 80 blades in the fourth stage.

TURBINE DISKS

The second- and third-stage turbine disks are made from corrosion- and heat-resistant nickel alloy. The fourth-stage disk is made from corrosion- and heat-

resistant steel. They are separated from each other by spacers and are attached to the front-compressor drive turbine shaft and the turbine rear hub by tierods as mentioned above. The second-stage disk has an integral spacer.

FRONT-COMPRESSOR DRIVE TURBINE SHAFT

The front-compressor drive turbine shaft is made from low-chrome steel alloy. It is a long, thin shaft, as it must pass through the first-stage turbine rotor shaft and must reach the front of the second-stage turbine disk to the rear hub of the front compressor. Its front end is supported inside the front-compressor hub, its middle by a bearing inside the rear-compressor turbine rotor shaft, and its rear end by the turbine assembly which, in turn, is supported by a bearing at the turbine rear hub.

The shaft is hollow and provides a passage for ninth-stage cooling air which passes through holes in the rear hub to cool the rear bearing seals, oil pump, and the rear face of the fourth-stage turbine disk. Oil is also piped through the shaft to its middle bearing. The forward end of the shaft is externally splined and internally threaded. The shaft external splines mate with the internal splines on the front-compressor rear hub, and the shaft internal threads mate with the external threads on the front-compressor drive turbine coupling.

A spacer is used between the compressor rear hub shaft and the front edge of the drive shaft to position the shaft correctly.

FRONT-COMPRESSOR COUPLING (Fig. 20-23)

The coupling's external shoulder butts against an internal shoulder in the front-compressor hub. The internal splines in the coupling are for the wrench. The coupling front end has external splines with three short slots. A ring having external and internal splines and

FIG. 20-23 *Front-compressor drive turbine coupling.*

FIG. 20-22 *Front-compressor drive turbine rotor.*

three inward projecting pins, fits over the forward end of the coupling, the pins projecting through the slots. A compression spring is located just forward of the spline-pinned ring and is held in place by an internal shoulder of a collar. The collar is held in the coupling by splines and a snap ring. The spring keeps a rearward pressure on the ring which will lock the ring's external splines to the internal splines in the compressor hub. These splines are just forward of the shoulder, and as long as the ring is locked, the coupling cannot be unscrewed.

In order to unscrew the coupling from the drive shaft, the ring must first be moved forward against the spring pressure until its external splines disengage the small internal spline that is inside of the compressor hub ahead of the internal shoulder. The pins that project through the slots in the coupling are used to move the ring forward. A special wrench is used that can pull the pins forward and then engage wrenching splines to turn the coupling.

EXHAUST SECTION *(Fig. 20-24)*

The exhaust section of the engine includes all items following the turbine except the tailpipe and other rearward attachments which are furnished by the airframe manufacturer.

The outer turbine exhaust case is constructed of nickel alloy. It bolts to the rear of the turbine case at its front flange, and its rear flange bolts to the tailpipe. Two heavy external flanges near the center of the case are used for engine mounting.

The outer case supports all the parts used in the inner case. A few parts are mounted directly on the outer case. The fourth-stage turbine outer seal is located in the front of the outer case, the flange of which is positioned between the rear flange of the turbine nozzle case and the forward flange on the exhaust case.

A turbine exhaust fairing assembly, consisting of an inner duct and four turbine exhaust struts, is positioned in the exhaust case. Four number 6 bearing support rods pass through the struts and through the holes in the outer case and are secured in strut supports between the engine mounting flanges mentioned above at the 12, 3, 6, and 9 o'clock positions. These rods are secured and positioned by a dual nut-locking arrangement in the strut supports. At the inner end, the rods are bolted to lugs on the number 6 bearing housing. When assembled, the struts envelop the rods and the oil tubes (to be discussed) for streamlining. At the 3 o'clock position and to the rear of the support rod, the number 6 bearing pressure oil tube passes from outside the exhaust case to the number 6 bearing support. At the 6 o'clock position, the number 6 bearing scavenge-oil tube is installed in the same manner.

A flange attached to the number 6 bearing support holds the sump adapter to which the number 6 bearing sump is attached. The entire sump area is enveloped by a heat shield. The fairing assembly area, internal to the struts, is also covered by a heat shield. An average pressure rake manifold is mounted around the case forward of the engine mounting flange. Just forward of the rear flange, the temperature thermocouples are installed. Attached to each are leads from a thermocouple harness which circles the case at this point.

NUMBER 6 BEARING SUPPORT AND SHIELDS

The number 6 bearing seals buildup and number 6 bearing inner race and rollers are mounted on the rear hub. The outer race is held in a housing which also serves as the seals housing. This housing is attached to and is held by the number 6 bearing support. Four support rods from the outer case thread into the rear of the support. Attached to the rear of the support is the sump adapter to which the sump is bolted. The rear heat shield is bolted to the rear heat-shield flange which is retained in the support by the adapter. Bolted to the front of the number 6 bearing support is the number 6 bearing airseal support. A knife-edge is riveted to its forward extremity to ride on a shoulder which is riveted to the rear hub, thus forming a gas seal.

NUMBER 6 BEARING OIL SUMP

The sump contains the number 6 bearing oil scavenge pump which is driven by a pinion gear attached to the rear hub. Inserted through the pinion is the oil nozzle which provides lubrication for the number 4½ bearing inside the turbine shaft. The sump bolts to the rear of the adapter and has a cover plate bolted to its rear side. O-ring seals are used between the sump adapter and the support and between the sump and the rear cover. The rear heat shield is bolted to the front heat shield at external flanges. The two heat shields cover all components inside the inner duct. All the metal parts are steel.

ACCESSORY AND COMPONENT DRIVES GEARBOX ASSEMBLY *(Figs. 20-25 and 20-26)*

The accessory and component drives gearbox consists of a front housing, a rear housing, and the internal gears and shaft gears. The gearbox assembly is mounted beneath the engine and secured to the diffuser case front flange. Power is supplied to the gearbox from the rear-compressor rotor shaft through an integral elbow on the rear housing. The oil-pump assembly is located at the lower right front of the gearbox and contains both pressure and scavenge sections.

EXHAUST

TURBINE EXHAUST CASE

TURBINE NOZZLE CASE

EXHAUST STRUT

FOURTH STAGE TURBINE BLADES

FIG. 20-24 *Exhaust section.*

FUEL CONTROL DRIVE

FUEL PUMP DRIVE

OIL PUMP ASSEMBLY

GEARBOX FRONT HOUSING

ALTERNATOR DRIVE ADAPTER PAD

FIG. 20-25 *Accessories gearbox front section.*

The engine fuel control mounts on a six-studded circular pad on the upper right front of the gearbox housing, and the fuel pump mounts on a similar pad on the upper left front. Gearing is provided to drive the fuel control, the fuel pump, rear-compressor tachometer, and a fluid pump. A six-studded accessory drive pad is positioned on an upward angle near the top on each side of the gearbox, and another is situated on the right rear face of the gearbox for the fluid pump. An optional accessory drive may be incorporated in either side upward drive.

Provisions are made for mounting either a constant speed drive (for installation on Boeing aircraft) or a generator with an adapter (for installation on Douglas aircraft) on the large alternator center front pad. At the left rear of the gearbox a six-studded pad is provided for a starter. The starter rotates the high-compressor rotor through the gearing and shafts.

ACCESSORY AND COMPONENT DRIVES GEARBOX FRONT SECTION

The oil-pump assembly, fuel control, fuel pump, starter drive shaft gears, and tachometer drive gear are located in the front housing. The duplex oil pump is mounted at the lower right front of the front housing. The pump is composed of two sections. The rear section is the pressure section, while the front section scavenges the gearbox assembly. The pressure pump section receives oil from the tank, pumps it through the filter and to all main bearings of the engine. The scavenge pump section clears the gearbox of scavenge oil and sends it to the oil tank. The right upward fluid drive (if incorporated) is driven by a gear bolted to the fuel control gearshaft and the left upward fluid drive (if incorporated) is driven by a gear bolted to the fuel pump drive gearshaft. An oil impeller rotary breather,

ACCESSORY AND COMPONENT DRIVES BEVEL GEARSHAFT

TACHOMETER DRIVE PAD

INNER BEARING LINER

GEARBOX
REAR HOUSING

STARTER DRIVE PAD

OIL DRAIN PLUG BOSS

ACCESSORY AND COMPONENT
DRIVES GEARSHAFT REAR
BEARING RETAINER PAD

ACCESSORY AND COMPONENT
DRIVES GEARSHAFT BALL BEARING

HYDRAULIC PUMP
DRIVE GEARSHAFT

HYDRAULIC PUMP DRIVE PAD

FIG. 20-26   *Accessories gearbox rear section.*

NO. 1 BEARING   NO. 2 BEARING   NO. 2½ BEARING   NO. 4½ BEARING   NO. 6 BEARING

NO. 3 BEARING   NO. 4 BEARING   NO. 5 BEARING

FIG. 20-27   *Location of the main bearings.*

a centrifugal device used to separate oil from air, is also attached to the fuel pump drive gear.

ACCESSORY AND COMPONENT DRIVES GEARBOX REAR SECTION

The rear housing contains the main accessory drive and idler gears, the tachometer drive, and the rear bearings for the horizontal gear trains.

Between the main accessory drive gear and the fuel control drive gear is the idler gear through which power is transmitted to the right side of the gearbox. Splined to the alternator drive shaft gear is the main accessory drive gear which mates with the angled accessory drive gear in the elbow section of the housing. The angled accessory drive gear transmits power from the high-speed compressor to the gearbox. The alternator drive shaft gear transmits power to the left side of the gearbox assembly through the starter drive shaft gear and the fuel pump drive gear. The tachometer drive is run by a tachometer drive gear internally splined to the fuel control drive gear.

BEARINGS *(Fig. 20-27)*

The bearings in the engine are of either the ball or roller type. Eight bearings are used on the principle rotating masses of the engine although in two instances, which we will discuss below, two bearings act as one. Twenty-five bearings are also used in fuel, oil, and accessory systems.

NUMBER 1 BEARING

The number 1 bearing is of the roller type and is located at the front hub of the front compressor. Its outer race is held in a housing by means of a spanner nut and nut-locking rivet. The housing is supported by the number 1 bearing front support and number 1 bearing seal and support assembly at the center of the inlet guide vane circle. Its inner race has a pinch fit on the front-compressor front hub and is further held in place by a spacer, a seal plate, a spanner nut, and a nut-locking rivet. The inner race is larger than its rollers to allow for engine dimension changes with temperature. An oil-seal assembly is used on the rear side of the bearing.

NUMBER 2 BEARING

The number 2 bearing is of the ball type. It is a duplex bearing with two bearings acting as one. They are a matched pair. Their outer races are carried in a steel housing. This housing is supported by three steel pieces that make up the bearing support at the rear-com-

pressor inlet vanes. These races are separated by an oil baffle and are held in place by an external shoulder in the housing and a spanner nut and tab washer. The inner races of both are split to aid installation. They are a pinch fit on the rear-compressor rear hub and are held in place by a hub shoulder, seal plate, oil baffle, and retaining nut. An oil-seal assembly is used on the front side of the bearing. Bearings number 1 and number 2 are the front-compressor rotor supports.

In order to reduce absorption of heat by engine oil, heat shielding and thermal-blanket insulation are provided for the number 2 bearing compartment on some engines. Bolts that secure the compressor intermediate front bearing housing to the rear face of the front bearing inner support also secure the compressor intermediate front bearing front heat shield to the front face of the support.

The compressor intermediate rear bearing heat shield consists of a front and rear heat shield, both of which are secured together and in turn are secured as a unit to the rear face of the compressor intermediate bearing rear support.

The thermal-blanket insulation is contained within the heat shield.

NUMBER 2½ BEARING

The number 2½ bearing shown in Fig. 20-27 is a small, single-row ball bearing and serves as part of the support for the number 2½ bearing housing. This housing is part of the seal system for the aft end of numbers 2, 2½, and 3 bearings. The outer race is held in the number 2½ bearing housing by a snap ring. Its inner race is on the front-compressor rear hub and is held in place between number 2 bearing inner race retaining nut and a spacer. This spacer in turn is held in place by the number 3 bearing inner race.

NUMBER 3 BEARING

The number 3 bearing also shown in Fig. 20-27 is of the roller type and forms the front hub support for the rear compressor. Its outer race is a force fit into the inside diameter of the rear-compressor front hub. A shoulder and a snap ring hold the race in place. The inner race and rollers are shrunk onto the outside diameter of the front-compressor rear hub. A retaining nut, secured by a rivet, jams this inner race against the spacer just in the rear of the number 2½ bearing inner race.

NUMBER 4 BEARING

The number 4 bearing is of the ball type. It is a duplex bearing with two bearings acting as one. It forms the support for the rear hub of the rear compressor. The outer races are mounted in a housing which is supported inside of the engine diffuser case. They are held in place by a shoulder and a spacer under the diffuser-case bolt ring. There is an oil baffle between the outer races. The inner races are the split type, a pinch fit to the outside diameter of the rear-compressor rear hub. These races are positioned by a shoulder on the shaft, a seal plate, an oil baffle between the races, a spacer ring, a bevel gear, and a retaining nut with a lock and snap ring. There is an oil-seal housing on the forward side of this bearing.

To reduce swirl and heat rejection in one model engine, a compressor rear bearing oil scavenge baffle assembly is provided. The baffle assembly is mounted on the longer studs of the compressor rear bearing support.

To reduce absorption of heat by the engine oil, heat shielding and thermal-blanket insulation are provided for the number 4 bearing compartment. The compressor rear bearing heat shield assembly consists of several individual heat shields welded together. The complete unit is bolted to the compressor rear bearing housing and extends over the bearing housing, the breather tube, the oil pressure and scavenge tubes, and along the tower shaft.

The thermal-blanket insulation is contained within the heat shield.

NUMBER 4½ BEARING

The number 4½ bearing is a small roller bearing which is located between the front- and rear-compressor turbine drive shafts to minimize the whip of the long (front) shaft. Its outer race is in the inside diameter of the rear-compressor drive turbine shaft. The race is held between a spacer on the shoulder on the inside diameter of the shaft and the turbine shafts bearing seals liner. The liner is torqued to specification. The bearing inner race and cage are shrunk onto the front-compressor drive turbine shaft. This race is held on the shaft by a shoulder on the shaft, the bearing seal assembly, a spacer and retaining nut, a tab washer, and a snap-ring assembly.

NUMBER 5 BEARING

The number 5 bearing is a roller-type bearing, located just forward of the rear-compressor turbine. It forms the support for the rear-compressor drive turbine shaft. The bearing outer race housing and its seal housing are carried by the turbine front bearing support and the nozzle case and outlet duct assembly. The outer race carries the bearing cage and rollers. It is held in its housing by a retaining nut which is torqued and riveted. The bearing inner race is shrunk onto the outside diam-

eter of the rear-compressor turbine shaft. This race is slightly wide to allow for engine temperature growth. The race is held in place by a shaft shoulder, airseal spacer, seal plate, retaining nut, and a retaining-nut tablock–snap-ring assembly.

NUMBER 6 BEARING

The number 6 bearing is a roller-type bearing which forms the support for the compressor turbine rear hub. The outer race is held in a housing which is bolted to the assembly. The support assembly is held by support rods which carry the load to the structure of the turbine exhaust case. The inner race, which holds the roller and cage, has a force fit on the front-compressor drive turbine rear hub. The inner race is located and held fast by the hub shoulder, two seal spacers, a seal plate, and the rear oil scavenge pump pinion flange. This flange is in turn bolted to a carrier sleeve which is threaded into the hub shaft.

OIL SYSTEM

The oil system for this engine is discussed in Chap. 15.

FUEL SYSTEM

A fuel system similar to the one used in the JT3D engine is described in Chap. 13.

IGNITION SYSTEM

The dc ignition system used on some engines is a high-energy, intermittent-duty, untimed electrical system designed to operate on an electrical input ranging between 14 and 29 volts. The dc ignition system is not used continuously. Once the flame is ignited in the combustion chambers, there is no further need for the dc ignition system until the next time the engine is started. This could be at the beginning of the next flight, or in the air following some trouble that would extinguish the flame. Fuel spray into the engine combustion chambers is continuous. As long as the spark ignites the fuel, it makes no difference as to the exact instant of ignition. Thus, timing is not required. This system produces two sparks per second and is turned on just before the fuel is admitted to the engine. As soon as ignition occurs and the flame is established, the dc ignition system is turned off.

The ignition system receives its input electric energy from the aircraft source through a lead connected to the receptacle mounted on the right-hand-center flange of the front-compressor case. From here, it is conducted via a lead in the electrical harness assembly to a 20-joule ignition exciter mounted on the upper-right-hand side of the engine between the front-compressor case front and middle flanges. The exciter stores energy converted from the dc input, and releases it as a fast high-voltage discharge. High-tension leads conduct the energy to two spark igniters installed into the number 4 and number 5 combustion chambers through holes in the lower rear of the diffuser case. The exciter provides the energy for the right and left spark igniters. This is done by means of a spark dividing network.

Some models use an ac ignition exciter in addition to the dc unit. This is a 4-joule unit which provides continuous ignition during flight to minimize the possibility of flameout during engine operation under adverse ambient conditions. After the dc unit previously discussed, has effected a satisfactory start, it is turned off. With the alternating current provided by the engine system, the ac ignition unit provides continuous ignition to the right spark igniter. The ac ignition unit has a nominal input of 115 volts, 400 cycles ac, but will operate under the range of 90 to 124 volts. It is a high-energy unit using stored energy. A radio suppressor built into the unit prevents radio frequencies generated within the unit from entering the supply circuit. (Refer to Chap. 16 for a more detailed examination of ignition systems.)

REVIEW AND STUDY QUESTIONS

1 Name several different airplanes using this engine.

2 List the engine's major specifications.

3 Where is the fan located? How is it driven?

4 Give a brief description of the engine operation and airflow.

5 Why are three turbines necessary to drive one of the compressors, while only one is needed to drive the other?

6 How is the chance for compressor stall reduced on this engine?

7 What type of combustion chamber is used? How does it differ from others of its type?

8 Describe the fuel manifold and fuel nozzle arrangement.

9 Very briefly describe the construction features of the following engine parts: front case, front- and rear-compressor rotors and cases, diffuser, combustion chamber and cases, turbine nozzle and case, turbine and case, exhaust duct, and accessories section.

10 How many main bearings are used? Name them and give their location.

11 Briefly describe the following engine systems: anti-ice, oil, fuel, and ignition.

Chapter 21

General Electric J79

The General Electric J79 (Fig. 21-1) is a very highly produced engine used in such airplanes as the McDonnell-Douglas F-4C, Lockheed F-104, Convair B-58, and the North American RA-5C (Vigilante). Since so many models of this engine are in use, and since they all have a similar basic construction, the description that follows is for the J79 jet engine in general.

SPECIFICATIONS

Number of compressor stages:	17
Number of turbine stages:	3
Number of combustors:	10
Maximum power at sea level:	15,000 to 18,000 lb
Specific fuel consumption at maximum power:	2.0 (approx.)
Compression ratio at maximum rpm:	12:1 to 13.5:1 (approx.)
Maximum diameter:	39 in.
Maximum length:	202 to 208 in.
Maximum dry weight:	3600 lb (approx.)

The J79 engine is an axial-flow turbojet engine with variable afterburner thrust. (See Fig. 2-23.) It incorporates a 17-stage compressor, of which the angles of the inlet guide vanes and the first 6 stages of stator vanes are variable; a combustion system, which consists of 10 individual combustion liners situated between an inner and outer combustion casing; a 3-stage turbine rotor, which is coupled directly to the compressor rotor; and an afterburner system, which provides afterburner thrust variation through fuel-flow scheduling and actuation of the variable-area, converging-diverging-type exhaust nozzle. The rotors are supported by three main bearings.

OPERATION

During operation, air enters the front of the engine and is directed into the compressor at the proper angle by the variable inlet guide vanes and variable stator vanes. The air is compressed and forced into the combustion section. A fuel nozzle extending into each combustion liner atomizes the fuel for combustion. The fuel-air mixture is initially ignited by a spark plug in one combustion liner, and is rapidly propagated to the remaining liners by cross ignition ducts which join adjacent liners. Once initiated, combustion is self-sustaining so ignition is turned off.

The gases which result from the combustion are directed into the turbine, which drives the compressor rotor. From the turbine, the exhaust gases flow into the afterburner where additional fuel may be injected and ignited to augment the thrust of the main engine. The exhaust gases then pass through, and are accelerated by, the exhaust nozzle.

The engine systems control engine thrust by regulating engine speed, stator angle, fuel flow, exhaust nozzle area, and exhaust gas temperature. Interconnecting signals integrate the various controls so that the systems function as a single unit in response to the throttle.

COMPRESSOR FRONT FRAME (Fig. 21-2)

The compressor front frame forms the air inlet passage for the engine and supports the front of the compressor rotor. The frame is made of stainless steel and consists of an outer shell, an inner hub, and 8 evenly spaced, hollow struts. The frame assembly includes the number 1 bearing area and the 20 inlet guide vanes and their actuating mechanism. The inner hub encloses the inlet gearbox assembly, the bearing seals, and an anti-icing air distribution manifold.

The outer shell of the frame contains 3 mounting pads to permit variations in aircraft mounting configuration, a gearbox mounting pad at the 6 o'clock position (Fig. 21-3) to support the transfer gearbox, and 20 evenly spaced holes which retain the spherical bearings assembled to the outer trunnions of the inlet guide vanes.

The inlet gearbox assembly, which is attached to the front face of the hub, becomes an integral part of the number 1 bearing sump. A split inlet guide vane inner support is attached to the rear face of the hub and retains the spherical bearings assembled to the inner trunnions of the inlet guide vanes. A manifold cover spans the space between the inner support and the number 1 bearing oil seal to enclose the anti-icing air manifold.

The front frame struts provide passageways for sump cooling air, anti-icing air, supply-and-scavenge-oil

1	ANTI-ICED INLET CASE AND STRUTS		BUSTOR, AND TURBINE CASINGS		VERGING-DIVERGING EXHAUST NOZZLE	8	REAR GEARBOX	11	FRONT GEARBOX FOR CARTRIDGE OR PNEU-MATIC STARTER
2	VARIABLE STATOR STAGES	4	AFTERBURNER	6	THREE-STAGE TURBINE	9	MAIN AND AFTERBURNER FUEL CONTROL		
3	SPLIT COMPRESSOR, COM-	5	VARIABLE-AREA CON-	7	COMBUSTION CANS	10	TRANSFER GEARBOX		

(a)

(b)

FIG. 21-1 *External and internal views of the General Electric J79-15 turbojet engine.*
(**a**) *Cutaway view.* (**b**) *Left and right side views.*

COMPRESSOR FRONT CASING

COMPRESSOR REAR CASING

COMPRESSOR REAR FRAME

COMPRESSOR FRONT FRAME

COMPRESSOR ROTOR

FIG. 21-2 *Compressor assembly.*

tubes, and the radial drive shaft to the transfer gearbox (Fig. 21-4).   The number 1 strut encloses a tube which ducts ninth-stage air to the oil seal.   The number 4 strut encloses tubes which duct oil supply to—and scavenge oil from—the number 1 bearing sump.   Strut number 5 encloses the radial drive shaft and provides a free-flow path for scavenge oil from the number 1 bearing sump.   Struts 2, 3, 7, and 8 duct anti-icing air into the hub; struts 1, 4, 5, and 6 contain a chamber near the leading edge that conducts the anti-icing air outward.   The number 1 strut contains a central passageway which is an extension of the number 1 bearing sump.   *NOTE:*   All struts are numbered in a clockwise direction beginning with the number 1 at the top or immediately to the right of the top, as the observer looks at the rear face of the frame.

FIG. 21-3 *Engine orientation.*

COMPRESSOR CASING ASSEMBLIES

The compressor casing assemblies consist of two cylindrical, stainless steel casings, split along a horizontal line for removal. Their flanges interlock such that the rear casing half must be removed before the front; however, both casing halves can be removed as one piece if the front casing must be removed. The front casing assembly contains the six stages of the variable stator vanes and their actuating linkage and the seventh-stage stator vanes, which have a fixed angle. The outer ribs of the casings provide mounting adaptors for engine accessories.

The shanks of the variable stator vanes protrude through holes in the front casing; plastic bushings on the inside and outside of the casing provide an airseal and bearing surface for the vanes. The first four stages of stator vanes are shrouded at the inner end to reduce vibration and air leakage.

The levers, which are attached to the vane shanks, are pinned to half-rings. The two half-rings of each stage are connected at the horizontal lines to form a complete circle. Each circle is linked to two bellcranks. All of the bellcranks on each side, including the inlet guide vane bellcranks, are interconnected by a master rod; such that the stator bellcrank and master rod assemblies actuate all stages of vanes simultaneously. The bellcranks are mounted on supports which are bolted to casing ribs, one at the 4 o'clock and the other at the 10 o'clock position on the casing.

The second-stage bellcrank on each support is attached to a vane actuator, which moves the stator vanes utilizing high-pressure fuel scheduled by the main fuel control. A permanent vane position indicator is attached to the fourth-stage actuating linkage at the seven o'clock position. The indicator is used to check the vane position and to rig the stator linkage.

The front casing has a manifold that conducts anti-icing air to the outer trunnions of the first-stage vanes. The air flows inward through the hollow trunnions and out through slots in the inner end of the vanes. Channel ribs near the rear flange of the front stator casing restrain the bases of the seventh-stage stator vanes. Each vane consists of an airfoil section welded to a hollow, T-shaped base.

The rear-compressor casing assembly includes the last 10 stages of stator vanes and one stage of exit guide vanes. Each stator vane consists of an airfoil section welded to a T-shaped base, similar to the 7th-stage vanes. An exit guide vane is mounted on the same base as each 17th-stage vane. The bases of the vanes slip into, and are restrained by, ribs in the casing.

The upper half of the rear casing has an air collection manifold. Ninth-stage air flows through holes in the casing and into the manifold, from which it is piped externally to the three bearing areas for sump cooling.

FIG. 21-4 *Strut usage.*

The lower casing half contains mounting lugs for the rear gearbox.

COMPRESSOR ROTOR *(Fig. 21-5)*

The compressor rotor consists of a front stub shaft; 17 disks, spacers, and sets of blades; a 7th-stage air baffle and ducts; 4 torque cones; and a rear stub shaft.

The front stub shaft is bolted to the front of the first-stage disk and provides a surface for the number 1 bearing and seal inner races. The hub of the shaft is internally splined to provide power to the accessory drive section.

The rotor blades are secured to the disks by single-tang dovetail connections. They are held in the dovetail slots by a blade retainer at the front of the rotor, the spacers throughout the rotor, and the 17th-stage airseal at the rear. The spacers transmit the torque forward from the 11th stage, and rearward to the 16th and 17th stages. The spacers between the 11th- and 15th-stage disks do not transmit torque, but continue the smooth contour of the rotor. The first four spacers form a mat-

ing surface for the shrouds on the stator vanes to form an airseal.

Holes through the seventh-stage spacer permit air to enter the rotor. An air baffle, bolted between the 7th- and 8th-stage disks, causes the air to continue rotating at the speed of the rotor. Air ducts allow the air to flow through the rotor to equalize the pressures on both sides of the disks and to duct it rearward through the stub shaft to cool the turbine rotor.

The torque cones transmit the torque from the small diameter at the 15th-stage disk outward to the large diameter of the 11th-stage disk. They also provide structural support for the larger disks and separate the different air pressures within the rotor. The rear stub shaft is bolted to the rear face of the 15th-stage disk. The inner races for air and oil seals and for the number 2 bearing are assembled to the stub shaft. The shaft is internally splined and threaded to receive the turbine shaft and turbine bolt.

The 17th-stage airseal is bolted to the rear face of the 17th-stage disk to prevent compressor discharge air from leaking into the area behind the rotor. The seal

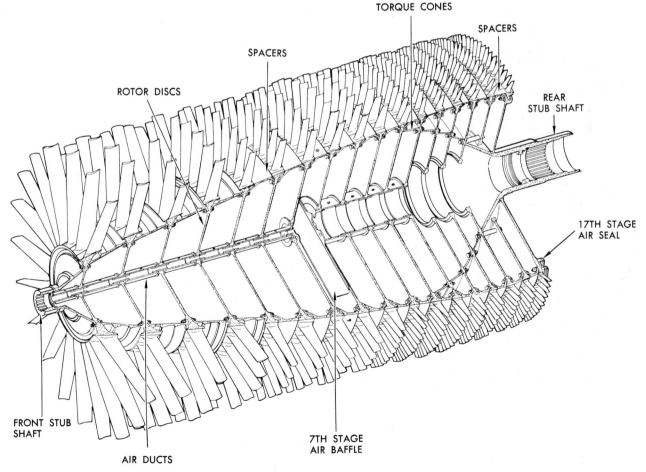

FIG. 21-5 *Compressor rotor.*

consists of a double, grooved-type race (labyrinth) which mates with the seal on the front flange of the compressor rear frame.

COMPRESSOR REAR FRAME *(Fig. 21-6)*

The compressor rear frame absorbs the thrust loading of the rotors and the radial force of the compressor-turbine coupling. It also forms an annular diffuser for the compressor discharge air. The frame consists of an outer shell connected by 10 equally spaced, hollow struts to an inner shell. The outer shell provides 10 mounting pads for the fuel nozzles and 10 bosses through which the pin bolts that secure the combustion liners pass.

The inner shell contains a double seal on the front flange that mates with the 17th-stage airseal of the rotor and two manifolds on the inner surface that strengthen the shell. The manifolds are used to extract compressor discharge air for aircraft use. The sump is discussed in the Bearings and Seals section.

The struts support the bearing sump and provide various service passages (see Fig. 21-4). Numbers 2, 4, 7, and 8 serve as passageways for extraction air for aircraft purposes. Numbers 3, 8, and 10 vent 17th-stage seal leakage air overboard. Number 1 contains a pair of concentric tubes, one of which conducts sump cooling air from the sump, the other conducts 9th-stage air into the sump cooling cavity. The number 5 strut also contains a pair of concentric tubes, one of which conducts oil supply to the sump, the other conducts scavenge oil from the rear portion of the sump. The number 6 strut contains a tube which conducts scavenge oil from the front portion of the sump.

COMBUSTION OUTER CASING *(Fig. 21-7)*

The combustion outer casing is split on the horizontal line to permit easy removal for inspection and removal of the liners. The upper half contains a port at the 12 o'clock position for extraction of anti-icing air. The lower half contains two spark-plug bosses—the one at the number 4 liner is used—and a combustion system drain. The drain allows excess fuel to drain from the combustion system. A port near the rear flange allows air to flow from the combustion casing to the pilot burner. A locking strip, which fits along the inside of the horizontal flange, strengthens the flange and prevents air leakage.

COMBUSTION LINERS *(Fig. 21-8)*

Each combustion liner consists of three parts riveted together; they are an inner liner, an outer liner, and a rear liner. The outer liner forms a snout which scoops compressor discharge air into the liner. Vanes in the snout produce a uniform distribution around the dome of the inner liner. A slot in the snout permits the fuel nozzle to extend into the inner-liner dome. The number 4 liner has a spark-plug hole through the inner and outer liner. The adjacent liners are joined near the front end by cross-ignition tubes and the flanges of adjacent liners are held by V-band clamps to form a sturdy assembly. The liners are restrained by pin bolts in the compressor rear frame.

The rear liners are oval shaped at the rear and are oblique to facilitate their removal. They fit into the inlet ports of the annular transition duct and are supported by it. The liners have thimble holes through which air is introduced to complete the combustion, and louvers that provide a flow of cooling air along the inner surface of the liner.

COMBUSTION INNER CASING *(Fig. 21-7)*

The inner casing is an internally stiffened cylinder that bolts between the compressor rear frame at the

FIG. 21-6 *Compressor rear frame.*

FIG. 21-7 *Combustion section.*

front and the first-stage turbine nozzle at the rear. It absorbs the torque developed on the turbine nozzle, and it combines the combustion airflow to an annular passage around the liners. Holes near the front of the casing permit air to flow into the chamber around the turbine shaft to cool the shaft.

ANNULAR TRANSITION DUCT (Fig. 21-7)

The transition duct provides a ring of 10 oval inlet ports and an annular exit, which is equal in area to the total of the 10 inlets. The duct is supported by the first-stage turbine nozzle, and is held in place by five pin bolts near the rear flange of the combustion inner casing.

The inlet ports of the transition duct support the rear end of the combustion liners. Small louvers between the inlet ports admit cooling air and allow flexibility to the duct to minimize cracking.

FIRST-STAGE TURBINE NOZZLE (Fig. 21-9)

The first-stage turbine nozzle is assembled as a part of the combustion section and is bolted to the rear flange of the inner combustion casing. The rear flange of the outer band contacts the turbine stator rib and re-

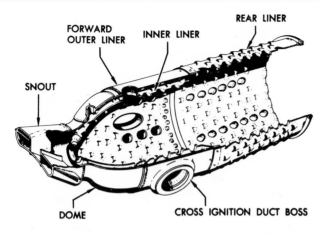

FIG. 21-8 *Combustion liner.*

strains the first-stage shroud. The outer band of the turbine nozzle is segmented to permit expansion.

The inner band of the nozzle is a one-piece structure from which the partitions are cantilevered. The inner band contains a corrugated baffle which mates with the transition duct and allows cooling air to flow across the band. The partitions are hollow, airfoil sections with internal baffles so that cooling air, passing through the partitions, maintains an even skin temperature.

TURBINE STATOR ASSEMBLY (Fig. 21-9)

The turbine stator is split on a horizontal line for easy removal. It includes the three turbine shrouds and the second- and third-stage nozzles assembled into the turbine casing. On some models, a turbine impingement manifold encircles the upper half of the second-stage shroud to direct high-pressure air onto the turbine blades for starting. A check valve in the supply

FIG. 21-9 *Turbine section.*

line prevents the turbine air from exiting into the manifold.

Flanges on the ribs within the casing hold the nozzles and shrouds. Each turbine nozzle is restrained by three pin bolts through each casing half. The partitions of the nozzle are supported by the outer rim. The rim protects the casing from the combustion gases. The inner band of the second- and third-stage turbine nozzles restrain the turbine seals that encircle the torque rings of the rotor. Some engines incorporate a turbine blade guard, consisting of a segmented soft metal half-ring that slips between the third-stage shroud and the upper turbine casing to prevent a fractured turbine blade from penetrating the casing and damaging the aircraft.

The nozzle partitions are hollow with internal baffling. The second-stage partitions have cooling air routed through them. The third-stage partitions are not air-cooled.

The turbine shrouds also slip into the ribs of the casing and interlock with the flanges of the turbine nozzles. The shrouds are half-rings or 60-deg segments with a bonded honeycomb surface which reduces air leakage around the tips of the turbine blades. Lockstops, welded in the casing, prevent the shrouds from rotating.

A turbine support ring mounts between the turbine casing and the combustion outer casing to maintain the axial distance for the stator assembly in respect to the rotor.

TURBINE ROTOR *(Fig. 21-10)*

The turbine rotor produces the rotary power to drive the compressor. It consists of the turbine shaft; three turbine wheels, sets of blades, clips, and locking strips; two torque rings; two baffle assemblies; and a turbine airseal. Honeycomb seals encircling the torque ring are a functional part of the stator assembly.

The turbine shaft is a hollow, conical shaft. The shaft has an external spline that engages the compressor rotor rear stub shaft and is internally threaded to receive the turbine bolt. The rear flange of the shaft is bolted to the front of the first-stage turbine wheel.

The turbine wheels are bolted to the torque rings which separate them. The wheels consist of thin disks with large open centers and widened rims. The rims have dovetail slots to retain the blades. The blades are assembled in pairs, two matching blades in each dovetail. The blade shanks keep the dovetail couplings out of the gas stream. Clips between the shanks prevent airflow between the blade pairs, and also damp their vibration. When bent, clips in the bottom of the dovetail retain the blades in the slots.

FIG. 21-10 *Turbine rotor and turbine/compressor bolt.*

The torque rings transmit torque from the rear wheels forward. The rings have a machined, three-ring seal on the outer surface and circumferential cooling rings on the inside. The seal mates with the turbine honeycomb seals to minimize air leakage across the surface of the torque rings. The cooling rings expose a greater amount of the torque rings to the cooling air in the rotor.

Turbine rotor baffle assemblies consist of a ring support, bolted to each side of the second-stage turbine wheel, and a disk, with four baffles attached to each side, attached to each ring support. The disks cause the cooling air to flow outward to the inner surface of the torque rings while the baffles prevent a change in angular velocity as the air flows outward and successively inward within the rotor. The disks have large open centers to permit the locknut wrench, which loosens the turbine bolt, to be inserted through the rotor.

A turbine inner baffle fills the center of the turbine rotor baffles. The inner baffle (refer to Fig. 21-10) consists of two disks attached to a tube. The rear of the inner baffle contains a spoked disk which is locked to the third-stage wheel by a pin. The center of the spoked disk has an internal spline that drives the number 3 bearing scavenge pump.

The turbine airseal is bolted to the rear face of the third-stage turbine wheel. The seal confines the sump cooling air to the cavity around the bearing sump. The hub of the third-stage wheel forms a stub shaft for the turbine rotor.

The turbine bolt is cylindrical and contains coarse threads, which engage threads within the compressor rotor rear stub shaft; fine threads, which engage threads within the turbine shaft; serrated locking fingers, which engage serrations within the turbine shaft to lock the bolt; and lugs on the inside that permit the locknut wrench to turn the bolt. (Refer to Fig. 21-10.) Since both sets of threads are engaged at the same time, turning the bolt gradually pulls the shafts together into a solid coupling.

TURBINE FRAME

The turbine frame shown in Fig. 21-9 forms an exhaust diffuser, supports the rear of the turbine rotor, and provides the main engine-to-aircraft mounting structure. The frame consists of an outer cone, an inner cone, and a sump housing connected by seven equally spaced, hollow struts. The struts are housed within turbine frame vanes to shield them from exhaust temperature.

The outer cone of the frame contains 12 bosses which support the thermocouples that measure the turbine discharge temperature. Four sets of engine mounting supports are bolted to the ribs to provide support connections for various mounting configurations. Three spherical bearing housings are bolted to the ribs for thrust transmission. Strut ends are cast to add rigidity to the union of the strut and the cone.

The turbine frame inner cone encloses the sump housing. The inner exhaust cone bolts to the rear flange of the frame inner cone. The number 3 bearing front airseal and spill baffle bolt to the front of the sump housing; the number 3 bearing rear airseal and the turbine cooling air baffle bolt to the rear.

All seven struts of the turbine rear frame (see Fig. 21-4) duct turbine cooling air to the engine compartment and, in addition, the number 2 strut encloses a tube that conducts ninth-stage air to the sump cooling cavity. A tube in strut number 6 vents the sump to the oil tank. A tube in strut number 3 conducts lubricating oil to the sump. Strut number 4 has a tube that conducts scavenge oil from the scavenge pump.

FORWARD EXHAUST DUCT ASSEMBLY
(Fig. 21-11)

The forward exhaust duct is bolted to the rear flange of the turbine frame. It supports a smooth, inner liner which incorporates a retaining clip at the rear edge to interlock with the front of the number 2 liner when the tailpipe is installed. The duct provides 21 mounting pads for the multijet fuel nozzles, and an opening for the pilot burner.

AFTERBURNER MANIFOLDS AND MULTIJET FUEL NOZZLES (Fig. 21-11)

The four afterburner manifolds encircle the forward exhaust duct. Each manifold has 21 outlet ports, one for each fuel nozzle. The multijet fuel nozzles consist of four tubes, one for each of the four manifolds, that are fused into a probe. Holes in the sides of the tubes spray the fuel at right angles to the exhaust gas flow. The inner ends of the probes are retained by bosses imbedded in the rear inner cone.

The rear inner cone is ceramic coated to protect it from the high-temperature exhaust gases. It bolts to the rear flange of the turbine frame inner cone. The rear inner cone supports the flameholder through seven mounting brackets on its outer surface.

The flameholder consists of three concentric, V-gutter rings connected by seven equally-spaced, radial links. The rings are staggered to ensure efficient burning without causing unnecessary airflow blockage.

PILOT BURNER

The pilot burner, or torch igniter, ignites the afterburner fuel in the exhaust section. The pilot burner attaches to the forward exhaust duct at the six o'clock position and extends into the inner and middle flameholder rings. A more complete description of the pilot burner is to be found on pages 366 to 367 and Fig. 21-23.

SPRAYBAR

FORWARD EXHAUST
DUCT LINER

FLAMEHOLDER

INNER REAR CONE

FORWARD EXHAUST DUCT

TORCH
IGNITER

FUEL MANIFOLDS

FIG. 21-11   *Afterburner assembly.*

TAILPIPE ASSEMBLY (Fig. 21-12)

The tailpipe assembly consists of the rear exhaust duct, the numbers 2, 3, and 4 liners and the exhaust nozzle. The rear exhaust duct has four support brackets at the front for the exhaust nozzle actuators, and four brackets at the rear to support the exhaust nozzle outer shroud. The liners are retained in the duct by tracks which engage clips on the liners.

The liners are ceramic coated to withstand the high afterburner temperatures. The number 2 and number 3 liners are corrugated and have cooling louvers to route cooling air along the inner surface of the liners. The liners are retained by clips that interlock with mating tracks in the duct.

The exhaust nozzle assembly consists of 24 nozzle flaps and seals interconnected by flap actuators and bellcranks to the support ring. Attached to the support

NO. 2 LINER

NO. 3 LINER

NO. 4 LINER

REAR EXHAUST DUCT

EXHAUST EJECTOR NOZZLE ASS'Y

FIG. 21-12 *Exhaust or tailpipe assembly.*

ring are 24 shroud flaps and seals. The support ring telescopes into the outer shroud. Through this arrangement, movement of the support ring toward the rear of the engine causes a simultaneous increase in the opening area of the primary and secondary exhaust nozzles.

The nozzle flaps bolt to the rear flange of the rear exhaust duct and, with the seals, form the primary exhaust nozzle. The shroud flaps and seals form the secondary nozzle.

NUMBER 1 BEARING AREA

The number 1 bearing, which is housed in the compressor front frame, is a roller bearing and restrains radial loads only; thus it permits the rotor to expand axially without transmitting stress to the surrounding structures. The front gearbox is included in the sump area, so no engine oil and airseals appear in front of the number 1 bearing. Behind the bearing is a dual, carbon-rubbing seal. Ninth-stage air is contained in the area between the seal rows to pressure load the seal segments against the race, to minimize oil loss from the sump. The forward seal-race contact surface is cooled by a spray of lubricating oil.

The oil that collects in front of the bearing flows through the open bottom strut of the front frame and into the transfer gearbox, while that behind the bearing is scavenged by a line leading to a separate element of the scavenge pump.

NUMBER 2 BEARING AREA (Fig. 21-13)

The number 2 bearing, which is housed in the compressor rear frame, is a ball bearing and restrains both the radial and the thrust loading of the rotors. It is contained in a sump enclosed by carbon-rubbing oil seals, which consist of a single row of carbon segments mounted in a housing, and held circumferentially by a coil spring (see Fig. 21-13). The seal segments have a dam on the edge nearest the bearing that forms the seal, while positioning pads contact the race and maintain the proper sealing position of the segments. The seal-race contact surface is cooled by a spray of lubricating oil. The oil that is supplied to the sump is scavenged from the front and the back of the sump through separate tubes to provide positive scavenging.

The sump cooling air pressure is confined to a cavity surrounding the sump by an airseal on each side of the sump. The airseal consists of several rims (rotating part) that contact a soft metal on the seal (stationary part). The pressure drop across each rim reduces the amount of air leakage from the cavity into the compressor rear frame. The air pressure thus contained minimizes oil loss from the sump.

FIG. 21-13 *Typical oil seal.*

NUMBER 3 BEARING AREA

The number 3 bearing, which is a roller bearing, is housed in the turbine frame and restrains radial loads only. The sump area is formed by carbon-rubbing seals and is scavenged through two separate tubes. The air pressure around the sump is confined by the rear turbine airseal and the rear number 3 bearing airseal. All of the seals are similar to those of the number 2 bearing, except the carbon seals contain a second row of segments for backup.

FRONT GEARBOX (Fig. 21-14)

The front gearbox is housed within the hub of the front frame and is connected directly to the front stub shaft of the compressor rotor through a spline. It contains a spline on the front which drives the aircraft constant-speed drive, and it is connected to the transfer gearbox by a radial drive shaft. The gearbox housing

FRONT GEARBOX ASSEMBLY

RADIAL DRIVE SHAFT

HORIZONTAL SHAFT (FRONT)

REAR GEARBOX ASSEMBLY

TRANSFER GEARBOX ASSEMBLY

HORIZONTAL SHAFT BEARING

HORIZONTAL SHAFT (REAR)

FIG. 21-14   *Accessory drive system.*

contains an anti-icing pad at the top to supply anti-icing air to the aircraft nose dome.

TRANSFER GEARBOX   (Fig. 21-14)

The transfer gearbox is mounted at the bottom of the compressor front frame, and receives power from the front gearbox through a radial drive shaft housed in the number 5 strut of the compressor front frame. It converts a radial drive to several horizontal drives and supplies the power to drive aircraft hydraulic pumps, a tachometer-generator, engine fuel pumps, a control alternator, and an oil scavenge pump. A combination cartridge/pneumatic starter is mounted on the rear face. A horizontal shaft transmits power to the rear gearbox.

DRIVE SHAFT SUPPORT BEARING   (Fig. 21-14)

The horizontal drive shaft support bearing is spline-connected to the front and rear horizontal drive shafts to prevent deflection of the shafts. The bearing housing is bolted to the bottom of the compressor front casing.

REAR GEARBOX   (Fig. 21-14)

The rear gearbox is attached to the bottom of the compressor rear casing and is hinge-mounted to compensate for the difference in the rates of expansion of the casing and the rear gearbox. It supplies power to drive the engine oil pumps, a nozzle hydraulic pump, an oil scavenge pump, and the main fuel control. It receives power from the transfer gearbox through the horizontal drive shaft.

MAIN FUEL SYSTEM (*Fig. 21-15*)

The main fuel system regulates the flow of fuel that is sprayed into the combustion section of the engine. In addition to regulating fuel flow, the system produces signals that (1) schedule the position of the compressor variable vanes, which govern the amount of airflow through the compressor, and (2) prevent afterburner system operation until engine speed and throttle position are proper. The system also supplies servo fuel at regulated pressure to the nozzle area control, and provides fuel for the afterburner-system torch igniter.

The path of fuel through the main fuel system is: The fuel flows from the airplane fuel supply system, through the engine inlet connector, and into the main fuel pump. The pump filters the fuel and delivers it at high pressure to the main fuel filter. The fuel flows from the filter to the main fuel control, which regulates the amount of fuel that will be used to operate the engine, and bypasses the excess fuel back to the main fuel pump. The metered fuel flows from the control through the fuel-flow transmitter, the main oil cooler, the pressurizing and drain valve, and the fuel nozzles. The nozzles spray the fuel into the combustion section of the engine.

MAIN FUEL PUMP (*Fig. 21-16*)

The main fuel pump is bolted to the right-hand pad on the rear side of the transfer gearbox. The pump filters the low-pressure fuel and delivers it at high pressure for use in the main fuel system.

The pump consists of an impeller-type boost pumping element, a low-pressure filter with a bypass valve that allows fuel to bypass the filter if filter inlet pressure exceeds filter discharge pressure by 33 psi, a gear-type main pumping element, and a pressure relief valve that limits pump discharge pressure to 1125 psi above the main pumping element inlet pressure.

Fuel flows through the pump inlet into the boost pumping element; the impeller increases the pressure and delivers the fuel to the outside of the low-pressure filter; it then flows inward through the filter and into the main pumping element which discharges the fuel at high pressure. A small amount of fuel at main pumping element inlet pressure is ported from the pump to cool the temperature amplifier. Excess fuel that is bypassed by the main fuel control is returned to the main pumping element inlet for recirculation through the fuel system.

FIG. 21-15 *Main fuel system.*

FILTER BOWL

FILTER BYPASS VALVE

FILTER INLET PRESSURE PORT

BYPASS AND BOOST CAVITY

MOUNTING FLANGE

A

TO A

DRIVE SPLINE

MAIN GEAR ELEMENT

DRAIN PLUG

FILTER ELEMENT

CLAMP

INLET

BOOST IMPELLER

OUTLET

FIG. 21-16 *Main fuel pump.*

BYPASS INDICATOR SWITCH

The bypass-indicator-switch mounting bracket is bolted near the four o'clock position on the forward end of the front-compressor casing. A set of electrical contacts in the switch closes when the low-pressure filter in the main fuel pump is becoming clogged.

The differential pressure switch senses the filter fuel inlet and outlet pressure. If the inlet pressure exceeds outlet by 25 psi, the contacts close; this completes a 28-volt circuit that actuates an indicator in the cockpit, so the filter can be inspected and cleaned before the following flight.

MAIN FUEL FILTER

The main fuel filter is bolted to the forward side of the main fuel control, which is clamped to the mounting pad on the forward side of the rear gearbox. The filter removes contamination from the high-pressure fuel in the main fuel system.

The filter contains a main element that filters all the fuel which enters the filter inlet, and smaller servo element that refilters the fuel that is to be used as a servo fluid in various engine controls. Each element has a bypass valve that allows fuel to bypass its filter if the pressure differential across the element exceeds 25 psi. The filter discharges the servo fuel and the main engine fuel through separate ports into the main fuel control.

MAIN FUEL CONTROL

The main fuel control is clamped to the mounting pad on the forward side of the rear gearbox. (See Chap. 12.) The control uses five signal inputs—throttle position, engine speed, compressor inlet air temperature (CIT), compressor discharge air pressure (CDP), and the position of the compressor variable vanes—to control the engine main fuel scheduling and the amount of airflow through the compressor section.

The functions of the control are

1 Governs engine speed.
2 Cuts off fuel when the throttle is in the OFF position.
3 Limits the least amount of fuel that can flow to operate the engine when the throttle is at or above the IDLE position. This allows the thrust output of the engine to be reduced at altitude without combustion flameout, and also provides a suitable amount of fuel during an engine automatic start.
4 Schedules fuel flow during acceleration and deceleration, to prevent compressor stall, combustion flameout, and excessive speed fluctuation.
5 Increases engine idle speed, when the CIT is high, to maintain airflow through the compressor.
6 Decreases engine scheduled top speed, when the CIT is low, to limit pressure in the engine.

7 Reduces fuel flow when CDP is high, to prevent an excessive amount of airflow through the compressor.

8 Controls the position of the compressor variable vanes, to maintain compressor efficiency under various operating conditions.

9 Prevents afterburner-system operation until main engine conditions are suitable.

Fuel that enters the servo inlet port of the control is used to actuate the variable vanes and the torque booster, and is also used as a servo fluid for positioning valves and pistons inside the main fuel control, the compressor-inlet-temperature sensor, and the nozzle area control.

Fuel that enters the main fuel inlet port is divided by the metering valve into bypass or excess fuel and metered fuel. The bypass fuel is returned to the main fuel pump; the metered fuel flows to the fuel nozzles to be sprayed into the combustion section.

COMPRESSOR-INLET-TEMPERATURE SENSOR

The compressor-inlet-temperature sensor transmits a signal representing inlet air temperature to the main fuel control. The sensor consists of a sensing coil that mounts in the compressor front frame and extends into the compressor inlet near the eight o'clock position, a sensor unit that is attached to the forward side of the main fuel control, and two metal-covered flexible tubes.

The sensing coil, two bellows in the sensor unit, and both tubes are filled with a temperature-sensitive fluid. Variations in temperature cause the volume of the fluid to change and expand or contract the bellows. The position of the bellows, an indication of inlet temperature, is transmitted through linkage to the main fuel control.

The flexible tube that is not connected to the sensing coil is used to counterbalance any effect that temperature inside the engine compartment has on the other tube.

A detailed examination of the Woodward 1307 fuel control is made in Chap. 12.

PRESSURIZING AND DRAIN VALVE *(refer to Fig. 12-33)*

The pressurizing and drain valve is bolted to the rear side of the main oil cooler, near the four o'clock position on the compressor rear casing.

During an engine start, the valve prevents fuel from flowing to the fuel nozzles until fuel pressure is high enough to operate the flow-scheduling mechanisms in the main fuel system. At engine shutdown, the valve allows fuel in the fuel nozzle manifold to drain, to prevent post-shutdown fires in the combustion section, but keeps the rest of the main fuel system primed.

Metered fuel from the main fuel control flows from the main oil cooler into the forward side of the valve; fuel at control bypass pressure is ported to the rear side of the valve. When metered fuel pressure is 90 psi higher than bypass fuel pressure, the valve allows metered fuel to flow to the fuel nozzles and cuts off flow from the drain. If the pressure differential becomes less than 90 psi, the valve shuts off metered fuel flow and allows fuel in the fuel nozzle manifold to drain.

FUEL NOZZLES *(refer to Fig. 12-24a)*

The 10 fuel nozzles, which are bolted to flanges around the compressor rear frame, spray fuel into the forward end of the combustion liners. Each nozzle contains a filter, a flow divider, and two separate passages from which the fuel is discharged in a single cone-shaped spray.

When inlet fuel pressure to the nozzle is less than 90 psi, the fuel flows through the filter, into the smaller of the passages, and is discharged into the combustion liner.

When inlet pressure reaches 90 psi, the flow divider valve opens and allows filtered fuel to flow into the larger passage too. The fuel discharged from both passages converges at the nozzle tip and is sprayed into the liner.

A shroud around the end of the nozzle deflects a small amount of air onto the tip of the nozzle to cool it and to retard the accumulation of carbon on the face of the nozzle.

MAIN IGNITION SYSTEM *(Fig. 21-17)*

The main ignition system consists of two circuits that are independent of each other except that a single cockpit switch energizes them both. The circuits, which operate only while the engine is being started, furnish the ignition for the fuel-air mixture in the combustion liners. Each circuit has its own ignition unit, shielded cables, and spark plug.

The two boxes containing the main ignition units are mounted next to each other near the four o'clock position on the compressor rear casing. The rear box energizes the spark plug in the number 5 combustion liner; the forward box energizes the plug in the number 4 liner. (The forward box also contains the circuit for transforming alternating current to energize the spark plug in the torch igniter of the afterburner system. This circuit is unrelated to the main ignition unit circuit.)

When the main engine ignition switch is closed, 28-volt direct current flows to both of the main ignition units. (See Fig. 16-10.) Each unit includes a step-up transformer controlled by a vibrator to produce the desired voltage; a half-wave rectifier to control current flow; a storage capacitor to accumulate sufficient energy

FIG. 21-17 *Main and afterburner ignition systems.*

FIG. 21-18 *Main spark plug.*

to produce the spark potential; and a gap which ionizes at approximately 3000 volts and allows the high-potential current to flow across it.

The main spark plugs (Fig. 21-18), which ignite the fuel-air mixture in the combustion liners during engine starts, screw into bosses in the outer combustion casing. The inner end of one plug extends into the number 4 combustion liner, the other into the number 5 liner.

The spark-plug electrodes are shunted by a ceramic semiconductor that ionizes the spark gap when the output of the ignition unit is impressed across it. This creates a low-resistance path across which the built-up energy in the ignition unit storage capacitor is discharged. This discharge is rapid and, consequently, the spark intensity is high.

AFTERBURNER FUEL SYSTEM (*Fig. 21-19*)

The afterburner (AB) fuel system increases the thrust output of the engine by spraying and igniting fuel in the exhaust tailpipe. Heating and expanding the exhaust gases increases their velocity.

Fuel from the aircraft supply system is furnished to the AB system through the engine inlet fuel connector. The valve in the inlet of the AB fuel pump prevents the fuel from entering the pump except during AB-system operation. When the engine throttle lever is positioned

in the AB range (above the 76-deg position) and engine speed exceeds 90.3 percent, the main fuel control transmits a fuel signal that opens the inlet valve and allows fuel to enter the AB fuel pump.

The engine-driven AB fuel pump, which rotates continuously during engine operation but pumps fuel only while the inlet valve is open, discharges the high-pressure fuel to the AB fuel filter. The fuel flows from the filter into the AB fuel control.

The control regulates the amount of fuel for AB operation and divides its output into two separate flows, core and annulus. The core fuel from the control flows through the AB oil cooler to the pressurizing valve. The annulus fuel flows from the control directly to the pressurizing valve.

The fuel pressurizing valve consists of four valves which divide the core fuel flow into primary core and secondary core and the annulus fuel flow into primary annulus and secondary annulus. This division ensures that adequate pressures are maintained to prevent vaporization within the spraybar tubes. Each pressurizing valve ports fuel to a fuel manifold, which delivers fuel to the 21 spraybars.

The AB fuel-air mixture is ignited by a torch igniter, which extends into the forward exhaust duct. The flame of the torch igniter is provided by combining fuel which is piped from the main fuel system; air, which is

FIG. 21-19 *Afterburner fuel system.*

piped from the outer combustion casing; and ignition, provided by the AB ignition system. Continuous ignition is provided during AB operation to ensure satisfactory burning.

Torch igniter fuel is scheduled or interrupted by the ON-OFF valve in response to AB pump discharge pressure increase or termination. The fuel is metered within the ON-OFF valve and is routed through a check valve prior to entering the torch igniter.

AFTERBURNER FUEL PUMP (*Fig. 21-20*)

The AB fuel pump is located at the seven o'clock position on the rear face of the transfer gearbox. The gear-driven impeller-type pump supplies fuel, under pressure, to the AB fuel system.

A valve, located in the inlet of the pump, regulates the passage of fuel from the fuel supply system into the pump. The valve, in turn, is controlled by an actuator, which is positioned according to pressure differential across the piston. When the differential exceeds 80 psi, the valve opens to allow fuel to enter the pump.

When AB operation is terminated, the main fuel control vents the actuator high-pressure (ON-OFF) signal line to reference pressure. Since both sides of the piston then are subject to an equal pressure, the actuator spring moves the piston and closes the valve. The inlet valve is fully closed when the fuel pressure differential on the piston decreases to less than 20 psi.

PUMP VENT VALVE (*Fig. 21-19*)

The pump vent valve is assembled to the signal-hose tee installed in the vent port of the AB fuel pump.

The pump vent valve drains the AB fuel pump cavity

and vents the torch igniter ON-OFF valve signal line to ambient pressure during nonafterburning operation. It closes to prevent fuel from escaping during AB-system operation.

AIRCRAFT REFERENCE FUEL FILTER (*Fig. 21-19*)

The aircraft reference fuel filter is located at the tee connector in the reference fuel return port of the AB fuel pump. The filter prevents contamination from entering the main and AB fuel systems during reverse fuel flow that occurs during engine start.

During normal engine operation, reference pressure fuel is returned to the AB fuel pump from the main fuel control and the AB fuel control. Reference pressure fuel returning to the AB fuel pump is bypassed around the filter element. When the engine is being started a reverse flow of fuel occurs in the reference fuel return line. During this reverse flow, the fuel from the aircraft fuel supply system that flows to the control system is filtered.

AFTERBURNER FUEL FILTER (*Fig. 21-19*)

The AB fuel filter is located at the seven o'clock position on the compressor rear casing. This filter removes contamination from the afterburner fuel.

The filter is an in-line filter. It incorporates a pressure-relief valve that allows fuel to bypass if the filter element becomes clogged.

AFTERBURNER FUEL CONTROL (*Fig. 21-21*)

The AB fuel control is located at the eight o'clock position on the compressor front casing and regulates

FIG. 21-20 *Afterburner-fuel-pump schematic.*

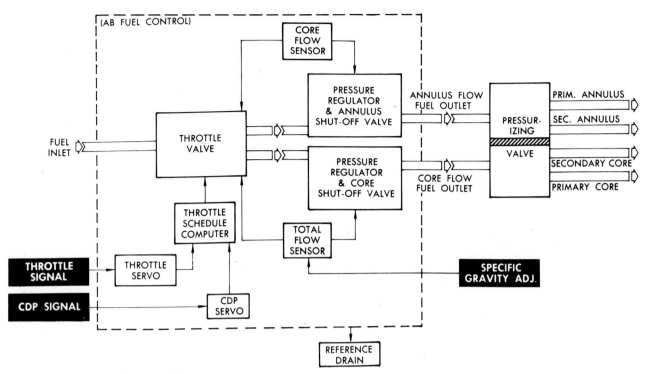

FIG. 21-21 *Afterburner-fuel-control block diagram.*

fuel flow for the AB as a function of throttle angle and compressor discharge air pressure (CDP).

The AB fuel control regulates AB fuel flow between the minimum necessary for combustion and the maximum allowable, and divides the flow into core and annulus supplies. The fuel control varies fuel flow by regulating the area of a metering orifice while maintaining a constant pressure differential across the orifice. Core fuel from the control flows through the AB oil cooler and to the pressurizing valve.

When the pressure differential between the total flow and the core flow reaches 40 psi, the control schedules the additional fuel to the annulus manifold. The fuel/air ratio within the core area is maintained by scheduling the size of the core throttling valve orifice proportionate to CDP. The annulus fuel flow is piped directly to the AB fuel pressurizing valve.

AFTERBURNER FUEL PRESSURIZING VALVE
(Fig. 21-19)

The AB fuel pressurizing valve keeps the system components filled with fuel and divides the flow between primary and secondary flows. It is located at the six o'clock position on the turbine casing.

The valve consists of four pressurizing pistons. Fuel is directed to two of them by the core fuel line and to the other two by the annulus fuel line. Fuel is admitted to the primary core manifold when core fuel pressure exceeds 121 psi, and to the secondary core manifold when it exceeds 265 psi. Fuel is admitted to the primary annulus manifold when annulus fuel pressure exceeds 101 psi, and to the secondary annulus manifold when it exceeds 245 psi.

When CDP drops below 76 psi, the fuel pressures are so low that only the primary core and primary annulus manifolds discharge fuel.

FUEL MANIFOLDS AND SPRAYBARS *(Fig. 21-22)*

The fuel manifolds and spraybars, located just aft of the turbine frame, direct sprays of fuel into the exhaust gas stream.

Fuel is distributed by 4 fuel manifolds to 21 spraybars. Each nozzle incorporates four tubes, one for each manifold. Holes in the sides of the tubes spray fuel into the AB. Core tubes spray fuel near the center of the tailpipe; the annulus tubes spray fuel near the outside of the tailpipe.

TORCH-IGNITER ON-OFF VALVE *(Fig. 21-19)*

The torch-igniter ON-OFF valve controls torch-igniter fuel flow to permit torch-igniter combustion only during AB operation.

The torch-igniter ON-OFF valve is located at the bottom of the compressor rear frame, in the torch-igniter fuel supply line. It is a two-position, hydraulically operated fluid metering valve. It contains a relieving-type inlet filter and a flow-metering cartridge.

SPRAYBAR — SPACER RING — RETAINING RING

PRIMARY SECTOR INLET TUBE · SECONDARY UNIFORM INLET TUBE

SECONDARY SECTOR INLET TUBE · PRIMARY UNIFORM INLET TUBE

FIG. 21-22 *Fuel manifold and spraybars.*

The torch-igniter ON-OFF valve is actuated by discharge fuel pressure from the AB fuel pump. When the engine throttle is advanced to afterburner range, a pressure signal from the main fuel control actuates the AB ignition switch and opens the inlet valve, admitting fuel to the AB fuel pump. The pump discharge pressure closes the pump vent valve and applies the pressure signal to the torch-igniter ON-OFF valve operating piston. Opposing this piston movement is engine main fuel manifold pressure plus a compression spring. The signal pressure overcomes these opposing forces and moves the piston to open the valve. As the piston travels to its stop, fuel displaced by the piston is discharged from the valve and fills the downstream piping to the torch igniter. With the piston in its extreme travel position, fuel flow to the torch igniter is metered by the cartridge orifice pack to support combustion in the torch igniter.

When the throttle is retarded below the AB range, fuel flow to the pump is interrupted and the pump discharge is vented overboard by the pump vent valve. This action reduces the signal pressure to the torch-igniter ON-OFF valve and allows the valve to close from the combined pressures of the compression spring and inlet fuel against the piston. With the piston in the closed position, the valve is again primed for refilling the downstream piping the next time AB operation is called for.

TORCH-IGNITER CHECK VALVE *(Fig. 21-19)*

The torch-igniter check valve permits fuel to flow to the torch igniter but prevents post-shutdown fires in the torch igniter.

The check valve is set to open at a pressure differential of 6 to 8 psi. It will permit fuel flow to the torch igniter at the rate of 200 lb/hr with a pressure drop of 10 psi maximum.

TORCH IGNITER *(Fig. 21-23)*

The torch igniter is located at the bottom of the tailpipe directly behind the spraybars. During AB operation, the torch igniter provides an intense flame that ensures positive combustion of AB fuel.

Fuel metered by the torch-igniter ON-OFF valve enters the fuel nozzle, which is located in a small combustion chamber. Some of the air, which is piped to the torch igniter, flows through a tube, to the fuel nozzle where it forces the fuel into the torch-igniter liner in a fine spray. This forced spray reduces the formation of carbon deposits on the fuel nozzle face.

The remainder of the air that is piped to the torch igniter enters the strut and flows to the inner liner, where it is mixed with the atomized fuel. The resultant mixture is ignited by a spark plug in the combustion chamber, and the burning mixture emerges from the open end of the liner as an intense flame. The rear of the torch-igniter liner spreads the flame and reduces the velocity of the surrounding fuel-air mixture. A tab on the rear of the torch-igniter liner conducts the flame to the middle flameholder ring.

Torch-igniter operation is continuous during afterburning. Because both fuel and air are scheduled to the torch igniter on the basis of CDP, the intensity of the torch-igniter flame is unaffected by altitude and airspeed.

AFTERBURNER IGNITION SYSTEM *(Fig. 21-17)*

The AB ignition system furnishes the ignition for the fuel-air mixture in the torch igniter. The resultant combustion ignites the fuel sprayed into the tailpipe by the AB spraybars. The system, which operates continuously during AB operation, consists of an ignition switch, an ignition unit, shielded cables, and a spark plug.

AFTERBURNER IGNITION SWITCH

The AB ignition switch is located near the rear end of the compressor front casing, just below the left horizontal bolt flange. During nonafterburner engine operation, main-fuel-system bypass pressure holds the switch contacts open. When the throttle is moved to the AB range and engine speed is within limits, the main fuel control transmits a high-pressure fuel signal to open the fuel inlet valve of the AB fuel pump and to initiate AB ignition. When the high-pressure signal exceeds reference pressure by 70 psi, the contact points

FIG. 21-23 *Torch igniter or pilot burner.*

in the switch close completing the circuit to the AB ignition unit. When the pressure differential drops to less than 40 psi, the contact points in the switch open and break the circuit.

AFTERBURNER IGNITION UNIT *(refer to Fig. 16-11)*

The box containing the AB ignition unit is mounted near the four o'clock position on the compressor rear casing. (The box also contains the main ignition unit circuit for transforming direct current, to energize the spark plug in number 4 combustion liner. This circuit is unrelated to the AB ignition unit circuit.)

When the AB ignition switch is closed, 115-volt alternating current flows to the AB ignition unit. The unit includes a step-up transformer to produce the desired voltage; a full-wave rectifier to control current flow; a storage capacitor to accumulate sufficient energy to produce the spark potential; and a gap which ionizes at approximately 3000 volts and allows the high-potential current to flow across it.

AFTERBURNER SPARK PLUG

The AB spark plug is located in the torch igniter, which is mounted at the six o'clock position of the tailpipe. The spark-plug electrodes are shunted by a ceramic semiconductor that ionizes the spark gap when the output of the ignition unit is impressed across it. The ionization creates a low-resistance path across which the built-up energy in the ignition unit storage capacitor is discharged. This discharge is rapid and, consequently, the spark intensity is high.

VARIABLE-NOZZLE SYSTEM *(Fig. 21-24)*

The variable-nozzle system controls the engine thrust output and protects the engine parts from overtemperature damage by regulating the position of the exhaust nozzle flaps.

Movement of the throttle during engine operation is transmitted through a cable to the nozzle area control. The control uses this mechanical signal of throttle posi-

FIG. 21-24 *Variable-nozzle system.*

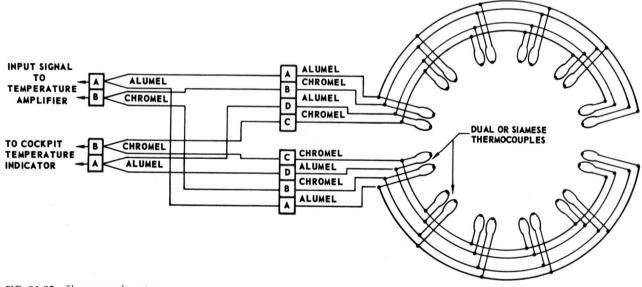

FIG. 21-25 *Thermocouple system.*

tion to schedule the position of the nozzle. However, when the exhaust gas temperature (EGT) limit is exceeded, or during a rapid acceleration, the temperature amplifier transmits an electrical signal to the nozzle area control that overrides the throttle-controlled schedule. A cable attached to the exhaust nozzle support ring continuously provides a feedback signal, which indicates the position of the nozzle flaps, to the nozzle area control.

When the signals to the nozzle area control indicate that a change in the position of the nozzle flaps is required, the control output rod moves the lever arm on the nozzle pump. When the lever arm moves (clockwise movement opens the nozzle), the pump sends high-pressure oil to either the head end (open) or rod end (close) of the nozzle actuators. As the actuator pistons move the nozzle, the feedback signal is nullifying the movement signal; when the nozzle flaps reach the desired position, the output of the pump maintains the actuator at this setting.

The components in the variable-nozzle system are: control alternator, thermocouples, temperature amplifier, nozzle area control, nozzle pump, nozzle actuators, lube and hydraulic oil pump and filters, pressure-relief valve, and nozzle hydraulic oil filters.

CONTROL ALTERNATOR (Fig. 21-24)

The control alternator is mounted on the rear side of the transfer gearbox near the seven o'clock position. The engine-driven alternator furnishes the power supply and speed signal for the temperature amplifier. The voltage and frequency of the alternator output are proportional to engine speed.

THERMOCOUPLES (Fig. 21-25)

Two semicircular harnesses, each containing six dual thermocouples, are mounted around the turbine frame. The thermocouples, which extend into the exhaust gas stream just to the rear of the third-stage turbine blades, produce thermoelectric currents that are proportional to temperature. The output of 12 of the thermocouple loops (6 in each harness) is used as a temperature signal in the temperature amplifier; the output of the other 12 energizes the exhaust gas temperature indicator in the cockpit.

TEMPERATURE AMPLIFIER (Fig. 21-24)

The temperature amplifier is mounted on the forward end of the compressor front casing near the eight o'clock position. A small amount of fuel from the main fuel system is used to cool the components inside the amplifier.

Electrical signals provided by the thermocouples and the control alternator furnish indications of the engine exhaust gas temperature (EGT), the rate of change of EGT, engine speed, and the rate of change of engine speed. The amplifier uses these four indications of engine operating conditions to produce an electrical output signal that is used in the nozzle area control to determine the proper position for the exhaust nozzle flaps.

A reference temperature adjustment on the temperature amplifier is set to limit EGT, as sensed by the thermocouples, to 625°C at 100 percent engine speed. (To improve acceleration during flight at altitude, the limiting temperature decreases when engine speed is less than 100 percent. For example, at 80 percent engine speed, the temperature at which limiting begins has dropped to approximately 535°C.) The temperature signal transmitted by the thermocouples is compared to the reference temperature signal. When the thermocouple signal is less than the reference signal, the amplifier transmits a signal to the nozzle area control, but the signal has no effect on nozzle flap position. However, if the thermocouple signal exceeds the reference signal, the amplifier output overrides the throttle-position schedule, and the amplifier output signal causes the nozzle area control to open the nozzle flaps enough to lower the EGT to the limiting temperature.

The amplifier output signal also (1) compensates for lag in the variable-nozzle system during a rapid acceleration, (2) reduces rollback of engine speed when afterburner operation is initiated, and (3) reduces the amount of overspeed when afterburner operation is terminated.

NOZZLE AREA CONTROL (Fig. 21-24)

The nozzle area control, which is mounted near the eight o'clock position on the rear end of the compressor rear casing, controls the position of the exhaust nozzle flaps by regulating the output of the nozzle pump.

The control receives mechanical signals that indicate the position of the throttle and of the exhaust nozzle flaps, and an electrical signal that is transmitted by the temperature amplifier.

Movement of the engine throttle rotates a cam in the control; the contour of the cam represents the mechanically scheduled nozzle flap position. Any position of the throttle corresponds to a scheduled setting for the nozzle flaps. However, the electrical signal can override this mechanical schedule and cause the nozzle flaps to move to a more open position when necessary.

Throttle movement or the electrical signal from the temperature amplifier, that necessitates a change in nozzle flap position is transmitted through gearing and servo mechanisms to the output rod of the nozzle area control. As the nozzle flaps move, a feedback signal, which indicates the position of the flaps, is canceling the movement signal. When the flaps reach the required position, the output rod is scheduling the nozzle pump to maintain an output that holds the nozzle actuators at this position.

Regulated pressure fuel from the main fuel control is used as the fluid in the nozzle area control servo mechanisms. A potentiometer in the control transmits a signal indicating position of the nozzle flaps to an indicator in the aircraft cockpit.

NOZZLE PUMP (Fig. 21-24)

The nozzle pump, which is bolted to the rear side of the rear gearbox near the seven o'clock position, is a variable displacement, variable pressure, reversible flow, piston-type pump. It supplies engine oil to the nozzle actuators, to maintain the nozzle flaps at a position or to reposition them as necessary.

The output of the pump is controlled by a lever arm that is attached to the output rod of the nozzle area control. The direction of lever arm moves (clockwise —open) determines whether the output of the pump will go to the head end (open) or rod end (close) of

the nozzle actuators. The amount the lever arm moves varies the pressure and volume of the oil flowing to the actuators. The lever arm is spring-loaded so it will return to a mid-travel position when there is no signal from the nozzle area control; in the mid-travel position the pump output is zero.

NOZZLE ACTUATORS (Fig. 21-26)

The four nozzle actuators are attached to brackets on the forward end of the exhaust tailpipe assembly. The actuators, which are located near the 2, 5, 8, and 11 o'clock positions on the tailpipe, move the nozzle flaps as scheduled by the nozzle area control.

Oil from the nozzle pump flows to either the head or rod end of each of the actuators. The fluid pressure moves the actuator piston to open or close the exhaust nozzle flaps.

Flexible shafts inside the head-end pressure tubes, which connect adjacent actuators, ensure simultaneous and parallel movement of all the actuator pistons: movement of the piston rotates a worm gear in the forward end of each of the actuators; as the worm gear turns, it rotates the flexible shafts which transmit the movement to the adjacent actuators.

An orifice through the piston of each actuator allows

FIG. 21-26 *Tailpipe assembly, external view.*

a small amount of oil to flow from one side of the piston to the other, to reduce the temperature of the oil in the actuator.

HYDRAULIC RELIEF VALVE (Fig. 21-24)

The discharge end of the hydraulic relief valve is attached to the outlet fitting of the rear-gearbox scavenge pump. The pump is bolted to the rear side of the rear gearbox near the six o'clock position.

The poppet-type check valve prevents pressure of the inlet oil to the nozzle pump from becoming too high. If the pump inlet pressure exceeds scavenge-oil pressure by 95 psi, the valve opens and dumps excess oil into the scavenge system. The valve also prevents scavenge oil from entering the nozzle system.

NOZZLE HYDRAULIC OIL FILTER (Fig. 21-24)

The nozzle hydraulic oil filters prevent contamination from passing with the hydraulic oil from the exhaust nozzle actuators to the nozzle pump, or from the pump to the actuators. The two identical filters are bolted to a bracket on the rear side of the nozzle pump—one filter is attached to the pump head-end port, the other to the pump rod-end port.

Each filter allows oil to flow through its filter element in either direction. A bypass valve in each filter allows unfiltered oil to bypass the filter element if the element becomes clogged.

VARIABLE-VANE SYSTEM (Fig. 21-27)

The variable-vane system schedules the position of the inlet guide vanes and the other six stages of variable vanes to maintain compressor efficiency during various operating conditions.

The variables that are used in scheduling the vane position are the temperature of the compressor inlet air (CIT) and engine speed. When the airflow requirements for operating the engine are low (during low engine speed and/or high CIT), the vanes are scheduled to a position that limits the amount of airflow through the compressor. As engine speed increases and/or CIT decreases, the engine requires a larger volume of air and the vanes are opened to minimize airflow restriction. Between approximately 65 and 95 percent corrected engine speed (measure of airflow) the vanes are positioned in accordance with the variable-vane schedule. Below 65 percent corrected engine speed the vanes are fully closed; above 95 percent the vanes are fully opened.

FIG. 21-27 *Variable-vane system.*

The variable vanes are positioned by two actuators, which use high-pressure fuel from the main fuel control to move the vane linkages.

A variable-vane schedule cam inside the main fuel control is positioned by forces that indicate engine speed and CIT. When a change in vane setting is required, the resultant of these forces on the cam opens a valve that allows high-pressure fuel to flow to the actuators. As the actuators vary the position of the vanes, a signal indicating vane position is transmitted through a flexible cable back to the main fuel control. When the vanes reach the desired position, the feedback signal has cancelled out the movement signal and the valve cuts off flow to the actuators. Some engines incorporate a vane closure valve to prevent engine stall when the aircraft guns are fired. During this period the CIT increases because of the ingestion of hot gas from the guns. The vane closure valve closes the vanes 4 deg, thus bringing the compressor away from stall.

VARIABLE-VANE ACTUATORS

The two variable-vane actuators are attached to brackets near the 4 and 10 o'clock positions on the compressor front casing (see Fig. 21-2). The actuators move the compressor variable vanes as scheduled by the main fuel control.

High-pressure fuel from the main fuel control flows to the head or rod end of each of the actuators. The fluid pressure moves the actuator piston to open or close the variable vanes. An orifice through the actuator piston allows a small amount of fuel to flow from one side of the piston to the other, to cool the actuator.

LUBRICATION SYSTEM (*Fig. 21-28*)

The lubrication system ensures adequate lubrication for the bearings and gears of the engine. The system can be divided into three subsystems:

1 The lube supply subsystem delivers filtered oil under pressure to the three main bearing areas and the three gearboxes. The oil is sprayed onto the bearings, gears, and oil seals to cool and lubricate them. Lubrication oil flows from the oil tank to the lube and hydraulic pump. The lube pump discharges the oil into the lube filter element of the lube and hydraulic filter. The oil flows from the filter to the bearing areas and gearboxes, where it is sprayed through nozzles onto the gears, bearings, and oil seals.

2 The scavenge subsystem recovers the oil from the lubrication areas and from the variable-nozzle sys-

tem. The scavenged oil is filtered, cooled, and returned to the oil tank for reuse. Each bearing sump and gearbox area has two scavenge-oil outlets—one in the forward end and one in the rear—to ensure removal of the oil whether the aircraft is diving, climbing, or flying level. The oil scavenged from these areas flows to three pumps: one pump is located on the rear side of the transfer gearbox, another on the rear side of the rear gearbox, the third to the rear of the number 3 bearing on the turbine frame. The output of the three scavenge pumps, plus oil returned from the exhaust nozzle actuation system, is delivered to the scavenge-oil filter. The oil flows from the filter through an aircraft furnished air/oil cooler, the AB fuel/oil cooler, and the main fuel/oil cooler, and back to the oil tank.

3 The pressurization subsystem (Fig. 21-29) regulates air pressure inside the oil tank, bearing sumps, and gearboxes, to ensure proper operation of the oil seals and to keep pressure in these areas at a safe level. Because the total capacity of the three scavenge pumps exceeds the output capacity of the lube pump, the scavenge pumps remove air, in addition to the oil, from the lubrication areas. This scavenge pump overcapacity causes a relatively low air pressure in the sumps and gearboxes, and high-pressure air leaks across seals into the areas. The amount of seal leakage varies between engines. If seal leakage air exceeds the amount required to maintain proper sump and gearbox pressure, excess air flows from the sumps, through the sump vent check valve, oil tank, tank pressurizing valve, and sump pressurizing valve to ambient pressure. However, if seal leakage is not sufficient to maintain the internal operating pressure, the sump and tank pressurizing valve allows enough air to enter the system to maintain the proper pressure.

OIL TANK

The oil tank, which is mounted between the 12 and 3 o'clock positions on the compressor front casing, stores the oil used in the lubrication system, the variable-exhaust-nozzle system, and the aircraft-furnished constant-speed drive.

Oil for the lubrication system flows through a port in the bottom of the tank into the lube pumping element of the lube and hydraulic pump. During normal flight, oil is supplied to the system as long as any remains in the tank. However, during inverted flight no oil is supplied to the lubrication system.

Oil for the nozzle system is contained in a compartment in the lower part of the tank. A flexible tube picks up the oil, which flows out of the tank to the hydraulic pumping element of the lube and hydraulic pump.

LUBRICATION LINES

HYDRAULIC LINES

CONSTANT SPEED DRIVE (CSD) SUPPLY LINES

VENT OR PRESSURIZATION LINES

LOW PRESSURE SCAVENGE LINES

HIGH PRESSURE SCAVENGE LINES

* INLET FILTERS

1 SCAVENGE FILTER
2 CHECK VALVE
3 AB OIL COOLER
4 AB FUEL PUMP
5 TRANSFER GEARBOX SCAVENGE PUMP
6 TRANSFER GEARBOX
7 CONSTANT SPEED DRIVE (A/C)
8 NO. 1 BEARING AND INLET GEARBOX
9 CSD FILTER (A/C)
10 AIR/OIL COOLER (A/C)
11 DAMPER BEARING
12 OIL PRESSURE TRANS-MITTER (A/C)
13 NOZZLE PUMP
14 NOZZLE HYDRAULIC FILTER
15 NO. 2 BEARING
16 REAR GEARBOX

17 REAR GEARBOX SCAVENGE PUMP
18 LUBE AND HYDRAULIC FILTER
19 LUBE AND HYDRAULIC PUMP
20 HYDRAULIC PRESSURE RELIEF VALVE
21 NOZZLE ACTUATOR (TYPICAL OF 4)
22 NO. 3 BEARING
23 NO. 3 BEARING SCAVENGE PUMP
24 MAIN OIL COOLER
25 LUBE PRESSURE RELIEF VALVE
26 TANK PRESSURIZING AND SUMP VACUUM RELIEF VALVE
27 OIL TANK
28 SUMP VENT CHECK VALVE

TO/FROM AMBIENT

FIG. 21-28 *Lubrication system.*

FIG. 21-29 *Sump-pressurizing system.*

During normal flight, oil flows freely from the tank into the compartment; however, if the quantity of oil in the tank drops to less than 0.9 gal, no more oil flows into the compartment and the supply to the nozzle system stops. During inverted flight a check valve prevents oil in the compartment from flowing back into the rest of the tank, and enough oil remains to continue to operate the nozzle system for about 30 sec.

A flexible tube, located near the center of the tank, picks up oil for the constant-speed drive. During normal flight if the amount of oil in the tank drops to less than 2.5 gal, the level of oil is below the inlet of the tube and oil supply for the drive is terminated. The flexible tube picks up oil for the constant-speed drive regardless of flight attitude.

The scavenge oil, which is being returned to the tank, contains a large amount of air that is removed in a deaerator chamber inside the tank. The air in the tank is regulated to reduce oil foaming and to provide a positive inlet pressure for the supply pumps.

A check valve in the sump vent port fitting prevents air in the tank, which normally has a higher pressure than sump pressure, from flowing into the sumps. However, if sump pressure becomes higher than tank pressure, the check valve allows airflow into the tank.

LUBE AND HYDRAULIC PUMP

The lube and hydraulic pump, which is bolted to the rear side of the rear gearbox near the five o'clock position, is a positive-displacement, rotary-vane-type pump. It contains two pump elements, one for the lubrication system and the other for the variable-nozzle system.

Lubrication system oil flows from the oil tank into the element nearest the drive-shaft end of the pump. The pump discharges the oil into the lube-oil filter of the lube and hydraulic filter assembly. The capacity of the lube pump element is 11.8 gal/min.

Nozzle-system oil flows from the oil tank into the rear element. The pump, which has a capacity of 4.1 gal/min, discharges the oil into the hydraulic oil filter of the lube and hydraulic filter assembly. The pump element contains a relief valve that prevents its discharge pressure from exceeding inlet pressure by more than 110 psi.

LUBE AND HYDRAULIC FILTER

The lube and hydraulic filter is an assembly of two filters—one filters lubrication system oil, the other filters variable-exhaust-nozzle system oil. The two filtering elements are removable and cleanable, but cannot be interchanged.

The filter for each system incorporates a bypass valve, a check valve, and a shutoff valve. Normally, oil flows from the lube and hydraulic pump through the filter elements and out the discharge ports. However, if either filter element becomes clogged, its bypass valve will open and allow unfiltered oil to flow to its discharge port. The check valves close when the engine is stopped to prevent oil leakage from the tank into the systems during shutdown. The shutoff valves close when the filter elements are removed for inspection or cleaning to prevent loss of oil from the systems.

A fitting on the lubrication-system side of the filter provides a tap for connecting a line to the aircraft-furnished lube pressure transmitter.

LUBE PRESSURE-RELIEF VALVE

The lube pressure-relief valve, which is attached to the lube oil inlet fitting of the lube and hydraulic pump, protects the aircraft-furnished oil-pressure transmitter from high oil pressures.

When the engine is started during cold weather, lube oil pressure is high due to the increased viscosity of the oil. If the differential between lube pump inlet and discharge pressures exceeds 95 psi, the relief valve

opens to prevent the pressure in the transmitter line from damaging the transmitter. However, the relief valve has a very little effect on actual system pressure, because a restriction in the fitting at the lube filter allows very little oil to flow into the transmitter line. When the oil warms and becomes more fluid, the relief valve closes and the transmitter measures actual lube-system oil pressure.

TRANSFER-GEARBOX SCAVENGE PUMP

The transfer-gearbox scavenge pump, which is mounted on the rear side of the transfer gearbox at the six o'clock position, contains two positive-displacement, gerotor-type pumps. The number 1 pump element, which is nearest the drive shaft end, has a capacity of 11 gal/min. It scavenges oil from inside the transfer gearbox. The other pump element has a capacity of 2.7 gal/min, and scavenges oil that flows into the oil outlet at the rear of the number 1 bearing sump. Each pump has a separate inlet, but both discharge oil through the same outlet.

REAR-GEARBOX SCAVENGE PUMP

The rear-gearbox scavenge pump is mounted on the rear side of the rear gearbox at the six o'clock position. It contains three positive-displacement, vane-type pumps. The number 1 pump element, which is nearest the drive-shaft end, has a capacity of 11 gal/min. It scavenges oil from inside the rear gearbox. The number 2 pump element has a capacity of 5.2 gal/min and scavenges oil that flows into the rear oil outlet of the number 2 bearing sump. The number 3 pump element has a capacity of 3.9 gal/min and scavenges oil that flows into the forward oil outlet of the number 2 bearing sump. Each pump has a separate inlet, but all three discharge oil through the same outlet.

NUMBER 3 BEARING SCAVENGE PUMP

The number 3 bearing scavenge pump, which is mounted on the rear of the turbine frame hub, contains two positive-displacement, vane-type pumps, each with a capacity of 3 gal/min. The forward pump element scavenges oil that flows into the forward oil outlet of the number 3 bearing sump. The rear element scavenges oil that flows into the rear oil outlet of the sump. The two elements discharge the oil into the same outlet.

SCAVENGE-OIL FILTER

The scavenge-oil filter, which is located near the nine o'clock position on the compressor front casing, removes contamination from the scavenge oil before it flows to the aircraft-furnished air/oil cooler.

Oil from the three scavenge pumps and the nozzle actuators flows into the filter inlet, through the filtering element, and out the discharge port. If the filtering element becomes clogged, a relief valve opens and allows unfiltered oil to flow out the discharge port. A check valve, which is assembled into the discharge port of the filter, prevents oil from flowing from the oil tank into the scavenge system while the engine is shut down.

AFTERBURNER FUEL/OIL COOLER

The AB fuel/oil cooler is mounted on the compressor rear casing near the nine o'clock position. Fuel that is discharged from the "core" outlet port on the AB fuel control is used in the cooler to reduce the temperature of the scavenge oil.

The fuel enters the fuel inlet port, flows through thin-walled tubes and out the fuel outlet port. Scavenge oil enters the oil inlet port, flows around the fuel-filled tubes and out the oil outlet port.

A bypass valve allows oil to flow from the oil inlet directly to the oil outlet, without going through the fuel tube portion of the cooler, if the temperature of the inlet oil is less than 110°F or if the pressure of the inlet oil exceeds outlet oil pressure by more than 40 psi.

MAIN FUEL/OIL COOLER

The main fuel/oil cooler is mounted on the compressor rear casing near the four o'clock position. Metered fuel from the main fuel system is used in the cooler to cool the scavenge oil. The main fuel/oil cooler is identical to the AB fuel/oil cooler.

TANK PRESSURIZING AND SUMP VACUUM RELIEF VALVE *(Fig. 21-29)*

The tank pressurizing and sump vacuum relief valve is located on the compressor rear casing near the two o'clock position. It contains two relief valves that regulate air pressure inside the oil tank, gearboxes, and bearing sumps. One valve vents air from the oil tank whenever tank air pressure exceeds ambient pressure by more than 4.5 psi; the other valve allows ambient air to bleed into the sumps and gearboxes if ambient pressure exceeds sump pressure by more than 2.5 psi.

ANTI-ICING SYSTEM *(Fig. 21-30)*

The anti-icing system directs compressor discharge air into the struts of the compressor front frame, the inlet guide vanes, and the first-stage compressor vanes. The temperature of this air prevents the formation of ice that might prove damaging to the engine.

Compressor discharge air passes through a port in the outer combustion casing into the anti-icing air tube, which directs it to the anti-icing valve. When the anti-icing control switch is closed, the anti-icing valve opens and the anti-icing air flows through struts number 2, 3, 7, and 8 into a manifold within the hub of the front frame. The air passes from the manifold through a port in the front-gearbox casing, struts number 1, 4, 5, and 6, and into the 20 inlet guide vanes. The air is discharged into the primary airstream through holes near the outer end of the four struts and through openings in the trailing edge of the inlet guide vanes.

At the compressor front casing, the anti-icing air flows through five tubes into a manifold located over the first-stage vanes. The air passes from the manifold through the variable vanes and returns to the primary airstream through two slots at the inner end of each vane.

ANTI-ICING VALVE

The anti-icing valve, which is mounted at the top of the compressor rear casing, regulates the flow and pressure of anti-icing air.

When the engine anti-icing switch in the airplane cockpit is positioned at DE-ICE, a solenoid in the valve is energized; this allows the main poppet valve to be unseated and anti-icing air to flow through the valve. The valve regulates the pressure of the anti-icing air to below 28 psi, and a pressure-relief valve prevents the pressure in the valve from exceeding approximately 35 psi.

ANTI-ICING INDICATOR SWITCH

The anti-icing indicator switch, which is mounted near the 11 o'clock position on the compressor front casing, furnishes a signal to indicate when the anti-icing valve is open and allowing anti-icing air to flow to the forward parts of the engine. The pressure of the air inside the anti-icing air tube forward of the anti-icing valve actuates a set of contacts inside the switch. When the anti-icing valve is closed, no anti-icing air flows past the valve and the contacts are open. When the valve is opened, the pressure of the anti-icing air causes the set of contacts to close; this completes a 28-volt circuit that activates the indicator in the airplane cockpit.

CONTROL LINKAGE SYSTEM *(Fig. 21-31)*

The control linkage system transmits input and feedback signals to the engine controls. The system is composed of four linkages, throttle, variable-vane feedback, variable-nozzle feedback, and nozzle area control to nozzle pump.

FIG. 21-30 *Anti-icing system.*

THROTTLE LINKAGE

The aircraft throttle lever is connected through linkage to the torque booster, which is attached to the throttle input shaft of the main fuel control. Also attached to the input shaft is a sheave inside the cable box housing. A flexible shaft that passes around the sheave also engages sheaves in the cable boxes on the nozzle area control and afterburner fuel control. As the throttle lever is moved, the movement is transmitted through the cable and sheaves to the three controls to synchronize the various systems' schedules.

TORQUE BOOSTER

The torque booster, which is mounted on the main fuel control, assists the pilot in positioning the throttle linkage by amplifying the force applied to the booster input shaft.

High-pressure fuel from the main fuel control is the actuating fluid in the torque booster. Rotation of the booster input shaft moves a pilot valve that directs the high-pressure fluid to one end of a piston and relieves pressure on the other end. The fuel pressure moves the piston, which rotates the booster output shaft.

FIG. 21-31 *Control-linkage-system schematic.*

When the output shaft reaches the desired setting, the pilot valve is positioned so it cuts off flow to the piston, and movement ceases.

VARIABLE-VANE FEEDBACK LINKAGE

The variable-vane feedback linkage conveys a signal of variable-vane position back to the main fuel control, which schedules movement of the vanes. The signal is transmitted through a flexible cable; one end of the cable is connected to a variable-vane bellcrank; the other end engages a sheave that is attached to a spring-loaded shaft on the main fuel control.

When the control schedules a change of vane position, a valve is opened that allows high-pressure fuel to flow to the vane actuators. As the actuator pistons move the vanes, the flexible cable feedback signal is neutralizing the movement by closing the valve. When the vanes reach the scheduled position, the valve is closed and fuel flow to the vane actuator stops.

VARIABLE-NOZZLE FEEDBACK LINKAGE

The variable-nozzle feedback linkage transmits a signal of the position of the variable-nozzle flaps back to the nozzle area control, which schedules movement of the flaps. The signal is conveyed through a two-piece flexible cable: one end of the cable is fastened to the exhaust nozzle support ring; the other end engages a sheave that is attached to the feedback shaft

on the nozzle area control. The sheave is spring-loaded to maintain tension on the flexible cable.

When the nozzle area control schedules a change of nozzle flap position, the output rod of the control extends (open nozzle) or retracts (close nozzle) and rotates the lever arm on the nozzle pump. The pump sends high-pressure oil to the head-end (open) or the rod-end (close) of the nozzle actuators. As the actuator pistons move the nozzle, the flexible cable feedback signal is canceling the movement signal in the control. When the nozzle flaps reach the scheduled position, the pump lever arm has returned to a setting that maintains the actuators at this position.

NOZZLE AREA CONTROL TO NOZZLE PUMP LINKAGE

The nozzle area control to nozzle pump linkage consists merely of the ball-socket-joint coupling that is screwed onto the output rod of the nozzle area control, and the bolt, washer, and nut that connect the coupling to the lever arm on the nozzle pump.

ENGINE AIRFLOW DESCRIPTION

During engine operation, air is drawn or rammed into the inlet, where it is directed onto the first-stage rotor blades by the inlet guide vanes. The successive stages of the compressor increase the pressure of the air, while forcing it to the rear. The angles of the first six stages of vanes and the inlet guide vanes are variable to maintain the efficiency of the compressor over a wide range of operating conditions.

The pressure rise of each stage of compression depends upon the speed of rotation of the rotor, which is reflected by engine speed; the density of the air, which is reflected by compressor inlet temperature; and the angle at which the air strikes the blades and vanes. The position of the vanes during any engine-speed/compressor-inlet-temperature condition is established by the main fuel control.

As the air travels to the rear, some of it bleeds inward through holes in the seventh-stage rotor spacer, and some outward through holes in the ninth-stage vane bases in the upper casing half. The seventh-stage air extraction is used as pressure-equalization air in the compressor rotor and turbine-cooling air. The ninth-stage air extraction becomes sump cooling air for the three bearing sumps.

As the air leaves the rear of the compressor, it is straightened by the outlet guide vanes to prevent swirling in the combustion section. The compressor rear frame is a diffuser which decreases the air velocity and increases its pressure. The rear frame contains air extraction manifolds to supply air to the aircraft.

The air within the combustion section supports the combustion of fuel and cools engine assemblies. A snout on each of the combustion liners directs air into the outer liners. The vanes in the snout distribute the air uniformly around the domes of the inner liners. Some of the air passes through the cowls on the fuel nozzles to hold the flame away from the nozzle tips, some through the louvers in the dome of the liners to atomize the fuel, and some through louvers in the liner to separate the flame from contact with the surface of the liner. Thimble holes in the inner liner direct the air inward to center the flame.

The remainder of the air continues to flow to the rear, surrounding the combustion liners. A small amount flows inward through holes in the inner casing, to cool the turbine shaft. It flows across a baffle on the inner rim of the first-stage turbine nozzle and onto the front face of the first-stage turbine blade shanks.

Air enters through louvers in the combustion rear liners to keep the flame from contacting the inner surface, and through thimble holes to ensure complete combustion. Combustion is completed at a point early enough to prevent the flame from being directed onto the first-stage turbine nozzle. The air surrounding the combustion liners cools the outer surface of the transition liner and some of it passes through louvers between the ports.

Air flows through the baffles on the rear flange of the combustion liners and along the inner surface of the transition-liner ports. It also enters a baffle on the rear of the transition liner and flows over the inner and outer bands of the first-stage turbine nozzle.

Some air enters the outer end of the first-stage nozzle vanes, passes inward through the vane, and is directed onto the front of the first-stage turbine blade shanks. Some air continues to flow rearward through holes in the inner rib of the turbine casing and inward through second-stage turbine nozzle vanes. It is directed onto the rear of the first-stage turbine blade shanks.

The first-stage nozzle vanes increase the velocity of the gas stream from the combustion section and direct it onto the first-stage turbine blades. The second-stage vanes reduce the swirling, again increase the velocity of the gas stream, and direct it onto the second-stage blades. The third-stage vanes reduce the swirling, accelerate the gas stream, and direct it onto the third-stage blades. The energy extracted, as a reaction to the high-velocity gases striking the blades, produces the rotary motion that drives the compressor.

Turbine shrouds and turbine seals prevent excessive leakage of gases around the tips of the blades and over the torque rings of the rotor. Strut covers, surrounding the struts of the turbine frame, reduce the swirling of the gases entering the exhaust section. The turbine frame diffuses the gas stream as it enters the tailpipe.

Thermocouples, mounted in the turbine frame, produce a signal that is proportional to the temperature of the turbine discharge (exhaust gas) temperature. The signal is used for cockpit indication and for control of the exhaust-nozzle area.

The air in the exhaust section is diffused between the inner rear cone and the forward exhaust duct liner. The air is divided into cooling air, which flows between the liners and the duct, and exhaust air, which flows through the liners. The cross section of the airstream changes from annular to circular within the duct.

Spraybars, extending into the exhaust-gas stream, add fuel which is ignited to augment the thrust of the basic engine when afterburner operation is selected. The flameholder produces a turbulence that enhances burning of the fuel. The torch igniter, receiving its air supply from the outer combustion casing, maintains the flame.

The cooling air between the liners and the ducts passes through louvers in the liner to shield its inner surface from direct contact with the flame. It also flows along the inner surface of the primary nozzle flaps and seals.

The exhaust nozzle causes the velocity of the airstream to increase by restricting its flow. The velocity of the exhaust gases past the throat (smallest area) is limited to the speed of sound within the gases. Since the speed of sound increases in proportion to an increase in temperature, the afterburner produces thrust by increasing both the temperature and the velocity of the gases.

The converging portion of the nozzle, formed by the primary flaps, accelerates the gases to a sonic velocity.

The diverging portion of the nozzle, formed by secondary air directed by the shroud flaps, controls the rate of expansion, and thus in effect accelerates the gases beyond the throat. The nozzle area is determined by the throttle position, until the temperature of the exhaust gases reach the reference temperature schedule of the engine; then the throttle control of the nozzle is over-ridden by a temperature-limiting system to maintain the exhaust-gas temperature according to the reference temperature schedule. The high velocity of the exhaust gases, passing from the throat of the nozzle to the exit, acts as an aspirator to cause air to flow along the outside of the engine. This is called secondary air.

The secondary air cools the engine and accessories, and forms the diverging (aerodynamic) exhaust nozzle. The air enters the engine compartment, around the engine inlet, and passes along the outside of the engine. It removes any fumes or leakage air from the engine compartment. The air is drawn into the outer shroud, between the primary and the secondary (shroud) nozzle flaps, and forms a nozzle around the expanding exhaust gases. The air mixes with the primary air and increases the total amount of airflow. Secondary air controls the rate of expansion of the exhaust gases beyond the primary nozzle throat and reduces the gas temperature. The shroud flap seals, and a seal between the fuselage and the outer shroud, reduce air leakage from around the outside of the aircraft, which would reduce the secondary airflow.

AIR EXTRACTION (refer to Fig. 21-4)

Air is extracted from the compressor for many uses. It is piped or ducted to supply air for turbine cooling, anti-icing, and for airplane uses. Some air passes inward through holes in the seventh-stage rotor spacer. It is ducted throughout the rotor to equalize the air pressures on the disks. It passes through the rear stub shaft and into the turbine shaft to cool the shaft and the front of the first-stage turbine wheel. The air flows through the center of the first-stage wheel, outward on the rear face of the wheel, across the inside of the first-stage torque ring, and inward on the front face of the second-stage wheel. The air flows through the center of the second-stage wheel, outward on the rear face of the wheel, across the inside of the second-stage torque ring, and inward on the front face of the third-stage wheel. The air flows through the center of the wheel, into the turbine cooling air baffle, and outward, through all seven struts of the turbine frame, into the engine compartment.

Cooling air for the three bearing areas flows outward from the compressor into the ninth-stage air manifold. It is externally piped to a tube in the number 1 strut of the compressor front frame, to a tube in the number 1

strut of the compressor rear frame, and to one in the number 2 strut of the turbine frame. The air minimizes oil leakage from the bearing sumps, surrounds the number 2 bearing sump to prevent the heat of the compressor discharge air from being transmitted to the sump, and surrounds the number 3 bearing sump to prevent the heat of the turbine discharge air from being transmitted to the sump. The air that leaks across the oil seals enters the bearing sumps.

The sump cooling air is confined in the compressor rear frame cavity by the number 2 bearing front and rear airseals. The seal-leakage air enters the 17th-stage seal leakage air cavity. The cooling air is confined in the turbine frame cavity by the rear turbine airseal at the front and the number 3 bearing airseal at the rear. The seal leakage enters the turbine discharge air from the front seal and the turbine cooling air at the rear seal.

Air, for use in the airplane, is extracted from the compressor discharge. The air enters the stiffening manifolds in the compressor rear frame inner shell. It is ducted through the numbers 2, 4, 7, and 9 struts of the rear frame.

ANTI-ICING AIR (refer to Figs. 21-4 and 21-30)

The anti-icing air prevents or removes ice formation in the engine inlet. The air is extracted through a port at the top of the outer combustion casing. It is piped to the anti-icing valve, which regulates the flow and pressure. It is piped from the valve to the first-stage compressor vanes anti-icing manifold, and to pads on the front frame, where it is ducted into the hub by four struts. The air is confined by a manifold cover in the hub of the frame and is distributed through the hollow shanks of the inlet guide vanes and the remaining four struts of the front frame. A port at the top of the gearbox casing conducts anti-icing air to the aircraft nose dome.

REVIEW AND STUDY QUESTIONS

1 Name several airplanes using this engine.
2 List the engine's major specifications.
3 Give a brief description of the engine operation and airflow.
4 Very briefly describe the construction features of the following engine parts: front frame, compressor rotor and cases, diffuser, combustion liner and cases, turbine stator and rotor, afterburner, and variable-area exhaust nozzle.
5 How is the chance for compressor stall reduced on this engine?
6 How many main bearings does the engine have?

7 How is excessive oil consumption in the bearing compartment controlled?

8 Briefly describe the following systems: anti-icing, oil, fuel, and ignition.

9 List the functions of the fuel control.

10 Describe the operation of the afterburner.

11 What is the purpose of the vane closure valve? Why is it needed?

12 Describe how and why the fuel flow, throttle position, afterburner operation, and nozzle position are all integrated.

13 Where is air extracted on this engine? For what purpose is the air used?

Chapter 22

Lycoming T-53

The Lycoming T-53 (Fig. 22-1), installed in the Grumman OV-1 and several models of the Bell UH-1 and 204 helicopter, has been selected for review because of its several distinctive features. A later, more powerful model, the T-55, has many of the same construction features and is used in the Vertol CH47A helicopter and the YAT-28E.

SPECIFICATIONS

Number of compressor stages:	5 axial, 1 centrifugal
Number of turbine stages:	2 or 4
Number of combustors:	1
Maximum power at sea level:	1100 to 1400 shp
Specific fuel consumption at maximum power:	0.58 to 0.68
Compression ratio at maximum rpm:	6:1
Maximum diameter:	23 in.
Maximum length:	47 in. approx.
Maximum dry weight:	500 lb approx.

The Lycoming T-53 gas turbine engine is a free-turbine power plant. Basically, all models of these engines are of the same configuration, but differ in some parts or assemblies. A major difference on later versions of the T-53 is the use of two gas-producer turbines and two free-power turbines instead of one of each type. The description and information given applies to all models except where noted.

The engine described here is a shaft turbine design with a single-stage, free-type power turbine and a single-stage gas-producer turbine that drives a combination axial-centrifugal compressor. The combustor is an external annular vaporizing type. Five major sections of the engine are air inlet, compressor, diffuser, combustor, and exhaust.

One model difference is the incorporation of a transient airbleed in conjunction with a faster acceleration schedule, modified airbleed actuator system, spring-mounted number 1 bearing, and a bypass fuel filter.

OPERATION (Fig. 22-2)

Air enters the inlet housing assembly and flows into the compressor section, where it is compressed by the five-stage axial-compressor rotor assembly and the centrifugal-compressor impeller. The compressed air flows through the diffuser housing and into the combustion chamber, where it mixes with fuel from the vaporizers. Air is then discharged through the turbines and exhaust diffuser.

Combustion gases drive two separate and independent turbine stages. The first-stage turbine drives the compressor rotor (N_1), which compresses and forces air rearward into the combustion chamber where it mixes with fuel. The second-stage turbine supplies the driving force for the power output gearshaft through reduction gearing.

The engine is started by energizing the starter, the starting-fuel solenoid valve, and the ignition system. Starting fuel, flowing into the combustion chamber through two starting-fuel nozzles, is ignited by the two igniter plugs adjacent to the nozzles at the 4 and 8 o'clock positions in the combustion chamber. At 8 and 13 percent N_1 speed, the fuel-regulator foot valve opens and main fuel flows into the combustion chamber through 11 fuel vaporizers and is ignited by the burning starting fuel.

Rotor speed (N_1) increases as the additional fuel mixes with compressed air and burns. When rotor speed reaches ground idle (40 to 44 percent), the igniter plugs are deenergized and the solenoid valve is deactivated, shutting off the starting fuel. During this period, the starter should be deenergized.

Combustion gases pass through the first-stage turbine nozzle assembly, impinge upon the blades of the first-stage turbine rotor, and pass through the second-stage turbine nozzle and cylinder assembly and onto the blades of the second-stage turbine rotor assembly. Approximately two-thirds of the gas energy passing through the first-stage turbine rotor is used to drive the compressor rotor assembly; the rest is used by the second-stage turbine rotor to drive the power shaft.

The second-stage power turbine rotor is splined to the power shaft and secured to it by the power-shaft bolt. At the inlet end of the engine, the power shaft is splined into the sun shaftgear, which drives the output reduction gears and power-output gearshaft.

FIG. 22-1 *The Lycoming T-53.*

1 INLET HOUSING ASSEMBLY	**7** COMBUSTION-CHAMBER ASSEMBLY	**13** EXHAUST DIFFUSER	AND TACHOMETER DRIVE SUPPORT AND GEAR ASSEMBLY
2 NO. 1 MAIN BEARING	**8** SCOOPS	**14** NO. 4 MAIN BEARING	
3 COMPRESSOR VANE		**15** MANIFOLD	
4 COMPRESSOR ROTOR ASSEMBLY	**9** FIRST-STAGE TURBINE	**16** POWER SHAFT	**20** OUTPUT SHAFT BEARING
5 INTERSTAGE BLEED COM-PRESSOR AND IMPELLER HOUSING	**10** FUEL VAPORIZER	**17** ACCESSORY DRIVE GEARBOX	**21** OUTPUT REDUCTION CARRIER AND GEAR ASSEMBLY
	11 SECOND-STAGE TURBINE NOZZLE AND CYLINDER ASSEMBLY	**18** ACCESSORY DRIVE CARRIER ASSEMBLY	**22** TORQUEMETER REAR PLATE AND CYLINDER
6 DIFFUSER HOUSING	**12** SECOND-STAGE TURBINE	**19** OVERSPEED GOVERNOR	

DIRECTIONAL REFERENCE *(Fig. 22-3)*

The following directional references are used in this section.

1 *Front*—End of engine from which output power is extracted.

2 *Rear*—End of engine from which exhaust gases are expelled.

3 *Right and left*—Determined by observing the engine from the exhaust end.

4 *Bottom*—Determined by location of accessory drive gearbox.

5 *Top*—Directly opposite, or 180 deg from, the accessory drive gearbox. (The hot-air solenoid valve is at the top of the engine.)

6 *Direction of rotation*—Determined as viewed from the rear of the engine. Direction of rotation of the compressor rotor and

first-stage turbine is counterclockwise. The second-stage turbine and the power-output gearshaft rotate clockwise.

7 *O'clock*—Position expressed as viewed from rear of the engine.

The major assemblies of the engine (Fig. 22-4) include the:

Inlet housing
Overspeed governor and tachometer drive assembly
Accessory gearbox assembly
Output reduction carrier and gear assembly
Compressor and impeller housing assemblies
Compressor rotor assembly
Diffuser housing
Combustor turbine assembly
Piping and accessories

INLET AIR AND COMPRESSED AIR FLOW

COMBUSTION GAS FLOW

FIG. 22-2 *Engine airflow.*

FIG. 22-3 *Directional references.*

drive gearbox. The overspeed governor and tachometer drive assembly is mounted on the outer-housing left side.

FIG. 22-4 *Engine major assemblies.*

1	OUTPUT REDUCTION CARRIER AND GEAR ASSEMBLY	9	DIFFUSER HOUSING
2	OVERSPEED GOVERNOR AND TACHOMETER DRIVE SUPPORT AND GEAR ASSEMBLY	10	REAR-BEARING HOUSING
		11	FIRST-STAGE TURBINE NOZZLE AND FLANGE ASSEMBLY
3	ACCESSORY DRIVE CARRIER ASSEMBLY	12	FIRST-STAGE TURBINE ROTOR
4	OVERSPEED GOVERNOR AND TACHOMETER DRIVE	13	POWER-TURBINE NOZZLE AND CYLINDER ASSEMBLY
5	INLET HOUSING ASSEMBLY	14	COMBUSTION CHAMBER
6	ACCESSORY DRIVE GEAR- BOX ASSEMBLY	15	V-BAND COUPLING
		16	SECOND-STAGE TURBINE ROTOR ASSEMBLY
7	COMPRESSOR AND IMPELLER HOUSING ASSEMBLIES	17	SECOND-STAGE TURBINE SUPPORT
		18	FIRE SHIELD
8	COMPRESSOR ROTOR ASSEMBLY	19	SUPPORT CONE
		20	COMBUSTOR TURBINE ASSEMBLY

The following descriptions of the major engine assemblies are coordinated with Fig. 22-4.

INLET-HOUSING ASSEMBLY

The inlet-housing assembly (5) is divided into two principal areas. The outer housing, supported by air struts, forms the outer wall of the air inlet area and houses the deicing manifold. The inner housing forms the inner wall of the air inlet area. The inlet-housing assembly encloses the output reduction carrier and gear assembly, the output shaft bearing, the number 1 main bearing, the overspeed governor and tachometer drive support and gear assembly, the accessory drive carrier assembly, and the torquemeter rear plate and cylinder. The inlet housing provides mounting for the accessory

OVERSPEED GOVERNOR AND TACHOMETER DRIVE ASSEMBLY

The overspeed governor and tachometer drive assembly (4) generates the indication and control signals for the power turbine. The output of the tachometer-generator, mounted on the overspeed governor and tachometer drive assembly, is transmitted to an airframe tachometer indicator, which reflects power turbine speed. The overspeed governor, in conjunction with the fuel control, maintains the power turbine speed within permissible limits. The assembly is mounted at nine o'clock position on the exterior of the inlet housing and is driven through shafts and gearing from the power turbine power-output shaft. The assembly also provides a mount for and drives the torquemeter booster pump.

ACCESSORY DRIVE GEARBOX ASSEMBLY

The accessory drive gearbox assembly (6) is mounted at the six o'clock position on the exterior of the inlet housing. It is driven by a shaftgear mated to a driving gear on the compressor rotor. The gearbox provides the drive for the oil pump, fuel control, compressor rotor tachometer-generator, and starter-generator (not part of the engine). A magnetic-chip-detector drain plug is installed in the bottom of the gearbox.

OUTPUT REDUCTION CARRIER AND GEAR ASSEMBLY

The output reduction carrier and gear assembly (1), mounted at the front of the inlet housing, consists of the support housing, carrier assembly, three planet-reduction gear assemblies, a torquemeter, and power-output gearshaft. The sun shaftgear, which is splined to the power shaft, drives the three helical planet-reduction gears mounted in the carrier and gear assembly. The reduction gears, in turn, drive the power-output gearshaft. The rear plate of the torquemeter is attached to the carrier.

COMPRESSOR AND IMPELLER HOUSING ASSEMBLIES

The compressor and impeller housings (7) each consist of two halves. The housings enclose the five-stage axial compressor and the single-stage centrifugal compressor impeller of the compressor rotor assembly. The axial-compressor stator vane assemblies are bolted to the compressor housing halves. An airbleed actuator is mounted on the right side of the impeller housing. An airbleed-connecting manifold and adapter assembly ducts bleed air from the diffuser housing to the impeller housing. Customer air is available from this adapter assembly, which also directs engine anti-icing air through a port in the impeller housing.

COMPRESSOR ROTOR ASSEMBLY

The compressor rotor assembly (8) consists of five compressor rotor disk and blade assemblies, five compressor rotor spacers, and one centrifugal compressor impeller assembly, all retained upon the compressor rotor sleeve. The first-stage turbine rotor is mounted on the rear-compressor shaft. The compressor rotor assembly encloses, but is not connected to, the power shaft.

DIFFUSER HOUSING

The diffuser housing (9) conducts air from the compressor to the combustion chamber. It supports the number 2 main bearing (compressor rotor rear bearing) and the first-stage turbine nozzle and flange assembly. Air is bled from the aft face of the diffuser vanes, through a connecting manifold, to supply anti-icing and customer bleed air.

COMBUSTOR TURBINE ASSEMBLY

The combustor turbine assembly (20) consists of the combustion-chamber assembly, power turbine nozzle and cylinder assembly, second-stage turbine support assembly, fire shield, and support cone. The combustion-chamber assembly consists of the combustion-chamber housing, combustion-chamber liner, and fuel vaporizers. The second-stage turbine support is made up of the second-stage turbine rotor assembly and the exhaust diffuser. The second-stage turbine rotor assembly consists of the second-stage turbine disk and blades, the numbers 3 and 4 bearings, and the number 3 bearing seal. The welded exhaust diffuser contains hollow struts through which cooling air is supplied to the numbers 3 and 4 bearings housings and the rear face of the second-stage turbine disk.

PIPING AND ACCESSORIES

Piping and accessories include the following:

1 Main and starting fuel manifolds and associated hoses
2 Fuel control, temperature-sensing element, and inlet-air-pressure sensing hose
3 Main wiring harness
4 Starting-fuel solenoid valve
5 Ignition unit, ignition lead and coil assembly, and igniter plugs
6 Hot-air solenoid valve and airbleed components
7 Interstage airbleed piping
8 Lubrication manifold
9 Pressure and scavenge-oil hoses
10 Torquemeter booster pump
11 Oil pump
12 Oil filter
13 Clamps, brackets, screws, and other attaching parts
14 Bypass fuel filter (on some models)
15 Combustion-chamber drain valve
16 Exhaust thermocouple harness
17 Starting-fuel nozzles
18 Exhaust diffuser cover

The engine systems are as follows:

1 Lubrication
2 Internal cooling
3 Pressurizing and anti-icing
4 Fuel, fuel control
5 Electrical
6 Interstage airbleed

LUBRICATION SYSTEM (*Fig. 22-5*)

The engine lubrication system consists of the main oil-pressure supply system and the scavenge-oil system. The principal components of the lubrication system are the main oil pump, oil filter, torquemeter booster pump, overspeed governor and tachometer-drive scavenge pump, and associated external lines and internal passages. The maximum oil inlet temperatures for various models run from 93°C (200°F) to 99°C (210°F). The engine lubrication system will operate satisfactorily with an engine oil inlet temperature between −54 and 99°C (−65 and 210°F). Recommended oils meet Mil-L-7808 or Mil-L-23699 specifications.

MAIN OIL-PRESSURE SUPPLY SYSTEM

An aircraft-mounted oil tank supplies engine-lubricating oil. Oil enters the oil pump, mounted on the accessory drive gearbox, and discharges through internal passages to the oil filter. Filtered oil is directed into two main flow paths.

One oil flow passes through internal passages in the inlet housing to supply lubricating oil to the front section of the engine, including the reduction gearing, torquemeter, accessory drive gearing, and the number 1 main bearing. The second oil-flow path through external lines to the rear section of the engine lubricates the numbers 2, 3, and 4 main bearings.

In the inlet-housing section, oil is directed through the accessory drive carrier flanges into an annular

FIG. 22-5 *Lubrication system schematic.*

passage located in the rear support flange of the carrier. Oil from this passage is directed for forced-feed spray lubrication to the carrier gears and power-shaft support bearing. A transfer tube from the accessory drive carrier assembly lubricates the number 1 main bearing and accessory drive pinion gear. Oil under constant pressure lubricates the support bearing.

A third transfer passage from the manifold is directed through an inlet-housing strut to the torquemeter pump. A pressure-regulating valve limits the rotary-pump output pressure by circulating the excess pressurized oil back to the inlet housing. The pressure oil from the torquemeter pump is directed back through an inlet-housing strut to the torquemeter valve.

An offset passage in the overspeed governor and tachometer drive assembly mounting flange supplies oil to the strainer and metering cartridge in the overspeed governor, which directs metered oil to the overspeed governor and tachometer drive gear train. An additional transfer passage from the output gearshaft rear-support bearing directs oil to the power takeoff mounting flange by means of internal passages in the inlet housing.

Oil flow to the rear section of the engine is supplied from an oil pressure port at five o'clock position on the inlet housing through an external flexible oil line to an external, rigid manifold mounted on the forward face of the diffuser housing. Oil is directed from the right side of this manifold through a strainer mounted on the diffuser housing to the number 2 main bearing. From the left side of the manifold, oil is directed through a flexible hose, strainer, and the oil-supply nozzle through the upper strut in the exhaust diffuser to lubricate the numbers 3 and 4 main bearings.

SCAVENGE-OIL SYSTEM

All internal scavenge oil from the inlet-housing section drains through hollow support struts to the bottom strut in the inlet housing, through a screen and transfer tube, and into the accessory drive gearbox. Scavenge oil from the output reduction carrier and gear assembly flows by gravity into the hollow inlet-housing struts. Scavenge oil from the number 1 main bearing is pumped to the inlet-housing struts by a paddle pump mounted on the rear of the bearing. Scavenge oil from the number 2 main bearing, aided by two impellers mounted on each side of the bearing, flows through a scavenge-oil tube in the diffuser housing and is directed to the accessory drive gearbox by an external scavenge-oil line. Scavenge oil from numbers 3 and 4 bearings, aided by two impellers located in the bearing housing, returns to the accessory drive gearbox through an external scavenge-oil line and an oil tube that extends through the bottom of the exhaust diffuser. The scavenge oil flows from the accessory drive gearbox through the aircraft oil cooler and back to the oil storage tank.

TORQUEMETER

The torquemeter is a hydromechanical torque-measuring device located in the reduction gearing section of the inlet housing. The torquemeter uses lubricating oil, but is not part of the lubrication system. It consists of a stationary plate, a movable plate attached to the planet gear carrier, and 18 steel balls positioned in conical pockets located in both plates. Rotation of the planetary gears causes the carrier-mounted plate to rotate slightly. The torquemeter balls are displaced from their individual pockets, forcing the rear torquemeter plate to move rearward. The rearward motion of the plate unseats a spring-loaded poppet valve that allows high-pressure oil to enter the torquemeter cylinder chamber, equalizing the force exerted by the displaced carrier. Torquemeter oil pressure from the cylinder and gearbox air pressure are directed to the aircraft torque-pressure transmitter, which indicates differential torque oil pressure in pounds per square inch. The differential torque oil pressure is proportional to the torque delivered to the output gearshaft.

OIL PUMP

Some model engines use a two-element gear-type lube and scavenge-oil pump, driven by a single, splined drive shaft. One element supplies main lubricating oil pressure; the other element returns scavenge oil to the aircraft-mounted oil tank. Others use a power-driven rotary lube and scavenge pump (vane type). The vane-type pump can also be used as an alternate for the gear-type pump. A common splined shaft drives both elements. A pressure-relief valve in the oil pump is adjusted to deliver a minimum of 60 to 80 psi oil pressure (measured at the oil filter discharge port) at sea level, normal rated power. This setting is rated for a maximum inlet oil temperature of 93°C (200°F) or 99°C (210°F). At pressures below relief-valve setting, oil pressure is directly proportional to compressor rotor speed. Oil pressure also varies with altitude.

OIL FILTER

The wafer-disk-type oil filter is bolted to the accessory drive gearbox. The filter contains a bypass valve, set to open at a 15 to 20 psi differential pressure, that allows the oil flow to bypass the filter elements and supply oil to the engine if the filter is clogged.

TORQUEMETER BOOSTER PUMP

The torquemeter booster pump, containing the pressure and the scavenge elements, is mounted on and driven by the overspeed governor and tachometer drive assembly. Each element is an individual pumping unit and draws oil from a separate source. The pressure element receives engine-lubricating oil at 60 to 80 psi and delivers it, through a filter, to the torquemeter valve at a pressure of 140 to 160 psi; excess oil flows back to the inlet side of the pump. A relief valve in the overspeed governor and tachometer drive assembly sets the outlet pressure. The scavenge element receives oil from the overspeed governor and tachometer drive gear housing and delivers it to the oil return passages in the inlet-housing assembly.

CHIP DETECTOR

A chip detector is installed in the lower right side of the accessory drive gearbox. The chip detector will provide an indication of the presence of metal particles in the engine lubrication system when a continuity check is performed.

INTERNAL COOLING AND PRESSURIZATION
(Fig. 22-6)

The internal cooling system provides cooling air to internal engine components and pressurizes the numbers 1, 2, and 3 main bearing and intershaft oil seals. Compressed bleed air from the centrifugal compressor section flows through internal passages to the front of the number 2 bearing housing, then under the air deflector to the rear of the bearing housing to pressurize the rear seal on the number 2 main bearing. Some of the air flows out through openings to cool the forward face of the first-stage turbine rotor. It then passes into the gas stream.

Some of the compressed air, bled from the centrifugal compressor, flows through holes in the compressor rotor rear shaft into the space between the compressor rotor shaft and the power shaft. The air bleeds rearward between the shafts, then up across the rear face of the first-stage turbine rotor. A part of the air passes through the second-stage turbine sealing ring, upward across the forward face of the second-stage turbine rotor, and into the exhaust stream.

The remainder of the compressed air (bled from the centrifugal compressor), passes through holes in the compressor rotor rear shaft into the space between the compressor rotor sleeve and the power shaft. Some of this air flows forward into the center of the seal behind number 1 bearing and to the intershaft seal located

forward of the number 1 bearing. The remainder of this air flows into the power shaft. This air flows rearward through a hole drilled in the power shaft through-bolt and then into the hollow interior of the second-stage turbine rear shaft. The air bleeds through holes in the second-stage turbine shaft to pressurize the seal in front of number 3 bearing.

The rear face of the second-stage turbine rotor and the housing for numbers 3 and 4 bearings are cooled by ambient air entering between the exhaust diffuser support cone and inner cone. The air moves forward through holes in the exhaust diffuser support cone, through exhaust diffuser struts, into the area around the numbers 3 and 4 bearing housing. The air moves forward around the numbers 3 and 4 bearing housing baffle, around the power-turbine cooling air deflector, past the second-stage turbine wheel rear face, and into the exhaust stream.

ANTI-ICING SYSTEM (Fig. 22-6)

The anti-icing system supplies hot air under pressure to prevent icing of the inlet-housing areas when the engine is operating under icing conditions. Pressurized hot air from the air diffuser flows through holes in the aft face of the diffuser vanes and collects in the air diffuser internal bleed air manifold, where it passes to an external manifold located at the one o'clock position on the diffuser housing. A connecting manifold, consisting of an external elbow and tubing, is attached to the external bleed air manifold and to an adapter located on top of the impeller housing. The connecting manifold passes air through the impeller housing to the hot-air solenoid valve.

The hot-air solenoid valve is mounted on top of the compressor and impeller housing assembly. The solenoid-operated valve controls the flow of anti-icing hot air from the diffuser housing to the inlet housing to prevent the formation of ice. During engine operation, the hot-air solenoid valve is normally energized in the CLOSED position by manually actuating a switch in the cockpit. In the event of electrical power failure, the fail-safe, spring-loaded valve returns to the OPEN position to provide continuous anti-icing air.

After leaving the hot-air solenoid valve, anti-icing air flows forward through a regulator tube into a hollow annulus (port) on top of the inlet housing. This hot air is then circulated through five of the six hollow inlet-housing support struts to prevent ice formation in the inlet housing area. Hot air also flows into an annulus in the rear of the inlet housing where it passes through the hollow inlet guide vanes to prevent icing. After passing through the inlet guide vanes, the air flows into the compressor area. In the event of electrical power

LEGEND

ANTI-ICING AIR

COMPRESSOR AIR, INTERNAL COOLING

ATMOSPHERIC AIR

FIG. 22-6 *Internal cooling and anti-icing air systems.*

failure, anti-icing becomes continuous. Hot scavenge oil, draining through the lower strut into the accessory drive gearbox, prevents ice formation in the bottom of the inlet-housing area. The anti-icing system is designed to accommodate air at static pressure and to reduce the possibility of the entrapment of solid or liquid particles.

The fuel system consists of the

1 Fuel control
2 Starting-fuel solenoid valve
3 Main- and starting-fuel manifolds and hoses
4 Bypass fuel filter (on some models)
5 Starting-fuel nozzles
6 Fuel vaporizers
7 Pressure-operated drain valve

STARTING-FUEL SYSTEM (*Fig. 22-7*)

During engine start, the starting-fuel system delivers starting fuel to the combustion chamber. Energizing the primer fuel switch opens the starting-fuel solenoid valve, allowing scheduled fuel from the fuel regulator to flow through the starting-fuel manifold, two starting-fuel nozzles, and into the combustion chamber where

it is ignited by two igniter plugs. At ground idle speed, the ignition system is deenergized, causing the solenoid valve to close and stop the flow of starting fuel. The starting-fuel nozzles are self-purging and automatically remove excess fuel.

MAIN-FUEL SYSTEM (*Fig. 22-7*)

The main-fuel system delivers metered fuel from the fuel regulator to the main-fuel manifold where it is discharged through 11 fuel vaporizers into the combustion chamber. Main fuel is ignited by the burning starting fuel.

FUEL-CONTROL ASSEMBLY

The fuel-control assembly consists of a fuel regulator, which incorporates an emergency (manual) control system, and an overspeed governor. The fuel regulator is a hydromechanical device containing a dual-element fuel pump, compressor rotor speed governor, an acceleration and deceleration control, an airbleed signal mechanism, and a fuel shutoff valve. Functionally, the fuel regulator is divided into a flow-control section

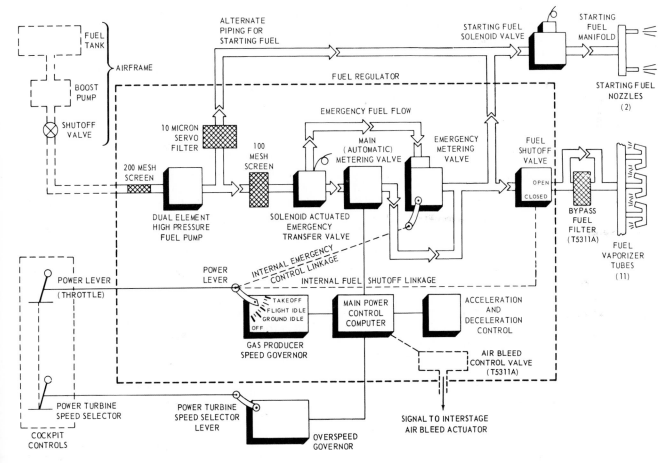

FIG. 22-7 *Typical fuel system schematic.*

and a computer section. The flow-control section consists of the components that meter engine fuel flow. The computer section comprises elements that schedule the positioning of the metering valve of the flow-control section as a function of the input signals to the regulator. The overspeed governor provides the fuel control with an N_2 speed signal. Fuel flow is then metered to maintain the desired N_2 speed plus or minus 50 rpm. The overspeed governor also serves as an override mechanism to reduce fuel flow in case of a power-turbine overspeed.

STARTING-FUEL SOLENOID VALVE

The starting-fuel solenoid valve is mounted on a bracket that is secured to the compressor housing at the 10 o'clock position. When energized, the valve allows starting fuel from the fuel control to flow to the starting-fuel nozzles. Under normal conditions, the starting-fuel solenoid valve is energized until ground idle speed is reached.

STARTING- AND MAIN-FUEL MANIFOLDS

The starting- and main-fuel manifolds are bracketed together and mounted at the rear of the combustion-chamber housing. The starting-fuel manifold receives fuel from the fuel regulator, through the starting-fuel solenoid valve, and delivers it to the starting-fuel nozzles. The main-fuel manifold receives fuel from the fuel regulator, through the main-fuel hose and bypass filter (some models only), and delivers it to the 11 fuel vaporizers.

BYPASS FUEL FILTER *(some models only)*

A bypass fuel filter, located on the lower left side of the combustion-chamber housing, filters fuel from the fuel regulator by means of a corrosion-resistant, 200-mesh, stainless steel element. As fuel passes through the filter element, contaminants are deposited on the inner wall of the filter element. In the event that clogging of the element occurs, fuel will bypass around the element into a hollow annulus within the filter housing and supply the main fuel manifold.

STARTING-FUEL NOZZLES

Two starting-fuel nozzles, located at the 4 and 8 o'clock positions in the rear of the combustion-chamber housing, deliver atomized fuel to the combustion chamber during starting. A ball check valve permits air from the combustion chamber to purge the nozzle when starting fuel stops flowing.

FUEL VAPORIZERS

Eleven equally spaced fuel vaporizers deliver main fuel to the combustion chamber. The fuel vaporizers receive fuel from the main-fuel manifold, combine it with compressed air, and deliver vaporized fuel and air to the combustion chamber.

COMBUSTION-CHAMBER DRAIN VALVE

The combustion-chamber drain valve is located at the 6 o'clock position on the combustion-chamber housing. The drain valve is spring-loaded open to allow drainage of residual fluids after engine shutdown. Internal pressure during engine operation keeps the valve closed.

FUEL-CONTROL SYSTEM *(Fig. 22-7)*

The fuel-control system consists of a primary control for the gas-producer section and an overspeed governor for the power-turbine section. An integral dual fuel pump and an emergency (manual) control system are incorporated in the primary control unit. The fuel control incorporates acceleration and deceleration controls and a droop-type governor for steady-state speed control. The main metering valve of the fuel regulator is the controlling unit by which the main fuel flow is metered to the engine. Its position is determined by the action of the gas-producer speed governor, the power-turbine overspeed governor, or the acceleration-deceleration control, depending upon engine requirements. In regulating the main metering valve, the governor or control that demands the least fuel flow overrides all others, except the deceleration control, to ensure a minimum fuel-flow rate.

The functions of the gas-producer speed control are to govern ground and flight idle operations, to limit the maximum power of the engine, and to maintain steady-state conditions through all power regimes. The gas-producer speed governor is driven, through gears, at a speed proportional to the gas-producer rotor speed. It regulates gas-producer rotor speed to the value selected by the power lever. Acceleration fuel-flow limits are scheduled over the entire operating range by scheduling maximum fuel flow as a function of gas-producer rotor speed and compressor inlet pressure and temperature. The absolute maximum fuel flow for acceleration or steady-state operation is determined by the maximum fuel-flow stop setting. The deceleration fuel-flow limits are scheduled as a function of gas-producer rotor speed and compressor inlet pressure. The absolute minimum fuel flow for deceleration or steady-state operation is determined by the minimum fuel-flow stop setting.

The power-turbine rotor is protected against overspeed operation by the power-turbine overspeed control (overspeed governor). The power-turbine governor is driven, through gears, at a speed proportional to power-turbine rotor speed. Limits for the power-turbine governor are set by adjustable stops.

FUEL FLOW

Fuel enters the dual fuel pump after passing through the inlet screen. It is then pumped through the check valves and the outlet screen to the transfer valve. With the transfer valve in the normal position for automatic operation, fuel flows to the main metering valve at a pressure controlled by the main pressure-regulating valve. The position of the main metering valve and hence the flow of fuel is automatically controlled by the computer section of the fuel control. The metered fuel flows through the open shutoff valve and the fuel discharge port to the engine main-fuel manifold and the fuel vaporizer tubes in the combustion chamber. When the transfer valve is in the emergency position, fuel flows through and is metered by the emergency (manual) metering valve. Fuel pressure is controlled by the emergency pressure regulating valve, and fuel is delivered through the open shutoff valve to the fuel discharge port and to the engine. The area of the valve opening and the resulting flow of fuel are determined by the position of the power lever controlled from the cockpit.

OPERATION OF THE EMERGENCY (MANUAL) FUEL SYSTEM *(Fig. 22-7)*

If the automatic fuel-control system fails, a changeover to the emergency (manual) fuel system should be made in accordance with the airframe instructions. When the emergency system is in operation, the main metering valve is bypassed and fuel is metered to the engine by the manual-system metering valve, which is positioned from the pilot's compartment by the power lever. Acceleration and deceleration control is not provided in the emergency system; therefore the power lever should not be moved rapidly when the emergency fuel system is in operation. Engine overspeed or possible flameout could result. The emergency fuel system does not affect the operation of the starting-fuel system if engine restart is required.

FUEL-CONTROL POWER LEVER

The power lever on the fuel control modulates the engine from *off* to *takeoff* power. The total travel of the lever is 100°. There is a 3° dwell at ground idle position and a 4° dwell at flight idle position.

Off:	0°
Ground idle:	23° to 26°
Flight idle:	38° to 42°
Normal:	83°
Takeoff:	100°

FUEL

These engines are designed to operate on Grade JP-4 or JP-5 fuel, military specification Mil-J-5624, or fuel types A or B, commercial specification ASTM D1655.

ELECTRICAL SYSTEM AND MAIN WIRING HARNESS *(Fig. 22-8)*

The main wiring harness contains connections for the ignition unit, hot-air solenoid valve, starting-fuel solenoid valve, inlet-oil temperature bulb, fuel-control transfer solenoid valve, and power-turbine and gas-producer tachometer-generators. Quick-disconnect plugs are incorporated on the harness.

IGNITION SYSTEM *(Fig. 22-8)*

The high-energy, medium-voltage ignition system consists of an ignition unit, an ignition lead and coil assembly, and igniter plugs. The system requires 14-volts dc minimum input at 3.0 amp.

The ignition unit is attached to a bracket located at 10 o'clock on the impeller-housing rear flange. The ignition unit converts low voltage through a vibrator transformer to a high voltage that passes through the ignition lead and coil assembly. The high voltage that is produced ionizes a gap in each igniter plug to produce a spark.

The ignition lead and coil assembly transmits high voltage from the ignition unit to the igniter plugs in the combustion chamber. The spark splitter coil, located below the ignition unit, distributes electric current equally to each igniter plug.

Two igniter plugs are installed in receptacles in the aft end of the combustion chamber at the 4 and 8 o'clock positions. The igniter plugs produce high-voltage sparks to ignite the fuel-air mixture in the combustion chamber.

INLET-OIL TEMPERATURE-SENSING BULB *(Fig. 22-8)*

An inlet-oil temperature-sensing bulb is installed in the main oil pump. This bulb is connected through the wiring harness to a cockpit indicator.

FIG. 22-8 *Electrical system schematic. NOTE: Typical airframe wiring diagram is shown above line A. The engine wiring diagram is shown below line A.*

EXHAUST THERMOCOUPLE HARNESS
(*Fig. 22-8*)

An exhaust thermocouple harness, consisting of an electrical connector, shielded manifold, and three chromel-alumel thermocouples, is provided with the engine. The thermocouples, inserted through the exhaust diffuser into the path of exhaust gas at the 2, 4, and 10 o'clock positions, transmit exhaust-gas temperatures to a cockpit indicator.

INTERSTAGE AIRBLEED SYSTEM (*Fig. 22-9*)

An interstage airbleed system is provided to facilitate acceleration of the compressor rotor assembly. Principal components of the system are an airbleed actuator, an airbleed valve (on some engines), and a bleed band assembly. The actuator controls operation of the compressor bleed air by tightening or loosening the bleed bands that encircle a ring of bleed air holes in the compressor housings at the exit guide vane location. The airbleed system on one model of this engine incorporates a transient control feature. The bleed bands open during all engine accelerations and open at speeds

below 70 percent N_1 speed at standard day sea level conditions as directed by the sensors in the fuel control. On some engines, the bleed bands are closed at speeds above 75 to 80 percent N_1.

FIG. 22-9 *Schematic of one form of airbleed actuator.*

INTERSTAGE AIRBLEED SYSTEM COMPONENTS
(*Fig. 22-9*)

The airbleed actuator is mounted on the right side of the compressor-housing assembly. Air pressure for operation of the airbleed actuator is obtained from a bleed port on the right side of the air-diffuser housing.

The airbleed valve (some models) is mounted on the airbleed actuator and senses the ratio of compressor discharge pressure to the compressor inlet air pressure. When the ratio reaches a preset point, the airbleed valve provides compressor discharge air pressure for operation of the airbleed actuator.

The bleed band assembly consists of two band halves bolted together. It is positioned around the rear portion of the axial-compressor housings and secured by clips bolted to the compressor housings. The looped ends of the bleed band assembly are attached to the airbleed actuator.

REVIEW AND STUDY QUESTIONS

1 What airplanes use this engine?
2 List the engine's major specifications.
3 Give a brief description of the engine and its operation.
4 Very briefly describe the construction features of the following parts: inlet-housing assembly, accessories section, compressor rotor and housing, diffuser, combustor, and turbine assembly.
5 How many main bearings are used?
6 How is the chance for compressor stall reduced in this engine?
7 Briefly describe the following systems: oil, fuel, ignition, torquemeter, and anti-icing.

Chapter 23

Allison 501-D13

The Allison Division of the General Motors Corporation has produced the 501-D13 (Fig. 23-1) in various configurations for several years.   It is used in the Lockheed Electra and Convair Conversion, while a more powerful version, the T-56 is installed in the Lockheed C130 and P-3B.

SPECIFICATIONS

Number of compressor stages:	14
Number of turbine stages:	4
Number of combustors:	6
Maximum power at sea level:	3750 eshp
Specific fuel consumption at maximum power:	0.54
Compressor ratio at maximum rpm:	9.2 : 1
Maximum diameter:	41 in.
Maximum length:	146 in.
Maximum dry weight:	1645 lb

The Allison 501-D13 engine is rated at 3750 eshp at standard day conditions with an rpm of 13,820 (100 percent), and a turbine inlet temperature of 971°C. The engine consists of a power section, a reduction gear, and a torquemeter assembly.   The power section and reduction gear are connected and aligned by the torquemeter assembly, and added rigidity is provided by two tie struts.   The propeller is mounted on a single-rotation number 60A propeller shaft.

INTRODUCTION

The power section is composed of a compressor assembly, accessory drive housing assembly, combustion assembly, and turbine assembly. The compressor assembly and the accessory drive housing assembly are referred to as the cold section of the engine, while the combustion assembly and turbine assembly are called the hot section.   The power section includes the oil, electrical, airbleed, anti-icing, fuel, and control systems.

The compressor assembly is an axial-flow type, incorporating a 14-stage compressor rotor and vane assembly encased in a 4-piece compressor casing (quadrant).   An air inlet housing, secured to the forward end of the compressor casing, receives air from the aircraft duct and directs this air to the compressor rotor. Provisions are made for the anti-icing of the air inlet-housing struts and the inlet anti-icing vanes which guide air into the rotor.   A compressor diffuser, secured to the rear end of the compressor casing, guides the air from the rotor into the combustion assembly.

The accessory drive housing assembly gear train receives its drive from the compressor extension shaft. Through a gear train, the power section rpm is reduced to that required to drive certain accessories.   The speed-sensitive valve, speed-sensitive control, and oil pump are mounted on the front cover of the accessory drive housing assembly.   The fuel control and fuel pump are mounted on the rear side of the accessory drive housing.

The combustion assembly, attached to the compressor diffuser, incorporates six cylindrical shaped combustion liners positioned between inner and outer combustion casings.   The combustion liners mix the fuel and air, support combustion, and guide the exhausting gases into the turbine assembly.

The turbine assembly, attached to the inner and outer combustion casings, consists of a four-stage turbine rotor and vane assembly encased in the turbine inlet casing, turbine vane casing, and turbine rear-bearing support.   The rotor absorbs the necessary energy from the expanding exhaust gases to drive the compressor rotor, accessories, reduction gear assembly, and propeller.   The turbine inlet casing supports the turbine front bearing, thermocouples, and houses the first-stage turbine vane assemblies.   The turbine vane casing houses the second-, third-, and fourth-stage vane assemblies.   The turbine rear bearing is supported and retained by the rear-bearing support which guides the exhausting gases into the aircraft tailpipe.

The torquemeter assembly, attached between the air inlet housing and the reduction-gear assembly, consists of a housing and shaft assembly.   The housing serves as the structural support which aligns the power section with the reduction-gear assembly.   The two tie struts provide the necessary rigidity to maintain this alignment.   The shaft assembly transmits torque from the power section to the reduction-gear assembly.   A pickup assembly, attached in the forward end of the housing, detects the torque transmitted through the shaft assembly.   The pickup-assembly signals are directed to a flight-deck torquemeter indicator which

Struts

Compressor
section

Combustion
section

Turbine
section

(a)

Reduction
gear

Torquemeter

(b)

Power
unit

FIG. 23-1 (**a**) *Sectioned and* (**b**) *external view of the Allison 501-D13 (T56) turboprop engine.*

registers the torque in shaft horsepower delivered into the reduction-gear assembly.

The reduction gear incorporates a single propeller drive shaft, a negative torque signal system, a thrust-sensitive signal system (auto feather), a propeller brake, a two-stage reduction-gear train, an accessories drive gear train, and an independent dry sump oil system.

The overall reduction-gear ratio of the two stages of reduction is 13.54:1, and thus the propeller rotates at an efficient rpm. Aircraft accessories are mounted on the rear side of the reduction-gear assembly, as well as an engine-furnished reduction-gear oil pump and filter assembly.

DIRECTIONAL REFERENCES AND DEFINITIONS

1 *Front*—The propeller end.

2 *Rear*—The exhaust end.

3 *Right and left*—Determined by standing at the rear of the engine and facing forward.

4 *Bottom*—Determined by the power-section accessories drive housing, which is located at the forward end of the power section.

5 *Top*—Determined by the breather located at the forward end of the power section.

6 *Rotation*—The direction of rotation is determined when standing at the rear of the engine, and facing forward. The power section rotor section turns in a counterclockwise direction, and the propeller rotation is clockwise.

7 *Accessories rotation*—Determined by facing the mounting pad of each accessory.

8 *Combustion-liner numbering*—The combustion liners are numbered from 1 through 6 in a clockwise direction when viewing the engine from the rear. The number 1 liner is located at the top vertical center line.

9 *Compressor- and turbine-stages numbering*—Numbered beginning from the forward end of the power section and progressively moving rearward. The compressor has 1 through 14 stages, and the turbine 1 through 4 stages.

10 *Main-rotor-bearings numbering*—Numbered beginning at the forward end of the power section, moving rearward, with number 1 being at the forward end of the compressor rotor, number 2 at the rear of the compressor rotor, number 3 at the forward side of the turbine rotor, and number 4 at the rear of the turbine rotor.

11 *Igniter-plug location*—There are two igniter plugs used, and these are located in combustion liners numbers 2 and 5.

COMPRESSOR ASSEMBLY

This assembly consists of a compressor air inlet-housing assembly, compressor housing assembly, compressor rotor assembly, diffuser, and diffuser scavenge-oil pump assembly.

The compressor air inlet housing (Fig. 23-2) is a magnesium-alloy casting, and is designed to direct and distribute air into the compressor rotor. It also provides the mounting location for the front-compressor bearing, the engine breather, the accessories drive housing assembly, the anti-icing air valves, the torquemeter housing, and the inlet anti-icing vane assembly. The inlet anti-icing vane assembly is mounted on the aft side of the air inlet housing, and is utilized to impart the proper direction and velocity to the airflow as it enters into the first stage of the compressor rotor. These vanes may "ice up" under ideal icing conditions. Therefore, provisions are made to direct heat to each of the vanes. Air, which has been heated due to compression, may be extracted, if so desired, from the outlet of the compressor (diffuser) and directed through two tubes to the anti-icing valves mounted on the compressor air inlet housing. The inlet anti-icing vanes

are hollow, and mate with inner and outer annuli, into which the hot air is directed. From the annuli, the air flows through the vanes, and exits into the first stage of the compressor through slots which are provided in the trailing edge of the vanes.

The compressor rotor is an axial-flow type and consists of 14 stages. It is supported at the forward end by a roller bearing, and at the rear by a ball bearing (Fig. 23-3).

The entire compressor housing assembly (Fig. 23-4) is fabricated from steel and consists of four quarters permanently bolted together in halves. The split lines of the housing are located 45 deg from a vertical center line. The compressor vane assemblies are installed in channels in the compressor housing, and are securely located and held in position by bolts. The inner ring of the vane assemblies supports the inter-stage airseals which form a labyrinth seal, thus preventing air from one stage bleeding back to the previous one. Between each of the vane assemblies, the housing is coated with a special type of sprayed aluminum to provide a minimum compressor rotor blade-tip clearance, thus increasing compressor efficiency. The outlet vane assembly consists of an inner and an outer ring supporting two complete circles of vanes. These are used to straighten airflow prior to entering the combustion section. The compressor housing is ported around the

FIG. 23-2 *Compressor air inlet housing.*

FIG. 23-3 *Compressor rotor.*

FIG. 23-4 *Compressor housing.*

circumference. Four bleed air valves are mounted on the outside of the compressor case at the fifth stage, and four at the tenth stage. Those valves at the fifth stage are manifolded together, as are those at the tenth stage. These valves are used to unload the compressor during the start and acceleration, or when operating at low-speed taxi idle. (Refer to Chap. 5.)

The compressor diffuser, of welded-steel construction, is bolted to the flange at the aft end of the compressor housing assembly. It is the midstructural member of the engine (Fig. 23-5). One of three engine-to-aircraft mountings is located at this point. Six airfoil struts form passages which conduct compressed air from the outlet of the 14th stage of the compressor to the forward end of the combustion liners. These struts also support the inner cone which provides the mounting for the rear-compressor bearing (ball), the seals, the rear-compressor bearing oil nozzle, the diffuser scavenge-oil pump, and the forward end of the inner combustion chamber. Air is extracted from ports on the diffuser for anti-icing and operation of the 5th- and 10th-stage bleed air valves and the 14th-stage bleed air valve. During the starting cycle, air is bled from the diffuser through the 14th-stage bleed air valve to promote better starts. Bleed air is also extracted from this point by the airframe manufacturer for aircraft anti-icing, and for cross-feeding from one engine to another for engine starter operation. The six fuel nozzles are mounted on and extend into the diffuser, and a fire shield is provided at the rear splitline.

COMBUSTION ASSEMBLY *(Fig. 23-6)*

This assembly consists of an outer and an inner combustion chamber that form an annular chamber in which six combustion liners are located. Fuel is sprayed continuously during operation into the forward end of each combustion liner. During the starting cycle, two igniter plugs, located in combustion liners numbers 2 and 5, ignite the fuel-air mixture. All six liners are interconnected near their forward ends by crossover tubes. Thus, during the starting cycle after ignition takes place in numbers 2 and 5 combustion liners, the flame propagates to the remaining liners. Liners, which do not utilize an igniter plug, have at the same location a liner-support assembly that positions the combustion liner and retains it axially. The outer combustion chamber provides the supporting structure between the diffuser and the turbine section. Mounted on the bottom of the outer combustion chamber are two combustion-chamber drain valves, which drain fuel after a false start or at engine shutdown.

TURBINE UNIT ASSEMBLY *(Fig. 23-7)*

This assembly includes six major items, namely: turbine inlet casing, turbine rear-bearing support, turbine rotor, turbine scavenge-oil pumps, turbine vane casing, and turbine vane assemblies.

The turbine inlet casing is attached at its forward end to the outer and inner combustion chambers. It is

FIG. 23-5 *Compressor diffuser.*

FIG. 23-6 *Combustion section.*

designed to locate and house the forward turbine bearing (roller), the seal assembly, front-turbine-bearing oil jet, and the turbine front scavenge-oil pump. The casing is divided into six equal passages by six airfoil struts. Each of these passages provides the means of locating and supporting the aft end of a combustion liner. Located around the outer casing are 18 holes, with one thermocouple assembly positioned in each. Thus, three thermocouple assemblies are available at the outlet of each combustion liner. These 18 thermocouple assemblies are dual, and thus two complete and individual circuits are available. One is used to provide a temperature indication (referred to as turbine inlet temperature) to the flight deck, the other is used to pro-

FIG. 23-7 *Turbine unit.*

1ST STAGE TURBINE BLADE

4TH STAGE TURBINE BLADE

1ST STAGE TURBINE WHEEL

SPACER RING

TURBINE CLAMP NUT

BALANCE RING (segmented and used as required)

TURBINE SHAFT

TIE BOLT SPACER TURBINE SHAFT

LOCK PIN (secures balance ring segments)

DOWEL PIN

LOCK PIN (secures balance ring segments)

1ST TO 2ND STAGE TURBINE SPACER

BALANCE RING (segmented and used as required)

FIG. 23-8 *Turbine rotor.*

TURBINE REAR BEARING SUPPORT

O RING

TURBINE TO COMPRESSOR TIE BOLT

SCAVENGE PUMP DRIVE SHAFT COUPLING POSITIONING PIN

SEALS

PLUG

TIE BOLT LOCK NUT

OIL PUMP DRIVE SHAFT

INNER EXHAUST CONE

PRESSURE OIL LINE

LOCK PIN

O RING

SCAVENGE PUMP DRIVE SHAFT COUPLING

O RING

BUSHING

O RING

METALLIC O RING

OIL PUMP SUPPORT

LOCK RING

TURBINE REAR SCAVENGE OIL PUMP

INNER EXHAUST CONE INSULATION

FIG. 23-9 *Turbine rear bearing support.*

vide a signal to the electronic fuel-trimming system (part of the fuel system). The circuits measure the average temperature of all 18 thermocouples, and thus a very accurate indication of the gas temperature entering the turbine section is at all times available. This is important, as the power being produced under any given set of conditions is dependent upon turbine inlet temperature.

The turbine rotor assembly (Fig. 23-8) consists of four turbine wheels which are splined on a turbine shaft. The entire assembly is supported by a roller bearing at the forward end, and a roller bearing at the aft end. A turbine coupling shaft assembly connects the turbine rotor to the compressor rotor, and thus power, extracted by the four stages of the turbine, is transmitted to the compressor rotor, driven accessories, reduction-gear assembly, and propeller. All four stages of blades are attached to the wheel rims in broached serrations of five-toothed, "fir tree" design. The first-stage turbine wheel has the smallest blade area, with each succeeding stage becoming larger.

The turbine vane casing encases the turbine rotor assembly, and retains the four stages of turbine vane assemblies. It is the structural member for supporting the turbine rear bearing support. The vanes are airfoil design, and serve two basic functions. They increase the gas velocity prior to each turbine wheel stage, and also direct the flow of gases so that they will impinge upon the turbine blades at the most efficient angle.

The turbine rear bearing support (Fig. 23-9) attaches to the aft end of the turbine rear vane casing. It houses

the turbine rear bearing (roller), the turbine rear scavenge pump and support, and the inner exhaust cone and insulation. It also forms the exhaust (jet) nozzle for the engine.

ACCESSORIES DRIVE HOUSING ASSEMBLY
(Fig. 23-10)

This is a magnesium-alloy casting mounted on the bottom of the compressor air inlet housing. It includes the necessary gear trains for driving all power-section-driven accessories at their proper rpm in relation to engine rpm. Power for driving the gear trains is taken from the compressor extension shaft by a vertical shaft gear. The following accessories are driven from this housing:

1 Speed-sensitive control
2 Speed-sensitive valve
3 Oil pump
4 Fuel control
5 Fuel pump

A number of nondriven accessories and components are furnished with the engine. These may be broadly classified into fuel system, airbleed, ignition, oil, and torquemeter systems (Fig. 23-11).

Fuel system

1 High-pressure fuel filter
2 Low-pressure fuel filter

FIG. 23-10 *Accessories case and oil pump.*

3 Primer valve

4 Fuel manifold pressure switch

5 Coordinator

6 Relay box (aircraft-mounted)

7 Temperature datum control (aircraft-mounted)

8 Temperature datum valve

9 Fuel nozzles (6)

10 Drip valve

11 Drain valves (2)

Airbleed system

1 Anti-icing solenoid valve

2 Anti-icing air valves (2)

3 Fifth- and tenth-stage compressor bleed air valves (8)

4 Fourteenth-stage starting bleed air valve

5 Fourteenth-stage bleed air control valve

Ignition system

1 Ignition exciter

2 Ignition relay

3 Igniter plugs (2)

Oil system

1 Oil filter (power section)

2 Oil filter (reduction gear)

Torquemeter system

Torquemeter indicator

REDUCTION-GEAR ASSEMBLY (*Fig. 23-12*)

The prime function of the reduction-gear assembly is that of providing the means of reducing power-section rpm to the range of efficient propeller rpm. It also provides pads on the rear case for mounting and driving the following aircraft-furnished accessories:

1 Starter

2 Cabin supercharger (engine numbers 2 and 3)

3 Alternator (115 volts, 400 cycle)

4 Tachometer-generator

5 Propeller alternator (engine-propeller rpm signal)

6 Hydraulic pump or dc generator (if required)

NOTE: In addition to the aforementioned accessories, there is an engine furnished oil pump, which is mounted on the rear case.

The reduction gear has an independent lubrication system, which includes a pressure pump and two scavenge pumps. Oil supply is furnished from an aircraft-furnished tank which also supplies the power section.

The reduction gear assembly is remotely located

FIG. 23-11 *Accessories location.*

FIG. 23-12 *Reduction gearbox.*

FIG. 23-13 *Propeller brake.*

from the power section and is attached by a torquemeter housing and two tie struts. The remote location offers a number of decided advantages, which include the following:

1 Better air inlet ducting, which increases engine efficiency and performance
2 The opportunity of readily mounting the gearbox offset up or down for high- or low-wing aircraft
3 The advantage of additional space for mounting driven accessories without affecting frontal area
4 Containing the engine in the minimum frontal area
5 The ability to utilize an electronic torquemeter

The reduction-gear housing is a magnesium-alloy casting. It has an overall reduction-gear ratio of 13.54:1, and this is accomplished through a two-stage stepdown. The primary stepdown is accomplished by a spur gear train having a ratio of 3.125:1, and the secondary stepdown is by a planetary gear train with a ratio of 4.333:1. The propeller shaft, size SAE 60A, rotates in a clockwise direction when viewed from the rear. In addition to the reduction gears and accessories drives, the reduction-gear assembly includes the following major units:

1 *Propeller brake*—Used to stop windmilling of feathered propeller, and to reduce time for propeller to come to rest after ground shutdown.
2 *Negative torque system (NTS)*—Designed to prevent excessive propeller drag.

3 *Thrust-sensitive signal (TSS)*—A device which will provide automatic feathering when armed during takeoff.
4 *Safety coupling*—A safety device backing up the NTS system.

PROPELLER BRAKE (*Fig. 23-13*)

The propeller brake is designed to prevent the propeller from windmilling when it is feathered in flight, and to decrease the time for the propeller to come to a complete stop after ground shutdown. It is a friction-type brake, consisting of a stationary inner member and a rotating outer member which, when locked, acts upon the primary-stage reduction gearing. During normal engine operation, reduction-gear oil pressure holds the brake in the released position. This is accomplished by oil pressure (hydraulic force) which holds the outer member away from the inner member. When the propeller is feathered or at engine shutdown, as reduction-gear oil pressure drops off, the effective hydraulic force decreases and a spring force moves the outer member into contact with the inner member.

NEGATIVE TORQUE SYSTEM (NTS) (*Fig. 23-14*)

The negative torque system is designed to prevent the aircraft from encountering excessive propeller drag. This system is part of the reduction gear, and is completely mechanical in design and automatic in opera-

FIG. 23-14 *Negative torque signal device.*

tion. A negative torque value in the range of 250 to 370 hp, transmitted from propeller into the reduction gear, causes the planetary ring gear to move forward, overcoming a calibrated spring force. As the ring gear moves forward, it actuates two rods which move forward through openings in the reduction-gear front case. Only one rod is used to actuate the propeller NTS linkage. When actuated, the propeller increases blade angle (toward feather) until the abnormal propeller drag and resultant excessive negative torque are relieved. The propeller will never go to the feather position, when actuated by the NTS system, but will modulate through a small blade angle range such that it will not absorb more than approximately 250 to 370 hp. As the negative torque is relieved, the propeller returns to normal governing.

THRUST-SENSITIVE SIGNAL (TSS) *(Fig. 23-15)*

The thrust-sensitive signal (TSS) provides for initiating automatic feathering at takeoff. The system must be armed prior to takeoff if it is to function, and a blocking relay is provided to prevent auto feathering of more than one propeller. The system is armed by the *auto feather arming switch* and a throttle-actuated switch. The setting of the throttle switch is such that, if operation is normal, the propeller will be developing consider-

ably in excess of positive 500 lb of thrust. This prevents auto feather except when a power failure occurs.

The system is designed to operate (if armed) when the propeller is delivering less than 500 lb of positive thrust. The propeller shaft tends to move in a forward axial direction as the propeller produces thrust. Axial travel is limited by mechanical stops. Forward movement of the shaft compresses two springs. As power decreases to 500 lb of thrust, the springs' force moves the shaft axially in a rearward direction. This movement is multiplied through mechanical linkage, and transmitted mechanically to a pad on the left side of the reduction-gear front case. An electrical switch mounted on the case, when actuated, energizes the feathering circuit.

SAFETY COUPLING *(Fig. 23-16)*

The safety coupling could readily be classified as a backup device for the negative torque signal system (NTS). It has a negative torque setting of approximately 1500 hp. In the event that the NTS system or propeller would not function properly, the safety coupling would uncouple the reduction gear from the power section. By so doing, the drag effect would be greatly reduced. The safety coupling is located and attached to the forward end of the torquemeter shaft, which transmits power-section horsepower into the reduction-gear

FIG. 23-15 *Negative torque and thrust-sensitive assembly.*

HOUSING

OUTER MEMBER

INNER MEMBER

INTERNAL RETAINING RING

PINION INPUT GEAR SHAFT

TORQUEMETER MOUNTING

INTERNAL RETAINING RING

OUTER MEMBER SHAFT

BEARING BUSHING

SPRING SEAT

SPRINGS

INPUT SHAFT OIL LUBE TUBE

INTERNAL SPHERICAL RING

EXTERNAL SPHERICAL RING

COUPLED

DECOUPLED

FIG. 23.16   *Safety coupling.*

POWER SUPPLY 115V 400 C.P.S.

PHASE DETECTOR TORQUEMETER

CAL A

TOR A B

CAL B

CAL SW S I

J 101

J 102

HP X 1000

TORQUEMETER PICK-UP

FRONT BEARING

CENTER BEARING

TORQUEMETER HOUSING

OUTER SHAFT LOCATING KEY

TORQUEMETER INNER SHAFT (TORQUE SHAFT)

TORQUEMETER OUTER SHAFT (REFERENCE SHAFT)

INTERMEDIATE BEARING

OUTER SHAFT EXCITER WHEEL

INNER SHAFT EXCITER WHEEL

FIG. 23-17   *Torquemeter assembly.*

assembly. During normal operation, the safety coupling connects the torquemeter shaft (power being produced by power section) to the reduction-gear assembly by helical splines. Aiding in the normal windup of these splines, as induced by power input and direction of rotation, is a set of four springs. When negative torque occurs, in excess of the preset value, an unwinding force overcomes the spring force and the helical splines move apart. This action disengages power section from the reduction gear. The safety coupling is designed to reengage when power-section and reduction-gear rpm are approximately the same.

TORQUEMETER ASSEMBLY AND TIE STRUTS
(*Fig. 23-17*)

The torquemeter housing provides alignment, and two tie struts provide the necessary rigidity between the power section and the reduction-gear assembly. The tie struts are adjustable through two eccentric pins which are located at the reduction-gear end. These pins are splined to enable a positive locking method after proper alignment is established by torquemeter housing. The torquemeter provides the means of accurately measuring shaft-horsepower input into the reduction-gear assembly. It has an indicated accuracy of ±35 hp from zero to maximum allowable power, which represents ±1 percent actual horsepower at standard day static takeoff power. The torquemeter consists of the following major parts.

1 Torquemeter inner shaft (torque shaft)
2 Torquemeter outer shaft (reference shaft)
3 Torquemeter pickup assembly (magnetic pickup)
4 Torquemeter housing
5 Phase detector
6 Indicator

The principal operation of the torquemeter is that of measuring electronically, the angular deflection (twist), which occurs in the torque shaft, relative to the zero deflection of the reference shaft. The actual degree of angular deflection is measured by the pickup assembly, and transmitted to the phase detector. The phase detector converts the pickup signal into an electrical signal, and directs it to the indicator located on the instrument panel.

LUBRICATION SYSTEMS (*refer to Fig. 15-10*)

The 501-D13 power section and reduction-gear assembly have separate and independent lubrication systems which utilize a common airframe-furnished oil-supply system.

The engine manufacturer supplies the airframe manufacturer with the amount of oil flow required by the

reduction gear and the power section, and also the heat rejection from the reduction gear and power section. The airframe manufacturer, with this information, designs an aircraft oil-supply system which will provide the required volume flow and the necessary oil cooling. In addition, the airframe manufacturer must provide the following cockpit indications for each engine.

1 Power-section oil pressure
2 Reduction-gear oil pressure
3 Oil inlet temperature (inlet to engine lubrication system)
4 Oil quantity

POWER-SECTION LUBRICATION SYSTEM
(*Fig. 23-18*)

The power section contains an independent lubrication system, with the exception of airframe-furnished parts which are common to power section and reduction gear. The power-section system includes the following, with each of their respective locations as indicated.

1 *Main oil pump*—This includes the pressure pump, a scavenge pump, and the pressure-regulating valve which is located on the forward side of the accessories drive housing assembly.
2 *Oil filter*—Located on the forward side of the accessories drive housing assembly.
3 *Check valve*—Located in the oil-filter assembly.
4 *Bypass valve* (filter)—Located in the accessories drive housing assembly.
5 *Three scavenge pumps*—Located in the diffuser, turbine inlet casing, and the turbine rear-bearing support.
   NOTE: Late-model engines locate the scavenge pumps externally (Fig. 23-18b).
6 *Scavenge relief valve*—Located in the accessories drive housing assembly.
7 *Breather*—Located on top of the air inlet housing.

Oil is supplied from the aircraft tank to the inlet of the pressure pump. Before the oil is delivered to any parts requiring lubrication, it flows through the oil filter. System pressure (filter outlet pressure) is regulated to 50 to 75 psi by the pressure-regulating valve. A bypass valve is incorporated in the system in the event that the filter becomes contaminated, thereby obstructing oil flow. A check valve prevents oil from seeping into the power section whenever the engine is not running.

The scavenge pump, which is incorporated in the main oil pump, and the three independent scavenge pumps are so located that they will scavenge oil from the power section in any normal attitude of flight. The scavenge pump, located in the main oil pump, scavenges oil from the accessories drive housing. The other three scavenge oil from the diffuser, and from the front and rear sides of the turbine. The outputs of the diffuser and the front-turbine scavenge pumps join that

(a)

(b)

FIG. 23-18   *Two types of power unit oil systems.*   (**a**) *Power unit oil system with internal scavenge pumps.*   (**b**) *Power unit oil system with external scavenge pumps.*

of the main scavenge pump. The output of the rear-turbine scavenge pump is delivered to the interior of the turbine-to-compressor tie bolt and the compressor rotor tie bolt. This oil is directed to the splines of the turbine coupling shaft assembly, and to the splines of the compressor extension shaft. Thus, the output of the rear-turbine scavenge pump must be rescavenged by the other three scavenge pumps. A scavenge relief valve is located so that it will prevent excessive pressure buildup in the power-section scavenge system. The combined flows of scavenged oil from the power section and reduction-gear scavenge systems must be cooled, and returned to the supply tank. A magnetic plug is located on the bottom of the accessories drive housing, and another at the scavenge-oil outlet on the forward side of the accessories drive housing.

REDUCTION-GEAR LUBRICATION SYSTEM
(*Fig. 23-19*)

The reduction-gear lubrication system includes the following, with each of their respective locations as indicated:

1 *Pressure pump*—Located on the left rear side of the reduction gear.
2 *Filter*—Located in pump body assembly.
3 *Filter bypass valve*—Located in pump body assembly.
4 *Check valve*—Located in pump body assembly.
5 *Two scavenge pumps*—One located in the bottom of the rear case; the other in the front case below the prop shaft.
6 *Two pressure-relief valves*—One for the pressure system; the other for the scavenge system. The scavenge relief valve is located in the common outlet of the scavenge pumps; the other in the rear-case housing near the oil filter outlet.

Oil flows from the pressure pump through a filter, and to all parts within the reduction gear which require lubrication. In addition, oil pressure is used as hydraulic pressure in the propeller brake assembly. A filter bypass valve guarantees continued oil flow in the event that the filter becomes contaminated. A check valve prevents oil flow into the reduction gear after engine shutdown. A relief valve, which is set at 180 psi to begin opening and to be fully open at 250 psi, prevents excessive system pressure. This valve is not to be construed as being a regulating valve, as its only function is that of limiting pressure.

The location of the scavenge pumps provides for scavenging in any normal attitude of flight. The output of the two scavenge pumps returns the oil by a common outlet to the aircraft system. A relief valve, which is set at the same values as the one in the reduction-gear

REAR CASE
OIL JET NOZZLE
BEARING DIAPHRAGM
FRONT CASE
OIL SEAL
CHECK VALVE
OIL PUMP AND FILTER ASSEMBLY
PROP SHAFT
FILTER BY-PASS VALVE
PROP BRAKE ASSEMBLY
REAR CASE INNER DIAPHRAGM
NOSE SCAVENGE PUMP
SUN GEAR LUBE TUBE
SCAVENGE OIL PRESSURE RELIEF VALVE
MAIN SCAVENGE PUMP
OIL SCREEN
MAGNETIC PLUG

⊙ PRESSURE OIL   ◕ SCAVENGE OIL

FIG. 23-19 *Reduction-gear oil system.*

pressure system, limits the maximum scavenge pressure. A magnetic plug is located on the bottom rear of the reduction-gear assembly and provides a means of draining it.

ANTI-ICING SYSTEM (*Fig. 23-20*)

The system includes an anti-icing solenoid valve located on the top of the compressor housing, two anti-icing-valve assemblies located one on either side of the compressor air inlet housing, and the necessary lines and passages from the compressor diffuser to the anti-icing valves. The system is entirely manual in operation, being selected by the crew from the flight deck by a switch called the *engine air scoop and inlet vanes anti-icing* switch. When selected, compressor discharge air, which has been heated due to compression, will flow to the two anti-icing valves. From this point, the air flows to the inlet anti-icing vane assembly, the compressor air inlet-housing struts, the fuel-control temperature probe deicer (located in the air inlet housing below the left horizontal strut), and the upper half of the torquemeter housing shroud. The fuel-control total pressure probe, located in the left horizontal strut of the air inlet housing, is anti-iced by heat conduction. Whenever engine anti-icing is selected, each engine will be independent of the other as each will have a switch. During anti-icing, approximately 1 percent of air will be bled which will result in a horsepower decrease of approximately 3 percent.

FIFTH- AND TENTH-STAGE BLEED AIR SYSTEM (ACCELERATION BLEED SYSTEM) (*Fig. 23-21*)

This is an entirely automatic system which bleeds air from the fifth and tenth stages during engine start and acceleration, and at low speed taxi. It is used to unload the compressor from 0 to 13,000 rpm in order to prevent engine stall and surge. The system includes four pneumatically operated bleed air valves located at the fifth stage and four located at the tenth stage, a speed-sensitive valve mounted on the forward side of the accessories housing assembly, and the necessary manifolding and plumbing. The bleed air valves at the fifth stage are manifolded together with the outlet being provided through the nacelle, forward of the engine baffle assembly (firewall at diffuser). The tenth-stage bleed air valves empty into another manifold, which is ducted to the aft side of the engine baffle assembly. The speed-sensitive valve is a flyweight type, which responds to engine rpm. When running at less than 13,000 rpm, the valve is so positioned that all bleed air valve piston heads are vented to the atmosphere. This allows the compressor fifth- and tenth-stage pressures to move the pistons to their open position, bleeding air overboard. When running at 13,000 rpm or better, the speed-sensitive valve directs 14th-stage air to the bleed air valve piston heads. Since 14th-stage pressure is always greater than 5th- or 10th-stage pressures, the bleed air valve pistons move to the closed position, thus preventing airbleed from the 5th and 10th stages.

FIG. 23-20 *Anti-icing system.*

(a)

(b)

FIG. 23-21 *Fifth- and tenth-stage bleed valve operation.* (**a**) *Bleed valve closed.* (**b**) *Bleed valve open.*

During low-speed taxi operation, the 5th and 10th stage bleed air valves will be in the open position, thus bleeding air.

FOURTEENTH-STAGE BLEED AIR SYSTEM (STARTING BLEED SYSTEM)

To facilitate the ignition of fuel and air during the starting cycle and to aid in initial acceleration after "light-off," a 14th-stage bleed is utilized. The system includes the 14th-stage bleed air valve and bleed air control valve which are mounted on the compressor diffuser. The 14th-stage bleed air valve is spring-loaded in the open position, and closed by compressor discharge pressure directed from the 14th stage by the bleed air control valve. At approximately 5000 engine rpm, air pressure from the 14th stage moves the bleed control valve to a position which allows 14th-stage air pressure to close the 14th-stage bleed air valve.

SPEED-SENSITIVE CONTROL

The speed-sensitive control is mounted on the forward side of the accessories drive housing assembly. The control is a flyweight type which incorporates three microswitches. At certain settings, electrical circuits are "made" or "broken" which make the entire engine starting procedure an automatic one. At 2200 rpm, the following take place:

1 The fuel control cutoff valve actuator opens the cutoff valve at the outlet of the fuel control.
   NOTE: Fuel and ignition switch must be on in the cockpit.
2 Ignition system—ON, providing it is armed by fuel and ignition switch.
3 Drip valve—Energized to closed position.
4 Fuel-pump paralleling valve—Closed fuel pumps placed in parallel; engine fuel pump light should go ON, indicating operation of the secondary pump.
5 Primer valve—Opens, this takes place only when primer switch is held to the ON position.

At 9000 rpm, the following occurs:

1 Ignition system—OFF.
2 Drip valve—Deenergized: remains closed due to fuel pressure.
3 Paralleling valve—Open: fuel pumps placed in series; engine fuel pump light should go OFF, indicating operation of the primary pump.
   NOTE: If fuel primer valve were used, it will automatically close at 50 psi fuel manifold pressure.

At 13,000 rpm, the following occurs:

1 The electronic fuel-trimming system is changed from temperature limiting with a maximum temperature of 871°C to temperature limiting with a maximum temperature of 977°C.
2 Resets maximum possible "take" of fuel by the temperature datum valve to 20 percent, rather than previous 50 percent.

IGNITION SYSTEM

Ignition is required only during the starting cycle, since the combustion process is continuous. Once ignition takes place, the flame in the combustion liners acts as the ignition agent for the fuel-air mixture.

This ignition system is classified as a condenser-discharge, high-energy type. The system includes an exciter and an ignition relay which are mounted on the top of the compressor housing, the lead assemblies, and two igniter plugs. It operates on 14 to 30 volts dc input. Actually there are two independent systems, as the exciter is a dual unit with individual leads going to the two igniter plugs. During the starting cycle as rpm reaches 2200, the speed-sensitive control automatically completes an electrical circuit to the ignition relay. This closes the circuit to the exciter, thus providing electric energy to the igniter plugs. When engine rpm reaches 9000, these circuits are deenergized through the action of the speed-sensitive control. Operation of the ignition system requires that the fuel and ignition switch in the cockpit be in the ON position. (Refer to Fig. 16-4.)

FUEL SYSTEM *(refer to Fig. 13-3)*

The fuel system includes the following, and their locations are as indicated (Fig. 23-22).

1 *Fuel pump*—Right rear side of accessories housing
2 *Low-pressure fuel filter*—Attached to right forward side of compressor-housing assembly
3 *High-pressure fuel filter*—Attached to bottom of fuel pump
4 *Fuel control*—Left rear side of accessories housing assembly
5 *Fuel-primer valve*—Bracket-mounted on center rear side of accessories drive housing assembly
6 *Manifold pressure switch*—Left side of compressor housing above fuel control
7 *Coordinator*—Attached to rear side of fuel control
8 *Temperature datum valve*—Bottom of compressor housing, aft of fuel pump
9 *Temperature datum control*—Airframe mounted
10 *Relay box*—Airframe mounted
11 *Fuel nozzles (6)*—Mounted to compressor diffuser
12 *Drip valve*—Bottom of fuel manifold, aft end of compressor housing
13 *Drain valves (2)*—Bottom, front, and rear outer combustion chamber

The fuel system must deliver metered fuel to the six fuel nozzles, as required to meet all possible conditions of engine operation either on the ground or in flight. This imposes a number of requirements on the fuel system. Some of these requirements are as follows:

1 The capability of starting under all ambient conditions.
2 Requirements for rapid changes in power.

3 A means of limiting the maximum allowable turbine inlet temperature.

4 A system which will enable the operator to select a desired power setting (turbine inlet temperature) and have it automatically maintained regardless of altitude, free-air temperature, forward speed, and fuel Btu content.

5 A system which incorporates an rpm-limiting device in the event of propeller governor malfunction.

6 A system which must control fuel flow during the rpm range in which the engine compressor is susceptible to stall or surge.

7 A system which coordinates propeller blade angle during ground operation (taxi range—start, taxi, and reverse—0 to 34° coordinator quadrant) with fuel flow.

8 A system which is capable of operating, if necessary, on the hydromechanical fuel control. However, if this is necessary, closer monitoring of throttle and engine instruments will be required.

Rather than attempt a flow description, each accessory or component will be covered in a normal sequence of flow. Since a few of the units are not associated with flow, these will be brought up in a logical sequence.

FUEL PUMP AND LOW-PRESSURE FUEL FILTER *(refer to Fig. 12-21)*

Fuel is supplied to the engine fuel pump from the aircraft system. It enters into a boost element and is then directed to the low-pressure filter.

The low-pressure fuel filter is a paper-cartridge-type filter that incorporates two bypass valves (relief safety valves) which open in the event of unusual fuel contamination. The paper cartridge is of the type that must be replaced at certain inspection periods.

The fuel-pump assembly includes, in addition to the boost element, two spur-gear-type high-pressure pumps (Fig. 23-23). These are commonly referred to as the primary and the secondary elements. During normal operation, these pumps are in series. However, during engine starting (2200 to 9000 rpm), the pumps are placed in parallel by the action of a paralleling valve in the high-pressure filter. The paralleling of the pumps is used to increase fuel flow during low rpm. Failure of either primary or secondary pump will not affect normal operation, as either pump has sufficient capacity of fuel flow for takeoff power.

HIGH-PRESSURE FUEL FILTER *(Fig. 23-24)*

The high-pressure fuel filter assembly consists of two check valves, a paralleling valve, a fuel filter, a pressure switch, and a bypass valve. The fuel filter assembly accomplishes the following:

1 Filters the output of primary and secondary pumps

2 Connects the two pumps in parallel during the starting cycle (2200 to 9000 rpm)

FIG. 23-22 *Fuel-system schematic.*

FIG. 23-23 *Fuel pump.*

3 Connects the two pumps in series during normal operation, with the primary pump supplying high-pressure fuel flow to the power section

4 Will automatically enable the secondary pump to "take over" upon failure of the primary pump

5 Provides a means of checking primary- and secondary-pump operation during the starting procedure

6 Provides a means of indicating primary-pump failure (by the engine fuel pump light)

FUEL CONTROL   *(refer to Fig. 12-8)*

The fuel control is a hydromechanical metering device which is designed to meet the following requirements:

1 Changes fuel flow with factors affecting air density as sensed at the engine inlet.

2 Meters fuel flow during starting (in conjunction with the temperature datum valve).

FIG. 23-24 *High-pressure fuel filter.*

3 Meters fuel flow during engine acceleration to aid in preventing compressor stall or surge, and is scheduled to prevent excessive turbine inlet temperature.

4 Controls power available in reverse.

5 Meters fuel to assist in controlling rpm during low- and high-speed taxi.

6 Provides an overspeed governor for ground operation, and for flight operation in the event of propeller governing malfunction.

7 Provides for manual selection of power (turbine inlet temperature) by movement of the throttle.

8 Permits any selection of power in the flight range and turbine inlet temperature (34 to 90° coordinator control) to be automatically maintained regardless of altitude, free-air temperature, and forward speed.

9 Meters 120 percent of engine fuel requirements, based upon compressor inlet air temperature and pressure, rpm, and throttle setting.

10 Allows cutoff of fuel flow manually or electrically.

PRIMER VALVE AND MANIFOLD PRESSURE SWITCH *(Fig. 23-25)*

The fuel primer system includes a primer valve which is solenoid-actuated, a manifold pressure switch, and necessary aircraft wiring and primer switch. This system may be used during the starting cycle. It is placed in operation by the spring-loaded primer switch on the flight deck. If the primer system is used, it will provide an increased initial fuel flow. This is accomplished by permitting fuel to flow through the primer valve, bypassing the metering section of the fuel control and entering just prior to the fuel-control cutoff valve. This fuel flows through the cutoff valve and is directed through the temperature datum valve, then to the manifold and fuel nozzles. The pressure switch, which senses manifold fuel pressure, breaks the elec-

FIG. 23-25 *Control-system schematic.*

trical circuit to the primer-valve solenoid when the fuel pressure reaches 50 psi.   An electrical interlock in the control system prevents energizing of the primer system after the engine is once started.

COORDINATOR (*Fig. 23-25*)

This coordinates the fuel control, propeller, and the electronic fuel-trimming system.   The operation of the coordinator is controlled by mechanical linkage from the flight deck, normally through the throttle, and, for special conditions, by the emergency shutdown handle.

The coordinator includes a discriminating device, two microswitches, a temperature datum control scheduling potentiometer, a coordinator lock, and the necessary gears and electrical wiring.   Throttle movement controls the main shaft of the coordinator, which in turn, controls the following:

1 The amount of fuel flowing from the fuel control under any given set of conditions (by mechanical linkage to the fuel control).

2 The propeller blade angle during all ground operation (taxi range: 0 to 34° on coordinator quadrant).   This is accomplished by mechanical linkage to the propeller.

3 Controls potentiometer output signal from 65 to 90° (coordinator quadrant).   This schedules turbine inlet temperature.

4 Controls two microswitches which are set, one at 65° and the other at 66°.   The 65° switch transfers the electronic fuel-trimming system from temperature limiting to temperature control.   The one set at 66° arms the temperature-trim switch which permits locking of the temperature datum valve brake.   This enables the operator to "lock in" a fuel correction with any power setting above 66°.

5 Propeller beta followup mechanism.

The discriminating device permits the use of the same mechanical linkage between the coordinator and the propeller for throttle or emergency shutdown handle operation.   The discriminator allows the throttle to position the propeller linkage at all times other than emergency shutdown.   When the emergency shutdown handle is pulled, the propeller linkage will always be actuated to feather by means of the discriminator regardless of throttle setting.

ELECTRONIC FUEL-TRIMMING SYSTEM

The electronic fuel-trimming system contributes the following:

1 Positive overtemperature protection during starting and acceleration.

2 Allows engine to operate closer to the maximum turbine inlet temperature because of accurate monitoring of fuel scheduling.

3 Permits selection of any desired turbine inlet temperature in the control range (760 to 971°C) to be automatically maintained without any throttle change.

4 Permits use of kerosine, Allison specification EMS-64A or JP4 fuel

without requirement for rerigging or recalibration of the fuel control.

5 Permits use of power unit bleed air for anti-icing purposes without the necessity of changing power settings to avoid the possibility of overtemperature.

6 Will trim fuel flow to compensate for erroneous compressor inlet air temperature or pressure sensing by the fuel control which could be caused by aircraft installation.

7 Provides a more uniform throttle setting for all engines.

8 Provisions for "locking in" a fuel correction prior to landing for a more balanced power from all engines.

The system trims the 120 percent fuel flow from the fuel control as required for any condition of engine operation.   There are two ranges of operation, namely *temperature limiting* and *temperature control*.

Temperature limiting serves to prevent the possibility of exceeding critical turbine inlet temperature limits during starting or acceleration.   Whenever operating with the throttle in the 0 to 65° position (coordinator quadrant), the engine is operating in limiting.   Temperature limiting also occurs when operating with a locked-in fuel correction above 65° (coordinator quadrant).

Two different limits are required: a lower one of 871°C needed below 13,000 rpm when the fifth- and tenth-stage compressor bleed air valves are open; a higher temperature limit of 977°C permits locking-in of a fuel correction at any throttle setting above 65° (coordinator quadrant) without having an overtemperature signal. Thus, the following operational conditions exist:

1 Temperature limit of 871°C when starting and accelerating up to 13,000 rpm

2 Temperature limit of 871°C when operating at low-speed taxi

3 Temperature limit of 977°C during high-speed taxi

4 Temperature limit of 977°C up to 65°C (coordinator quadrant)

5 Temperature limit of 977°C when rpm is greater than 13,000 and temperature trim switch is in locked (locked-in fuel correction)

Temperature control permits the use of the throttle to schedule a desired turbine inlet temperature when operating above 65° (coordinator quadrant).   Temperature control requires rpm in excess of 13,000 with temperature trim switch in CONTROLLED (*no* locked-in fuel correction).

COMPONENTS REQUIRED FOR OPERATION OF THE ELECTRONIC FUEL-TRIMMING SYSTEM (*Fig. 23-26*)

A number of engine and airframe components are required for operation of the electronic fuel-trimming system, and include the following:

1 Temperature datum valve

2 Temperature datum control

3 Relay box

FIG. 23-26 *Electrical-system schematic.*

4   Thermocouples (18 in parallel)
5   Coordinator (potentiometer and microswitches)
6   Speed-sensitive control (13,000-rpm switch)
7   Throttle (flight deck)
8   Temperature trim light (flight deck)
9   Temperature trim switch (flight deck)
10   Engine-temperature datum control switch (flight deck)

The temperature datum valve receives 120 percent of engine fuel flow requirement. Obviously some fuel must be bypassed by the temperature datum valve. When 20 percent is bypassed, the term *null* is used to describe this condition. When more than 20 percent is bypassed, a *take* condition exists, and if less than 20 percent is bypassed, a *put* condition exists.

In order for the electronic fuel-trimming system to function, the temperature datum control must receive a temperature signal and a reference signal. The temperature signal always comes from 18 thermocouples at the turbine inlet. The reference signal can be from one of three sources: start (871°C) from a potentiometer in the temperature datum control; normal (977°C) from a potentiometer in the temperature datum control; or from a variable potentiometer in the coordinator (approximately 760 to 971°C turbine inlet temperature). The variable potentiometer in the coordinator is positioned by movement of the throttle on the flight deck in

the range of 65 to 90° (coordinator quadrant). When the temperature signal (18 thermocouples) is less than the reference signal (start or normal), the temperature datum control sends no signal to the temperature datum valve. Hence, the valve remains in the *null* position since there is no overtemperature condition (bypass 20 percent).

If the temperature signal (18 thermocouples) is greater than the reference signal (start or normal), the temperature datum control sends a signal to the temperature datum valve to *take* fuel (bypasses more than 20 percent).

During temperature control, if the temperature signal exceeds the reference signal from the coordinator potentiometer, the temperature datum control sends a signal to the temperature datum valve to *take* fuel (bypasses more than 20 percent).

When operating in the control range and the temperature signal is less than the reference signal from the coordinator potentiometer, the temperature datum control sends a *put* (bypasses less than 20 percent) signal to the temperature datum valve.

Thus, in temperature limiting, the signal to the temperature datum valve can only be one which will cause the valve to move to a *take* position. However, in temperature control, the signal may result in placing the valve in either a *take* or *put* position.

The following are conditions of engine operation which will result in *null, put,* or *take:*

1   When no correction is necessary, a null condition exists (bypass 20 percent).

2   When turbine inlet temperature is less than desired in the temperature-control range, a maximum of 15 percent put is possible (bypass 5 percent).

3   During starting, and acceleration up to 13,000 rpm, the maximum take may be as high as 50 percent (bypass 70 percent). However, when engine rpm reaches 13,000, the speed-sensitive control deenergizes a circuit which resets the maximum possible take to 20 percent (bypass 40 percent).

NOTE: During starting and engine acceleration, it is necessary to provide a means of taking a greater percentage of fuel than when the engine is operating at, or near, its maximum rpm.

TEMPERATURE DATUM VALVE   *(Fig. 23-27)*

The temperature datum valve is an electrically operated fuel-trimming device. It is located in the fuel system so that all fuel, flowing from the fuel control to the nozzles, must pass through it. The valve operates on ac current fed from the temperature datum control. Fuel, in excess of that required by the engine, is bypassed and returned with excess fuel from the fuel control to the inlet of the primary and secondary fuel pumps. As previously mentioned, it is necessary to have available, two distinct ranges of fuel *take*. To accomplish

this, a solenoid-operated control valve is an integral part of the temperature datum valve. The solenoid is energized by 28 volts dc through the speed-sensitive control when the engine is operating in the 0- to 13,000-rpm range. At 13,000 rpm, the solenoid is deenergized, which resets the *take* stop to 20 percent of the nominal fuel-flow requirements. A brake is also included in the temperature datum valve. When the temperature trim switch is placed in the locked position and the throttle is in the range of 65 to 90° (coordinator quadrant—approximately 760 to 971°C), the valve will then supply fuel flow correction in the 0 to 65° (coordinator quadrant) range. In the event that an overtemperature condition occurs while the switch is in locked, the control system automatically unlocks the brake and bypasses more fuel to prevent an overtemperature condition. (Refer to Fig. 12-13.)

TEMPERATURE DATUM CONTROL   *(Fig. 23-25)*

The temperature datum control is an electronic control, using 115-volt, 400-cycle alternating current. The control may be thought of as a comparator in that it compares actual with desired or limited turbine inlet temperature signals. If an out-of-balance condition exists, the control signals the temperature datum valve to *put* (increase) or *take* (decrease) fuel flow as required to bring the temperature back to that which is scheduled.

FIG. 23-27   *Temperature-datum-valve schematic.*

Operation of the temperature datum control requires having the engine-temperature datum control switch (located on the flight deck) in the NORMAL position.

The temperature datum control contains four potentiometers, the necessary electrical wiring, and four external adjustments. The external adjustments are referred to as the *bias, slope, start limiting,* and *normal limiting.* The bias and slope adjusts the temperature schedule for engine operation between 65 and 90° (coordinator quadrant) which is known as the control range. The other two adjust the start-limiting temperature and the normal-limiting temperature.

RELAY BOX

The relay box contains the relays which are required by the engine for proper sequencing of all control components.

THERMOCOUPLES *(Fig. 23-28)*

There is a total of 18 dual thermocouples, forming two individual circuits. One circuit provides turbine inlet temperature to the flight-deck instrument, and the other provides an actual temperature indication to the temperature datum control. Due to the fact that each circuit is a parallel one made of 18 thermocouples, the temperature indication is an average of all 18.

COORDINATOR POTENTIOMETER AND MICROSWITCHES

The coordinator potentiometer is a variable one and provides the desired turbine inlet temperature signal to the temperature datum control in the range of 65 to 90° (coordinator quadrant—approximately 760° to 971°C). The variable signal is a result of throttle movement on the flight deck positioning this potentiometer.

The microswitch, set at 65°, transfers the electronic fuel-trimming system from temperature limiting to temperature control. The one at 66° arms the temperature trim switch which allows locking of the temperature datum valve brake.

SPEED-SENSITIVE CONTROL (13,000-RPM SWITCH)

At 13,000 rpm, it deenergizes the solenoid-operated control valve in the temperature datum valve, thus switching from a maximum *take* of 50 percent to one of 20 percent.

THROTTLE *(Fig. 23-25)*

The throttle provides the means of complete power control during all normal conditions of operation.

Movement of the throttle actuates mechanical linkage to the coordinator which has a total quadrant travel of 0 to 90°. Ground operation, which includes start, ground idle, taxi, and reverse, is in the range of 0 to 34°. Flight operation is between 34 and 90° at all times. Temperature limiting schedule is 0 to 65° and temperature control schedule is 65 to 90°. *NOTE:* All of the aforementioned ranges are in coordinator quadrant degrees. Total flight station throttle travel is somewhat less.

TEMPERATURE TRIM SWITCH *(Fig. 23-25)*

The temperature trim switch, when placed in the locked position, causes the datum valve brake to move to locked. However, this occurs only with the throttle in a position greater than 66° (coordinator quadrant). When the switch is moved to the controlled position, it releases the brake.

TEMPERATURE TRIM LIGHT *(Fig. 23-25)*

The temperature trim light will be on from 0 to 65° (coordinator quadrant), indicating operation in the temperature-limiting range. From 65 to 90° (coordinator quadrant), it will be off, indicating operation in the temperature control range. It will also be off from 90 to 0° (coordinator quadrant) when the temperature-datum-valve brake is in the locked position. However, if an overtemperature condition occurs with the temperature-datum-valve brake locked at any power setting, the light will come on. When the temperature trim light is off, it indicates that the electronic fuel-trimming system is making a fuel flow correction (put or take); and when the light is on, it indicates that no correction (null) is being made or there is an overtemperature condition. *NOTE:* If the engine temperature datum control switch is in emergency NULL or OFF, the light indication should be disregarded.

ENGINE-TEMPERATURE DATUM CONTROL SWITCH *(Fig. 23-25)*

The engine-temperature datum control switch must be placed in the NORMAL position for the electronic fuel-trimming system to function. When placed in emergency NULL, the system is inoperative and the temperature datum valve returns to the null position, bypassing 20 percent of the 120 percent furnished by the fuel control. The metering of fuel is now accomplished solely by the fuel control. Closer monitoring of turbine inlet temperature should be done, and the operator should remember that overtemperature protection is lost. The switch has a third position, namely, OFF. When in this position, the same conditions apply as in

FIG. 23-28 *Thermocouple assembly.* (**a**) *Thermocouple harness.* (**b**) *Typical thermocouple.*

the emergency NULL position, except for the fact that the temperature datum valve is locked into whatever position it was prior to the switch being moved. *NOTE:* The switch should always be turned on before engine starting. The switch should always be placed in the OFF position after engine shutdown.

FUEL NOZZLES *(refer to Fig. 12-28)*

The fuel nozzles are duplex-type, dual orifice nozzles. The six nozzles are mounted in the diffuser, and one extends into the forward end of each of the six combustion liners. The fuel nozzle must provide a controlled pattern of fuel flow, and also a maximum degree of atomization. At the tip of the nozzle, an air shroud surrounds the dual orifices. The air shroud contains a number of air holes through which air is circulated at high velocity, thus preventing the formation of carbon around the orifices.

DRIP VALVE *(refer to Figs. 23-11 and 23-22)*

The drip valve is located at the lowest point in the fuel manifold. It is designed to drain the manifold at engine shutdown, thus preventing fuel from draining into the combustion liners after the fuel-control cutoff valve is closed. The drip valve is a solenoid-operated valve, which is closed by completion of the electrical circuit by the 2200-rpm switch in the speed-sensitive control. At 9000 rpm, the electrical circuit is broken and fuel manifold pressure, acting upon the valve, continues to hold it in the closed position. At engine shutdown, when manifold pressure drops to a value of 8 to 10 psi, the valve opens due to spring force.

DRAIN VALVES *(refer to Fig. 23-11)*

There are two drain valves which are located at the forward and aft ends on the bottom of the outer combustion chamber. These valves are set at 2 to 4 psi air pressure, and are held closed by combustion-chamber air pressure during all engine operation. At engine shutdown, these valves open and thus prevent accumulation of fuel in the outer combustion chamber after a false start, or after engine shutdown.

THROTTLE POSITION *(Fig. 23-25)*

The throttle provides the means of selecting the following:

1 *Start blade angle*—This is the minimum torque blade angle and is desired for best starting characteristics.
2 *Ground idle*—This is a blade angle and power setting which requires a minimum of wheel braking.

3 *Maximum reverse*—The throttle is in the full aft position which produces a blade angle and power setting for a maximum aircraft braking after touchdown. Movement of the throttle forward and toward the start blade angle produces lesser amounts of braking force.
4 *Taxi range*—From the maximum reverse position to the flight-idle detent. At this time, the propeller is a multiposition, selective blade-angle propeller. For each and every change of the throttle, a new blade angle is selected.
5 *Flight range*—From the flight-idle detent to the full forward position. In this range, the propeller is a nonselective, automatic rpm governor. The throttle in this range serves primarily as the means of changing fuel flow.

The throttle is connected by aircraft linkage to the engine coordinator control, and any movement of the throttle will move this linkage. The coordinator control then has the function of coordinating the operation of the fuel system with that of the propeller.

The coordinator has a quadrant marked off from 0 to 90° and has the following markings.

1 Maximum reverse: 0°
2 Ground idle: 9°
3 Flight idle: 34°
4 Takeoff: 90°

Coordinator-quadrant degrees are usually called throttle degrees since the throttle actually sets the coordinator at any setting that it may have. The cockpit throttle quadrant has less than 90° travel and, therefore, measuring the degrees that the throttle moves in the cockpit will not correspond to the throttle degrees which one may read about in the publications of the engine manufacturer.

The coordinator-quadrant degree indications for the various ranges are as follows:

1 High-speed taxi range: 0°–34°
2 Low-speed taxi range: 9°–30°
3 Flight range: 34°–90°
4 Temperature-limiting range: 0°–65°
5 Temperature-control range: 65°–90°

NOTE: Power-unit rpm in the low-speed taxi range is 10,000 + (30/−10), and power-unit rpm in the high-speed taxi range is in excess of 13,000. To obtain low-speed taxi, the coordinator pointer must be between 9 and 30° and the cockpit low-speed taxi switch must be in the low position.

REVIEW AND STUDY QUESTIONS

1 List several airplanes that use this engine.
2 Give a brief description of this engine and its operation.
3 Very briefly describe the construction features of the following parts: compressor assembly, combustion assembly, turbine unit assembly, and accessories drive assembly.

4 Discuss the reduction-gear assembly including the description of the propeller brake, negative torque system, thrust-sensitive signal, and safety coupling.

5 What is the function of the torquemeter? Describe its operation.

6 How many main bearings does this engine have?

7 Briefly describe the following systems: lubrication (reduction gear and main), anti-icing, bleed air, ignition, and fuel, including the electronic trim system.

8 Describe the coordinator control and its operation.

9 List the throttle positions and tell what mode of engine operation each position selects.

CHAPTER 24

Continental J69-T-25

The construction of this engine (Fig. 24-1) is somewhat different from the larger turbojet engines in use at this writing, due principally to the novel design of the combustion chamber and fuel distribution system. Two J69's are installed in the Air Force's primary trainer, the Cessna T-37. Other models of this engine are installed in versions of the Ryan Firebee target drone.

SPECIFICATIONS

Number of compressor stages:	1
Number of turbine stages:	1
Number of combustors:	1
Maximum power at sea level:	1025 lb
Specific fuel consumption;	
at maximum power:	1.14
Compressor ratio at maximum rpm:	4:1
Maximum diameter:	24.9 in.
Maximum length:	50 in.
Maximum dry weight:	364 lb

The J69 engine consists of the following sections, accessories, and parts (Fig. 24-2):

1 Accessory case
2 Compressor housing
3 Turbine housing

External accessories include (Fig. 24-3):

1 Starter-generator (airframe supplied)
2 Starting-fuel system
3 Ignition system
4 Fuel pump
5 Fuel control
6 Oil pump
7 Oil filter

In addition to these parts are fuel, air, and oil lines. The engine is mounted with one top mount at the rear and two front mounts, approximately on the shaft axis.

OPERATION (Fig. 24-4)

NOTE: All numbers refer to Fig. 24-4.

In starting, the starter-generator drives through gears to spin the turbine shaft assembly (1). Air drawn into the inducer and compressor rotors (11, 12) is flung outward radially into the radial and axial diffusers (14, 16) which convert the velocity of the air into pressure. This pressure developed at the inlet to the turbine housing (21) forces the air into the combustion chamber (20). Main fuel sprays from the fuel distributor (2) into the combustion chamber to mix with this air. When ignition of the air-fuel mixture takes place, the hot gases flow out through the combustion chamber and are then directed by fixed vanes of the turbine inlet nozzle (24) to impinge upon the blades of the turbine rotor (25). The resultant torque speeds up the turbine shaft assembly to draw in and compress additional air. This new air enters the combustion chamber to mix with fuel. The mixture burns in the presence of the previously established flame so that the cycle is continuous. After the engine is working under continuous flame operation (3500 rpm), the starting-fuel solenoid valve and the ignition system must be deenergized. The starter is cut out at about 5000 rpm. The hot products of combustion pass through the exhaust diffuser (29) and through the aircraft tailpipe to produce thrust.

An ignition system and a separate fuel system are provided for starting. Fuel is fed from the fuel control through a solenoid valve to the starting-fuel nozzles (17) installed in the lower portion of the turbine housing. Adjacent to each of the two nozzles is an igniter plug (18) which is energized by an ignition coil. These components are located at the outlet from the axial diffuser assembly, outside of the combustion chamber. Starting fuel is injected from the nozzles into the incoming air, and this mixture is ignited by the spark at the plugs. The flame follows air path B (described later) into the combustion chamber. This starting combustion occurs at 1500 to 2000 rpm. As the shaft speeds up, main fuel issues from the rotating fuel distributor to build up flame in the combustion chamber. After flame is established in the combustion chamber, a control switch must cut off the ignition and the starting fuel. The ignition-control switch and starter-control switch are not supplied with the engine.

CONSTRUCTION (Fig. 24-4)

The turbine shaft assembly (1) is carried in a single ball bearing (3) in the compressor housing (15) at the intake end and in a single roller bearing (30) at the exhaust end. The rear bearing is supported on three tangentially arranged link-type supports (26) designed to ensure centering under temperature-expansion con-

FIG. 24-1 *Cutaway view of the Continental J69-T-25.*

ditions by a small rotation of the rear housing. The supports are encased in three streamlined struts (28) of the exhaust diffuser. These streamlined struts are hollow in order to carry cooling air to the rear bearing area. The cooling air passes around the outside of the rear-bearing housing and also through passages in the turbine shaft assembly to provide cooling of the hollow rear section of this shaft assembly. This airflow is induced by tubular passages (31), located at the back of the turbine rotor, which act as an ejector-type centrifugal fan. One of the streamlined struts contains oil passages (27) carrying oil to and from the rear bearing. It also has an atmospheric vent for balancing pressures at the rear bearing. The front portion of the turbine shaft assembly is hollow. Through this the main fuel supply for the engine is carried through a fuel seal (4) to the fuel distributor (2) at the combustion chamber (20), where the centrifugal effect of the rotating distributor ejects the fuel into the combustion chamber.

The turbine housing (21) is the structural frame of the engine. The annular combustion-chamber structure (22, 23) is installed inside the turbine housing over the center portion of the turbine shaft assembly. The products of combustion are directed from the combustion chamber into the turbine inlet nozzle (24) (stationary vanes), through the turbine rotor (25), and then pass on to the exhaust diffuser. The front of the turbine housing is enclosed by the compressor housing (15), installed over the compressor rotor (12) and the inducer rotor (11). The compressor housing carries the front bearing (3) and the gear train which drives the various accessories at the intake end. The starter-generator and its drive (7) are mounted at the forward center of the accessory case (6) which is mounted to the front of the compressor housing.

Mounted on the accessory case are the fuel pump, oil pump, oil filter, and fuel control. The tachometer

drive is taken from this area. Provisions are also available for mounting a hydraulic pump. (The pump is not supplied with the engine.) A gear train (5) serves to drive the various accessories mounted on the accessory case.

The turbine-shaft-assembly parts are machined. The blades of the compressor and inducer rotors are integral with the hub metal, while the turbine rotor blades are removable and replaceable. The turbine housing, turbine inlet nozzle, radial diffuser, and exhaust diffuser are of welded built-up construction, whereas the compressor housing, accessory case, its cover, oil-pump drive adaptor, starter-generator adaptor, axial diffuser, and rear-bearing housing, its supports, the various labyrinth seals, the front bearing cage, and the oil pump are machined items. The combustor shells and structure are of sheet metal construction in nature, but using high-temperature-resistant alloy metal.

AIRFLOW *(Fig. 24-4)*

Air entering the inlet (9) flows past the three struts (10) in the compressor housing air passage to the inducer rotor (11). The inducer rotor whirls the air in the direction of rotation of the compressor rotor (12) just before the air enters the compressor rotor. In the compressor rotor, the air is flung outward radially at high velocity to pass through the radial diffuser assembly (14). The airflow is then turned 90° and directed through the axial diffuser assembly (16) which is parallel to the turbine shaft assembly. Following the reduction in velocity in the diffusers and the resultant increase in pressure, the air now enters the interior of the turbine housing at A.

Part B of the air coming out of the axial diffuser passes down behind the compressor cover (13) to enter the combustion chamber through the louvers in the outer

FIG. 24-2   *Major engine components.*

1   ELECTRICAL CABLE GROUP
2   IGNITION GROUP
3   FIREWALL AND HOSES GROUP
4   FUEL PUMP GROUP
5   FUEL CONTROL GROUP
6   OIL PUMP GROUP
7   OIL FILTER ASSEMBLY
8   OIL PUMP DRIVE GROUP
9   STARTER-GENERATOR DRIVE GROUP
10   ACCESSORY CASE GROUP
11   EXHAUST DIFFUSER AND REAR BEARING GROUP

12   ACCESSORY DRIVE GEARSHAFT AND FRONT BEARING CAGE GROUP
13   COMPRESSOR HOUSING GROUP
14   RADIAL DIFFUSER AND COMPRESSOR COVER GROUP
15   COMBUSTOR SHELL AND INLET NOZZLE GROUP
16   TURBINE AND COMPRESSOR SHAFT ASSEMBLY
17   TURBINE HOUSING GROUP
18   COMPRESSED AIR FILTER ASSEMBLY

1	STARTER-GENERATOR	9	FUEL CONTROL
	MOUNT LOCATION	10	OIL PUMP
2	AIR INTAKE	11	OIL FILTER
3	ACCESSORY CASE	12	FUEL LINES
4	COMPRESSOR HOUSING	13	AIR LINES
5	TURBINE HOUSING	14	OIL LINES
6	STARTING FUEL SYSTEM	15	REAR MOUNT
7	IGNITION SYSTEM	16	FRONT MOUNT
8	FUEL PUMP		

FIG. 24-3 *External parts of Continental J69-T-25.*

combustor shell (22) just forward of the fuel distributor (2). These louvers are spaced and designed to provide thorough mixing of air and fuel. Part C of the incoming air passes around the outer combustor shell (22) of the combustion chamber, following its shape approximately, and is thereby led to the hollow vanes of the turbine inlet nozzle (24). This air cools the vanes while passing into the chamber formed by the inner combustor shell (23) and the turbine shaft assembly. The front end of the inner combustor shell is perforated so the air C

(heated in the chamber) flows into the combustion chamber just aft of the fuel distributor. The air following paths B and C is known as *primary* air and it is this air which forms the air-fuel mixture in the combustion chamber. As this mixture heats in the presence of the established flame, it ignites. The combustion chamber is approximately L-shaped in cross section. As the products of combustion turn the corner of the L, air inlet tubes (19) feed incoming air D directly into the flow. This dilution holds down peak temperatures. The air following path D is known as *secondary air,* since it does not directly enter the combustion process. The total volume now passes through the turbine inlet nozzle (cooled by primary air), to the turbine rotor (25) from which it passes on out the exhaust diffuser (29).

OIL SYSTEM *(Fig. 24-5)*

Oil from the engine oil tank (not supplied with the engine) is led to the main oil pump where the pressure section develops main oil pressure. The output of the pressure pump is led through an antileak valve to the main oil filter. This filter system incorporates a pressure-regulating arrangement as well as bypass provisions to pass oil beyond the filter element if it should become clogged. From the oil-filter output, oil for the rear bearing is carried by an external hose. Another external hose picks up return oil from the rear bearing to carry this oil to the rear-bearing scavenge section of the oil pump. The rear-bearing housing incorporates a vent passage as well as passages to feed the oil to and from the rear bearing. At the front of the engine, oil is led from the main oil-filter output through passages to the front bearings and front-end gears. Oil is also fed to the accessory gear train that fans out across the lower part of the compressor housing. Oil from the front bearings and upper gears drains down to the accessory case from which one scavenge section of the oil pump pulls return-oil. All scavenge sections of the oil pump lead return-oil back to the engine oil tank through an antileak valve. This valve prevents tank oil from draining back into the engine after engine shutdown. The front-end section is vented by a passage to the top of the upper gear housing.

FUEL FLOW *(Fig. 24-6)*

The aircraft fuel system includes the fuel tanks, booster pump(s), a fuel strainer, a shutoff valve, and fuel flowmeters in the flow of fuel up to the engine. The engine fuel system starts with the fuel pump. This pump, driven off the accessory gear train, has a centrifugal booster stage which is intended to provide boost pressure if the boost provisions in the aircraft system should fail. It also reduces vapor effects by raising total

FIG. 24-4 *Sectional view. NOTE: The starting fuel nozzle (17) and the igniter plug (18) are in lower part of engine, but are shown on top to facilitate sectioning.*

1	MAIN SHAFT ASSEMBLY		REPLACEMENT COVER	16 AXIAL DIFFUSER
2	FUEL DISTRIBUTOR	9	AIR INLET	17 STARTING FUEL NOZZLE
3	FRONT BALL BEARING	10	COMPRESSOR HOUSING	18 IGNITER PLUG
4	FUEL SEAL		STRUT	19 AIR INLET TUBE
5	ACCESSORY GEAR TRAIN	11	INDUCER ROTOR	20 COMBUSTION CHAMBER
6	ACCESSORY CASE	12	COMPRESSOR ROTOR	21 TURBINE HOUSING
7	STARTER-GENERATOR	13	COMPRESSOR COVER	22 OUTER COMBUSTOR SHELL
	DRIVE	14	RADIAL DIFFUSER	23 INNER COMBUSTOR SHELL
8	STARTER-GENERATOR	15	COMPRESSOR HOUSING	24 TURBINE INLET NOZZLE

25 TURBINE ROTOR
26 REAR BEARING HOUSING
SUPPORT
27 OIL PASSAGE
28 STREAMLINE STRUT
29 EXHAUST DIFFUSER
30 REAR ROLLER BEARING
31 TUBULAR AIR PASSAGE

boost pressure. The centrifugal booster stage feeds two gear-pump pressure sections operating in parallel. Either section will provide full pressure and flow for the engine, and each section is independent of the other. From the main fuel pump, fuel is carried by a hose to the fuel filter built into the fuel-control unit. This filter incorporates two separate filtering elements with provisions to bypass the fuel if the elements should become clogged. A differential pressure indicator is installed in one of the filtering elements to sense the increase in back pressure as the elements become dirty. An easily read, calibrated button protrudes from the indicator to show the amount of back pressure. When the button is full out (40 to 45 psi), the filters must be cleaned and the button reset. A manually operated flushing valve permits closing off the rest of the fuel system when reverse flushing of the filter is accomplished. This valve is at the filter outlet.

FUEL CONTROL

Within the fuel control there are two separate fuel paths:

1 From the flushing valve outlet, starting fuel is led through a starting-fuel filter to a pressure regulator, then to the starting-fuel solenoid valve. From this valve, starting fuel passes through adjustable bleed

PRESSURE

SCAVENGE

VENT

TANK FLOW

REAR BEARING OIL JETS

REAR BEARING AIR VENT

SCAVENGE OIL FROM REAR BEARING

PRESSURE OIL TO REAR BEARING

ANTI-LEAK VALVE

OIL RETURN CONNECTION TO TANK

OIL FILTER DRAIN

OIL IN CONNECTION FROM TANK

BLIND HOLE

△ DENOTES PASSAGE HAS PIPE PLUG

FRONT MAIN BEARING OIL JET

OIL PUMP

OIL JET TO PUMP AND TACH GEAR TRAIN

ACCESSORY DRIVE OIL JET

OIL VENT TO TANK CONNECTION

ACCESSORY CASE BREATHER

OIL SEAL VENT

ACCESSORY DRIVE DRAIN

PRESSURE OIL FROM PUMP

OIL JETS TO GEARS (2 REQD.)

ANTI-LEAK VALVE

ACCESSORY CASE SCAVENGE

PLUG

ACCESSORY CASE DRAIN

OIL PRESSURE REG VALVE

OIL FILTER BY-PASS VALVE

OIL PRESSURE CONNECTION

FIG. 24-5 *Oil system.*

FIG. 24-6 *Fuel-system schematic.*

valves to the external piping that leads the fuel to the starting-fuel nozzles.

2 The main fuel path feeds to the acceleration control, to the governor valve, then to the cutoff valve from which flow is to the pressurizing valve and thence into the engine fuel tube. The acceleration control is designed to influence fuel input during acceleration and also to compensate for changes of altitude or other ambient air conditions. The governor valve influences flow to hold the speed called for by the throttle-lever setting. The governor valve is servo-operated and responds to pressure signals developed in the speed-sensing element. The latter also sends pressure signals to the bypass valve. The function of the bypass valve is to maintain a design pressure differential across the metering elements (which are the acceleration control and the governor valve). This pressure differential is maintained by bypassing fuel back to the fuel-pump inlet. Since the design pressure differential must change with speed, the bypass valve is made responsive to a signal from the speed-sensing element. The pressurizing valve is designed to open only above a minimum pressure and so prevents "dribble" of fuel or drainage of the control unit when the engine comes to a stop.

The fuel control also contains check valves, "trim" provisions, and passages for return of fuel bleed-off or seepage.

ENGINE CONTROL

The fuel control is the key element affecting engine control. Provided the proper volume and pressure of fuel are fed into the fuel-control unit, it regulates and meters engine fuel input to cover all operating conditions automatically.

The following main conditions are controlled:

1 *Starting*—The separate starting-fuel path sets up fuel flow to the starting-fuel nozzles. The fuel-control starting-fuel solenoid valve opens this path and closes it in response to signals from a control element not supplied with the engine.

2 *Acceleration to idle*—The acceleration control sets up fuel flow to the main fuel distributor such as to speed the engine up from starting speed to idle without surge or overtemperature. As the engine reaches the speed set by the throttle-lever position, the governor valve will come into action to hold the speed as set.

3 *Above idle*—The acceleration control is designed to control fuel input for all changing conditions for all operations from idle up to full speed without allowing surge or overtemperature. It compensates for acceleration, for change of altitude, and for other changes of ambient air characteristics. The governor valve, in all cases, acts to hold engine speed to the value set by the throttle-lever position.

ELECTRICAL SYSTEM (*Fig. 24-7*)

The electrical system of the engine includes the starter-generator and its lead assembly; the ignition coil, igniter plugs, and their leads; the starting-fuel solenoid valve incorporated in the fuel control; the tachometer; and the accessory electrical lead assembly. The remaining elements that constitute the complete electrical system are provided by the aircraft manufacturer.

FIG. 24-7 *Electrical-system schematic.*

REVIEW AND STUDY QUESTIONS

1   What airplane uses this engine?
2   List the engine's major specifications.
3   Give a brief description of the engine and its operation.
4   How many main bearings does this engine have?
5   Very briefly describe the construction features of the following parts: accessory case, compressor housing and rotor, diffuser, combustor liner, turbine housing, turbine and shaft, and exhaust diffuser.
6   What provision is made to reduce compressor stall?
7   Briefly describe the following systems: lubrication, ignition, fuel, and electrical.

Appendixes

Appendix A

Conversion factors

TO CONVERT FROM—	TO—	MULTIPLY BY—
Acres	Square feet	4.356×10^4
"	Square meters	4.047×10^3
"	Square miles	1.562×10^{-3}
"	Square rods	1.6×10^2
Amperes	Faradays/second	1.04×10^{-5}
Amperes/square foot	Amperes/square centimeter	0.00108
Ampere-hours	Coulombs	3600
Amperes/square centimeter	Amperes/square foot	929
Angstrom units	Inches	3.94×10^{-9}
"	Meters	1×10^{-10}
"	Microns	1×10^{-4}
Atmospheres	Centimeters of Hg at 0°C	76
"	Inches Hg at 0°C	29.92
"	Feet of water at 4°C	33.9
"	Kilograms/square centimeter	1.033
"	Pounds/square inch	14.696
"	Pounds/square foot	2116
"	Bars, hectopieze	1.013
Barrels (U.S. liquid)	Gallons	31.5
Bars	Centimeters of Hg at 0°C	75.01
"	Pounds/square inch	14.5
Btu	Foot-pounds	778.26
"	Horsepower hours	3.93×10^{-4}
"	Kilowatt hours	2.931×10^{-4}
"	Kilogram calories	2.52×10^{-1}
"	Kilogram meters	1.076×10^2
"	Joules	1055
Btu/second	Watts	1055
Centimeters	Inches	0.394

TO CONVERT FROM—	TO—	MULTIPLY BY—
Centimeters	Mils	393.7
"	Feet	0.0328
Centimeters of Hg	Inches of water at 4°C	5.354
"	Feet of water at 4°C	4.46×10^{-1}
"	Pounds/square inch	1.934×10^{-1}
"	Pounds/square foot	27.85
"	Kilograms/square meter	135.95
"	Atmospheres	0.013158
Centimeters/ second	Feet/minute	1.9685
"	Feet/second	3.281×10^{-2}
"	Miles/hour	2.237×10^{-2}
Centipoise	Pounds-second/foot	6.72×10^{-4}
"	Kilograms-hour/meters	3.6
Chain	Links	100
"	Feet	66
Circle	Degrees	360
"	Radius	6.28319
Circular mils	Square centimeters	5.07×10^{-6}
"	Square inches	7.854×10^{-7}
"	Square millimeters	5.067×10^{-4}
"	Square mils	7.854×10^{-1}
Cord	Cubic feet	128
Cubic centimeters	Cubic feet	3.53×10^{-5}
"	Cubic inches	0.061
"	Gallons (U.S.)	2.64×10^{-4}
"	Liters	9.999×10^{-4}
"	Fluid ounces	0.0338
"	Pints	0.0021
"	Quarts (liquid)	0.0011
Cubic feet	Cubic centimeters	28,317
"	Cubic inches	1728
"	Gallons (U.S.)	7.48
"	Liters	28.32
"	Quarts	29.92
"	Cubic yards	3.704×10^{-2}
Cubic feet of water (60°F)	Pounds	62.37
Cubic feet/minute	Gallons/second	0.1247
"	Liters/second	4.719×10^{-1}
"	Cubic meters/minute	2.832×10^{-2}
Cubic inches	Cubic centimeters	16.39
"	Cubic feet	5.787×10^{-4}
"	Gallons (U.S.)	0.0043
"	Liters	0.0164
"	Fluid ounces	0.554
"	Quarts (liquid)	0.0173
Cubic meters	Cubic inches	61,023
"	Cubic yards	1.308
"	Cubic feet	35.31
"	Gallons (U.S.)	274.17
Cubic yards	Cubic feet	27
"	Cubic meters	7.646×10^{-1}
"	Gallons	2.022×10^2
"	Cubic inches	46,656
Curies	Disintegrations/second	3.7×10^{10}

TO CONVERT FROM—	TO—	MULTIPLY BY—
Degrees (arc)	Radians	1.745×10^{-2}
Degrees/second	Revolutions/minute	0.1667
"	Radians/second	0.017453
Dynes	Grams	1.020×10^{-3}
"	Pounds	2.248×10^{-6}
"	Poundals	7.233×10^{-5}
Electron volts	Ergs	1.602×10^{-12}
Ergs	Btu	9.478×10^{-11}
"	Dyne centimeters	1
"	Electron volts	6.242×10^{11}
"	Foot-pounds	7.376×10^{-8}
"	Gram centimeters	1.020×10^{-3}
"	Joules	10^{-7}
"	Kilogram calories	2.388×10^{-11}
Faradays	Coulombs	9.65×10^{-4}
Faradays/second	Amperes	96,500
Fathoms	Feet	6
Feet	Centimeters	30.48
"	Inches	12
"	Meters	0.3048
"	Yards	3.333×10^{-1}
"	Miles	1.894×10^{-4}
"	Nautical miles	1.646×10^{-4}
Feet of water at 4°C	Atmospheres	2.95×10^{-2}
"	Pounds/square inch	4.335×10^{-1}
"	Pounds/square foot	62.43
"	Kilograms/square meter	3.048×10^{2}
"	Inches of Hg at 0°C	8.826×10^{-1}
"	Centimeters of Hg at 0°C	2.24
Feet/minute	Miles/hour	1.136×10^{-2}
"	Kilometers/hour	1.829×10^{-2}
"	Centimeters/second	5.08×10^{-1}
Feet/second	Miles/hour	0.6818
"	Kilometers/hour	1.097
"	Meters/minute	18.29
"	Centimeters/second	30.48
"	Knots	0.5925
Foot-pounds	Btu	1.285×10^{-3}
"	Joules (absolute)	1.35582
"	Meter-kilograms	1.383×10^{-1}
"	Kilowatt hours	3.766×10^{-7}
Foot-pounds/minute	Horsepower	3.030×10^{-5}
Foot-pounds/second	Horsepower	1.818×10^{-3}
"	Kilowatts	1.356×10^{-3}
Fluid ounces	Drams	8
"	Cubic centimeters	29.6
Furlongs	Feet	660
"	Yards	220
"	Rods	40
Gallons (U.S. liquid)	Quarts (liquid)	4
"	Cubic centimeters	3785.4

TO CONVERT FROM—	TO—	MULTIPLY BY—
Gallons (U.S. liquid)	Cubic inches	231
"	Cubic feet	1.337×10^{-1}
"	Liters	3.785
"	Imperial gallons	8.327×10^{-1}
"	Fluid ounces	1.28×10^{2}
"	Pints	8
"	Pounds (av) of water at 17°C	8.31
Gallons (U.S. dry)	Cubic inches	268.8
"	Cubic feet	1.556×10^{-1}
"	U.S. gallons (liquid)	1.164
"	Liters	4.405
Gallons (imperial)	Cubic inches	277.4
"	U.S. gallons	1.201
"	Liters	4.546
Grains	Grams	0.0648
"	Ounces (avoir.)	0.0023
"	Ounces (troy)	0.0021
"	Pennyweights (troy)	0.0417
"	Pounds (avoir.)	1/7000
"	Pounds (troy)	1/5760
Grams	Grains	15.43
"	Milligrams	1000
"	Ounces (avoir.)	0.0353
"	Ounces (troy)	0.0321
"	Pennyweights	0.643
"	Pounds (avoir.)	0.022
"	Pounds (troy)	0.0027
"	Kilograms	10^{-3}
"	Dynes	980.67
Grams/cubic centimeter	Pounds/cubic inch	0.03613
"	Pounds/cubic foot	62.43
"	Kilograms/cubic meter	1000
Grams/centimeter	Kilograms/meter	0.1
"	Pounds/foot	6.721×10^{-2}
"	Pounds/inch	5.601×10^{-3}
Grams/liter	Ounces/gallon (troy)	0.122
"	Ounces/gallon (avoir.)	0.134
"	Parts/million	1000
"	Pennyweights/gallon	2.44
Grams of U^{235} fissioned	Kilowatt hours heat gen.	23,000
Gram calories	Btu	3.969×10^{-3}
Hands	Inches	4
Hectares	Square meters	10^{4}
"	Acres	2.471
Hectopieze	Inches of Hg	29.53
Horsepower	Foot-pounds/minute	33,000
"	Foot-pounds/second	550
"	Meter-kilograms/second	76.04
"	Metric horsepower	1.014
"	Kilowatts	7.457×10^{-1}
"	Btu/hour	2545.08
"	Btu/second	7.068×10^{-1}
Horsepower (metric)	Meters/kilogram second	75

TO CONVERT FROM—	TO—	MULTIPLY BY—
Horsepower (metric)	Horsepower	9.863×10^{-1}
"	Kilowatts	7.355×10^{-1}
"	Btu/second	6.971×10^{-1}
Horsepower hours	Btu	2.545×10^{3}
"	Foot-pounds	1.98×10^{6}
"	Meter-kilograms	2.737×10^{5}
Inches	Centimeters	2.54
"	Feet	83.33×10^{3}
"	Mils	1000
Inches of Hg at 0°C	Atmospheres	3.342×10^{-2}
"	Inches of water at 4°C	13.6
"	Feet of water	1.133
"	Pounds/square inch	4.912×10^{-1}
"	Pounds/square foot	70.73
"	Kilograms/square meter	3.453×10^{2}
Inches of water at 4°C	Atmospheres	2.458×10^{-3}
"	Inches of Hg at 0°C	7.355×10^{-2}
"	Centimeters of Hg at 0°C	1.868×10^{-1}
"	Pounds/square inch	3.613×10^{-2}
"	Pounds/square foot	5.202
"	Kilograms/square meter	25.4
Joules	Btu	9.48×10^{-4}
"	Foot-pounds	7.376×10^{-1}
"	Kilogram calories	2.389×10^{-4}
"	Kilogram meters	1.020×10^{-1}
"	Watt hours	2.778×10^{-4}
"	Horsepower hours	3.725×10^{-7}
"	Ergs	10^{7}
Kilograms	Grains	15,432.4
"	Grams	1000
"	Ounces (avoir.)	35.27
"	Ounces (troy)	32.15
"	Pennyweights	643.01
"	Pounds (avoir.)	2.205
"	Pounds (troy)	2.679
Kilogram calories	Btu	3.968
"	Foot-pounds	3087
"	Meter-kilograms	4.269×10^{2}
Kilograms/cubic meter	Pounds/cubic foot	62.43×10^{-3}
"	Grams/cubic centimeter	10^{-3}
Kilograms/square centimeter	Pounds/square inch	14.22
"	Pounds/square foot	2.048×10^{3}
"	Inches of Hg at 0°C	28.96
"	Feet of water at 4°C	3.28×10^{-7}
Kilometers	Feet	3.281×10^{3}
"	Miles	6.214×10^{-1}
"	Nautical miles	5.4×10^{-1}
"	Centimeters	10^{5}
Kilometers/hour	Feet/second	9.113×10^{-1}
"	Knots	5.396×10^{-1}
"	Miles/hour	6.214×10^{-1}
"	Meters/second	2.778×10^{-1}

TO CONVERT FROM—	TO—	MULTIPLY BY—
Kilowatt hours heat gen.	Grams of U^{235} fissioned	4.35×10^{-5}
Kilowatts	Btu/second	9.48×10^{-1}
"	Foot-pounds/second	7.376×10^{2}
"	Horsepower	1.341
"	Kilogram calories/ second	2.389×10^{-1}
Knots	Nautical miles/hour	1
"	Feet/hour	6076.1033
"	Feet/second	1.688
"	Miles/hour	1.151
"	Kilometers/hour	1.853
"	Meters/second	5.148×10^{-1}
Leagues (U.S.)	Nautical miles	3
Link	Inches	7.92
Liters	Cubic centimeters	1000.027
"	Cubic feet	0.035
"	Cubic inches	61.025
"	Gallons (U.S.)	0.264
"	Gallons (imperial)	0.22
"	Ounces (fluid)	33.81
"	Pints	2.11
"	Quarts (liquid)	1.057
Meters	Centimeters	100
"	Miles	6.214×10^{-4}
"	Feet	3.281
"	Inches	39.37
"	Kilometers	0.001
"	Yards	1.094
Meter-kilograms	Foot-pounds	7.233
"	Joules	9.807
Meters/second	Feet/second	3.281
"	Miles/hour	2.237
"	Kilometers/hour	3.6
Microamperes	Unit charges/second	6.24×10^{12}
Microohms	Megaohms	1×10^{-12}
"	Ohms	1×10^{-6}
Microns	Inches	3.937×10^{-5}
"	Millimeters	0.001
Miles	Feet	5280
"	Kilometers	1.609
"	Nautical miles	8.69×10^{-1}
"	Furlongs	8
Miles/hour	Feet/second	1.467
"	Meters/second	4.47×10^{-1}
"	Kilometers/hour	1.609
"	Knots	8.69×10^{-1}
Miles/hour squared	Feet/second squared	2.151
Miles/hour/ second	Feet/second squared	1.4667
Millibars	Inches of Hg at 0°C	2.953×10^{-2}
Milligrams	Grains	0.0154
"	Grams	0.001
"	Kilograms	1×10^{-6}
"	Ounces (avoir.)	3.5×10^{-5}
"	Ounces (troy)	3.215×10^{-5}

TO CONVERT FROM—	TO—	MULTIPLY BY—
Milligrams	Pennyweights	6.43×10^{-4}
"	Pounds (avoir.)	2.21×10^{-6}
"	Pounds (troy)	2.68×10^{-6}
Milligrams/liter	Parts/million	1
Milliliters	Cubic centimeters	1.000027
"	Cubic inches	0.061
"	Liters	0.001
"	Ounces (fluid)	0.034
Millimeters	Centimeters	0.1
"	Inches	0.039
"	Meters	0.001
"	Microns	1000
Mils	Centimeters	0.0025
"	Inches	0.001
"	Microns	25.4
Nautical miles	Feet	6076.1
"	Miles	1.151
"	Meters	1852
Ounces (avoir.)	Grains	437.5
"	Grams	28.35
"	Ounces (troy)	0.911
"	Pennyweights	18.23
"	Pounds (avoir.)	1/16
"	Pounds (troy)	0.076
Ounces/gallon (avoir.)	Grams/liter	7.5
Ounces (troy)	Grains	480
"	Grams	31.1
"	Milligrams	31103.5
"	Ounces (avoir.)	1.097
"	Pennyweights	20
"	Pounds (avoir.)	0.069
"	Pounds (troy)	1/12
Ounces/gallon (troy)	Grams/liter	8.2
Ounces (fluid)	Cubic centimeters	29.57
"	Cubic inches	1.8
"	Gallons	1/128
"	Liters	0.0296
"	Milliliters	29.57
"	Pints	1/16
"	Quarts	0.031
Ounces/gallon (fluid)	Cubic centimeters/liter	7.7
Pennyweights	Grains	24
"	Grams	1.56
"	Milligrams	1555
"	Ounces (avoir.)	0.0549
"	Ounces (troy)	0.05
"	Pounds (avoir.)	0.0034
"	Pounds (troy)	0.0042
Pennyweights/ gallon	Grams/liter	0.41
Pints	Cubic centimeters	473.2
"	Cubic feet	0.017
"	Cubic inches	28.88
"	Gallons	0.125
"	Liters	0.473
"	Ounces (fluid)	16

TO CONVERT FROM—	TO—	MULTIPLY BY—
Pints	Quarts	0.5
Poles	Feet	16.5
"	Yards	5.5
Pounds (avoir.)	Grains	7000
"	Grams	453.6
"	Kilograms	0.454
"	Ounces (avoir.)	16
"	Ounces (troy)	14.58
"	Pennyweights	291.67
"	Pounds (troy)	1.215
"	Poundals	32.174
"	Slugs	3.108×10^{-2}
Pounds (troy)	Grains	5760
"	Grams	373.24
"	Kilograms	0.373
"	Ounces (avoir.)	13.17
"	Ounces (troy)	12
"	Pennyweights	240
"	Pounds (avoir.)	0.823
Pounds of water at 17°C	Cubic feet	0.016
"	Cubic inches	27.68
"	Gallons	0.1198
Pounds/cubic foot	Kilograms/cubic meter	16.02
Pounds/cubic inch	Pounds/cubic foot	1728
"	Grams/cubic centimeter	27.68
Pounds/square inch	Inches of Hg at 0°C	2.036
"	Feet of water at 4°C	2.307
"	Atmospheres	6.805×10^{-2}
"	Kilograms/square meter	7.031×10^{2}
Quarts (liquid)	Cubic centimeters	946.4
"	Cubic inches	57.75
"	Cubic feet	0.033
"	Gallons	0.25
"	Liters	0.946
"	Ounces (fluid)	32
"	Pints	2
Radians	Degrees (arc)	57.3
Radians/second	Degrees/second	57.3
"	Revolutions/second	15.92×10^{-2}
"	Revolutions/minute	9.549
Revolutions	Radians	6.283
Revolutions/minute	Radians/second	1.047×10^{-1}
Rods	Foot	16.5
"	Yard	5.5
Slugs	Pounds	32.17405
Spans	Inches	9
Square centimeters	Circular millimeters	127.32
"	Circular mils	197,350
"	Square feet	0.001
"	Square inches	0.155
"	Square millimeters	100
Square feet	Square centimeters	929.03
"	Square inches	144
"	Square yards	1.111×10^{-1}
"	Acres	2.296×10^{-5}

TO CONVERT FROM—	TO—	MULTIPLY BY—
Square inches	Circular mils	1.2732
"	Square centimeters	6.45
"	Square feet	1/144
"	Square mils	1×10^{-6}
"	Square yards	1/1296
Square kilometers	Square miles	3.861×10^{-1}
Square meters	Square feet	10.76
"	Square yards	1.196
Square miles	Square kilometers	2.59
"	Acres	640
Square rods	Square yards	30.25
Square yards	Square feet	9
"	Square inches	1296
"	Square meters	8.361×10^{-1}

TO CONVERT FROM—	TO—	MULTIPLY BY—
Stones (British)	Pounds (avoir.)	14
Tablespoons	Fluid ounces	0.5
U^{235} fissions/ second	Watts	3.21×10^{-11}
Unit charges/ second	Microamperes	1.6×10^{-13}
Watts	Btu/second	9.481×10^{-4}
"	U^{235} fissions/second	3.12×10^{10}
Yards	Meters	9.144×10^{-1}
"	Feet	3
"	Inches	36
Years (sidereal)	Days (mean solar)	365.256

Commonly used gas turbine engine symbols and abbreviations

SYMBOL	DEFINITION	UNITS
A	Cross-sectional flow area	sq in., sq ft
a	Angle of attack	Degrees
a	Linear or angular acceleration	ft/sec², rad/sec²
C	Coefficient	None
C-D	Converging-diverging	None
CDP	Compressor discharge pressure	psi
CDT	Compressor discharge temperature	°F, °C, °R
CIT	Compressor inlet temperature	°F, °C, °R
c	Speed of sound	ft/sec
c_p	Specific heat at a constant pressure	Btu/lb/°F
c_v	Specific heat at a constant volume	Btu/lb/°F
D	Diameter	ft, in.
EGT	Exhaust-gas temperature	°F, °C, °R
EPR	Engine pressure ratio	None
eshp	Equivalent shaft horsepower $= \text{shp} + \dfrac{F_n \times V_a}{550}$	hp
F	Thrust	lb
F_g	Gross thrust	lb
F_j	Jet thrust	lb
F_n	Net thrust $= F_g - F_r + F_j$	lb
F_r	Ram drag of engine airflow	lb
f/a	Fuel/air ratio	lb/lb
f	Frequency	1/sec
g	Acceleration due to gravity	ft/sec²
g	Mass conversion factor	32.174
H	Enthalpy, heating value	Btu/lb
IGV	Inlet guide vane	None
hp	Horsepower (shp, fhp)	hp
J	Joule's constant $= 778.26$	ft-lb/Btu
M	Mass W/g	lb

SYMBOL	DEFINITION	UNITS
M	Mach number $= V/c$	None
N	Engine rotational speed	rpm
OAT	Outside air temperature	°F, °C, °R
OGV	Outlet guide vane	None
P	Power	Btu/sec, hp
P	Absolute pressure (psia)	lb/sq in., in. Hg
PTA	Post-turbine augmentation	None
PTI	Pre-turbine injection	None
R	Gas constant for air $= 53.35$	ft-lb/(lb)(°F)
R	Reynolds number	None
SFC	Specific fuel consumption (ESFC, BSFC)	lb/(hr)(hp)
s	Specific entropy	Btu/lb-°R
thp	Thrust horsepower	hp
TSFC	Thrust specific fuel consumption	lb/(lbt)(hr)
T	Absolute temperature	°R
t	Time	sec
u	Specific internal energy	Btu/lb
u	Rotor linear velocity	ft/sec
V	Velocity	ft/sec
V	Volume	cu ft
v	Specific volume	cu ft/lb
W	Weight (force)	lb
w	Rate of flow	lb/sec, lb/hr
Δ	Difference	None
δ	Relative absolute pressure $= P/P_o$	None
η	Efficiency	percent
γ or κ	Ratio of specific heats c_p/c_v	None
μ	Microns	None
π	3.1416	None
θ	Relative absolute temperature T/T_o	None

Commonly used subscripts

SYMBOL	DEFINITION
a	Air
am	Ambient
av	Average
ax	Axial
b	Combustion chamber (burner)
bl	Bleed
c	Compressor
cr	Critical
d	Diffuser, duct
e	Effective (as in area), exhaust, exit
f	Fuel
g	Gross, gas, or products of combustion
i	Inlet, indicated
init	Initial
j	Jet
n	Net
o	Sea-level standard values (59°F, 15°C, 518.7°R and 2116 lb/sq ft, 14.7 psi, 29.92 in. Hg)
p	Propeller, aircraft, constant pressure, propulsion
R	Relative
r	Ram
s	Static, sound
sl	Sea level
t	Total, turbine
th	Thermal
v	Velocity, volume
0, 1, 2, etc.	Engine station location (See Appendix E-4, gas turbine engine station notation.)

Glossary

ambient Refers to condition of atmosphere existing around the engine, such as ambient pressure or temperature.

ampere A unit of measurement of current flow. It is directly proportional to the voltage, but inversely proportional to the resistance to flow (ohm).

centrifugal force The outward force an object exerts on a restraining agent when the motion of the object is rotational.

centripetal force The inward force a restraining agent exerts on an object moving in a circle. It is the opposite of, and equal to, centrifugal force.

choked nozzle A nozzle whose flow rate has reached the speed of sound.

density Mass per unit volume.

energy The capacity for doing work.

horsepower A man-made unit of power equal to 33,000 ft-lb of work per minute.

hot start Overtemperature during starting.

hung start Failure to reach normal-idling rpm during starting.

inertia The opposition of a body to having its state of rest or motion changed.

jam acceleration Rapid movement of the power lever, calling for maximum rate of rotor-speed increase.

jet silencer A device used to reduce and change the lower-frequency sound waves emitting from the engine's exhaust nozzle, and thus reducing the noise factor.

joule An electrical unit of energy or work.

mass The amount of matter contained within a substance.

molecule The smallest particle of a substance which can exist and still retain all of the characteristics of that substance.

momentum The tendency of a body to continue after being placed in motion.

ohm A unit which measures resistance to electrical current flow, and is equal to volts divided by amperes.

overspeed Rpm is excess of design 100 percent rpm.

overtemperature Temperature in excess of maximum allowable design temperature at the turbine exit.

power The rate of doing work; work per unit of time.

ram The amount of pressure buildup above ambient pressure at the engine's compressor inlet, due to forward motion of the engine through the air (air's initial momentum).

ram ratio The ratio of ram pressure to ambient pressure.

ram recovery The ability of an engine's air inlet duct to take advantage of ram pressure.

sonic speed Speed of sound under ambient or local conditions.

specific heat The ratio of the thermal capacity of a substance to the thermal capacity of water.

stable operation Condition where no appreciable fluctuation, intentional or unintentional, is occurring to any of the engine's variables such as rpm, temperature, or pressure.

subsonic speed Speed less than that of sound.

supersonic speed Speed in excess of that of sound.

thermocouple A pair of joints of two dissimilar metals across which a dc voltage is produced when one joint is warmer than the other.

thrust A reaction force in pounds.

thrust, gross The thrust developed by the engine, not taking into consideration any presence of initial-air-mass momentum.

thrust, net The effective thrust developed by the engine during flight, taking into consideration the initial momentum of the air mass prior to entering the influence of the engine.

thrust reverser A device used to partially reverse the flow of engine's nozzle discharge gases, and thus create a thrust force in the rearward direction.

thrust specific fuel consumption The fuel that the engine must burn per hour to generate any 1 lb of thrust.

thrust, static Same as gross thrust, without any initial air-mass momentum present due to engine's static condition.

torque A force, multiplied by its lever arm, acting at right angles to an axis.

transient conditions Conditions which may occur briefly while accelerating or decelerating, or while passing through a specific range of engine operation.

vector A line which, by scaled length, indicates magnitude, and whose arrow head represents direction of action.

volt A unit of measurement of electrical force. It is a function of the flow current (ampere) and the amount of resistance to flow (ohm) present.

watt A unit which measures power, and is equal to voltage multiplied by amperes.

work A force acting through a distance.

Appendix E

Tables and charts

E-1
Typical table of torque values (lb-in.)

TAP SIZE	TENSION-TYPE NUTS: AN-365 AND AN-310	SHEER-TYPE NUTS: AN-364 AND AN-320
FINE-THREAD SERIES		
8–36	12–15	7–9
10–32	20–25	12–15
1/4–28	50–70	30–40
5/16–24	100–140	60–85
3/8–24	160–190	95–110
7/16–20	450–500	270–300
1/2–20	480–690	290–410
9/16–18	800–1000	480–600
5/8–18	1100–1300	600–780
3/4–16	2300–2500	1300–1500
7/8–14	2500–3000	1500–1800
1–14	3700–5500	2200–3300
1 1/8–12	5000–7000	3000–4200
1 1/4–12	9000–11,000	5400–6600
COARSE-THREAD SERIES		
8–32	12–15	7–9
10–24	20–25	12–15
1/4–20	40–50	25–30
5/16–18	80–90	48–55
3/8–16	160–185	95–100
7/16–14	235–255	140–155
1/2–13	400–480	240–290
9/16–12	500–700	300–420
5/8–11	700–900	420–540
3/4–10	1150–1600	700–950
7/8–9	2200–3000	1300–1800

E-2
Partial listing of aircraft gas turbine engines

ENGINE	MANUFACTURER	ENGINE	MANUFACTURER
TURBOFANS		*TURBOJETS*	
TF30	Pratt & Whitney	I-A	General Electric
TF33	Pratt & Whitney	J30	Westinghouse
TF35	General Electric	J31	General Electric
TF39	General Electric	J32	Westinghouse
JT3D	Pratt & Whitney	J33	Allison
JT8D	Pratt & Whitney	J34	Westinghouse
JT9D	Pratt & Whitney	J35	Allison
JTF10A	Pratt & Whitney	J37	Curtiss-Wright
CJ805-23	General Electric	J40	Westinghouse
CF700	General Electric	J41	Packard
		J42	Pratt & Whitney
		J43	Westinghouse
TURBOPROPS		J44	Fairchild
		J45	Westinghouse
T30	Westinghouse	J46	Westinghouse
T31	General Electric	J47	General Electric
T32	Pratt & Whitney	J48	Pratt & Whitney
T33	Frederick Flader	J49	Packard
T34	Pratt & Whitney	J51	Curtiss-Wright
T35	Curtiss-Wright	J52	Pratt & Whitney
T36	Chrysler	J53	General Electric
T37	General Electric	J54	Westinghouse
T38	Allison	J55	Frederick Flader
T39	Allison	J57	Pratt & Whitney
T40	Allison	J58	Pratt & Whitney
T41	General Electric	J59	Curtiss-Wright
T42	DeLaval	J61	Curtiss-Wright
T43	Curtiss-Wright	J63	Ranger
T44	Allison	J65	Curtiss-Wright
T45	Pratt & Whitney	J67	Curtiss-Wright
T46	Fairchild	J69	Continental
T47	Curtiss-Wright	J71	Allison
T48	Pratt & Whitney	J73	General Electric
T49	Curtiss-Wright	J75	Pratt & Whitney
T50	Boeing	J79	General Electric
T51	Continental	J81	Westinghouse
T52	Pratt & Whitney	J83	Fairchild
T53	Lycoming	J85	General Electric
T54	Allison	J89	Allison
T55	Lycoming	CJ805	General Electric
T56	Allison	JT3C	Pratt & Whitney
T57	Pratt & Whitney	JT4A	Pratt & Whitney
T58	General Electric	TJ38	Curtiss-Wright
T60	Boeing	J93	General Electric
T63	Allison		
T64	General Electric		
T72	Continental		
T74	Pratt & Whitney		
501D	Allison		

E-3

Variation of the speed of sound with temperature

Speed of sound (c_s) in dry air
$k = 1.4$
$c_s = \sqrt{gkRt_{am}}$
T_{am} = abs temp in °R

E-4

Gas turbine engine station notation

Single - rotor turbojet

Dual-rotor turbofan

Dual - rotor turbojet

Single-rotor turbojet

For engines with afterburners, station 5 is the entrance to the exhaust duct, station 6 is the entrance to the afterburner combustion chamber, station 7 is the entrance to the jet nozzle, and station 8 is the plane of the jet nozzle.

Dual-rotor turbojet

For engines with afterburners, station 7 is the entrance to the exhaust duct, station 8 is the entrance to the afterburner combustion chamber, station 9 is the entrance to the jet nozzle, and station 10 is the plane of the jet nozzle.

E-5

Psychometric chart

1 *Read wet bulb temperature on slant line.*
2 *Read dry bulb temperature on vertical line at point of intersection of slant and vertical lines.*
3 *Read absolute humidity on horizontal line.*

E-6
Fuel utilization

Pounds of fuel per nautical mile $\left(\dfrac{lb\ fuel}{n.\ mile}\right) = \dfrac{F(SFC)}{V}$

E-7
Decimal equivalents

INCH FRACTION	DECIMAL	CIRCLE A, in.²	mm	INCH FRACTION	DECIMAL	CIRCLE A, in.²	mm
1/64	.0156	.0002	.397	33/64	.5156	.2088	13.097
1/32	.0312	.0008	.794	17/32	.5312	.2217	13.494
3/64	.0469	.0017	1.191	35/64	.5469	.2349	13.891
1/16	.0625	.0031	1.587	9/16	.5625	.2485	14.288
5/64	.0781	.0048	1.984	37/64	.5781	.2625	14.686
3/32	.0937	.0069	2.381	19/32	.5937	.2769	15.081
7/64	.1094	.0094	2.778	39/64	.6094	.2916	15.478
1/8	.1250	.0123	3.175	5/8	.6250	.3068	15.875
9/64	.1406	.0154	3.572	41/64	.6406	.3223	16.272
5/32	.1562	.0192	3.969	21/32	.6562	.3382	16.669
11/64	.1719	.0232	4.366	43/64	.6719	.3545	17.065
3/16	.1875	.0276	4.762	11/16	.6875	.3712	17.462
13/64	.2031	.0324	5.159	45/64	.7031	.3883	17.859
7/32	.2187	.0376	5.556	23/32	.7187	.4057	18.256
15/64	.2344	.0431	5.953	47/64	.7344	.4235	18.653
1/4	.2500	.0491	6.350	3/4	.7500	.4418	19.050
17/64	.2656	.0553	6.747	49/64	.7656	.4604	19.447
9/32	.2812	.0621	7.144	25/32	.7812	.4794	19.844
19/64	.2969	.0692	7.540	51/64	.7969	.4987	20.241
5/16	.3125	.0767	7.937	13/16	.8125	.5185	20.637
21/64	.3281	.0845	8.334	53/64	.8281	.5386	21.034
11/32	.3437	.0928	8.731	27/32	.8437	.5591	21.431
23/64	.3594	.1014	9.128	55/64	.8594	.5800	21.828
3/8	.3750	.1105	9.525	7/8	.8750	.6013	22.225
25/64	.3906	.1198	9.922	57/64	.8906	.6229	22.622
13/32	.4062	.1296	10.319	29/32	.9062	.6450	23.019
27/64	.4219	.1398	10.716	59/64	.9219	.6675	23.416
7/16	.4375	.1503	11.112	15/16	.9375	.6903	23.812
29/64	.4531	.1612	11.509	61/64	.9531	.7134	24.209
15/32	.4687	.1726	11.906	31/32	.9687	.7371	24.606
31/64	.4844	.1842	12.303	63/64	.9844	.7610	25.003
1/2	.5000	.1964	12.700	1	1.000	.7854	25.400

E-8
Drill sizes—decimal equivalents

DRILL NO.	DIA., in.	DRILL NO.	DIA., in.	DRILL NO.	DIA., in.
A	.234	J	.277	S	.348
B	.238	K	.281	T	.358
C	.242	L	.290	U	.368
D	.246	M	.295	V	.377
E	.250	N	.302	W	.386
F	.257	O	.316	X	.397
G	.261	P	.323	Y	.404
H	.266	Q	.332	Z	.413
I	.272	R	.339		
1	.2280	28	.1405		
2	.2210	29	.1360	55	.0520
3	.2130	30	.1285	56	.0465
4	.2090	31	.1200	57	.0430
5	.2055	32	.1160	58	.0420
6	.2040	33	.1130	59	.0410
7	.2010	34	.1110	60	.0400
8	.1990	35	.1100	61	.0390
9	.1960	36	.1065	62	.0380
10	.1935	37	.1040	63	.0370
11	.1910	38	.1015	64	.0360
12	.1890	39	.0995	65	.0350
13	.1850	40	.0980	66	.0330
14	.1820	41	.0960	67	.0320
15	.1800	42	.0935	68	.0310
16	.1770	43	.0890	69	.0292
17	.1730	44	.0860	70	.0280
18	.1695	45	.0820	71	.0260
19	.1660	46	.0810	72	.0250
20	.1610	47	.0785	73	.0240
21	.1590	48	.0760	74	.0225
22	.1570	49	.0730	75	.0210
23	.1540	50	.0700	76	.0200
24	.1520	51	.0670	77	.0180
25	.1495	52	.0635	78	.0160
26	.1470	53	.0595	79	.0145
27	.1440	54	.0550	80	.0135

Screw dia. = (screw no. × 0.013) + 0.060

E-9
Greek alphabet

A, α	Alpha		N, ν	Nu
B, β	Beta		Ξ, ξ	Xi
Γ, γ	Gamma		O, o	Omicron
Δ, δ	Delta		Π, π	Pi
E, ϵ	Epsilon		P, ρ	Rho
Z, ζ	Zeta		Σ, σ,s	Sigma
H, η	Eta		T, τ	Tau
Θ, θ	Theta		Y, υ	Upsilon
I, ι	Iota		Φ, ϕ	Phi
K, κ	Kappa		X, χ	Chi
Λ, λ	Lambda		Ψ, ψ	Psi
M, μ	Mu		Ω, ω	Omega

E-10
Prefix multiples

PREFIX		MULTIPLIER	
Tera-	One trillion	1,000,000,000,000	10^{12}
Giga-	One billion	1,000,000,000	10^{9}
Mega-	One million	1,000,000	10^{6}
Myria-	Ten thousand	10,000	10^{4}
Kilo-	One thousand	1000	10^{3}
Hecto-	One hundred	100	10^{2}
Deka-	Ten	10	10
Octa-	Eight	8	
Hexa-	Six	6	
Penta-	Five	5	
Tetra-	Four	4	
Tri-	Three	3	
Deci-	One-tenth	1/10	10^{-1}
Centi-	One-hundreth	1/100	10^{-2}
Milli-	One-thousandth	1/1000	10^{-3}
Micro-	One-millionth	1/1,000,000	10^{-6}
Nano-	One-billionth	1/1,000,000,000	10^{-9}
Pico-	One-trillionth	1/1,000,000,000,000	10^{-12}

E-11

General properties of air

P = Absolute pressure — lb/sq ft
P_o = Standard absolute pressure — lb/sq ft
T = Absolute temperature
T_o = Standard absolute temperature
V = Velocity — ft/sec
g = Acceleration of gravity — ft/sec^2

n = Exponent of compression
q = Impact pressure — lb/ft^2
ρ = Density — lb sec^2/ft^4
μ = Absolute viscosity lb sec/ft^2
ν = Kinematic viscosity — ft^2/sec
σ = Density ratio — ρ/ρ_o

$$P = \rho g R T$$

$$\frac{P}{P_o} = \frac{\rho}{\rho_o}\frac{T}{T_o} = \left(\frac{\rho}{\rho_o}\right)^n = \left(\frac{V_o}{V}\right)^n$$

$$\frac{T}{T_o} = \left(\frac{P}{P_o}\right)^{\frac{n-1}{n}} = \left(\frac{V_o}{V}\right)^{n-1}$$

$$\frac{\rho}{\rho_o} = \left(\frac{T}{T_o}\right)^{\frac{1}{n-1}} \quad \text{For adiabatic change} \quad n = 1.39$$

Specific Weight of Air in lb/ft^3

$$g\rho = .07651 \frac{P}{P_o}\frac{T_o}{T} = 1.325 \frac{P \text{ in in. Hg}}{T \text{ in } F_{abs}}$$

Density of Air in lb sec^2/ft^4 or slugs/ft^3

$$\rho = .002378 \frac{P}{P_o}\frac{T_o}{T} = .041187 \frac{P \text{ in in. Hg}}{T \text{ in } F_{abs}}$$

Air Density Ratio

$$\rho/\rho_o = \frac{P}{P_o}\frac{T_o}{T} = 17.32 \frac{P \text{ in in. Hg}}{T \text{ in } F_{abs}}$$

Specific Heat of Air in Btu per lb per degree F

at constant pressure, $C_p = .240$
at constant volume, $C_v = .1715$
for atmospheric temperature range
$\gamma = C_p/C_v = 1.40$

Gas Constant for Air

$$R = 53.345 \text{ ft-lb/lb F}_{abs}$$

$$= \frac{1545.4 \text{ ft-lb/lb - mole F}_{abs}}{\text{mol wt}}$$

Molecular weight of air = 28.97

Impact Pressure

for incompressible flow $q = \frac{1}{2}\rho V^2$

for compressible flow $qc = \left(\frac{P_r}{P_{am}} - 1\right)^{P_{am}}$

$$T_r = \left(\frac{T_r}{T_{am}} - 1\right)^{T_{am}}$$

Speed of Sound in Air

$c_{tps} = \sqrt{\gamma g R T}$ $\qquad c_{tps} = 49.04\sqrt{T}$
$c_{knots} = 29.05\sqrt{T}$ $\qquad c_{mph} = 33.5\sqrt{T}$
where T is air temperature in °R
$c_{SL} = 661.74$ knots $= 761.52$ mph $= 1117$ fps

Absolute Viscosity for Air

$$\mu = \rho\nu$$

$$10^{10}\mu = 3583 + 9.870 \text{ t in degrees C}$$

$$= 3408 + 5.483 \text{ t in degrees F}$$

Approximate value (at sea level)

$$q = 25\left(\frac{V}{100}\right)^2 \text{lb/sq ft}$$

$$= 5\left(\frac{V}{100}\right)^2 \text{in. water}$$

Where V is in mph

Temperature rise resulting from adiabatic compression at impact

$$T = 1.792\left(\frac{V}{100}\right)^2 \text{ in degrees F}$$

Where V = True air speed in mph

E-12
Weights and measures

LENGTH

12 inches = 1 foot
 9 inches = 1 span
 4 inches = 1 hand
 3 feet   = 1 yard
 5½ yards = 16½ feet = 1 rod or pole
40 rods   = 220 yd = 1 furlong
 8 furlongs = 5280 ft = 1 mile
 3 miles   = 1 league

Nautical

6080.2 ft = 1 nautical mile
1 nautical mile per hour = 1 knot
6 feet = 1 fathom

Surveyor's

7.92 inches = 1 link
100 links = 66 ft = 1 chain
80 chains = 1 mile

WEIGHTS

Avoirdupois

16 drams = 437.5 grains = 1 ounce
16 ounces = 7000 grains = 1 pound
112 pounds = 1 hundredweight
2240 pounds = 1 long ton
2000 pounds = 1 short ton

Troy

24 grains = 1 pennyweight
20 pennyweights = 1 ounce
12 ounces = 5760 grains = 1 pound

Apothecaries

20 grains = 1 scruple
3 scruples = 1 dram
8 drams = 1 ounce
12 ounces = 5760 grains = 1 pound

VOLUME

1728 cubic inches = 1 cubic foot
  27 cubic feet = 1 cubic yard
 128 cubic feet = 1 cord of wood

Liquid

4 gills . = 1 pint
2 pints = 1 quart
4 quarts = 1 gallon
7.4805 gallons = 1 cubic foot

Dry

2 pints = 1 quart
8 quarts = 1 peck
4 pecks = 1 bushel

Apothecaries

60 minim = 1 liquid dram
 8 drams = 1 liquid ounce
16 ounces = 1 pint

Shipping

100 cubic feet = 1 Register ton
 40 cubic feet = 1 U. S. shipping ton

AREA

144 square inches = 1 square foot
9 square feet   = 1 square yard
30¼ square yards = 1 square rod
160 square rods = 43,560 square feet = 1 acre
640 acres   = 1 square mile

ENGLISH — METRIC EQUIVALENTS

Length

1 centimeter = 0.3937 inches
2.54 centimeters = 1 inch
0.3048 meters = 1 foot
1 meter = 3.278 feet
1 kilometer = 0.6214 miles
1.61 kilometers = 1 mile

Area

1 sq cm = .1550 sq in.
6.452 sq cm = 1.0 sq in.
0.093 sq meters = 1 sq ft
1 sq meter = 10.76 sq ft
4047 sq meters = 1 acre
1 hectare = 10,000 sq meters = 2.471 acres

Volume

1 cu cm = 0.061 cu in.
16.39 cu cm = 1 cu in.
0.0283 cu meter = 1 cu ft
1 cu meter = 35.31 cu ft
1 cu meter = 1.308 cu yd

Weight

0.648 gram = 1 grain
1.0 gram = 15.43 grains
28.35 grams = 1 oz
1 kilogram = 2.205 pounds

Liquid Measure

29.57 cu cm = 1 fluid ounce
1 liter = 33.81 fluid oz = 1.057 qt
3.8 liters = 1 gal

E-13
Fahrenheit-Centigrade conversion table

Look up reading in middle column; if in degrees Centigrade, read Fahrenheit equivalent in right-hand column; if in degrees Fahrenheit, read Centigrade equivalent in left-hand column.

−60 to 43			44 to 93			94 to 510			520 to 1010			1020 to 1510			1520 to 2010			2020 to 2510			2520 to 3000		
C		F	C		F	C		F	C		F	C		F	C		F	C		F	C		F
−51	−60	−76	6.7	44	111.2	34.4	94	201.2	271	520	968	549	1020	1868	827	1520	2768	1104	2020	3668	1382	2520	4568
−46	−50	−58	7.2	45	113.0	35.0	95	203.0	277	530	986	554	1030	1886	832	1530	2786	1110	2030	3686	1388	2530	4586
−40	−40	−40	7.8	46	114.3	35.6	96	204.8	282	540	1004	560	1040	1904	838	1540	2804	1116	2040	3704	1393	2540	4604
−34	−30	−22	8.3	47	116.6	36.1	97	206.6	288	550	1022	566	1050	1922	843	1550	2822	1121	2050	3722	1399	2550	4622
−29	−20	−4	8.9	48	118.4	36.7	98	208.4	293	560	1040	571	1060	1940	849	1560	2840	1127	2060	3740	1404	2560	4640
−23	−10	14	9.4	49	120.2	37.2	99	210.2	299	570	1058	577	1070	1958	854	1570	2858	1132	2070	3758	1410	2570	4658
−17.8	0	32	10.0	50	122.0	37.8	100	212.0	304	580	1076	582	1080	1976	860	1580	2876	1138	2080	3776	1416	2580	4676
−17.2	1	33.8	10.6	51	123.8	38	100	212	310	590	1094	588	1090	1994	866	1590	2894	1143	2090	3794	1421	2590	4694
−16.7	2	35.6	11.1	52	125.6	43	110	230	316	600	1112	593	1100	2012	871	1600	2912	1149	2100	3812	1427	2600	4712
−16.1	3	37.4	11.7	53	127.4	49	120	248	321	610	1130	599	1110	2030	877	1610	2930	1154	2110	3830	1432	2610	4730
−15.6	4	39.2	12.2	54	129.2	54	130	266	327	620	1148	604	1120	2048	882	1620	2948	1160	2120	3848	1438	2620	4748
−15.0	5	41.0	12.8	55	131.0	60	140	284	332	630	1166	610	1130	2066	888	1630	2966	1166	2130	3866	1443	2630	4766
−14.4	6	42.8	13.3	56	132.8	66	150	302	338	640	1184	616	1140	2084	893	1640	2984	1171	2140	3884	1449	2640	4784
−13.9	7	44.6	13.9	57	134.6	71	160	320	343	650	1202	621	1150	2102	899	1650	3002	1177	2150	3902	1454	2650	4802
−13.3	8	46.4	14.4	58	136.4	77	170	338	349	660	1220	627	1160	2120	904	1660	3020	1182	2160	3920	1460	2660	4820
−12.8	9	48.2	15.0	59	138.2	82	180	356	354	670	1238	632	1170	2138	910	1670	3038	1188	2170	3938	1466	2670	4838
−12.2	10	50.0	15.6	60	140.0	88	190	374	360	680	1256	638	1180	2156	916	1680	3056	1193	2180	3956	1471	2680	4856
−11.7	11	51.8	16.1	61	141.8	93	200	392	366	690	1274	643	1190	2174	921	1690	3074	1199	2190	3974	1477	2690	4874
−11.1	12	53.6	16.7	62	143.6	99	210	410	371	700	1292	649	1200	2192	927	1700	3092	1204	2200	3992	1482	2700	4892
−10.6	13	55.4	17.2	63	145.4	100	212	413.6	377	710	1310	654	1210	2210	932	1710	3110	1210	2210	4010	1488	2710	4910
−10.0	14	57.2	17.8	64	147.2	104	220	428	382	720	1328	660	1220	2228	938	1720	3128	1216	2220	4028	1493	2720	4928
−9.4	15	59.0	18.3	65	149.0	110	230	446	388	730	1346	666	1230	2246	943	1730	3146	1221	2230	4046	1499	2730	4946
−8.9	16	60.8	18.9	66	150.8	116	240	464	393	740	1364	671	1240	2264	949	1740	3164	1227	2240	4064	1504	2740	4964
−8.3	17	62.6	19.4	67	152.6	121	250	482	399	750	1382	677	1250	2282	954	1750	3182	1232	2250	4082	1510	2750	4982
−7.8	18	64.4	20.0	68	154.4	127	260	500	404	760	1400	682	1260	2300	960	1760	3200	1238	2260	4100	1516	2760	5000
−7.2	19	66.2	20.6	69	156.2	132	270	518	410	770	1418	688	1270	2318	966	1770	3218	1243	2270	4118	1521	2770	5018
−6.7	20	68.0	21.1	70	158.0	138	280	536	416	780	1436	693	1280	2336	971	1780	3236	1249	2280	4136	1527	2780	5036
−6.1	21	69.8	21.7	71	159.8	143	290	554	421	790	1454	699	1290	2354	977	1790	3254	1254	2290	4154	1532	2790	5054
−5.6	22	71.6	22.2	72	161.6	148	300	572	427	800	1472	704	1300	2372	982	1800	3272	1260	2300	4172	1538	2800	5072
−5.0	23	73.4	22.8	73	163.4	154	310	590	432	810	1490	710	1310	2390	988	1810	3290	1266	2310	4190	1543	2810	5090
−4.4	24	75.2	23.3	74	165.2	160	320	608	438	820	1508	716	1320	2408	993	1820	3308	1271	2320	4208	1549	2820	5108
−3.9	25	77.0	23.9	75	167.0	166	330	626	443	830	1526	721	1330	2426	999	1830	3326	1277	2330	4226	1554	2830	5126
−3.3	26	78.8	24.4	76	168.8	171	340	644	449	840	1544	727	1340	2444	1004	1840	3344	1282	2340	4244	1560	2840	5144
−2.8	27	80.6	25.0	77	170.6	177	350	662	454	850	1562	732	1350	2462	1010	1850	3362	1288	2350	4262	1566	2850	5162
−2.3	28	82.4	25.6	78	172.4	182	360	680	460	860	1580	738	1360	2480	1016	1860	3380	1293	2360	4280	1571	2860	5180
−1.7	29	84.2	26.1	79	174.3	188	370	698	466	870	1598	743	1370	2498	1021	1870	3398	1299	2370	4298	1577	2870	5198
−1.1	30	86.0	26.7	80	176.0	193	380	716	471	880	1616	749	1380	2516	1027	1880	3416	1304	2380	4316	1582	2880	5216
−0.6	31	87.8	27.2	81	177.8	199	390	734	477	890	1634	754	1390	2534	1032	1890	3434	1310	2390	4334	1588	2890	5234
0.0	32	89.6	27.8	82	179.6	204	400	752	482	900	1652	760	1400	2552	1038	1900	3452	1316	2400	4352	1593	2900	5252
0.6	33	91.4	28.3	83	181.4	210	410	770	488	910	1670	766	1410	2570	1043	1910	3470	1321	2410	4370	1599	2910	5270
1.1	34	93.2	28.9	84	183.2	216	420	788	493	920	1688	771	1420	2588	1049	1920	3488	1327	2420	4388	1604	2920	5288
1.7	35	95.0	29.4	85	185.0	221	430	806	499	930	1706	777	1430	2606	1054	1930	3506	1332	2430	4406	1610	2930	5306
2.2	36	96.8	30.0	86	186.8	227	440	824	504	940	1724	782	1440	2624	1060	1940	3524	1338	2440	4424	1616	2940	5324
2.8	37	98.6	30.6	87	188.6	232	450	842	510	950	1742	788	1450	2642	1066	1950	3542	1343	2450	4442	1621	2950	5342
3.3	38	100.4	31.1	88	190.4	238	460	860	516	960	1760	793	1460	2660	1071	1960	3560	1349	2460	4460	1627	2960	5360
3.9	39	102.2	31.7	89	192.2	243	470	878	521	970	1778	799	1470	2678	1077	1970	3578	1354	2470	4478	1632	2970	5378
4.4	40	104.0	32.2	90	194.0	249	480	896	527	980	1796	804	1480	2696	1082	1980	3596	1360	2480	4496	1638	2980	5396
5.0	41	105.8	32.8	91	195.8	254	490	914	532	990	1814	810	1490	2714	1088	1990	3614	1366	2490	4514	1643	2990	5414
5.6	42	107.6	33.3	92	197.6	260	500	932	538	1000	1832	816	1500	2732	1093	2000	3632	1371	2500	4532	1649	3000	5432
6.1	43	109.4	33.9	93	199.4	266	510	950	543	1010	1850	821	1510	2750	1099	2010	3650	1377	2510	4550			

E-14
Table for finding θ and √θ (temperature correction factor)

RELATIVE TEMPERATURE

$$°F = °R − 460 \qquad °C = °K − 273 \qquad °C = \frac{5}{9}(°F − 32)$$

$$°F = \frac{9}{5}°C + 32 \qquad \theta = \frac{T}{T_0} = \frac{T}{519} \qquad \text{For interpolation, } 1°C = 1.8°F$$

T (°F)	θ	√θ	T (°F)	θ	√θ	T (°F)	θ	√θ	T (°F)	θ	√θ
200	1.272	1.128									
199	1.270	1.127	129	1.135	1.065	59	1.000	1.000	-10	0.867	0.931
198	1.269	1.126	128	1.133	1.064	58	0.999	0.999	-11	0.865	0.930
197	1.267	1.125	127	1.131	1..064	57	0.997	0.998	-12	0.863	0.929
196	1.265	1.124	126	1.129	1.063	56	0.995	0.997	-13	0.861	0.928
195	1.263	1.123	125	1.127	1.062	55	0.993	0.996	-14	0.859	0.927
194	1.261	1.123	124	1.125	1.061	54	0.991	0.995	-15	0.857	0.926
193	1.259	1.122	123	1.123	1.060	53	0.989	0.994	-16	0.856	0.925
192	1.257	1.121	122	1.122	1.059	52	0.988	0.993	-17	0.854	0.924
191	1.255	1.120	121	1.120	1.058	51	0.986	0.992	-18	0.852	0.923
190	1.253	1.119	120	1.118	1.057	50	0.984	0.991	-19	0.850	0.922
189	1.251	1.118	119	1.116	1.056	49	0.982	0.990	-20	0.848	0.921
188	1.249	1.117	118	1.114	1.055	48	0.980	0.989	-21	0.846	0.920
187	1.247	1.117	117	1.112	1.054	47	0.978	0.988	-22	0.844	0.919
186	1.245	1.116	116	1.110	1.054	46	0.976	0.987	-23	0.842	0.918
185	1.243	1.115	115	1.108	1.053	45	0.974	0.986	-24	0.840	0.917
184	1.242	1.114	114	1.106	1.052	44	0.972	0.985	-25	0.838	0.916
183	1.240	1.113	113	1.104	1.051	43	0.970	0.984	-26	0.836	0.914
182	1.238	1.112	112	1.102	1.050	42	0.968	0.984	-27	0.834	0.913
181	1.236	1.111	111	1.100	1.049	41	0.966	0.983	-28	0.832	0.912
180	1.234	1.111	110	1.098	1.048	40	0.964	0.982	-29	0.831	0.911
179	1.232	1.110	109	1.096	1.047	39	0.962	0.981	-30	0.829	0.910
178	1.230	1.109	108	1.095	1.046	38	0.960	0.980	-31	0.827	0.909
177	1.228	1.108	107	1.093	1.045	37	0.959	0.979	-32	0.825	0.908
176	1.226	1.107	106	1.091	1.044	36	0.957	0.978	-33	0.823	0.907
175	1.224	1.106	105	1.089	1.043	35	0.955	0.977	-34	0.821	0.906
174	1.222	1.105	104	1.087	1.042	34	0.953	0.976	-35	0.819	0.905
173	1.220	1.104	103	1.085	1.041	33	0.951	0.975	-36	0.817	0.904
172	1.218	1.104	102	1.083	1.041	32	0.949	0.974	-37	0.815	0.903
171	1.216	1.103	101	1.082	1.040	31	0.947	0.973	-38	0.813	0.902
170	1.214	1.102	100	1.080	1.039	30	0.945	0.972	-39	0.811	0.901
169	1.212	1.101	99	1.078	1.038	29	0.943	0.971	-40	0.809	0.900
168	1.210	1.100	98	1.076	1.037	28	0.941	0.970	-41	0.807	0.899
167	1.208	1.099	97	1.074	1.036	27	0.939	0.969	-42	0.805	0.897
166	1.206	1.098	96	1.072	1.035	26	0.937	0.968	-43	0.804	0.896
165	1.204	1.097	95	1.070	1.034	25	0.935	0.967	-44	0.802	0.895
164	1.202	1.096	94	1.068	1.033	24	0.934	0.966	-45	0.800	0.894
163	1.200	1.095	93	1.066	1.032	23	0.932	0.965	-46	0.798	0.893
162	1.199	1.095	92	1.064	1.031	22	0.930	0.964	-47	0.796	0.892
161	1.197	1.094	91	1.062	1.030	21	0.928	0.963	-48	0.794	0.891
160	1.195	1.093	90	1.060	1.029	20	0.926	0.962	-49	0.792	0.890
159	1.193	1.092	89	1.058	1.029	19	0.924	0.961	-50	0.790	0.889
158	1.191	1.091	88	1.056	1.028	18	0.922	0.960	-51	0.788	0.888
157	1.189	1.090	87	1.055	1.027	17	0.920	0.959	-52	0.786	0.887
156	1.187	1.089	86	1.053	1.026	16	0.918	0.958	-53	0.784	0.886
155	1.185	1.089	85	1.051	1.025	15	0.916	0.957	-54	0.782	0.885
154	1.183	1.088	84	1.049	1.024	14	0.914	0.956	-55	0.780	0.883
153	1.181	1.087	83	1.047	1.023	13	0.912	0.955	-56	0.778	0.882
152	1.179	1.086	82	1.045	1.022	12	0.910	0.954	-57	0.777	0.881
151	1.177	1.085	81	1.043	1.021	11	0.908	0.953	-58	0.775	0.880
150	1.176	1.084	80	1.041	1.020	10	0.907	0.952	-59	0.773	0.879
149	1.174	1.083	79	1.039	1.019	9	0.905	0.951	-60	0.771	0.878
148	1.172	1.082	78	1.037	1.018	8	0.903	0.950	-61	0.769	0.877
147	1.170	1.082	77	1.035	1.017	7	0.901	0.949	-62	0.767	0.876
146	1.168	1.081	76	1.033	1.016	6	0.899	0.948	-63	0.765	0.875
145	1.166	1.080	75	1.031	1.015	5	0.897	0.947	-64	0.763	0.874
144	1.164	1.079	74	1.029	1.014	4	0.895	0.946	-65	0.761	0.872
143	1.162	1.078	73	1.028	1.013	3	0.893	0.945	-66	0.759	0.871
142	1.160	1.077	72	1.026	1.012	2	0.891	0.944	-67	0.757	0.870
141	1.158	1.076	71	1.024	1.012	1	0.889	0.943	-68	0.755	0.869
140	1.156	1.075	70	1.022	1.011	0	0.887	0.942	-69	0.753	0.868
139	1.154	1.074	69	1.020	1.010	-1	0.884	0.940	-70	0.751	0.867
138	1.152	1.073	68	1.018	1.009	-2	0.883	0.939	-71	0.750	0.866
137	1.150	1.073	67	1.016	1.008	-3	0.881	0.938	-72	0.748	0.865
136	1.149	1.072	66	1.014	1.007	-4	0.879	0.937	-73	0.746	0.864
135	1.147	1.071	65	1.012	1.006	-5	0.877	0.936	-74	0.744	0.862
134	1.145	1.070	64	1.010	1.005	-6	0.875	0.935	-75	0.742	0.861
133	1.143	1.069	63	1.008	1.004	-7	0.873	0.934	-76	0.740	0.860
132	1.141	1.068	62	1.006	1.003	-8	0.871	0.933	-77	0.738	0.859
131	1.139	1.067	61	1.004	1.002	-9	0.869	0.932	-78	0.736	0.858
130	1.137	1.066	60	1.002	1.001				-79	0.734	0.857

Table for finding δ (pressure correction factor)

RELATIVE PRESSURE

In. Hg = 0.07355 × in. H_2O

$\delta = \dfrac{P}{P_0} = \dfrac{P}{29.92}$

In. Hg = 0.1414 × lb/sq ft

In. Hg = 2.036 × lb/sq in.

P IN. HG. ABS	δ	P IN. HG. ABS	δ	P IN. HG. ABS	δ	P IN. HG. ABS	δ
40.0	1.337						
39.9	1.334	32.9	1.100	25.9	0.8656	18.9	0.6317
39.8	1.330	32.8	1.096	25.8	0.8623	18.8	0.6283
39.7	1.327	32.7	1.093	25.7	0.8586	18.7	0.6250
39.6	1.324	32.6	1.090	25.6	0.8556	18.6	0.6216
39.5	1.320	32.5	1.086	25.5	0.8523	18.5	0.6183
39.4	1.317	32.4	1.083	25.4	0.8489	18.4	0.6150
39.3	1.313	32.3	1.080	25.3	0.8456	18.3	0.6116
39.2	1.310	32.2	1.076	25.2	0.8422	18.2	0.6083
39.1	1.307	32.1	1.073	25.1	0.8389	18.1	0.6050
39.0	1.303	32.0	1.070	25.0	0.8356	18.0	0.6016
38.9	1.300	31.9	1.066	24.9	0.8322	17.9	0.5983
38.8	1.297	31.8	1.063	24.8	0.8289	17.8	0.5949
38.7	1.293	31.7	1.059	24.7	0.8255	17.7	0.5916
38.6	1.290	31.6	1.056	24.6	0.8222	17.6	0.5882
38.5	1.287	31.5	1.053	24.5	0.8188	17.5	0.5849
38.4	1.283	31.4	1.049	24.4	0.8155	17.4	0.5815
38.3	1.280	31.3	1.046	24.3	0.8122	17.3	0.5782
38.2	1.277	31.2	1.043	24.2	0.8088	17.2	0.5749
38.1	1.273	31.1	1.039	24.1	0.8055	17.1	0.5715
38.0	1.270	31.0	1.036	24.0	0.8021	17.0	0.5682
37.9	1.267	30.9	1.033	23.9	0.7988	16.9	0.5648
37.8	1.263	30.8	1.029	23.8	0.7954	16.8	0.5615
37.7	1.260	30.7	1.026	23.7	0.7921	16.7	0.5581
37.6	1.257	30.6	1.023	23.6	0.7888	16.6	0.5548
37.5	1.253	30.5	1.019	23.5	0.7854	16.5	0.5515
37.4	1.250	30.4	1.016	23.4	0.7821	16.4	0.5481
37.3	1.247	30.3	1.013	23.3	0.7787	16.3	0.5448
37.2	1.243	30.2	1.009	23.2	0.7754	16.2	0.5414
37.1	1.240	30.1	1.006	23.1	0.7720	16.1	0.5381
37.0	1.237	30.0	1.003	23.0	0.7687	16.0	0.5348
36.9	1.233	29.9	0.9993	22.9	0.7654	15.9	0.5314
36.8	1.230	29.8	0.9960	22.8	0.7620	15.8	0.5281
36.7	1.227	29.7	0.9926	22.7	0.7587	15.7	0.5247
36.6	1.223	29.6	0.9893	22.6	0.7553	15.6	0.5214
36.5	1.220	29.5	0.9859	22.5	0.7520	15.5	0.5180
36.4	1.217	29.4	0.9826	22.4	0.7487	15.4	0.5147
36.3	1.213	29.3	0.9793	22.3	0.7453	15.3	0.5224
36.2	1.210	29.2	0.9759	22.2	0.7420	15.2	0.5080
36.1	1.207	29.1	0.9726	22.1	0.7386	15.1	0.5047
36.0	1.203	29.0	0.9692	22.0	0.7353	15.0	0.5013
35.9	1.200	28.9	0.9659	21.9	0.7319	14.9	0.4980
35.8	1.196	28.8	0.9626	21.8	0.7286	14.8	0.4946
35.7	1.193	28.7	0.9592	21.7	0.7253	14.7	0.4913
35.6	1.190	28.6	0.9559	21.6	0.7219	14.6	0.4880
35.5	1.186	28.5	0.9525	21.5	0.7186	14.5	0.4846
35.4	1.183	28.4	0.9492	21.4	0.7152	14.4	0.4813
35.3	1.180	28.3	0.9458	21.3	0.7119	14.3	0.4779
35.2	1.176	28.2	0.9425	21.2	0.7085	14.2	0.4746
35.1	1.173	28.1	0.9392	21.1	0.7052	14.1	0.4713
35.0	1.170	28.0	0.9358	21.0	0.7019	14.0	0.4679
34.9	1.166	27.9	0.9325	20.9	0.6985	13.9	0.4646
34.8	1.163	27.8	0.9291	20.8	0.6952	13.8	0.4612
34.7	1.160	27.7	0.9258	20.7	0.6918	13.7	0.4579
34.6	1.156	27.6	0.9224	20.6	0.6885	13.6	0.4545
34.5	1.153	27.5	0.9191	20.5	0.6852	13.5	0.4512
34.4	1.150	27.4	0.9158	20.4	0.6818	13.4	0.4479
34.3	1.146	27.3	0.9124	20.3	0.6785	13.3	0.4445
34.2	1.143	27.2	0.9091	20.2	0.6751	13.2	0.4412
34.1	1.140	27.1	0.9057	20.1	0.6718	13.1	0.4378
34.0	1.136	27.0	0.9024	20.0	0.6684	13.0	0.4345
33.9	1.133	26.9	0.8990	19.9	0.6651	12.9	0.4311
33.8	1.130	26.8	0.8957	19.8	0.6618	12.8	0.4278
33.7	1.126	26.7	0.8924	19.7	0.6584	12.7	0.4245
33.6	1.123	26.6	0.8890	19.6	0.6551	12.6	0.4211
33.5	1.120	26.5	0.8857	19.5	0.6517	12.5	0.4178
33.4	1.116	26.4	0.8823	19.4	0.6484	12.4	0.4144
33.3	1.113	26.3	0.8790	19.3	0.6450	12.3	0.4111
33.2	1.110	26.2	0.8757	19.2	0.6417	12.2	0.4077
33.1	1.106	26.1	0.8723	19.1	0.6384	12.1	0.4044
33.0	1.103	26.0	0.8690	19.0	0.6350	12.0	0.4011

Index

....

Page references in boldface indicate figures.